D1090505

BUILDING THE BEEF INDUSTRY

BUILDING THE BEEF INDUSTRY

♦

A CENTURY OF COMMITMENT

CHARLES E. BALL

EDITED BY

SUSANNAH S. BORG

FOREWORD BY

HUGH S. SIDEY

THE NATIONAL CATTLEMEN'S FOUNDATION
DENVER

On the Cover

Bronze, by William G. Duncan. *The bronze shown on the cover, although a complete sculpture itself, is part of a larger bronze sculpture created for the Cattlemen's Centennial.* *(See page 293.)* *The portion used was to represent the people of the Association. Here is a generational view of the industry, the older cowboy figure looms large in the background, while a younger, modern generation looks outward to meet the challenges of a new beef industry.*

The National Cattlemen's Foundation
National Cattlemen's Beef Association
P.O. Box 3469
Englewood, CO 80155

This book is meant to be a comprehensive history of the one hundred years of the association of cattlemen.
Every effort has been made to verify all facts and identify persons included in this book.
However, because it is a compilation of history from numerous sources, neither the Publisher, Author nor Editor can assume responsibility or liability for misinformation, misprints, omissions, or errors contained herein.

Produced for Publication by
THE SARATOGA PUBLISHING GROUP
PO Box 959, Saratoga, WY 82331
(800) 722-6932

ISBN 1-879894-15-7
Limited Edition ISBN 1-879894-16-5
Library of Congress Catalog Number: 97-066850

Printed in the United States of America.

When a stockman says he is for you,
he is for you. . .and that is all there is to it.

When a stockman says he wants something,
he gets up and says it in no uncertain sound.

He is a man who makes his opinions known,
and he is strong enough to make everybody understand it.

As a rule, he is at peace with the world.

He does not belong in the cliques and combines you find in our great cities.

He is as free as the wind. . .liberal to a fault,
kind to his neighbors, just to all men. . .

We started out together, our interests are identical. . .

We have no corners to run, no cards to stack;
we want justice, we want equity.

We want to treat everybody fairly
and court the friendship of all.

—John W. Springer
First Association President

The Monfort Legacy

Pioneers, Innovators, Entrepreneurs

After serving in World War I, Warren H. Monfort taught school in Illinois for a few years, where he observed the cattle and hog economy of the Corn Belt states. With new ideas of his own, he returned to the 80-acre family farm two miles north of Greeley, Colorado, confident that cattle feeding could be a profitable business and that he could do it better than the Corn Belt feeders.

In 1930 he bought his first eighteen head of feeder cattle. As he became more successful, he built more pens to feed more cattle. By the end of the 1940s he was consistently feeding 3,500 head of cattle—a very large feedlot at that time.

Warren H. Monfort *turned Greeley, Colorado, into a major cattle feeding center. An excellent cattleman, his eye and judgment of cattle were unmatched. Once his calves topped the market in Chicago, he knew he had made cattle feeding in Colorado more prosperous than feeding in the Corn Belt.*

Colorado, the better place to feed cattle. *After studying Corn Belt feeders, Warren H. Monfort was convinced that cattle feeding could be more efficient and more profitable in Colorado because the weather and hay were better.*

After World War II he started feeding steer calves and sold them on the Chicago market where they topped the market more often than those of any other feeder.

By bringing corn to cattle in Colorado rather than shipping cattle to be fed in the Midwest, he established a more efficient system. He also innovated the process by feeding ground grains, rather than whole, believing that cattle would gain weight more easily eating ground grain.

When corn procurement became difficult for the increasing numbers of cattle, his daughter, Marjory, and her husband Lloyd Wilson, moved to Cozad, Nebraska, where they built a large corn storage and buying station. With their large capacity, they could ship corn by rail in five car units, greatly reducing freight costs, thus adding profit to the feeding operation.

Because of the post-war demand for beef, the 1950s were a period of expansion and great changes in the feeding industry. Monfort, Inc. kept building pens, but marketing and shipping cattle became more difficult. It then made sense to build a packing house in Greeley.

When Kenneth Monfort left Colorado A&M in 1955 to join his father in business, Warren told his son, *I have built a large cattle feeding business, but it will be up to you to build a large packing plant business.*

The first plant was built in 1960. They hired Maurice Feldman, an experienced beef man from New York City, who was a good teacher for young Kenneth. They established a positive relationship with the great A&P stores on the eastern seaboard and business flourished.

By 1968 they had established the first 100,000-head feedlot in the United States and by 1970 they had constructed their second.

Producing and selling carcass beef was not suited to the modern trends of the retailers, so Kenneth built an addition to the plant in which they could break down carcasses into primal cuts and box them. "Boxed beef" became a big turning point for the industry. Retailers could finally get the specific cuts they wanted.

As convenient as boxed beef was for the retailer, it did not help the packing house at the time; it merely added overhead. So Monfort merged with Mapelli Brothers who understood

Family business was the way to do business *for the Monforts. Edith and Warren Monfort began a tradition that has lasted into the third generation. When a need arose to expand and develop business, another member of the family took up the cause. By the time Monfort of Colorado merged into ConAgra, Monfort represented a strong family operation reflecting the family traditions that have built the American cattle industry.*

DEDIC

***The family gathered** in July 1990 at Colorado State University for the dedication of the Monfort Endowment Chair in Meat and Animal Sciences. Standing in the rear center is Myra and Ken Monfort surrounded by children (loosely from left to right: Charlie Monfort and wife, Victoria, Dick Monfort and wife Chris, Kyle (Monfort) Futo and Rick and Kaye (Monfort) Montera and grandchildren.*

the wholesale and retail markets and knew where to put the boxed beef. Monfort then opened distribution centers in key cities under the Mapelli Brothers name. These centers allowed them to box beef for specific markets. Large restaurant chains needed several month's inventory of certain cuts, and Monfort had to turn to the futures market to protect forward sales. As they supplied restaurants more, they developed portion control and cryovacing of individual cuts, which also made it possible to open foreign markets. Monfort was soon the largest beef exporter to Japan.

Father and Son Built an Empire. *When Warren Monfort told his son it was up to him to build the packing business, because he had built the feeding business, Ken later quipped, "My father, being a cattleman, never quite thought as much of me after I became a packer."*

Because of Kenneth Monfort's innovative spirit, he constantly upgraded the packing house. and moved in other directions. About 1970, Monfort began their own trucking company for distribution, which grew quickly to more than 150 truck tractors and hundreds of refrigerated trailers.

Warren Monfort's health began to fail; in 1971 he resigned as chairman of the board. As the export business grew, Kenneth's youngest son, Charlie, headed up international sales. In addition to two sons, Charlie and Dick, Kenneth has two daughters: Kyle Futo, Wichita, Kansas, and Kay Montera, Eaton, Colorado.

The Mapelli Brothers Distribution Company began selling more product than the Greeley plant could produce so in 1979 the company built a second beef slaughtering plant at Grand Island, Nebraska. Kenneth's oldest son, Dick, who worked for the company as a feeder cattle buyer, became plant manager of the new plant.

There was no end to the expansion of facilities and equipment needed to compete in the world market. Then in the late 1970s and early 1980s, rising costs, low cattle prices, extremely high interest rates, plus the immense amount of money to be borrowed, convinced Kenneth that while Monfort of Colorado had assumed a large position in the industry, it was too much for one single family to continue.

In 1987, Monfort of Colorado was merged into ConAgra along with Swift International, and A. E. Miller Company. Kenneth became president of ConAgra Red Meats Division. He managed this red meat company until he retired in 1989, and his son, Dick, took over the Red Meat Division until he retired in 1995. Charlie Monfort still heads the International Division of ConAgra.

Rick Montera, Kenneth's son-in-law, made all feeder cattle purchases for many years and retired in 1995. Dick Monfort and Rick Montera are now large cattle feeders.

Ken Monfort, the Innovator. *The upstart packer became a leading beef company. Duly recognized, Ken became President of the American Meat Institute, served on the Beef Board and was an energetic member of NCA. He was also recipient of the Golden Spur Award.*

Through three generations, the Monfort family has been among the nation's leaders in the growth, development and prosperity of the beef industry. Warren Monfort's vision of what cattle feeding could be has been proven. The pioneering improvements in packing house equipment, boxed beef, and computerized inventories developed by Kenneth Monfort have had a major impact on moving the industry forward.

It is with deep gratitude that the National Cattlemen's Foundation recognizes The Monfort Family Foundation for having generously underwritten the major portion of this Centennial History.

TABLE OF CONTENTS

Foreword

More than anyone else the cowboy is the portrait of America. In him there is the call of the wind and the beckoning of open land, there is the lure of adventure and romance, the triumph of unique skill and discipline—and purpose. Too little has been said about purpose.

The cowboy of this nation was not spawned for novelists and Hollywood but by the beef industry, a creation of cattlemen, cowboys in concert. In its early days it may not have resembled much of of an organized entity in American society. But an industry it was, even then, in the hearts of lone horsemen rounding up wild cattle for food and sale, in the minds of a clutch of adventurers who could see profit at the end of a long and dangerous trail drive that took them to the crude rail terminals leaping across the plains. America wanted good beef at reasonable prices and the production challenges faced by the cattlemen were more daunting than those confronting any new industry like the railroads or automobiles.

The cattle "factory" was not a harborside building but millions of square miles of varigated land from Florida to Washington. The raw ingredients were not inert metals but often obstreperous and spirited animals bent on rebellion, subject to nature's ravages. The plant managers were themselves free-ranging, fiercely independent folk who were by nature suspicious of any organization or political group imposing restraint and cooperation.

This book is the remarkable story of the men and women who understood above all else that there had to be a viable national association for the survival of a beef industry. That industry had to take its place in the gigantic American marketplace, subject to all the vicissitudes of supply and demand, shaped and reshaped almost daily by technological developments like hamburger and huge cattle trucks and feedyards. It had to be a weighty voice in constant debate with the political forces in state capitals and in Washington, DC, where regulations ran rampant and all American interests collided with each other.

Building the beef industry was not a ritual without mistakes and not free of rancor as you

will see as you journey through these pages. Nor are the arguments over. But here is a drama of strong, caring people who not only wanted to serve this country better beef but wanted to preserve a way of life where families could live on their land and preserve it and claim for themselves the same sense of security and well being that Americans have always sought.

This dusty century of roundups, bawling stockyards, environmental precautions and breed refinement may be the easy century. The challenges ahead for the industry are more complex and pervasive than those faced by the 1,200 delegates who gathered in Denver in 1898 to found the National Live Stock Association of the United States, the progenitor of the National Cattlemen's Beef Association, which now reaches over 200,000 producers. Ranch land continues to succumb to the deep pockets of real estate developers, and regulations on health and slaughter cascade out of every concerned governmental body. The assault on red meat consumption is waged by fringe dietary and animal rights groups. Change is the only constant, accelerated by an information highway which has obliterated space, reclusiveness and the luxury of waiting. More than ever we stand united—or else.

Let this book be a guide for cooperative and enlightened effort in the years ahead. There is here besides the accounts and debates of many crucial meetings, the cowboy legends of hard work born along by hope and humor and the exhilaration of the company of the very special people who have made the beef industry great.

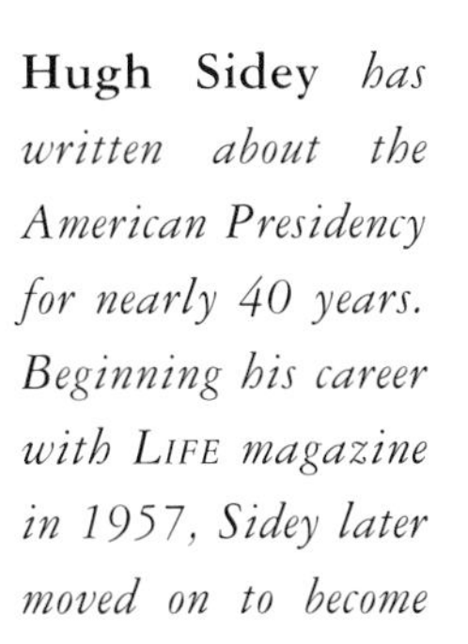

Hugh Sidey *has written about the American Presidency for nearly 40 years. Beginning his career with* LIFE *magazine in 1957, Sidey later moved on to become* TIME *magazine's political and White House correspondent, and eventually bureau chief. Mr. Sidey is now the Washington Contributing Editor and author of* TIME *magazine's column "The Presidency." Son of a country editor and reared on the family's weekly newspaper in Greenfield, Iowa, Sidey occasionally leaves Washington and goes back to work on the newspaper, "to keep in touch with the real America."*

Edward Hicks THE CORNELL FARM

About the Author

Charles E. Ball is uniquely qualified to write the history of national cattlemen. He has lived it, led it and written about it.

His experience with cattle began 60 years ago, as a 4-H Club member, and he has owned cattle ever since—first in the cow-calf business, then as a stocker operator, and in recent years as a feeder.

As an award-winning editor of *Farm Journal* during the 1950s and 1960s, he traveled the World, searching for and writing about innovative cattlemen. His first ANCA convention was 1956 in New Orleans, and he has attended most of them since.

As executive vice president of Texas Cattle Feeders Association, 1972-1988, he fought the battles and helped celebrate the victories of cattlemen. . . during the worst of times and the best of times. He studied association management and later became an association consultant, working for a number of state and national associations.

Ball is a native of Lamar County, Texas, where he won many 4-H Club honors. He graduated from Texas A&M College (1947) and Iowa State College (1948), after a three-year stint as a combat officer in the European Theater during World War II.

His earlier writing experience includes: editor of the *Texas A&M Agriculturist* (1947); managing editor of *Farm & Ranch-Southern Agriculturist* (1948-52); and regional editor of *Farm Journal* (1952-72). In addition, he has written for *The Saturday Evening Post* and *Reader's Digest*. Also, Ball was the author of two books, *Saddle Up!*, a "best selling" horse book, and *The Finishing Touch*, a history of cattle feeding in the Southwest.

Acknowledgments

As always with a project of this scope—and it has been a five-year journey of discovery and delight—many people pitched in to make it happen. So I am genuinely grateful:

To Rick Ewig and his staff at the American Heritage Center, University of Wyoming, where the archives of the Association are located and where a majority of my research occurred.

To the dedicated librarians at the National Live Stock and Meat Board, the National Agricultural Library, the National Archives, the Library of Congress, the Nebraska Historical Society, the Denver Public Library, the Amarillo Public Library and the Panhandle Plains Museum. All had valuable documents, plus the knowledge and patience to assist "an incessant researcher."

To my wife, Dawn, who assisted with the research, including the processing of more than 5,000 photocopies.

To my secretaries, Lucy Jalbert and Cynthia Riojas, who did the computer work and taught me computer-ese at the same time.

To the designers, Randy Taylor and Lynn Harster, who elevated this work from a mere history book to a centerpiece for the coffee table, and who worked through the many complicated details of the design and printing.

To the staff at Saratoga Publishing —editor Susannah Borg, artist Keith McLendon, photo researcher Ann Palen, proofreaders Carol Pederson and Kathy Lane—who worked tirelessly to make the layouts attractive, the photos surprising and the copy entertaining.

To the early reviewers of the manuscript who helped assure the accuracy of the content: Forrest Bassford, John Merrill, Tobin Armstrong, W.D. Farr, Bill McMillan, George Spencer, Dub Berry, Burton Eller and Earl Peterson.

To the living past presidents of the Association—27 of whom I interviewed—for their encouragement, their perspective and their inspiration.

Throughout this journey, I have been amazed at the similarity of issues facing cattlemen during the past 100 years. Because similar problems occurred and reoccurred, wise leaders will learn from the history made by their predecessors. That's why the past is worth preserving.

—Charles E. Ball

Acronyms Used Frequently Throughout the Text

ANCA *American National Cattlemen's Association*

ANCB *American National CowBelles*

ANCW *American National CattleWomen*

ANLSA *American National Live Stock Association*

BIC *Beef Industry Council*

BLM *Bureau of Land Management*

CBLFA *Corn Belt Livestock Feeders Association*

FDA *Food and Drug Administration*

NCA *National Cattlemen's Association*

NCBA *National Cattlemen's Beef Association*

NCF *National Cattlemen's Foundation*

NLFA *National Livestock Feeders Association*

NLSA *National Live Stock Association*

PLC *Public Lands Council*

USMEF *United States Meat Export Federation*

USDA *United States Department of Agriculture*

Centennial Task Force

The National Cattlemen's Foundation appointed The Centennial Task Force in 1995 to oversee the initial plans for the Centennial Celebration of the Association to be held in February 1998, and to raise funds to cover the costs of this history book project. To that end, the Task Force was highly successful, raising over $400,000 for the Foundation.

EDITORIAL BOARD

Don Butler
Chairman, National Cattlemen's Foundation and NCA Past President

W.D. Farr
National Cattlemen's Foundation Board of Directors and ANCA Past President

Hugh Sidey
Time Magazine

Roger Berglund
Former NCA Communications Director

Susannah S. Borg
Editor and Project Manager

Charles E. Ball
Author

TASK FORCE MEMBERS

Linda M. Davis, New Mexico, *Chairman*
Don Butler, Arizona, *NCF Chairman*
John Lacey, California, *1996 NCBA President*
Clark Willingham, Texas, NCBA Vice President
John Armstrong, Texas
Jim Berger, Wyoming
Scott Chandler, Colorado
W.D. Farr, Colorado
Ben Houston, Colorado
John Trotman, Alabama
Gordon Van Vleck, California
Susannah Borg, Florida, *Project Manager*

NATIONAL CATTLEMEN'S FOUNDATION STAFF

The NCF staff, during the course of this project, contributed greatly to its success and kept the work moving through the Association.

Earl B. Peterson
Pam Fyock
Christine Taylor
Nicky Henderson

REVIEWERS

Although the manuscript was reviewed in part by many persons and experts, the following persons reviewed the manuscript in full and offered comments, changes and confirmation of content.

Tobin Armstrong
Forrest Bassford
W.T. (Dub) Berry
Burton Eller
C.W. (Bill) McMillan
John (Chip) Merrill
Earl Peterson
George Spencer
Gordon Van Vleck

In Memoriam

As this book was going to press, Scott Chandler was killed in an accident on his ranch near Walsenburg, Colorado. Chandler, a well-known leader in the animal health field, was an energetic member of the Task Force and was instrumental in bringing forward many of the creative ideas and plans for the Centennial. At the time of his death, he was actively pursuing the setup of an event for the Centennial Convention. The industry, the Association, and the Centennial Task Force has suffered a great loss.

THE PRESIDENT'S BRONZE

1978

ARTIST: JERRY PALEN

THE MAN CASTS A LONG SHADOW.

BRONZE CREATED AS A SYMBOL OF THE PRESIDENCY OF THE NATIONAL CATTLEMEN'S ASSOCIATION AND GIVEN TO EACH PRESIDENT UPON RETIREMENT FROM 1978 THROUGH 1995.

EVOLUTION OF THE NATIONAL ASSOCIATION

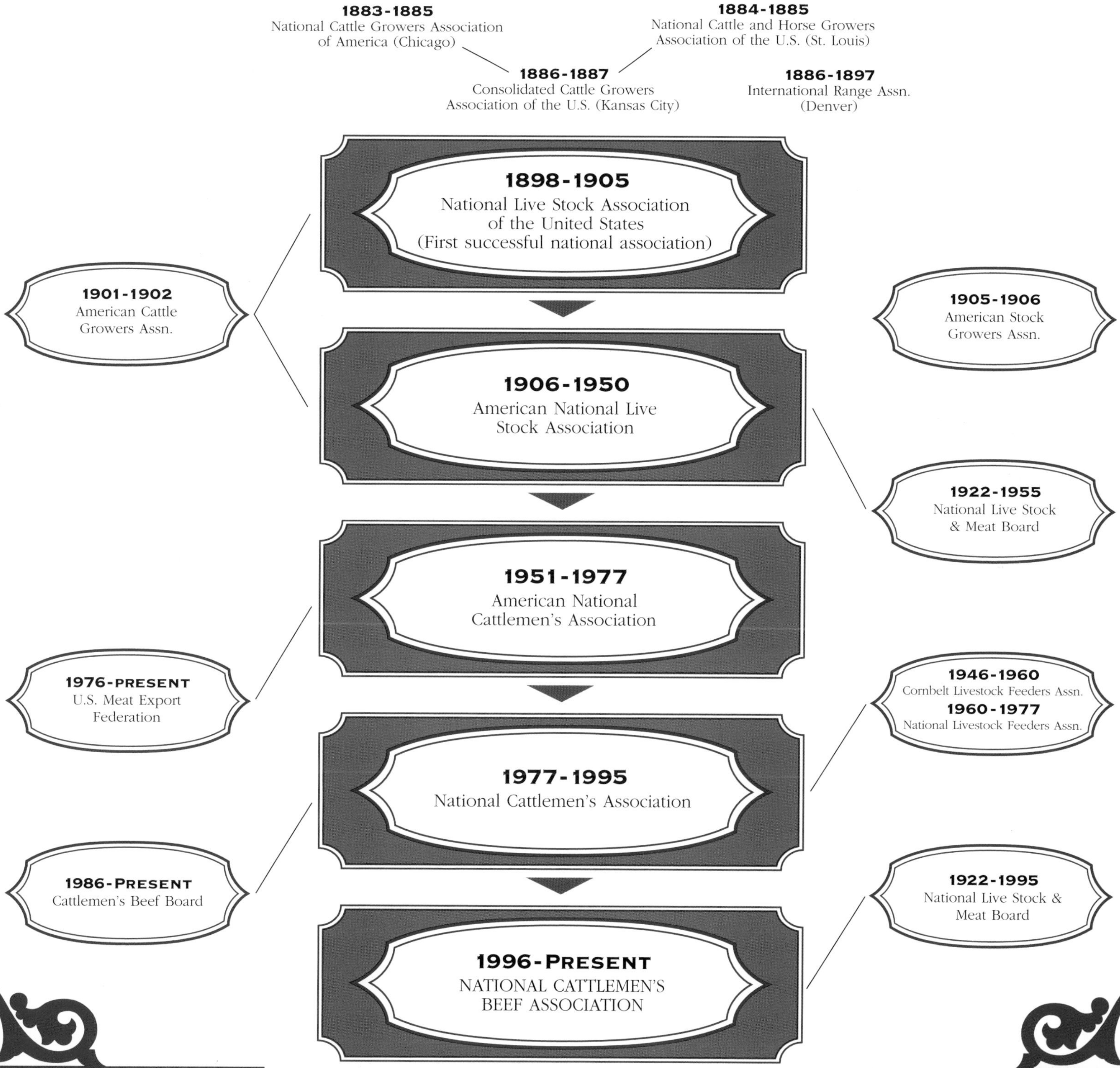

1883-1885
National Cattle Growers Association of America (Chicago)

1884-1885
National Cattle and Horse Growers Association of the U.S. (St. Louis)

1886-1887
Consolidated Cattle Growers Association of the U.S. (Kansas City)

1886-1897
International Range Assn. (Denver)

1898-1905
National Live Stock Association of the United States (First successful national association)

1901-1902
American Cattle Growers Assn.

1905-1906
American Stock Growers Assn.

1906-1950
American National Live Stock Association

1922-1955
National Live Stock & Meat Board

1951-1977
American National Cattlemen's Association

1976-PRESENT
U.S. Meat Export Federation

1946-1960
Cornbelt Livestock Feeders Assn.
1960-1977
National Livestock Feeders Assn.

1977-1995
National Cattlemen's Association

1986-PRESENT
Cattlemen's Beef Board

1922-1995
National Live Stock & Meat Board

1996-PRESENT
NATIONAL CATTLEMEN'S BEEF ASSOCIATION

Tom Lea CATTLE ARRIVE IN AMERICA

A New Industry is Born

On his second voyage to the New World in 1493, Columbus introduced cattle to the Western Hemisphere. After a two-month, 3400-mile voyage, he set anchor at Hispaniola and unloaded his cattle. There the cattle thrived. In 1519, Hernando Cortez took offspring of these cattle to Mexico to set up ranches. Often the cattle roamed wild and later came to the United States by way of Texas and California.

CHAPTER ONE

The Most Eventful Years

Historians and old-time cattlemen called the last two decades of the 1800s "the most eventful years in cattle industry history." As the 19th century clock ran down, the western cattle industry was struggling for its permanence on the sparse range. At long last cattlemen were debating the merits of joining together for their mutual benefit, if not for their own survival.

Experienced cattlemen as well as aspiring cattlemen, rich and poor, big or little, were attracted to the frontier by the "glamour" of the West and by promises of good return on cattle investments, a movement surpassed only by those of the earlier gold rushes.

Land promoters, who worked for the railroads or state immigration offices, were alleging "enormous profits" as were the cattle barons of the day.

On top of the hype for easy profits, the federal government was offering free land to homesteaders. By 1900, some 61,200 families had staked their claims; the culture of the range land changed.

But even these aspiring cattlemen, all rugged individuals, all necessarily brave and independent, soon discovered that the West was not all glamour. There were forces at work and a myriad of problems which they were not able to handle as individuals:

- Indian attacks or "defender" attacks, depending on the point of view.
- Range wars and fence cuttings between big cattle outfits and homesteaders, who the cattlemen contemptuously called "sodbusters," "squatters" or "nesters."
- Cattle rustling and "mavericking" by entrepreneuring cowhands, who learned from their bosses the temptations and rewards of putting their own brand on any stray that was unmarked and could be roped.
- Lack of law enforcement outside the settlements, which permitted outlaws to conduct holdups or other crimes and escape without pursuit.
- Cattle diseases spread by cattle movement, such as Texas Fever and Pleuropneumonia.

TIMELINE

1880 Western cattle boom begins.

Mechanical refrigeration first used.

1883 National Cattle Growers Association organized in Chicago.

Cody's first Wild West Show.

1884 National Cattle and Horse Growers Association held in St. Louis.

Bureau of Animal Industry (BAI) established.

Animal and Plant Health Inspection Service (APHIS), established.

1885 Pasteur vaccinates against rabies.

1886 Consolidated Cattle Growers meet at Kansas City.

Coca-Cola goes on sale.

1887 Ten-year drought cycle begins.

Congress authorizes BAI to buy and destroy diseased animals.

Interstate Commerce Act passed.

1889 Oklahoma Land Rush.

First dipping vats used on King Ranch in Texas.

Discovery of cause of Texas Fever.

The Record Stockman, a livestock publication, founded.

1890 Sherman Anti-Trust Act passed.

First meat inspection act.

1891 National Forest System founded.

1892 Texas A&M researchers found that ticks carried Texas Fever.

Successful use of desiccated beef thyroid for human medical therapy provides beef by-product market.

Bovine pleuropneumonia eradicated.

First successful tractor built by John Froelich, Iowa.

1895 Sears, Roebuck Company opens catalog business.

1897 Amalgamated Meat Cutters & Butcher Workmen founded.

ISSUES

Homesteaders
•
Loss of Open Range
•
Economic Difficulties
•
Packer Trust
•
Infectious Diseases
•
National Organization

CATTLE REACH AMERICA

Early American cattle originated in Europe but came to the Americas by many routes: Texas, Florida, California, Virginia and New England.

By the time cattle reached Texas and California from Mexico in the 1500s, a cattle industry was emerging in Florida. Weighing 600 to 800 pounds these cattle known as woods cattle, Florida Crackers or Florida Scrubs, flourished and are still around today.

In 1607, cattle arrived at Jamestown, but none survived. More came in 1611, at which time Governor Thomas Dale issued a proclamation: "No man shall dare kill any bull, cow, calf...whether his own or appertaining to another man." Thanks to this conservation and further imports, cattle became established in Virginia: an estimated 500 head by 1620 and 30,000 by 1639.

At the same time, animals from England and northern Europe began arriving in New England and appeared in New York in 1625. On Manhattan Island, a wall was built between the Dutch commune and their outlying farms to protect against wild animals and Indians. This is the wall for which today's Wall Street is named.

- The packer trust, a monopoly, which knew what was going on, and had the upper hand, leaving ranchers with no market information except hearsay.
- New railroads and railroad routes, which ranchers quickly became dependent upon but which charged monopolistic freight rates.
- Finally, there was the government at Washington, which seemed intent on helping homesteaders claim the best land and water, while taking the free grazing from established grazers.

Not one of these issues could a rancher resolve alone.

BANDING TOGETHER

Neighboring or "helping out" was practiced in a limited way, even though neighbors often lived many miles apart and horseback was the fastest mode of transportation and communication. But communication was a necessity were issues to be resolved.

One of the first cooperative efforts was the district roundup. This required the cooperation of several ranchers who would spend days planning and then executing. The actual roundup, which included the identification of unmarked animals, the proper branding and settlement of ownership and other disputes, took many days and much work on the part of all involved. Although somewhat successful, the roundup cried out for better and more methodical organization.

"**Early New England Farmer-Feeders Drove Their Cattle to Market**—*Boston, New York, Philadelphia, Baltimore—and sometimes tangled with carriages and pedestrians." (From* AMERICAN CATTLE TRAILS *1540-1900). Governor William Bradford wrote that the Pilgrims "brought three heifers and a bull to Plymouth in 1624," the first beginnings of any cattle of that kind in New England. During the following decade larger shipments were received, up to 50 and 60 head per ship. The novel economic value of color in cattle showed up early: a red calf was worth less than a black one, because there was greater probability of a red calf being mistaken as a deer and being attacked by wolves.*

Up the Trail

The Trail Drive

While there existed a general shortage of beef in the northern and eastern parts of the country at the end of the Civil War, there was no shortage in Texas. An estimated 6 million head, about one-fourth of all cattle in the country, were found there.

As the soldiers returned home and new settlers migrated to Texas to take advantage of the free land and free grazing, they eyed the potential markets to the north. Receiving pens were being constructed at the newly functional railroads in the midwest and packing plants were coming into their own in the major cities.

Trail Drives from Texas to Kansas *were commonplace during the 19th century. Once in Kansas the cattle were transferred to rail cars for the eastern markets. Typical droves numbered from 500 to 8,000 head of cattle; the trip took four to five months.*

Trail drives, which had begun in the 1840s and 1850s by the wagon trains and immigrants, were resumed by those seeking profit in the cattle industry. By 1890, it was estimated that 10 million head went "up the trail." More often they took steers for grazing or slaughter, but they also took breeding stock for the Northwest and long-term production in the new territories.

At least two national cattlemen association presidents got their start by trailing cattle. John B. Kendrick, upon completing one drive, met the daughter of a Wyoming rancher to whom he delivered cattle, married her and stayed. Ike T. Pryor, of Texas, wrote later in 1929 about the business of trailing:

> *In 1884, I drove 15 herds from southern Texas to the northwestern states and territories. These cattle were driven in droves of about 3,000 to each herd, with 11 men, and each man was furnished with six horses. The salaries were $30 a month for each of the men, including the cook, and $100 for the boss. Traveling about 450 to 500 miles a month, the cost, including provisions, to drive 3,000 head 3,000 miles was $3,000. Today, by train, it would cost $30,000 to move 3,000 steers from southern Texas to Montana.*

While the economics appealed to owners, it was a hard way to make a living. But many young men were looking for adventure, including a large number of Mexicans and blacks. They needed only a saddle and bedroll, everything else was furnished. Adventure they got, plus dust, mud, swollen rivers and stampedes. Indians would frequently demand pay for grazing their lands or a bribe in beef for not stampeding the drove. More brazen tribesmen would stampede the herd then charge for regathering them.

There were many well-known trails: the Shawnee Trail, the Chisholm Trail, Western Trail, Goodnight-Loving Trail, and many unnamed ones. Most drovers didn't like to refer to them by a person's name; to the drovers, it was just "up the trail."

The Need To Help One Another

Last of the 5000. *Responding to an owner's inquiry about their herd's condition, OH Ranch foreman Jesse Phelps asked a young wrangler, Charlie Russell, to sketch a picture to include in his response. Russell did this watercolor on a piece of pasteboard. Upon seeing how well he showed the situation, Phelps sent the sketch with no letter. When the owner received it, he went out and got drunk. The original, "Waiting for a chinook—Last of the 5000," is property of the Montana Stockgrowers Association, and hangs at the Historical Society of Montana, today valued at $260,000.*

The Worst Winter 1886-1887

In the 1880s, big corporations and absentee owners, lacking practical knowledge about the cattle business and driven by high cattle prices, had overstocked the range. The problem worsened in 1885 when President Cleveland, acting on protests from Indians that "Cattle Kings" were illegally grazing their reservations, ordered 200,000 head removed from Oklahoma and placed on the already overgrazed free ranges of the neighboring states. The 1885-1886 winter was severe in the Texas Panhandle, New Mexico and Colorado. A widespread drought followed in the summer of 1886. Cattle were thin and weakened.

In November 1886, snow fell over the Western Plains until a Chinook came down in January bringing warm winds that partially melted the snow. A howling blizzard then swept the Plains for four days, dropping temperatures to 32-below in Montana and 20-below in Colorado.

Melting snow froze into an impermeable crust over remaining forage. Cattle could not feed and drifted, then piled up against fences and in draws. Even ranchers who had feed could not get out to check herds. Unable to break through the ice, cattle died by the thousands.

Ranches reported 10 to 90 percent of their herds lost, although reliable accounts were 25 to 50 percent. One observer claimed it was possible to walk along the Platte River from Greeley to Julesburg (about 150 miles) by stepping from one dead carcass to another.

Bad as it was, historians agree this was an opportunity for managers reporting to absentee owners to make up for poor management and four or five years of inflated book counts. One manager reported a 125-percent loss: 50 percent steers and 75 percent cows.

The devastation contributed to the end of open range and led to a restructuring of the industry, with cattlemen recognizing the need to organize.

Fight Monopoly With Monopoly

In the 1880s, a group of cattlemen upset with the "packer monopoly" concluded, "The only way to fight monopoly is with monopoly."

So in 1887, the American Cattle Trust, patterned after the Standard Oil Trust that had initiated an economic revolution in 1882, was organized with offices in New York. Directors included some of the most substantial cattlemen in the West: John L. Routt, governor of Colorado; R.G. Head of New Mexico; C.C. Slaughter and John T. Lytle of Texas; Thomas Sturgis and Francis E. Warren of Wyoming; and an impressive group of eastern financiers.

Although not large enough to be really effective, the Trust was sizeable and vertically integrated. It included ranches in Texas, New Mexico, Colorado and Wyoming encompassing 218,934 head of cattle as well as feeding farms near Gilmore, Nebraska; a Chicago packing plant, purchased from Morris for $2,000,000; and contracts for canned beef with France and Belgium.

While this trust reflected the mood of cattlemen in that day, and probably for generations to follow, it was not a financial success and was liquidated in 1890.

Trouble with Homesteaders

The race to homestead the west became a problem to cattlemen as farmers in Missouri, Kansas and other states rebelled against Texas cattle passing through their property largely for fear of Texas Fever. Cattle drives were forced to bypass the homesteaders and cattlemen had to deal with the loss of free-range grazing.

The Johnson County War

In the late 1800s, conflicting claims for land and fence cuttings resulted in a number of deaths. One of the most notorious conflicts was the Johnson County War in Wyoming. In the spring of 1892, feelings between ranchers and homesteaders, complicated by a growing number of cattle thieves siding with the newcomers, reached a fever pitch.

"Settlers taking law into their own hands," *taken by S.D. Butcher in 1885. This re-enactment shows "free-rangers" cutting 15 miles of fence on the Brighton Ranch in Nebraska.*

Homesteads *of 160 acres and later of 320 and 640 acres were granted to Civil War veterans "who did not bear arms against the Union Army," and to heads of households over 21 years of age who promised to stay on the land for five years and improve it.*

The thieves and the nesters, according to the ranchers, were "mavericking" and building up herds at their expense. So the ranchers assembled a force of about 25 cattlemen, plus an equal number of hired guns from Texas, and planned to invade and chase out the "intruders."

But the townspeople, including the sheriff, sided with the "little people," and by the time the invaders arrived there were 200 to 300 armed defenders waiting. The fiasco received so much advanced attention, including numerous telegrams to Washington, that President Benjamin Harrison dispatched troops just in time to prevent widespread bloodshed. Only four men lost their lives, two on each side.

Looking for adventure, *many young men made their way "Up the Trail." John B. Kendrick and Ike T. Pryor, both eventually Association presidents, got their start trailing cattle north.*

Some better-read ranchers had learned of the first association in the Americas, the Mexican Mesta, organized in the early 1500s by Spanish settlers to protect their cattle and grazing interests. So a few visionaries began to talk about what "cattlemen in concert" might accomplish through cooperation and through organization.

State organizations led the trend towards association. The first state cattlemen's organization was the Colorado Stock Growers Association (now Colorado Cattlemen's Association) in 1867, followed by the Wyoming Stock Growers Association in 1873, the Cattle Raisers Association of Texas (now Texas and Southwestern Cattle Raisers Association) in 1877, and the Montana Stockgrowers Association in 1885.

These organizations attacked those issues best handled at the state level such as establishing ownership and catching cattle thieves, but other problems were becoming bigger than state associations could cope with. So talk began about the need for a national association.

A lasting national organization would not become reality until 1898 in Denver. But there were earlier efforts, which in retrospect seemed necessary for the trial-and-error approach, because there were no precedents for a national organization of such a complex industry.

The first national gathering of cattlemen was called by George Loring, United States Commissioner of Agriculture, in Chicago, November 15-16, 1883, at the time of the National Fat Stock Show. He was concerned about the 1881 embargo by the British government on American cattle and beef, allegedly because of pleuropneumonia. In a Congress-authorized inquiry, the Treasury Cattle Commission issued a report in 1882 determining that effective regulation of cattle diseases depended on federal rather than local authority. Loring was in fact advocating federal legislation to deal with contagious diseases.

Almost immediately, the proposed legislation drew controversy and division within the cattle industry. Texas cattlemen thought the real target was Texas Fever and that federal legislation would stop the movement of Texas cattle to the north. They joined with Chicago commission firms to oppose both the meeting and the legislation.

Colorado cattlemen did not participate in the meeting for another reason: they believed that the convention would be dominated by market and packer interests in the Midwest and they spread the warning to all cattlemen to avoid doing business with the Swift Brothers of Chicago.

> ***All that is needed is a modest amount of capital and the natural increase will repay an average annual profit of 20 to 25 percent. The whole secret of it is, it costs nothing to feed the cattle.***
>
> —General James S. Brisbin
> *THE BEEF BONANZA; OR HOW TO GET RICH ON THE PLAINS, 1880*

Swift had purchased steers from W.J. Wilson of Colorado and given him a $3,000 draft; however, while the steers were in route to Chicago, the market dropped and Swift refused payment on the draft. But the Colorado Stock Growers Association did send observers.

Over 170 delegates from 23 states and territories came and adopted several resolutions: the most significant was to send a committee to Washington to prepare and get passed a bill to establish a Bureau of Animal Industry within the Department of Agriculture. It was a hot issue in Washington and lobbied intensely both ways, but it passed on May 29, 1884, and the Bureau of Animal Industry became reality.

The Long Road to Organization

First Cattlemen's Association

In 1529, the town council of Mexico City, mostly cattle raisers, ordered the establishment of a cattlemen's association to control cattle theft and preserve their monopoly on cattle production. "The Mesta" became the first known livestock association in the Americas.

As a quasi-governmental organization, The Mesta promulgated several ordinances and regulations that sound familiar today, such as the rule that each owner shall have his own brand and such brand be registered in a brand book kept in Mexico City.

Later, as the cattle multiplied and moved further from Mexico City to common grazing grounds, cattle rustling became a problem. In 1537, the crown granted new and expanded authority to The Mesta:

> *To enact ordinances to benefit and increase the herds, and to remedy and punish frauds and crimes which are committed with much frequency.*

The Mesta thus enacted three new ordinances:

1. All brands had to be different, so the owners of animals could be identified.
2. When two owners had the same brand, The Mesta could arbitrarily give each a distinctive brand.
3. Cropping the ears of an animal for identification was prohibited because such identification could easily be altered.

In addition, authority was granted to The Mesta to require every cattleman with more than 20 head to become a member of The Mesta and to attend meetings, usually two a year, or send a representative.

States Lead The Way in the United States

State cattle and livestock associations were the first to recognize the benefit of joining together to confront the issues and resolve problems. Colorado Stock Growers Association (now Colorado Cattlemen's Association) led the way in 1867 followed by the Wyoming Stock Growers Association in 1873, then Texas and Montana. These associations formed the core group that was instrumental in eventually establishing a national organization.

(above) **The Planter House**, *a popular meeting place for Denver businessmen and cattlemen, became a club for a group of Colorado cattlemen who formed the first state association.*

(below) **The Cheyenne Club** *played host to Wyoming cattlemen and politicians, often the same people, and became home to the Wyoming Stock Growers Association.*

Delegates at the early conventions *came from a variety of backgrounds. Some came "up the trail," some represented international interests, some were easterners who could neither understand their issues nor agree with the majority of westerners, but each held their opinion and held it strongly. The only prevailing wind was the wind of dissension. After the 1884 Chicago convention, one delegate, Levi Leiter, was prompted to write another delegate, James Pratt of Nebraska and ask, "why you people in the West do not cooperate more and bicker less?"*

NATIONAL CATTLE GROWERS' ASSOCIATION

A second convention was called at Chicago in November 1884, at which time a permanent organization was to be established called the National Cattle Growers' Association of America. This was the first known attempt to form a national federation of cattle producer organizations. At that meeting, a constitution was adopted and officers were elected: President, D.W. Smith, a prominent Hereford breeder at Bates, Illinois; Vice President, General N.M. Curtis of Ogdensbury, New York; Secretary, Thomas Sturgis of Cheyenne, Wyoming, who also was secretary of the Wyoming Stock Growers Association; Treasurer, John Clay, Jr., a commission man in Chicago, who also managed several ranches in the West and later became president of the Wyoming Stock Growers Association (1890-95). Of the 19 directors, 16 were from the West or Midwest, lending credence to charges that the new organization was not truly national in representation. Despite this accusation, officers pleaded for unity and cooperation; at the same time they revealed the problems of organization that have beleaguered cattlemen over the years:

> *If all work together, nothing can prevail against them; the only foes they need to dread are internal suspicions and dissensions.*
>
> —D.W. Smith
> *President, National Cattle Growers' Association, 1884*

> *All of the business industries of the country have been quick to see and seize upon the advantages to be derived from an organization of their forces, but perhaps none of the great industries have been so slow and so inefficient in their organization as has been that one which, in point of numbers and of wealth, is the greatest of them all: the live stock industry.*
>
> *Much has been said and written in regard to the organization of an association which should embrace in one all of the various state and local associations of cattle growers in the*

Feeding Cattle. *In the 1890s Brownwood Cotton Oil Company Feedlot, Brownwood, Texas, proved that "aged" Longhorns can be fattened. The interests and issues of feeding operations were well placed in the dialogues and discussions of the early national conventions.*

United States. . .But there has ever been an unfortunate spirit of distrust and suspicion pervading this greatest of all the industries, which has during many years prevented that concert of action which was so desirable and important.

Of late years, however, we have begun to learn something of the sweet uses of adversity. Foreign governments have discriminated against us from without, and contagious diseases have threatened us from within; railroad and stock yards companies have preyed upon us; legislatures and congresses have turned deaf ears to our appeals, and we have been compelled to turn to each other for consolation and support.

—*Proceedings*, Chicago Convention, 1884

First National Convention of Cattlemen Medallion. *The convention held in St. Louis in 1884.*

According to its constitution, the National Cattle Growers Association limited its membership to associations and societies, stating that no one shall be eligible as a delegate who is not directly engaged in the breeding and growing of cattle. Dues included an entrance fee of $15 per association plus annual dues of 50 cents per member.

{But} when I recollect the millions for whom food is cheaper on account of your work, I. . .am glad of the cattle trade.

—General William T. Sherman

Addressing the 1884 National Convention of Cattlemen in St. Louis

Six committees, reflecting the issues of the late 1800s, were set up: Transportation, National and State Legislation, Statistics and General Information, Dairy Interests, Diseases of Live Stock, and Foreign Restrictions. These committees reflected concerns that remained with the industry throughout the next century and are as relevant a century later. Also relevant a century later was President D.W. Smith of Illinois's appeal for unity:

> *There is a great work to be done, but it can only be accomplished by the united, earnest and persistent efforts of cattle owners of the whole country. If all work together, nothing can prevail against them; the only foes they need to dread are internal suspicions and dissension.*

But the dissension between East and West prevailed in Chicago.

The stage was set to try again to have a "real convention of cattlemen," this time in St. Louis, to overcome the problems in Chicago. But as A.T. Atwater of the Hunter-Evans Commission firm in St. Louis wrote to Thomas Sturgis of Wyoming, *The bonafide cattleman and raisers who signed the call for the St. Louis convention {to be held later in 1884} decided*

General Preston Porter *addressing the National Convention of Cattlemen in St. Louis, 1884.*

that some action should show Chicago {Chicago convention} that she had trod upon the toes of the entire cattle raising district west of the Mississippi River, and so the dissension continued.

First National Convention of Cattlemen

On November 15, 1884, the day the Chicago convention ended, a new convention was called to be held in St. Louis. Organized and promoted by Colonel Robert D. Hunter, this convention was a large, gala affair, with bands, banquets and parties, and it was a long six days. Among the associations represented were the Cherokee Protective and Detective Association (from Indian Territory), Holstein Breeders Association of America, Western Kansas Stock Growers' Association Texas Live Stock Association, Wyoming Stock Growers' Association, Montana Stock Growers Association, Nevada Live Stock Association, American Agricultural Association (Missouri), New Mexico Stock Growers' Association, Utah and Idaho Live Stock Association, and more.

Speakers included many of the best known names in the cattle business, governors, ex-senators and army generals. General William T. Sherman, who commanded the Union troops in the Civil War, thrilled the delegates with a short talk:

> *You know your business better than I can tell you, he said modestly. I was one of those who sentimentally regretted the replacing*

of the buffalo and the black-tailed deer, the elk and the antelope by the long-horned cattle of Texas. But when I recollect the millions for whom food is cheaper on account of your work, I do not deplore, but am glad of the cattle trade.

Delegates from the Chicago convention arrived in St. Louis by train, after the festivities had started, and were disenchanted by the multitude in the flag-draped Exposition Hall. *. . .not half of which could hear the presiding officer*, sneered Thomas Sturgis. For this reason, the Chicago convention turned to the time honored Anglo-Saxon plan of representation by delegates. The Chicago group was also disappointed in the business agenda, which they felt was singularly limited to the national cattle trail. Texans were there in large numbers and had previously agreed to focus their debate and votes on that one issue.

Actually, many topics were on the agenda, reported in great length

A business that had been fascinating to me before, suddenly became distasteful. I wanted no more of it. I never wanted to own again an animal that I could not feed and shelter.

—Granville Stuart, Montana
Commenting on the Winter of 1886-1887

by the two St. Louis newspapers: protection from the government at Washington; contagious diseases and quarantine laws; unreasonable freight rates by the railroads; beef exports to the Continent; an embargo by European countries on American cattle and meat; placement of brands on cattle to avoid undue damage to the hides; Indian rights; cheap and good beef for the working class; and the need "for so vast and valuable an industry to become organized."

Yet Another National Association

The final business of the St. Louis Convention was the formation of a permanent organization, the National Cattle and Horse Growers Association of the United States, and the call for a Second Annual Convention to be held in St. Louis in November 1885 immediately following the convention of the National Cattle Growers Association of America in Chicago.

Officers of the new association were: President, Robert D. Hunter of St. Louis; Vice President, General J.S. Brisbin of Idaho; Treasurer, J.C. Moore of St. Louis; Secretary, A.T. Atwater of St. Louis.

Both associations, "the Chicago Association" and "the St. Louis Association," met the following year, but neither convention was as successful as the previous ones and it was decided that they should consolidate into the Consolidated Cattle Growers Association of the United States. The first convention of this new organization would be in Chicago and the second in Kansas City. John Clay of Chicago had written to Thomas Sturgis of Cheyenne, *There are but two cities fitted for our association's headquarters, Chicago and Kansas City, not St. Louis! We must work through thick and thin for Chicago.*

Consolidated Cattle Growers Association

These conventions of the consolidated groups were bland compared to the previous ones, because of smaller attendance (300 delegates from 33 states and territories at the first one—fewer at the second one) and lack of controversy. The primary topics included contagious diseases; oleomargarine legislation, which dairymen had pushed through Congress and which cattlemen said was "robbing the steer to pay the cow;" hide damage from improper branding; and the "real, great and essential" need for stockmen to organize into one strong national organization.

Issues More Important Than Organization

Contagious Pleuropneumonia was the dreaded disease at the time; however, Foot-and-Mouth disease and Rinderpest also were included in the act they were attempting to get passed. Pleuropneumonia had entered the United States in 1843 through one cow purchased off an English vessel and by 1884 had been found in several states. Cattlemen

Western cattlemen controlled enough capital *by 1884 to have retired the national debt. To give this concentration of power a unified voice, Colonel Robert D. Hunter, a well-known commission man, organized and promoted the National Convention of Cattlemen. Here the flag-draped assembly hall held more than 1300 delegates from 34 states and territories convened for this "Convention of Conventions" in St. Louis in 1884. According to one contemporary account, "the ladies, the talent, the wit and the beauty of St. Louis decked their halls and parlors to greet and make welcome the bronzed ranchmen of the plains."*

maintained that it was a great threat to the vast cattle industry, which had annual sales in excess of $250 million and a capital investment of $5 billion. They were attempting to get $1 million from Congress to enforce the program, including slaughter with indemnity. The industry was already losing $1 million per year in export sales, because of the European embargo on American cattle and cattle products. But opponents in Congress were raising two constitutional questions:

1. Would the search of premises and destruction of cattle be in violation of the constitution?
2. Would such federal action not violate in part the powers reserved to the states?

The Legislative Committee, in an eloquent report to the November 1887 convention in Kansas City, admitted that they were disappointed but edified by their lobbying experience in Washington:

> *Right at the threshold, {we} were encountered by rules of order, rules of procedure, rules of precedence, rules of etiquette, and a multitude of other rules hedging about and obstructing all approach to Congress; to violate any one of which was to invite almost certain ruin.*

They also reported another obstacle encountered in lobbying:

> *It is not too much to say that our efforts would have been crowned with entire success in the House, as in the Senate, but*

for the vicious course of one man, who by reason of his official position, assisted by the rules of the House, and favored by the speaker, was able to plant himself squarely across the road over which our bill must pass. It is humiliating to the just pride of American citizens that a single man, 'puffed up' with a little brief authority, consumed with egotism, insanely jealous of his official prerogatives, and imbued with that hatred of independent thought and action which has ever characterized small minds elevated to high stations, is able to thwart the wishes of a majority.

At the last minute, Congress did appropriate $500,000 a year for a pleuropneumonia program and the disease was eradicated by 1892.

The winter of 1886-1887, the worst ever recorded for cattlemen, left the industry so depressed that the infant Consolidated Cattle Growers' Association simply faded away.

It would be 11 years before another national association would surface. During this interim, one other organization was born and buried: the International Range Association, which some writers classified as national. Incorporated in February 1886 in Colorado, it had one purpose: to protect ranchers and the cattle on public lands. Richard C. Head, general manager of the giant Prairie Cattle Company at Trinidad, Colorado, was originator and president. Directors included 20 prominent cattlemen from Mexico to Dakota, but they were strictly western operators. At the March 1888 convention in Denver, Colonel H.M. Taylor of New Mexico remarked,

In the conduct of range matters, there are numerous questions of common interest to all stockmen of the plains in which our eastern brothers have and take no interest.

The East-West differences continued to simmer.

It was to this group of western operators that Edward M. McGillin first proposed the American Cattle Trust. In response, Alexander H. Swan, one of Wyoming's best known cattlemen, wrote a letter to the secretary that showed a basic understanding of the cattlemen's psychology and why concerted action had thus far been unattainable. Swan wrote,

I do not believe that concerted action can be depended upon by cattle owners of the northwest, west and southwest. . .My experience has been {regarding pooled beef shipments} that jealousies will arise, and no concerted and thoroughly organized co-operation can be depended upon.

With the rapid disappearance of the open range, the basis for the International Range Association was destroyed. So this organization, too, faded away. The proposition for a unified national cattlemen's organization remained unattainable.

THE MAVERICK

1985

ARTIST: TOMMY BEALL

FIRST BRONZE COMMISSIONED TO BENEFIT THE NATIONAL CATTLEMEN'S FOUNDATION.

SERIES: 300 BRONZES

Charles M. Russell WHITE MAN'S BUFFALO

Expanding Horizons

By the 1890s there was a new range. Great herds of buffalo were gone; Indians were relegated to reservations; barbed wire had carved out farms; and a growing network of rails replaced trail drives. Cattle were now a business owned by small as well as large producers. A new century was approaching and the world would change dramatically for the cattleman.

CHAPTER TWO

AN ASSOCIATION OF ASSOCIATIONS

As the 19th century was winding down, the mood of cattlemen was turning upward. The industry was experiencing a revival; cattle were selling at 100 to 300 percent above the demoralized prices of five to eight years earlier; ranchers were scurrying to restock the range; there was talk of "prosperity!"

But the picture remained confusing. Cattle ranches, coming out of the bad times of the 1880s, were reorganizing; settlers struggling financially needed cash crops to sell and turned to cattle. The people who made up the industry in 1897 were substantially different from those of even 10 or 15 years before. Three previous attempts to organize nationally had failed and there had simply not been the money and wherewithall to make it happen. The need remained. The industry was growing again and new issues warranted attention.

BEGINNING OF AN ERA

Sensing this revival and sitting in the hub of the western range country, the Livestock Committee of the Denver Chamber of Commerce and Trade Board were ready to take on a "leadership project." Two members of that committee, Charles F. Martin and John W. Springer, had kept the vision of a national association and now brought that idea before the committee.

Previously, Martin had managed the Associated Press in Denver. Before that, he had ranched, edited the *NEW MEXICAN STOCKMAN* in Springer, New Mexico, and authored *PROSE AND POETRY OF THE CATTLE INDUSTRY OF THE UNITED STATES*, considered one of the "Four Classics" in livestock literature. Martin was also familiar with the ill-fated Consolidated Cattle Growers association and was prepared to pull from past mistakes.

TIMELINE

1898 The Paris Exposition.

Spanish-American War begins.

United States annexes Hawaii.

1899 Spanish-American War ends.

1900 Congress passes Gold Standard Act; currency backed by gold reserves.

First International Livestock Exposition, Chicago.

National Debt at $1,263,417,000 or $16.60 per capita.

1901 Guglielmo Marconi sends first wireless messages across Atlantic.

Theodore Roosevelt becomes 26th President upon McKinley's assassination.

First large oil strike, at Spindletop Well, near Beaumont, Texas.

U.S. Steel formed by 10-company syndicate headed by J.P. Morgan and Elbert Gary.

1902 Rural free mail delivery becomes permanent.

Panama canal authorized; Spooner act allocates $40 million for construction.

National Farmers Union formed.

1903 Wright brothers fly first powered airplane at Kitty Hawk, NC.

Henry Ford starts Ford Motor Co.

First Pacific cable opened.

"The Great Train Robbery" produced: first motion picture employing movement of camera.

Pelican Island, Florida, established as first national wildlife refuge.

First transcontinental auto trip: Packard car arrives in New York City after 52-day journey from San Francisco.

1904 First livestock auction opened in Union, Iowa.

Caterpillar "truck" invented.

1905 National Forest Service moved from Interior to Agriculture Department.

ISSUES

Organization of National Live Stock Growers Association in 1898

•

Modernizers of the Industry

•

Monopoly of the Triad: Packers, Stockyards, and Railroads

•

Freight Rates

•

Public Domain

•

Government in Washington

Pieces taken from the Program for the 1898 National Live Stock Association Convention.

Springer, at the time a rancher on the outskirts of Denver, had enjoyed a distinguished career as an attorney and state representative in Illinois, a banker in Dallas, a Colorado nominee for vice president of the United States and a nationally-known orator.

Together, Springer and Martin were to introduce an association that they were determined could not fail. Following their leadership, the Livestock Committee of the Chamber called a National Stock Growers Convention, with the underlying goal to form a new and permanent national association. Thinking big, they envisioned that this would become an "association of associations" and would represent every branch of the livestock industry: cattle, sheep, goat, swine and horse growers, as well as all other groups who shared the diverse interests in the livestock and meat industry.

The gathering was set for January 25-27, 1898, in "The Queen City of the Plains," Denver, Colorado. Invitations were sent across the United States and into several foreign countries to all known groups and organizations with the criteria for sending delegates:

- Each state and territorial range organization of cattle, horse, sheep and swine breeders—one delegate for every 10,000 head of stock represented.
- Each state or territorial livestock sanitary board—three delegates
- Each agricultural college—one delegate
- Commission exchanges—one delegate for every 10 members
- Each livestock company—one delegate
- All other livestock clubs, organizations of "fine stock breeders" and others not attached to state or territorial organizations—one delegate for each organization
- Each livestock journal—one delegate

Other groups such as the irrigation organizations were added later. Conspicuously, packers were left off the guest list.

A total of 1,185 registered delegates showed up, and a similar number of guests. Considering the travel conditions, the turnout was remarkable. Their enthusiasm for a new organization motivated them to leave isolated ranches, midwestern and eastern farms and travel days to reach mid-winter Denver.

At the opening session, the silver-tongued Springer greeted the crowd:

> *While I see some in this great gathering whose locks are whitened with the struggles of the years agone, it is, however, a fact that the majority are in the prime of life, enthusiastic, practical and well satisfied with present conditions. . . . This is the new regime. By reason of it we are prospering as never before. . . . We shall, however, at this meeting perfect an organization, national in its scope, broad in its objects and absolutely free from the*

Springer *addresses the crowd and is caricatured in the newspapers.*

The National Stock Growers Convention.
Denver, Colo.
·1898·
Tues. Wed. Thurs. January 25, 26, 27.
Reduced Rates on All Railroads.

Stockyards Became the New Way to Market Cattle. *The Union Stock Yard and Transit Company of Chicago opened for business in late 1866 and in the following 33 years received over 278 million head of livestock, all kinds. It was the largest stockyard in the world.*

machinations of political promoters. We can have our state and county organizations. . .but it is certainly desirable that once each year we shall all come together as members of the National Live Stock Association of the United States to discuss collectively matters pertaining to the best interests of all individually. . . .We would then be able to speak by authority of the livestock interests of the Union.

Also at the opening session, Kansas moved to preserve their reputation when J.B. McCoy, the recognized founder of the Southwestern cattle trade and the builder of Abilene, rose to be recognized and began saying, "Kansas is never known to be still very long." Following cries, "Right you are!" he admonishes his fellow cattlemen, "organize or perish."

THE WORLD IS OURS

The program was astutely planned and orchestrated by the ex-journalist Martin. Leading off, after a blessing by "Parson Tom" Uzzell and a welcome by Colorado Governor Alva Adams, was a hard-hitting paper by rancher G.F. Patrick of Pueblo on "The Benefits To Be Derived from Interstate Organization." After attacking the trusts and the combines—the Armours and Cudahys, the Hammonds, Swifts and Morrisons—he built the case for one national association:

Turn in whatever direction you may, and large interests are protected by associated effort. . . .the insurance men. . .the national banks. . .the stockyards corporations. . .each speak to us with a single voice, hold us in the iron grip of a single strong hand. . . .The single shipper {cattleman}, in his effort for terms and conditions, is fighting an individual battle against a thousand combined in one, against hundreds of thousands of dollars controlled by a single mind, the will of the organization. It is an unequal battle. . . .Alone, the shipper is nothing; in combination, everything.

Then "The Benefits To Be Derived from State and County Organization," was delivered by J.R. Van Boskirk of Nebraska:

Indeed it would seem that success, in this age of intense competition and clashing of different interests, comes only from association of those having common interests, followed by cooperation, organization, leadership and attention to detail. . . .To awaken and put in action public opinion is the work of local associations. When every good citizen in a county belongs to an association pledged to give his influence, his money, his vote, to the maintenance of the sacred rights of all property, whether large or small, then public officers can be depended upon to do their duty thoroughly. . . .In a democratic community individuals are very powerless. . . .As individuals we can do nothing; combined with lawful purposes, we can accomplish any necessary end. . . .All that is needed is cooperation, organization, leadership and attention to details, and the world is ours.

Public Lands Already An Issue

The three-day program was brimming with inspirational and educational topics, including the ever-controversial public lands problem, which appeared on the agenda in 1898 and has appeared on every Association agenda since. Wyoming Governor William A. Richards explained why it was and would continue to be a festering issue:

The disposition of the public domain is a question that has been of the greatest importance to the people since the federation of states. . .In round numbers, 1,850,000,000 acres are included. Out of this area of public land has been carved 19 states and five territories lying west of the Mississippi River. . .If there was any hope that we could educate Congress up to a proper appreciation of our necessities within the lifetime of this generation, then I would have no objection to turning both the land and water over to the control of Congress, but I do not believe that we can do this. . .I believe our

The Brown Palace

General headquarters of the convention are at Brown Palace Hotel, rooms 235, 237,239. Committeemen in charge of every detail will be found there.

—from the *Program*, National Stock Growers Convention, 1898

The Cattlemen's Favorite Hotel

When cattlemen met in Denver in 1898 to form the National Live Stock Association (NLSA), most stayed at the new, six-year-old Brown Palace Hotel.

During the 20th century, more meetings of cattlemen have been held at the Brown Palace than at any other still-existing hotel and it remains a cattlemen's tradition to stay at the Brown.

It was here in 1905 that a splinter group organized the American Stock Growers Association (ASGA), and here in 1906 that ASGA merged with NLSA to become the American National Live Stock Association.

It was also here in the 1950s, during the National Western Stock Show, that Colorado Governor Dan Thornton exhibited his prize-winning Herefords in the famed hotel lobby (below), a lobby where cattlemen like to sit and admire the eight-story atrium.

Many presidents have visited the Brown, including Teddy Roosevelt and Dwight Eisenhower. For Ike, the chef developed a special dish, "Beef Tenderloin President," still served today, and a suite is reserved in his name.

The Last Great Buffalo Barbecue

The city fathers of Denver, in anticipation of a new national organization that would surely be headquartered in Denver, wanted to show its appreciation with "The Last Great Buffalo Barbecue," scheduled for Friday afternoon immediately after the close of the 1898 convention.

Following is a report on that unforgettable barbecue, gleaned from stories in *The Denver Post* and *The Rocky Mountain News*, January 25-28, 1898.

The plans were grandiose and, the committee thought, very thorough. "The biggest feast ever in Denver" certainly warranted the support of merchants, who bought blocks of tickets for their customers, employees and friends. The Burlington made available five special trains—one scheduled out every 15 minutes, beginning at 1:00 p.m.—essentially to transport the 2,000 delegates and guests from downtown to the Denver Union Stockyards where the barbecue was to be held. Following the delegates, as a matter of courtesy, the ticket-holding citizens would be transported. The delegates would be greeted by the First Regiment Band, amid the banners and bunting, playing Sousa's "Turn Loose the Dogs of War" march. Also, 48 uniformed policemen were on duty; and they had side-tracked a box car for a temporary jail, if needed.

To prepare and serve the savories were 35 chefs, 200 white-aproned waiters and 40 beer servers. They had garnered 11,000 pounds of meat, including 34 quarters of beef, four large buffalo, five elk, seven Rocky Mountain sheep, two bears, 400 kegs of beer, 1,000 gallons of coffee and other provisions: enough to liberally serve 20,000 hungry people.

The menu—fit for kings—was published in the newspapers:

Buffalo with Onion Basting
Wild Mutton with Mint Sauce
Venison with Burnt Sage
Elk
Beef with Garlic Basting
Possum and Sweet Potatoes

Tantalizing! So irresistible, in fact, that tickets became scarce and were scalped for as much as $2 per couple. Chamber of Commerce officials were so pleased with the response, they printed more tickets and, it later was revealed, distributed them indiscriminately. Many ended up in saloons, dance houses and lower resorts of that district, assuring the attendance of disreputables from the toughest classes.

An estimated 30,000 people showed up!

Regrettably, many of the local citizens, including the hoodlums, bullies and hobos, arrived early. They lined the tables 30 to 40 deep, clamoring for food and beer. When the beer servers decided to stop serving them—the hospitable thing to do since most of the guests had not arrived—wild disorder prevailed. The mob turned over tables, rustled the meat and commandeered the beer.

The police were overpowered, so the cowboys, being cowboys, instinctively "helped out." After the dust had settled, the sad news was that three-fourths of the people did not get fed and one delegate was charged with murdering a local citizen. The fiasco was an embarrassment to the local cattlemen's committee and to all honorable citizens of Denver.

Nevertheless, it was a party to be talked about for years and a memorable first convention for the National Live Stock Association.

experience with congressional appropriations will be in the future just what it has been in the past.

Business was limited at this convention, except for the all-important formation of a new organization, the adoption of bylaws and the election of officers.

The New Association

The National Live Stock Association (NLSA) of the United States was founded.

The new Association bylaws provided for membership of all state, county and local livestock associations; also for all branches or entities associated with the livestock industry. Each association would have one delegate at large, plus an additional delegate for each 10,000 head of stock represented by such association. The top delegate fee for the first year was $2.50. Annual dues were set at $10 per association, plus 25 cents for each 1,000 head represented. Thus, at the beginning, the important principle was established that dues would be on a sliding scale, based on the number of animals, rather than a flat rate.

The first state organization to join was the Colorado Stock Growers Association, one of the organizers of the convention, followed by the Cattle Raisers Association of Texas.

Elected officers were: President, John W. Springer of Colorado; Vice President, John M. Holt of Montana; Treasurer, George L. Goulding of Colorado; Secretary, Charles F. Martin of Denver.

In 1899, the NLSA was barely one year old, but the United States was 123 years old and the 19th century was drawing to a close. The timing provided irresistible rationale for looking back and looking ahead.

In reviewing the first year of activity, Springer stated, *The first aim of this Association has been to get as active members every live stock association and organization in the United States.* The progress toward that aim gave the leadership much pride. Secretary Martin reported 53 organizations as members, representing 5,000 persons, with 9 million head of stock and a combined investment of $300 million.

But an early pattern of membership established some limitations for this "national" association, limitations which would prevail for over half a century. Martin explained, *While the work being done is national in scope, the greater part of the cattle of commerce coming from the West has caused a preponderance of membership and interest to be confined to the West.*

Issues: The Reason for Association

While the first convention was essentially a planning session, the second convention set the pace for conventions thereafter. The need for the association was to confront, discuss and seek solutions to the issues at hand. In 1899 this process was well underway. President Springer noted the most important "modernizers" that had revolutionized the entire live stock industry in the last two decades and that now were the basis of the issues facing the industry at the turn-of-the-century.

1. Rapid and more humane railroad transportation.
2. High bred stock in all lines.
3. The modern packing house.
4. Refrigerator cars and ships.
5. National and state quarantines.
6. Thorough live stock inspection by states.
7. Bounties for pest extermination.
8. More sacred regard for law by stockmen.

> ***You cannot do much unless you form a close partnership with the press gang, and for one I want to be counted close up and counted often.***
>
> —NLSA President Springer

9. Rigid governmental sanitary measures.
10. Lower rates of interest on live stock paper.
11. Signal service reports as forecaster of storms.
12. More generally educated (better read) live stock men.

But he urged delegates not to use these developments as excuses but as the building blocks with which to move ahead:

The men, or set of men, who are continually looking backward for inspiration; who are chuck full of calamity forebodings; who

John W. Springer

First President
1898-1903

Our Moses, Our Brutus

John W. Springer served five years as president, longer than any other president. After three years, he asked to be replaced, but some of his peers called him "the ideal president" and went on to re-elect him two more times. Undoubtedly, he was a man of destiny: the right man at the right time to organize, lead and build a new Association to permanency. As his successor observed, *Mr. Springer's power and influence over men is unbounded; it has no limit.*

A nationally-known orator and a master organizer, he began his brilliant career as an attorney and state representative in Illinois, then as a banker in Dallas, before moving to Denver for his wife's health. In Denver, Springer was engaged in banking, mining, ranching and politics. After serving as mayor of Denver, he was a Colorado nominee for vice president of the United States. As President of NLSA,, he was a spellbinder. Some members referred to him as "Our Moses" others as "Our Brutus."

An eloquent speaker and inspiring personality, he unwaveringly pushed his organization, his industry and his brother stockmen to higher plateaus. A learned scholar himself, Springer believed and preached that education was the greatest need of the world, especially the West.

At the 1901 convention, he said,

In our early days of stock raising and farming, infantry methods of crude expediency tided many a stockman and farmer over financial battle. . . .today it requires the heavy artillery of college education.

And, he declared enthusiastically,

There is a smaller sphere for the uneducated man every decade, and a diminishing possibility of success for the man who does not read. The reading man is in the saddle. The thinking man is guiding our national destinies.

And on yet another occasion he enthralled his audience:

Woe to that leader who seeks to sidetrack the energies of the American people! Woe to the pessimist who continually predicts clouds, failures and defeat for American genius—he will drop out. . . .

Springer promoted "high-bred stock" and livestock shows, occasionally quoting one of his axioms:

. . .The stockman who gains the greatest reward will be he who places quality above quantity in all of his dealings in livestock. . . .Have the best of everything about you, and garner happiness rather than supreme selfishness. Make the world better for your having lived, and your children will rise up and pronounce your names with a benediction!

He never missed an opportunity to praise the press for their role in elevating the cattle industry.

You cannot do much, unless you form a close partnership with the press gang and for one I want to be counted close up and counted often.

Predictably, the press responded favorably. At the 1901 convention in Chicago, there were 70 representatives of the press and their names were printed in the permanent proceedings.

CHARLES F. MARTIN

FIRST SECRETARY
1898 -1904

FAITHFUL EVEN UNTO DEATH

Secretary Charles F. Martin, the second-half of the remarkable Springer-Martin team, was remembered as "the chief spirit of the NLSA for its first years." He was unassuming, efficient, well educated, a good communicator, knowledgeable of the industry and "faithful even unto death."

Born in Kentucky and reared in Iowa, Martin moved to Colorado while helping build the Santa Fe railroad. There he stayed, first as a cowboy, then as a sheep rancher, until 1880 when former Senator Stephen W. Dorsey, a well-known "cattle baron," enticed him to Springer, New Mexico, to edit the *NEW MEXICAN STOCKMAN*. At that time, the area was ruled by elements such as Billy the Kid and others. So when the youthful editor started a war for law and order, there were numerous threats and attempts upon his life. Conditions became so bad that United States troops were sent from Santa Fe to take over Springer. Even so, Martin withdrew to Denver where he soon became manager of the Associated Press, a position he held for eight years, until he helped organize the National Live Stock Association and became its first secretary.

Among Martin's greatest contributions to the permanency of the Association was his instigation of data retrieval and information dissemination. He believed that the need for information was at the heart of many issues and would eventually solve the industry's problems. He gathered information from every source available, reliable or not, and sent out the information through a bulletin service in the association. Although going through a number of names and formats, this service exists today and is the constant contact between the Association and its membership.

Martin was in frail health from consumption (tuberculosis) but his friends said his mental energy was out of all proportion to his physical strength. His contagious enthusiasm was refreshing.

As recorded in *PROSE AND POETRY OF THE CATTLE INDUSTRY OF THE UNITED STATES*, recognized by some as the most important book yet written on the range cattle industry,

> *There are few who are more widely and more favorably known . . . .His life seemed to be wrapped up in the interests and usefulness of the National Live Stock Association. He thought of nothing else, labored for nothing else; and died while going forth to serve it.*

On September 21, 1904, Martin left Denver for an Association meeting in Cheyenne. A few miles out, he suffered a hemorrhage of the lungs and was removed from the train in Greeley where he died, literally "in the harness."

Former President Springer memorialized Martin thus:

> *His voice, his pen, his influence, were always for a charge forward, and no man can truthfully say that Charlie Martin ever advised a retreat.*

The last letter Martin wrote was to Theodore Roosevelt. Springer delivered it in person. It relayed to the range-educated President three requests of importance to the stockmen of the country. According to Springer, *All three of our requests were urged upon the attention of Congress in a ringing message* [by President Roosevelt], *such as our people will never forget.*

thrive on opposition to any and all measures; who are constantly quoting ancient history, are not fit to lead progressive, enterprising, 20th century Americans.

This theme (preparing for the next century) would be reflected a hundred years later as the Association created a long-range plan for moving into the 21st century.

Let it be understood here and now, that the American stockman proposes to take care of himself, and that he is not supplicant at the doors of the federal Congress for any subsidy, for any bonus or for any policy which seeks 'forty acres and a mule'.

—NLSA President Springer
Addressing the 1903 convention

RAILROADS LAUDED AND DAMNED

Railroad transportation was at the head of the list, because railroads probably had done more to revolutionize the cattle industry than anything. And cattlemen knew it. Nevertheless, railroads seemed to be the proverbial target of condemnation—scarcely ahead of packers and stockyards—at all cattlemen's gatherings of that day.

M.A. Daugherty of Nebraska attempted to be objective in addressing the 1899 convention. After pointing out the mutual dependency of railroads and cattlemen, he said he had discovered a "chillness" toward each other, then went on to explain the importance and impact of railroads. Of the 940 delegates and 2,000 visitors attending this convention, over 100 were railroad agents.

Daugherty gave a brief history of the network of railroads that was rapidly covering the country. *The first trans-continental and the pioneer of all lines was the Union and Central Pacific*, according to Daugherty. Finished in 1868, this line became the main artery of commerce throughout the heart of the western half of America. Another great trans-continental line, the Atchison, Topeka & Santa Fe, headed across the continent in 1870, reaching Santa Fe, New Mexico, in 1880 and El Paso in 1881. The Burlington started building in Nebraska in 1869 and, after gridironing the state with 2,600 miles of tracks, continued on to Denver and Billings, Montana.

Railroads made the great stockyards possible, asserted Daugherty, *and changed the way cattle were marketed.* They brought an end to the great cattle drives from Texas, which from 1873 to 1885 averaged over 300,000 head annually. (Others estimated 500,000 head annually.)

The combination of railroads and stockyards resulted in a new phenomenon for that day, as noted by Daugherty,

A small percent of this immense aggregate of livestock is handled and slaughtered locally. It goes on hoof to the packing house, and from there is distributed throughout the world, often returning, dressed and cured, back to the original shipping points.

Then he concluded with this terse plea for cooperation:

To you railroad gentlemen, I say that we, as stockmen, simply ask justice. . . And to you, brothers, everywhere, I say, whenever you make a contract with these roads, be honest.

PACKERS PRAISED AND CONDEMNED

Along with expanded railroads and central stockyards came the big packing plants, with mass production techniques and refrigeration, which provided year-round markets. This triad—railroads, stockyards and packing plants—provided the backbone for the New West economy and created a boom such as the country had never before experienced, including prosperity for the cattle industry. Springer drew applause at the 1901 convention when he said,

It was a great day for our country when Armour, Swift, Morris, Cudahy, Hammond, Sulzberger and others notified the stockmen and the world that they would kill everything offered, waste nothing and supply the world's markets.

All of which seems incongruous with the constant complaints and perennial resolutions against railroads, stockyards and packers. As early as 1900, a resolution charged that competition among carriers had become minimized by the growing concentration of railroads into large systems and asked that "some tribunal be given absolute power over rates." The following year the Association wrote a memorial to the President, the Senate and the House of Representatives of the United States urging legislation to correct an injustice, because *the Interstate Commerce Commission does not have the power to fix rates, as was intended when it was created in 1887.* The animosity toward packers was even greater! Packers and railroads had become favorite targets for the Association, and would remain so for several decades.

First Lobbyist for Stockmen

Very early in the 20th Century, as the leadership became assured that they had a permanent organization, they initiated some lasting activities. One of the first and most significant was representation in the nation's capital. In 1901, Judge William M. Springer (no relation to President Springer) was engaged as legal counsel and lobbyist for $3,000 per year. That was enough to strain the Association's budget, which totalled $15,000 for the year, but "it had to be done." For a booming industry that represented $4.5 billion invested capital, they reasoned, an increase in assessments from 25 cents to 50 cents per 1,000 cattle represented was justified, even though it caused some local associations to drop their membership.

Early attempts at swaying public policy were positive endeavors for the Association. That sweet taste of legislative success prompted Springer to appeal for a larger legislative and legal fund. *In my judgement,* he said in 1903, *at least $10,000 should be kept available for such purposes.* Such a proposal would be repeated and reinforced many times

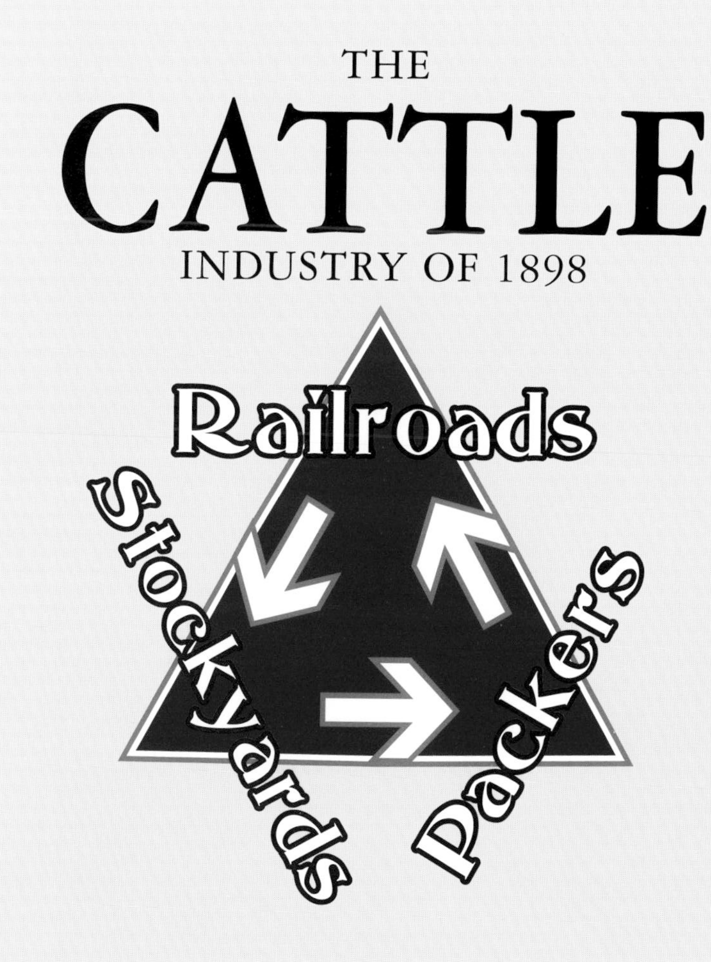

The cattle industry in 1898 was not only regional, focused almost entirely in the West, but also differed substantially from today's industry especially in how cattle were readied for and delivered to market.

The industry was organized to produce steers four or five years old which were shipped by train from local loading stations along the ever-growing network of rail lines to central markets as grass fat steers from July to November.

Stockyards provided the accumulation points for cattle coming in on the rail cars. Cattle were not fed as in today's definition, but rather sorted and distributed out to packers.There were no feeder or stocker cattle, and heifers were never slaughtered. What feeding there was in the Corn Belt was because midwestern farmers kept cattle to use up excess corn. But this was usually a sideline to their corn and hog economy.

Packers, too, had to be concentrated at the rail centers. They killed all kinds of livestock. Their customers were small butcher shops, which needed an assortment of product. The refrigerator cars were loaded with beef quarters hanging from the ceiling. The floor of the car had boxes of ham, bacon and lamb carcasses wrapped in cheese cloth and veal calf carcasses with the hide still on. Freight rates seemed high, but it was a one-way haul to the eastern markets. There was no back haul; stock cars had to go west empty.

Through the history of the industry cattlemen have worried about the size and ethics of railroad, packers, and eventually about buyers, feeders and any other group who seems to be operating outside of their control. At that time it was difficult for a rancher to realize that once the animal was slaughtered it became a very perishable product. It had to be moved into consumption no matter what the conditions, or lost entirely.

Honorary Lifetime Members

Colonel Alexander Majors

Colonel Joseph G. McCoy

Honorary Lifetime Members

During its 100-year history, the Association recognized only three men as Honorary Lifetime Members: Colonel Alexander Majors in 1899, Colonel Joseph G. McCoy in 1899 and General John J. Pershing in 1916.

Colonel Alexander Majors

Colonel Alexander Majors was for nearly 50 years one of the best known names in the West. In his active brain was conceived the overland freight line, the overland stage and the pony express.

His company, Russell, Majors & Waddell, supplied military and trading posts from the Missouri River across the Great Plains to Santa Fe, Salt Lake City and beyond. In 1858, the United States Government awarded them the largest overland transportation contract to that date. For the 16 millon pounds of freight, the company engaged 4,000 wagons, 40,000 oxen, 1,000 mules and 5,000 men. Among his employees were Kit Carson and William F. (Buffalo Bill) Cody.

Born in Missouri in 1814, he later lived in Leavenworth, Kansas City, California and Denver. In 1893, Majors published an autobiography, *Seventy Years on the Plains*. His picture in stained glass was placed in the dome of the Colorado State Capital in Denver.

At eighty years old, he spoke at the 1899 meeting of the association on the subject of "Winter Grazing" and was introduced as "probably the oldest cattleman in attendance."

Excerpts from that speech:

> *. . .I believe I am the first man, with two exceptions, that discovered that the domestic . .cow could be wintered upon the plains or in the valleys of the Rocky Mountains [the other two being Bent and Ward of Wyoming, with whom he communicated on the subject]. . . .I was freighting for the government. . . and they gave me a trainload of freight late in the season. I was compelled to leave my oxen in the country, and, to my astonishment, next spring found that they were in better condition than the cattle I had at home and was feeding at the time with corn. [For the next five years*

he successfully wintered around 10,000 head in Wyoming]. . . there wasn't such a thing as disease among the buffaloes. . .The buffaloes changed their feeding grounds almost every single day. . . .If you gentlemen who handle and manage stock on feed that is obtained in pastures will change as often as possible from one pasture to the other, and keep that up, you will find that you will be less liable to disease. . . .There is nothing more important than the paper [on sanitary conditions] that was read here a while ago. . . I was thirty years old before. . . Texas Fever was ever heard of; but when people began making drives of cattle from Texas further north, the condition of those cattle some time or other produced the same disease with our cattle further north. . . .My experience has been from the beginning, that the range you find in nature, the grasses, the herbs [will disappear] as soon as civilization takes possession of them.

He also assured the audience that proper range management would resolve the sheep and cattle grazing conflicts.

General John J. Pershing and Staff.

Colonel Joseph G. McCoy

Colonel McCoy built the town of Abilene, Kansas, and became the biggest cattle trader in the world.

Following the Civil War, he observed that the northern states had depleted their cattle numbers while Texas, having refused to sell to the Yankee Army, had built up surpluses. Then, when the Union Pacific Railway pushed through Kansas, McCoy saw the potential to help Texas trail drivers get more for their cattle and get beef to the northern consumers—at a price they could afford. The possibilities absorbed his every thought.

Making a deal with the Union Pacific, he set about building every facility needed for a thriving cattle shipping depot: holding and loading pens, barns, hotels and homes, thus creating the town of Abilene, Kansas. In addition to advertising the new enterprise, he sent scouts down the trail to intercept a drove and sell the trail boss on the advantages of diverting to Abilene.

McCoy was credited with handling as many as 700,000 head in a single year, shipping 10,000 cars eastward and in helping make Kansas City *the* market of the Missouri Valley. He also hired surveyors to lay out a trail extending from Abilene to Corpus Christi, a trail over which 10 million cattle would ultimately pass, as well as opening the Chisholm Trail and drives to Cottonwood Falls and Wichita, Kansas. In 1874, he wrote *Historic Sketches of the Cattle Trade of the West and Southwest.* NLSA recognized him as the "Founder of the Southwest cattle trade."

But adversity struck his enterprises, as it has many big cattle traders over the decades, and he left Abilene a crushed man.

General John J. Pershing

General John J. (Black Jack) Pershing was a national hero, the kind cattlemen admired. He fought the Apache and Sioux Indians; then fought in the Spanish American War and in the Philippines against the Moros. In 1916-1917 he led the expedition in Mexico against Pancho Villa.

During World War I he led the American Expeditionary Forces (AEF) to victory in Europe, emerging from the War as America's most celebrated hero.

His speech, well received at the 1916 Convention in El Paso was on patriotism and preparedness.

Nothing had revolutionized *the cattle industry as had the railroad. It permitted cattlemen to expand their business by reaching the big markets of the East; and at the turn of the century, it was the only feasible way to get beef from West to East. But for decades cattlemen would regard railroads as a major foe.*

during the subsequent decades, albeit not always funded. By 1993, however, the Association spent approximately $1.75 million on legislative activity, plus another $409,000 through their political action committee and took steps to fund a new legal fund.

> ***The law of supply and demands governs, but what the demand is or what the supply, every man is allowed to guess for himself... Men argue that there are fewer cattle in the country than the demand calls for, or vice versa, but their arguments are based entirely upon opinion.***
>
> —NLSA Secretary Martin

HOW MUCH GOVERNMENT HELP TO ACCEPT

While declaring their independence and abhorrence to government interference, the early cattle industry leaders were not adverse to government help. Although this difference exists within most industries, it has drawn the cynical attention of some media and legislators throughout the history of the Association. Even so, it is a dilemma for cattlemen: how much government help to request or accept has resurfaced many times.

While their actions sometimes appeared borderline, their philosophy was firmly on the side of rugged individualism. Like most Association presidents throughout the 20th century, Springer made this clear in his 1903 address:

> *Let it be understood here and now, that the American stockman proposes to take care of himself, and that he is not supplicant at the doors of the federal Congress for any subsidy, for any bonus or for any policy which seeks 'forty acres and a mule'.*

PRIORITY ON COMMUNICATIONS

A less controversial activity, which also had permanence, was the *NATIONAL LIVE STOCK BULLETIN*. It was the only source of information on markets, range conditions, cattle movement, exports and other statistics. Secretary Martin collected this information—sketchy as it was—from the railroads, stockyards, state boards of agriculture, members and elsewhere. The crucial need for such information was pointed out by Martin:

> *The law of supply and demand governs, but what the demand is or what the supply, every man is allowed to guess for himself. . . .Men argue there are fewer cattle in the country than the demand calls for, or vice versa, but their arguments are based entirely upon opinion.*

There was a government census every 10 years, but it was so general in reporting cattle numbers and so slow in being published that it was of little value. For example, the only breakdown in numbers was for "milch cows" and "other cattle." The Association considered it a great achievement when the census finally separated "work oxen" and classified beef cattle by age categories. The bulletin service has continued on throughout the years of the Association.

In 1905 the Springer-Martin era ended. There is no doubt that the force and abilities of those two colorful men launched the permanent Association and gave it the structure and purpose that would carry it through the next century.

Bull Butter vs. Cow Butter

The debate was traditional butter vs. oleomargarine, the latter made primarily from tallow and vegetable oil. Butter sold as high as 27 cents per pound while oleo sold as low as 15 cents per pound. A two-cent tax was already imposed on margarine; and the Grout Bill, sponsored by eastern congressmen at the urging of dairymen, would add another 10 cents for the margarine. Dairy interests claimed that margarine was not as healthful or as sanitary; while beef interests maintained there was no chemical difference and margarine was in fact more sanitary.

NLSA celebrated victory when the Grout Bill was defeated in 1901. But a similar "butter subsidy" bill was reintroduced the following year and the Dairy Union threatened to retaliate against the Association by "opposing every measure you ask to have enacted." Fighting words for NLSA!

The debate raged on. Arguments by cattlemen expressed strongly one opinion:

> *The power to tax was intended for the public good, and never was intended to destroy one industry to encourage and build up another industry. Since there is no difference in the two products, working men should not be forced to pay more for this pure and healthful food product (margarine)....All cows are dual purpose in this respect. They produce dairy butter from the milk and oleomargarine from their fat when dead.*

While dairymen voiced another:

> *It has become impossible for the eastern farmer to compete successfully with the western farmer, encouraged in effect by governmental subsidy. In the free use of public lands, the beef cattle and sheep industries are still receiving enormous governmental subsidies....Can any reasonable man accept and use free or cheap government land, which is practically a subsidy, and at the same time refuse to grant dairymen the just protection they so sorely need?*

The "butter subsidy" bill (additional tax on margarine) did pass in 1902—the first of many wins by the dairy industry.

Chicago *(left) was the largest market but not the oldest.* **Kansas City,** *the next largest stockyards, (large photo at top) were opened in 1870, followed by Omaha, East St. Louis, New York and Denver. In 1898, the Bureau of Animal Industry listed 27 Principal Stock Centers, which that year received 7,881,140 head of cattle.*

The Chicago Union Stockyards *(below) as seen in 1865.*

The Brighton Market *in Boston (directly above) began about 1800 and by the time the Western Railroad arrived in 1842, it was handling as many as 8,000 head per week.*

Joe Beeler WINCHESTER HOSPITALITY

Establishing The Domain

Whether the enemy was homesteaders or sheepmen, cattlemen fought hard to keep lands open for grazing. The need for these lands in an ever-shrinking range was the seed of the ongoing debate over use of public lands.

CHAPTER THREE

STAYING THE COURSE

After five years of Springer and Martin—a tough duo to follow—the industry and the Association fell into troubled waters. Prices dropped drastically from $24 per head in 1900 to $15 in 1905. Railroads attempted to raise freight rates, in spite of their deteriorating service. Membership support waned. Sheep wars and continued discontent further divided members over public lands. Export markets, particularly in France and Germany, were down. Reorganization of the Association was unsuccessful, and a splinter group left taking with it some of the most prestigious members.

The year just closed has been a momentous one for the live stock interests and for your Association, said a solemn Frank J. Hagenbarth, the second president, in his 1905 address. *Calamities and blessings have been mixed.* A man of reason, of humility, of guarded optimism, he appealed for understanding and harmony.

WHO'S TO BLAME?

Hagenbarth quoted a New Mexico cattleman, who wrote:

> *We have had a devil of a rough deal these last few years that we begin to doubt the honesty and good intentions of every one. It may not be the packers, it may not be the commission men, it may not be the sheepmen or even the railroads, but some way every man's hand seems to be against us these days.*

To which Hagenbarth added, *When level-headed men feel this way, all is not right.*

Searching for "blessings," he cited the fact that cattlemen had a friend in

TIMELINE

1906 Upton Sinclair writes *THE JUNGLE*, Leads to Meat Inspection Act.

FDA established to insure wholesome and truthfully labeled foods.

Earthquake and fire destroy most of San Francisco.

President Roosevelt awarded Nobel Prize for mediation of Russo-Japanese War.

National Live Stock Association and American Stock Growers Association merge.

1907 Financial panic results in bank runs and sharp decline in stock market.

Ziegfield's Follies open.

Congress sets minimum grazing fees on public lands.

1908 Ammonia fertilizer synthesized.

Ford introduces Model T for $850.

1909 Taft becomes 27th president.

1910 Boy Scouts of America founded.

Congress passes 16th ammendment, for income tax, ratified 1913.

Camp Fire Girls founded.

1911 Hoover Dam dedicated.

Ty Cobb hits .420.

Sherman Antitrust act used to break American Tobacco Co. and Standard Oil Co. monopolies.

Commercial production of synthetic fiber rayon begins.

Congress authorizes Forest Service to purchase two million acres per year for five years.

First truck delivery of livestock reaches Indianapolis.

1912 Titanic sinks killing 1,500 people.

New Mexico becomes 47th state.

Arizona becomes 48th state.

American Indian Jim Thorpe declared "World's Greatest Athlete" after winning decathlon and pentathlon events in Olympics at Stockholm.

ISSUES

Declining Prices
•
Division in Association
•
Sheep Wars
•
Meat Inspection Act
•
Regulating the Rails
•
Beef Exports and Imports
•
Public Domain
•
Permanent Organization for Cattlemen

the White House, Teddy Roosevelt, and that cattlemen now were using more thoroughbred animals to transform their scrubs into desirable meat animals.

Even for better cattle, the market continued to deteriorate. According to an Executive Committee report, cattle feeders in the Missouri and Mississippi Valley during the winter of 1902 and the spring of 1903 lost from $15 to $30 per head, for a total of over $750 million, "the only apparent reason being the unjust manipulation of prices at the market."

In addition, there was still the alarming talk about a merger of the seven big packers.

TIME TO CONFRONT

Clearly, it was time for "power to meet power." Members organized the Independent Packing Company, incorporated under the laws of Arizona with a capital of $5 million, to place producer-owned plants in the major market centers. The plan was that stockmen throughout the country would subscribe to the extent of $1 for each bovine animal owned, 25 cents for each sheep and 25 cents for each hog. It was a bold idea, but one which never materialized.

Another significant development, in the opinion of Hagenbarth, was a "great change in the trend of our thoughts concerning the public domain," that all grazing areas should be placed under governmental jurisdiction. Approximately 400 million acres of public lands remained that were fit for nothing but grazing, according to several proposals. If leased for two cents per acre, these fees would raise $8 million toward the development of irrigation in the West. "A way to develop the West without cost to the government," cattlemen maintained. It was another bold idea, but not salable in the nation's capital.

Our own mistakes have been many, acknowledged Hagenbarth on the short-sighted and unguarded policy of grazing the public lands, *where two blades of grass grew before but one grows now.*

But under the circumstances of free grazing, there was no incentive to practice conservation. If a rancher attempted to conserve the grass in a given area, in anticipation of a bad winter or a dry summer, someone else could move in with a herd or flock or both and graze it to the ground.

This is what led to the so-called "sheep wars," where ranchers often hired hoodlums to shoot or club to death hundreds of sheep. The sheepmen maintained, however, that they had as much right to the open range as the cattlemen. In fact, during times of depressed cattle prices, some cattlemen were known to switch to sheep.

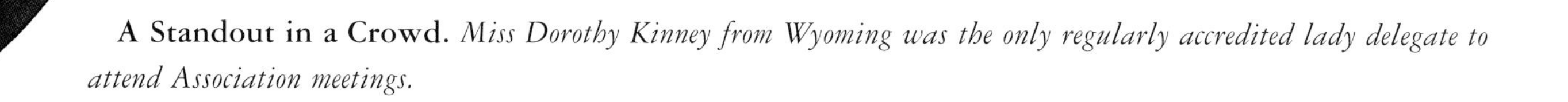

A Standout in a Crowd. *Miss Dorothy Kinney from Wyoming was the only regularly accredited lady delegate to attend Association meetings.*

One Association For All

Like many Utah producers at the time, Hagenbarth was both a sheep and a cattle man. Thus, he was convinced that the Association could best serve the producers of all livestock be it cattle, sheep, goats, hogs or horses. Likewise, clinging to its original objectives, he wanted the Association to represent all segments of the industry: producers, commission companies, stockyards, packers and railroads.

This philosophy, although sincere and somewhat idealistic, would cause Hagenbarth and the Association some later grief. The sheepmen had organized the National Wool Growers Association in 1865, and were reasonably pleased with it; the railroads had their association. The packers had organized, as had the grain dealers, the coal miners, the steel manufacturers and even the whiskey makers. Some speakers chided cattlemen that they were the only significant industry without their own association.

FRANK J. HAGENBARTH
President 1904-1905
Salt Lake City, Utah

A large rancher in Utah, Texas and Kansas, he was president of the National Live Stock Association when it still represented cattle, sheep, goats, hogs and horses. . .when the market plummeted to $15 per head. . .and when "rebels" split off to form the American Cattle Growers Association. Known as a man of reason, humility and patience, he later was called upon at conventions to "lift the spirits" of fellow cattlemen. He also was president of the National Wool Growers Association for 21 consecutive years.

For Cattle Growers Alone

As early as January 1901, at the Salt Lake City convention of the NLSA, several cattlemen held a rump session to discuss a separate association. Their first formal meeting was held the following March in Denver, to organize the American Cattle Growers Association. F.C. Lusk of Chico, California, was elected president and A.E. de Ricqles of Denver, secretary.

The Denver Times was rather blunt in its reporting, under the headline, "Sheep War Is Now On." The prime purpose of the new organization, said the *Times*,

> *. . .is the protection of the cattle industry from the ravages of the range-destroying sheep industry and to place the gigantic cattle business on a footing to maintain its proper place among the important pursuits of the country. . . .Plainly, the majority of the delegates have no sheep interests and no interest in sheep except to have them kept off of the cattle ranges.*

The Denver Post elaborated further on the purpose of the new Association:

> *An organization of cattle growers alone, barring yardmen, packing men, railway men, and particularly shutting out sheepmen. The proposition is that the Western range is not big enough for both cattle and sheep and that as cattle represent the greater interest financially. . .the sheepmen must find other sections for their range—some place in Alaska or Mexico—any place except the places the cattlemen want.*

Votes $10 Per Individual

According to the newspapers, the new organization was to be more democratic. It was composed of individuals, not of associations, and each individual member was to have one vote. This policy purportedly was to protect the interest of the small producer. It also was a slap at the older national association, which permitted member associations to buy as many votes as they wished for $10 per vote. [The Cattle Growers

The National Live Stock Association *Fifth Annual Convention in Session at Studebaker's Theater in Chicago, 1902.*

of Texas reportedly would cast 1,000 to 1,500 votes, while representatives from Montana and Wyoming sometimes would do the same.]

> ***...we begin to doubt the honesty and good intentions of everyone. It may not be the packers, it may not be the commission men, it may not be the sheepmen or even the railroads, but some way every man's hand seems to be against us these days.***
>
> *—Delegate from New Mexico Addressing the 1905 Convention*

However, one resolution at the new American Association did not appear very altruistic. Introduced by Colonel John P. Irish of California, it pledged the Association to the proposed law for leasing the public domain, "in the interest of the large stock owners and against the interest of the small owners."

The Denver newspapers reported on a second convention of the American Cattle Growers Association in 1902, when their membership was "nearly 450." However, no further accounts or official records have been found.

Will C. Barnes, one of the founders and first secretary of the American Stock Growers Association [organized three years later], later had one explanation for the controversy and lack of effectiveness. In 1926 Barnes wrote in *THE PRODUCER*:

> *We cowmen had a foolish idea, that the packers, the livestock commission men, the stockyard owners, and the railroad officials were responsible for most of our sorrows. There was no Forest Service then to blame it all on.*

Near the end of his term, in 1905, Hagenbarth attempted to reorganize the National Live Stock Association. His main concession was to eliminate the railroads from membership, but to retain the commission men, the stockyards and the packers. According to one report, the railroads and others offered the Association $40,000 to remain in.

Still, the idea of "one organization for all segments of the industry" did not have wide support. It was finally approved by the Committee on Reorganization by a vote of eight to seven. To any organization person, such a split vote spells trouble. When presented at the 1905 convention in Denver, there was a majority report and a minority report, followed by bitter debate.

Yet Another Organization Surfaces

The end result of the reorganization was that a number of cattlemen representing the larger Association members, such as the Cattle Raisers Association of Texas, walked out and went on to form another organization, the American Stock Growers Association.

Hagenbarth, a patient and persistent man, never stopped working for harmony. Quoting Emerson and Gladstone, he philosophized,

> *Consistency is the hobgoblin of petty minds. . . .Some people look upon a change of mind as though it were a disgrace. To me it is a sign of life. Only the dead never change.*

This philosophy and this approach ultimately paid off, for the following year the two national organizations would merge into one strong and lasting association, the American National Live Stock Association (ANSLA).

Following the troubles of the cattle industry in the 1904-1905 era, it appears that cattlemen had the right leader at the right time, as was to happen often in its history. And their new Association, the American National Live Stock Association, had a new begin-

The Sheep Wars

Whose Land Is It Anyway?

The invention of barbed wire and incentives given to settlers to homestead had broken up the free range. However, the tremendous amount of land owned by the federal government continued to be a problem throughout the history of the Association. One of the earliest conflicts, and definitely the most violent, over federal lands became known as "The Sheep Wars." Cattlemen wanted control over their leases of Federal land and hardly wanted to share it with other cattlemen, much less sheepmen. Sheep and cattle could not graze the same areas. Sheep would eat the grass down to a level that a cow could not graze, thereby ruining rangeland that was already crowded. But the sheepmen felt they had the same rights as cattlemen and continued to stake their claim on federal lands. Cattlemen sought to wipe out the sheepmen by intimidation and eventual killings of sheepherders and flocks of sheep.

Ironically many Association members were also sheep producers, and to some extent sheep were more profitable than cattle because they had two sources of income: wool and meat. Lambs could be sheared before going to market, and mutton was an accepted meat.

But as Honorary Lifetime Member Colonel Majors pointed out in the 1899 speech to the Convention, it was really a range management issue.

> *If the sheepmen had been a little more patient, and waited a little longer. . .there never would have been any fuss between the cattlemen and sheepmen. The cattle eat the first grass—the largest grass. When that goes away, he [cattleman] naturally takes his cattle away from that, and then the sheep man can come along and won't disturb him at all.*

ning. Hagenbarth, keeping firm to his original beliefs for a unified livestock association, went on to become president of the National Wool Growers Association for 21 consecutive years.

LEADERSHIP FOR A NEW BEGINNING

Murdo Mackenzie, the affable and cunning Scotsman, came to the United States in 1882, at age 35. He came first as assistant manager of the large Prairie Cattle Company, the first Scottish-owned ranch with headquarters in Trinidad, Colorado. Then, in 1891, he was hired as manager of an even larger Scottish firm, the Matador Land and Cattle Company, which had title to 445,457 acres, plus another 200,000 acres under lease. Under Mackenzie's management, the company continued to expand until 1916 when it owned 879,735 acres in Texas and a half-dozen other states, along with leased land. The Matador prevailed for seven decades, longer than any of the Scottish syndicates, but it, too, was finally broken up in 1951.

This step was taken with a view of getting the live stock producers united as much as possible. We are more anxious than ever to have individual support as well as support through the different associations.

—President Murdo Mackenzie

Address on the subject of why the Association needed individuals as well as associations

Mackenzie was a large, shrewd, forceful man, the kind of leader that commanded respect—the kind that the new, merged Association needed to get it back on course. After serving as the first and only president of the first splinter group, American Stock Growers Association, in 1905, he was elected president of the ANLSA after the merger. He would return three years later, in 1911, to be elected president again.

One of his first moves was to hire T.W. Tomlinson from Chicago for the post of Executive Secretary. Railroad freight rates were a major

Sam Houston Cowan—Association Lobbyist in Washington. *Judge William Springer had begun the long lobbying tradition for the Association when he was hired in 1901 as lobbyist in Washington. In 1905, when Murdo Mackenzie was elected president of the American Stock Growers Association—the cattlemen who had bolted from the NLSA—he immediately hired his friend Cowan as attorney and lobbyist. Cowan was also attorney-lobbyist for the Cattle Raisers Association of Texas, who continued to pay most of his salary and permitted him to represent both associations. Then when the American and National merged in 1906, Cowan stayed on until he retired in 1916. Considering that the cattlemen's first priority issue at that time was regulation of the railroads, it was not surprising that Cowan was recognized as "the greatest rate lawyer in the country." He never lost a case before the Interstate Commerce Commission (ICC). As a result, he became a friend of President Roosevelt, who offered him an appointment to the ICC. But he declined on the grounds that he wanted to continue the cattlemen's fight for fair freight rates.*

The first Federal Meat Inspection Act passed in 1906, *following Upton Sinclair's novel, The Jungle, a scathing exposé of the unsanitary conditions in Chicago packing plants. Cattlemen supported the effort because it gave beef a better acceptance in the marketplace. It was a great victory for the Association when it succeeded in having the federal government foot the bill for the inspectors.*

issue during those years and Tomlinson had gained a reputation of being a rate expert. During his 23-year tenure, the officers described him as "able and indefatigable," while railroad men often referred to him as "an encyclopedia."

Next, Mackenzie engaged his friend Sam H. Cowan of Fort Worth as attorney and lobbyist for the Association. Cowan, articulate and verbose, also was attorney for the Cattle Raisers Association of Texas; for whom Mackenzie had also served as president in 1902-1903.

During the next two decades, the names of Tomlinson and Cowan became an integral part of the frequent discussions about railroad rates. Railroad officials regarded these two with dread, while shippers felt they almost always could find some way of obtaining relief.

In his first presidential address, Mackenzie outlined some compromises made to accomplish the merger of the two rival associations. One was to admit individuals as well as associations. He explained:

> *This step was taken with a view of getting the live stock producers united as much as possible. We are more anxious than ever to have individual support as well as support through the different associations.*

This was an important policy, being both a practical move as well as a philosophical one. This has remained the policy of the Association unto this day.

Burning Issues

Mackenzie also outlined a number of burning issues. And a year later, in 1907, he ticked off most of them as "accomplishments of your Association." Railroad rates and problems were foremost but other landmark issues were tackled as well.

The first Federal Meat Inspection Act was passed in 1906. Meat inspection was welcomed by cattlemen. It forced packers to have clean

MURDO MACKENZIE
President 1906-1907, 1911
Trinidad and Denver, Colorado

An affable, cunning and forceful Scotsman, he became manager of the large Matador Land and Cattle Company, in Texas and a half-dozen other states. Instrumental in the first merger, Mackenzie was the first President of the resulting American National Live Stock Association, and later returned in 1911 to serve a second hitch. He then moved to Brazil to form the Brazil Land, Cattle and Packing Company, the largest ranch in the world, with nearly 10 million acres and 250,000 cows.

plants and assured the consumer of a good product, ultimately supporting more purchase of beef. However, they were not happy with the provision that packers pay for inspection when the packers openly said they would deduct that cost from the price paid to producers. ["user's fee"] The fight to have the cost borne by the federal government was a notable victory for the Association. It was successful in getting a $3 million appropriation to pay for federal meat inspection, thus establishing the tenuous principle that the government should pay for services that are in the public interest.

The export market in Europe was falling for two reasons: (1) Argentina was just developing their cattle industry and they were closer to the Atlantic Ocean than were the western ranchers, and (2) unrest in Europe with World War I brewing. An agreement on tariffs was reached with Germany, thus saving one of our largest export markets for beef. In 1900, the United States exported 8,849,800 pounds of canned meat to Germany; but by 1904, none. Germany claimed to shut out United States meat under the guise of keeping out diseases, but this action actually was retaliation for high tariffs on German manufactured products coming into the United States. Their willingness to begin imports of canned beef had mixed blessings and was for a purpose as we would later discover with the outbreak of World War I.

Public lands issues came a little closer to resolution. President Roosevelt made cattlemen's concerns a priority issue with a special message to Congress, as several bills were introduced. But Mackenzie told members it remained so controversial that the Association had *refrained from committing you one way or the other.* By 1908, a majority of western ranchers had even come to believe that range conditions were so unsatisfactory that government control or leasing was the only solution.

Protests against increased commission charges at the terminal markets were to no avail. Cattlemen organized the Co-operative Live Stock Commission Company to compete with existing commission companies. Although a separate organization from the ANLSA, the association did support it. It opened for business at Kansas City, St. Joseph and Chicago on September 1, 1906. The commissions charged were $2 per car less than charges established by the live stock exchanges, which lowered them to 50 cents per head on cattle with a maximum of $10 per car. It proved once again that struggling ranchers had little faith in anyone but themselves.

THE RENOWNED MACKENZIE

Mackenzie not only was popular with western cattlemen, he became world renowned and lived a good life. With headquarters in Colorado, he maintained fine homes in Trinidad and Denver, and traveled Europe.

His friendship with Teddy Roosevelt was a privilege cattlemen were to enjoy only a few times throughout their history, but it proved a beneficial one in these trying and exciting times.

While serving as president of the Association, Mackenzie met the international financier, Percival Farquahar, who envisioned that Europe was going to need much more beef. In 1911, he persuaded

A Friend in the White House

The Roosevelt Years

During Theodore Roosevelt's years as President, 1901-1909, the Association had a friend in The White House whose doors were always open to cattlemen. He assisted the Association with numerous issues and became good friends not only with ANSLA President Murdo Mackenzie (shown here sharing barbecue) but also with the Association lobbyist Sam Cowan and later with ANLSA President Dwight Heard. After all, following graduation from Harvard University in 1880, Roosevelt went west to become a rancher for a few years in North Dakota and Wyoming and he always considered himself "one of them."

Initially Roosevelt was the butt of jokes because of his Harvard accent, his dude dress and his thick eyeglasses. On his first roundup, he called out, *Hasten forward quickly there!* For weeks, the cowboys ordered each other around with *Hasten forward quickly there!*

> *On another occasion, he was approached in a hotel saloon by a bully who announced repeatedly, "Four Eyes is going to treat!" Finally, Teddy, who had been a champion boxer at Harvard, arose and muttered, Well, if I've got to, I've got to, and flattened the bully with a punch to the jaw. After that, he was called "Old Four Eyes," because it was considered an honor to have "old" used before your name.*

President Teddy Roosevelt wrote about Mackenzie in his book, *A Book Lover's Holidays in the Open:*

> *During my term as president he was, on the whole, the most influential of the western cattle growers. He was a leader of the far-seeing, enlightened element. He was a most powerful supporter of the government in the fight for the conservation of our national resources. . .for honest treatment of everybody and for the shaping of governmental policy in the interest of the small settler—the homemaker.*

"Bully" for Roosevelt

At the 1935 National Western Hereford Show, Murdo Mackenzie, then chairman of a commercial cow operation, outbid leading registered Hereford breeders buying the champion at an astronomical (for the depression) $3,100.

When asked how he justified paying so much for a bull. Murdo replied,

> *If we see a bull capable of adding as little as 50 cents to the value of each calf produced, the question isn't how much he costs, it's how much we lose if we don't buy and use him.*

Which led to the question, *What do you look for in buying bulls?* Mackenzie swung his chair to face the mounted head of a noted bull his company had used. *See that!* he demanded. Turning to the wall facing his desk he pointed to an unmistakable head picture of Teddy Roosevelt. *See that! See the similarity! I want to buy bulls with heads just like Teddy Roosevelt's.*

HENRY A. JASTRO
President 1908-1910, 1912-1914
Bakersfield, California

A German-Jewish immigrant, Jastro was one of the few Association presidents active in the Democratic Party. An imposing man physically, he also was known widely for his business acumen, prominence and influence. As manager of Kern County Land, Cattle and Water Company and two cattle companies in New Mexico, he and his companies finished 30,000 head of cattle, 25,000 sheep and 10,000 hogs annually. He also served on the Kern County Board of Supervisors for 24 years. Jastro Park, in Bakersfield, was named for him.

Mackenzie to go to Brazil and start in 1912 the Brazil Land, Cattle and Packing Company, with French financing, to produce beef for export. Within a very few years, he put together and was managing the largest ranch in the world.

Mackenzie would return to the United States in 1919 to challenge Association leaders on a new set of issues. Nevertheless, the Association flourished under his able leadership, and Mackenzie was yet another hard act to follow.

Strong Leadership Prevailed

Mackenzie was succeeded in 1908 to 1910 by yet another strong leader, another big man in stature and another big operator. Henry A. Jastro managed the Kern County Land, Cattle and Water Company of Bakersfield, California, as well as the Victoria and Boguillas Land and Cattle Companies of New Mexico. Together, these companies finished approximately 30,000 head of cattle, 25,000 sheep and 10,000 hogs annually.

Jastro, an imposing man physically, was a quiet, distinguished and powerful worker. The June 1919 issue of *The Producer,* the official publication of the ANLSA, said he was "recognized as the most prominent and influential livestock man in the United States, to whose efforts in its behalf the industry owes more, perhaps, than to those of any other individual."

The Mackenzie-Jastro-Mackenzie-Jastro Epoch

It was an unprecedented move, undoubtedly due to the leadership strength and national influence of the men involved, that Mackenzie and Jastro, two of the largest cattlemen in the country, would alternate as presidents of the Association during the years 1906 through 1914. This was the Mackenzie-Jastro-Mackenzie-Jastro epoch, an era when the Association spread its roots and became recognized as one of the most influential organizations in the nation.

The major issues they tackled, some of which ring amazingly timely today, include: beef exports, free trade versus fair trade, consumer rebellion against high food prices, the persistent public lands issue and continued disputes with the railroads.

The Rise and Fall of Beef Exports

Beef exports, on which United States cattlemen had become to rely, were beginning to create some apprehension. Said Jastro in 1909:

> *Our foreign trade in live animals and meat products is in a very unsatisfactory condition. The price of our surplus (exports) largely fixes the price of our livestock at home, and the importance of increased foreign outlets cannot be over estimated.*

Yet exports continued to show an alarming drop. Jastro said a year later:

The small butcher shop was the ultimate customer for the cattle industry, not the consumer. *The final step in the process, via producer, railroad, stokyard and packer was the delivery of carcasses to these shops, which then sold retail to the consumer. In the early 1900s the number of small shops grew. They split market areas, which might be better served by one larger market, and added on the additional overhead costs to the consumers. Consumers had to pay the price and the small shopkeepers made no money either.*

> *The United States now has six percent of the world's population and 17 percent of the world's cattle, with an almost unlimited potential to expand production. Since 1898, the value of our meat animals and packing house products exported has averaged about $200 million annually, equal to about one-seventh of our annual domestic production. {About 14 percent, compared to about five percent in the early 1990s.}*

In 1903, the United States supplied 70 percent of the total value of the meats exported from surplus countries (United States, Canada, Argentina, New Zealand and Australia). As Jastro put it, *Indeed, we have been preeminently the world's meat shop.*

But by 1912, overseas shipments had dwindled. Argentina took the lead in beef exports with a threefold increse in seven years.

But the main reason that exports had decreased was because cattle numbers in the United States had dropped 15 percent during the same period, and were down to 56 million head. There was very little surplus to export.

WHO WAS MAKING THE PROFIT?

The law of supply and demand, acting in a predictable way, caused the retail price of beef to increase. Also predictably, the higher prices precipitated consumer protests, plus a congressional investigation.

Cattlemen maintained that the slightly higher prices for cattle [$21.99 per head average in 1909, compared with $19.69 in 1904] were not enough to justify the significant increase in retail prices. But the Association acknowledged that consumers were paying too much; so, possibly as a diversionary tactic, they suggested in 1911 "another investigation of "who" was making the excessive profit?"

> ***Given a little time ranchers would respond to the better prices and increase the supply. But given the nature of the cow, this would take time.***
>
> —ANLSA President Jastro
>
> *Explaining to congressmen the law of supply and demand in the cattle industry.*

The Department of Agriculture had conducted an exhaustive investigation in 1909, into the producer-to-consumer price spread. In the words of Secretary of Agriculture James Wilson, the findings were:

- The retailer's delivery service is costly, and the business overdone.
- The multiplication of small shops is a burden to consumers and no source of riches to the small shopkeepers.
- When several small shops divide the retail business within an area one large shop could serve, the expense of the many shops for labor, rent and other things in excess of what would be sufficient for one, must go into the retail prices of the meat sold.

As cattle prices continued to climb to $38.97 per head average in 1914, Jastro attempted to explain to consumers and congressmen how supply and demand works in the cattle business. *Given a little time,* he said, *ranchers would respond to the better prices and increase the supply. But given the nature of the cow, this would take time.*

BEHIND THE SCENES

THOMAS W. TOMLINSON
EXECUTIVE SECRETARY
1905-1928

"Never a cog slipped" is the way associates described this man "of brilliant intellect." His quiet efficiency, his serene temper, his unfailing kindness gained him the admiration of everyone who saw him in action. *He knew everybody and everybody liked him.*

Born in Indiana in 1864, he earned a law degree from Cornell University. His first employment was with the Santa Fe Railroad, then the Union Stock Yards in Chicago and later the Chicago Live Stock Exchange. At these places, he was said to have gained "amazing familiarity with the intricacies of freight rates and other abstruse angles of the livestock business."

The American Stock Growers Association hired Tomlinson as its executive secretary. When the associations merged in 1906 into the American National Live Stock Association, he was retained as chief executive and remained so until his death in 1928.

The main ongoing problem for the Association was the railroads and their rates, which the ICC determined "unreasonable and illegal." Tomlinson and Association Attorney Sam Cowan (both hired the same year and died the same year in1928) became "yoke-mates" for twenty-five years. Combating their combined expertise, railroad officials regarded them with dread.

Tomlinson presented cases with acumen and won victories through sheer force of logic, yet leaving opponents as personal friends.

But he was at his best at annual conventions, where members were amazed at his memory for detail, his skill and consummate tact in smoothing over troubled waters.

LABOR UNIONS PROTEST

Such rationale was not good enough for some people, like John T. Russell, president of the United Master Butchers of America.

I blame the grower for the high cost of beef today, he bellowed in a 1913 speech in Cincinnati, *There is a combination of cattle raisers in the West, who have known for some years of the coming shortage of beef and have quietly waited for it, so that they might fill their purses at the expense of the meat-eating public.*

Russell was pushing for a lifting of the tariff on imported beef. In another speech, he made the threat that if the growers of this country did not get busy and raise more beef, pork and mutton, he would have to go to Washington and get legislation to force them to do so!

FREE TRADE VERSUS FAIR TRADE

Congress did respond to the consumers. It eventually lifted the tariff on hides and beef, hoping this would increase imports and lower prices.

Since the days of the Civil War, the cattle industry had relied on a protectionist tariff, as had most American industries selling finished products. Cattlemen claimed fat animals and hides as their finished products.

The debate began before 1909, when eastern shoe manufacturers and leather trusts started agitating to remove a 15 percent tariff on imported hides, while retaining their higher tariff on imported leather goods. The Association claimed that removing the tariff would cost producers $1.50 per animal, while lowering shoe prices only two to three cents a pair. They also felt the 15 percent a reasonable tariff to protect "such an essential industry as agriculture and livestock," when the average tariff was about 45 percent with some products over 100 percent.

Speaking for fair trade, First Vice President Dwight B. Heard of Arizona declared, *Cattlemen demand fair and just treatment—nothing more, nothing less.*

But the Association lost that battle, when in 1909 the tariff on hides was lifted. And as predicted, the price of shoes continued to increase.

INVESTIGATION OF HIGH MEAT PRICES

The big battle to save the tariff on imported beef was yet to come.

In 1910, the United States Senate appointed a Select Committee to investigate the so-called high prices of meat. Officers of the association subpoenaed to testify asked for *a square deal, no more and no less.*

Murdo Mackenzie, who in 1911 became president for the second time, explained the Association's position:

> *This nation requires for its support {Federal Budget} from $900 million to $1billion annually, and of this amount custom revenues or tariff duties furnish approximately $350 million.*
>
> *The imposition of an import duty on anything produced in this country in effect gives a protection or advantage to the home producers of such commodities by the amount of the tax. Our position is that we want the favors or burdens of this system equitably distributed, and that, so long as the present system of raising money for the support of the government by means of customs duties continues in effect, the livestock industry should receive its share of the favors.*

But cattlemen lost that battle, too.

In 1913 imported livestock, meats and wool were placed on the free list.

At the following convention in 1914, in Denver, there was much venting of frustration. [It sounded almost like a rehearsal for debates that would follow 80 years later regarding the North American Free Trade Agreement.] *Free trade cannot be considered other than a menace to the industry*, raged one speaker. *We are import crazy!*

Then he offered his version of the problem: *Gentlemen, we have too many lawyers, ignorant of the needs of this industry, in Congress. Lawyers are a national infliction, and you can't get rid of them.*

Indifference to the West

The cool, collected Jastro had a more plausible explanation:

> *The problem is deeper-seated than the tariff, and is chargeable to the indifference of Congress to the needs of the West.*

But now, in hindsight, it appears that even the wise Jastro may have overlooked the real cause of problems the Association was having with Congress. He and all presidents in the first half of

At Convention

Fort Worth Hat Fiasco

Known for his tales of early conventions, Will C. Barnes, first secretary of the American Stock Growers Association (merged into the ANLSA) and later a forester and writer, recorded the following in the October 1934 *American Cattle Producer* on an event at the 1911 Convention in Fort Worth.

> *At Denver in 1898, the 1,185 registered delegates (plus guests) were entertained one night with a prize fight, which closed with a battle-royal between seven husky colored individuals, all blindfolded. It lasted nearly an hour. . . .*
>
> *The next year, 1899, again at Denver, we had the celebrated "cactus ball." "A Night With the Bohemians" it was called on the handsome invitations. It was a night of "wine, women and song," with special emphasis on the first two. . . .*
>
> *In 1911, Fort Worth captured the convention. This meeting was notable mostly for the "Knights of Bovinia," also for a mix-up known locally as the 'Hat Riot.'*
>
> *About midnight some individual, tired of the affair went to the check-room for his sombrero. He was half-seas over and looking for trouble with a longing eye. The colored attendant asked him for his check. The gentleman swore he never had such a thing. The attendant, like the Chinese laundryman, smiled and said, 'No checkee, no hattee.'*
>
> *The Texan waxed exceedingly warm under the collar. 'The hell you say! I'll teach you some manners." Climbing heavily across the low counter, the incensed 'Tejaner' cornered the African, worked him over and tossed him over the counter.*
>
> *Then he proceeded to seek his headgear. Grabbing any handy hat, he tried them on one after the other. If they did not fit or suit his taste, he sailed them out of a near-by third story window to the street below. There they were gathered up by a mob of hack-drivers, street urchins and others who looked upon the descending hats as manna from heaven and carried them off as trophies.*
>
> *Needless to say, the local hat stores did a land-office business the next day.*

Regulating the Rails

Trouble with Trains

Most Association members had some complaint against the railroads, whether it be rates, service, or availability of cars.

The railroad problems were diverse. As Lyle Liggett, former ANLSA director of information, pointed out in his history of the Association at its 75th Anniversary:

> *They [the membership] were unhappy about rates, slow trains, no cars when needed and a lot of other things. They also disliked the law requiring feed, rest and water every 28 hours. 'Our cattle are range wild—it would be more inhumane to unload and load every 28 hours than if they were let go, say, for 40 hours,' ranchers declared. Mostly they were displeased because of inequities in rates between routings and companies; some charge one rate for a car, but it shot up when transferred to other lines serving destination points. Some charge rates by the length of the car; others by the number of head. Some bore the cost of feed, rest and water; others charged the shipper or consignee. Few lines gave livestock trains priority of passenger service, so stock cars spent many hours on the side track until the "Limited" came by. Indicative of the delays was the Association's later drive to require a minimum speed limit of 20 miles per hour for stock trains.*

So the Association took to task the need to regulate the trains.

They sought authority for the Interstate Commerce Commission (ICC) to regulate railroad rates. A couple of years earlier, the Cattle Raisers Association of Texas had taken their case to the ICC, which determined that rates were "unreasonable and illegal," but the ICC had no authority to do anything about it. In 1906, a law was passed to regulate rates which cattlemen had pushed through with the help of their friend, President Roosevelt.

The Highest Priced Steer. *Charles Wood, of Wood Brothers in Chicago, Illinois, poses with the highest priced range steer ever sold on the open market. In November of 1909 this steer, bought by Armour and Company, weighed in at 1470 pounds and sold for $8.25 per cwt.*

the 20th Century frequently made appeals to "cattlemen west of the Mississippi River" and for "the western states to stick together." Also, in early years, only a few members of the large Executive Committee were from as far east as Iowa and Missouri.

Such bias portrayed this as a western range association, at a time when there was lingering resentment in the East about "free range" and when the West was far short of the needed votes in Congress. It would be decades before changes were made and the Association became recognized as a truly national organization. In the meantime, general farm organizations were also speaking for producers: the American Farm Bureau Federation was organized in 1919, and the National Grange was organized in 1867.

Pervading Issues

In many areas, Jastro showed foresight and vision that has pervaded Association policies. In 1910 he advocated a full time representative or office in Washington.

Also, in 1914 he was among the first to speak up for consumers:

> *We must, by our policies, indicate a broader recognition of the rights of the consumer, and we shall then represent a keener appreciation on the basis of sound business.*

Even earlier (and before hamburgers), he said

> *. . .it was an industry responsibility to help housewives with more intelligent utilization of all the edible parts of a beef animal. Consumers perceive beef as being high because they think only of the expensive cuts. Yet the expensive cuts comprise only 20 percent of the carcass; and the other 80 percent, just as nutritious, often goes begging.*

Also, after helping to fight off an attempt by Congress to withdraw federal funding for meat inspection, he advised future cattle industry leaders:

> *The meat inspection system is for the benefit of the entire country—the consumer as well as the producer—and should continue to be made at the expense of the government. This is one of many matters which it is the province of the Association to carefully watch.*

Railroad rates and the public domain continued to be trouble spots. On the first, the Association had several victories, gaining legislation permitting the Interstate Commerce Commission to enforce lower rates for cattle and minimum speed limits by trains.

The public domain issue, however, was too formidable, even for giants of the industry like Mackenzie and Jastro. Eventually even they became convinced that, as had a majority of association members, *The only solution is government control, through leasing or otherwise.* But their efforts to accomplish this were thwarted by non-members. *Those in opposition remind me of train-robbers, who after accomplishing their purpose want to be let alone,* snarled Jastro in 1913. *So long as these men continue to derive benefits, as they are now doing, by devastating the public ranges, they care nothing for the interests of others.* Thus, public lands remained an unsolved problem.

Toward the end of each convention, during the Mackenzie-Jastro-Mackenzie-Jastro era, it became almost custom that one of these giants would stand before the delegates and say something like:

> *I now have the unpleasant duty to discuss with you the finances of our Association. You have heard its many accomplishments and how beneficial it is to every stockman in the nation. Do you want to maintain this Association or not? If so, are you willing to finance it? We need approximately $15,000 (sometimes they said $20,000) to continue next year. I hope you will respond generously, and I will start the subscriptions with $500 (sometimes $1,000).*

The minutes usually recorded: *And those present responded liberally for themselves and the associations they represented.*

That's how the Association would be financed, year after year.

UNITY

1985

ARTIST: HAROLD HOLDEN

COMMISSIONED BY THE NATIONAL

CATTLEMEN'S ASSOCIATION.

SERIES: 35 BRONZES

Thomas Hart Benton NEW MEXICO

The Winds of Change

The cattle industry had entered the 20th century. The nation turned outward as it entered a world war. The task of feeding troops and allies put the industry into accelerated production and it looked eagerly towards new markets. Technological advances would lead to new modes of transportation and agricultural production, and farms and ranches would slowly begin to mechanize.

CHAPTER FOUR

Patriotism Abroad, Battles At Home

When the American National Live Stock Association (ANLSA) met in El Paso in 1916, war had begun in Europe and there was great concern that the United States might soon become involved.

Patriotism abounded. The Association invited General John J. Pershing, the Army Chief of Staff who would later lead the American Expeditionary Forces in Europe, to be the honored speaker. Before his speech, General Pershing was made an Honorary Lifetime Member of the Association. Then, amid ovations, he spoke on patriotism and preparedness.

But cattlemen had battles to fight closer to home. Among them were the battle to eradicate foot-and-mouth disease and the battle with the beef trust, which was just heating up.

The presidents of ANLSA during World War I years were Dwight B. Heard of Phoenix, and Isaac T. "Ike" Pryor of San Antonio, men with widely varying backgrounds but both well qualified for their wartime tasks.

Heard of Arizona

Dwight Heard, born in Boston of a wealthy family, moved to Arizona in 1895, at age 26. Five years later, along with his father-in-law of Chicago, he established the Bartlett-Heard Land and Cattle Company. They purchased 8,000 acres to the south and east of the town of Phoenix and quickly made it into a show place for the production of purebred Hereford and Shorthorn bulls.

He was active in practically every agricultural pursuit and association in the state: cattle, cotton, hay, irrigation, good roads and more. After participat-

TIMELINE

1915 Transcontinental phone service established in United States.

1916 Albert Einstein announces theory of relativity.

National Livestock News Service established by Congress.

Stock Raising Homestead Act provides 640 acres per family, creating new wave of settlers.

Federal Land Bank created.

1917 Russian revolution: Lenin becomes leader of Communist government.

United States declares war on Germany; enters World War I.

1918 Armistice declared November 11, ending World War I.

Congress establishes daylight savings time to conserve electricity.

1919 Packer Consent Decree accepted.

Institute of American Meat Packers, now AMI, organized.

1920 18th Amendment prohibits production and sale of alcohol.

19th Amendment ratified; women gain vote.

League of Nations established.

American Professional Football Association (later NFL) formed.

1921 Packers and Stockyards Act passed.

Warren G. Harding becomes 29th president, later dies in office.

1922 National Live Stock and Meat Board founded.

1923 United States Steel replaces 12-hour working day with eight-hour day.

Calvin Coolidge becomes 30th president.

1924 Joseph Stalin rises to power and rules Soviet Union for 29 years.

J. Edgar Hoover appointed head of Bureau of Investigation (later FBI) and served until 1972.

1926 Admiral Richard E. Byrd flies to North Pole.

ISSUES

Supply and Demand
•
Food for the War
•
Food Administration
•
Meatless Day
•
The Beef Trust
•
Consent Decree
•
Packers and Stockyards Act
•
Beef Promotion
•
National Live Stock and Meat Board

ing in the build-up of the Salt River Valley, he hosted President Teddy Roosevelt in 1911, when he came to dedicate the Roosevelt Dam. As the President toured the Heard ranch, observers noted his pleasure in viewing the horses, cattle, irrigation, cotton, alfalfa, citrus and grapes.

Capitalizing on location, Heard developed many fine residential areas in Phoenix and the Salt River Valley, plus office buildings and a hotel in downtown Phoenix. His 8,000-acre ranch became the southern half of Phoenix, some of which in the 1990s was selling for $2 to $12 per square foot. With political influence in Washington, he helped defeat the joint Arizona-New Mexico statehood bill, and was thus given much credit for Arizona becoming a separate state in 1912.

That same year, Heard purchased the *Arizona Republican* (now the *Arizona Republic*), reportedly to help re-elect his friend Teddy Roosevelt as President. Before his death in 1929, he established the Heard Museum, which today remains one of the nation's outstanding museums for Indian culture and art.

Pryor of Texas

Ike Pryor, on the other hand, was reared in poverty, but he had one of the most colorful and successful careers in the history of the cattle business. Born in Tampa, Florida, in 1852, Ike was orphaned at age five and moved to Alabama to live with an uncle, from whom he ran away. At age nine, he found himself in the middle of the Battle of Murfreesboro in the Civil War. Picked up by the Third Ohio Cavalry, he was adopted as their mascot and paper boy. He then went on with the regiment to fight the Battles of Chattanooga and Lookout Mountain, where his pony was shot out from under him.

After the Civil War, Pryor made his way to Texas and at age 18 got a job as a plow hand on a farm near Austin, driving a six-yoke team of oxen for $15 per month. Never before had the young Pryor seen a herd of cattle, but he watched with awe the passing herds whose drovers said they were headed for Kansas, Colorado or Montana. So the next year, in 1874, Pryor made his first drive with 2,500 head to Coffeyville, Kansas. The following year he became a trail boss and owned part of the cattle. Upon his return to Texas, with a few dollars in his pocket and very liberal credit, he bought his first ranch in the Hill Country of Texas: 20,000 acres with 1,500 cattle.

Trail driving proved to be profitable for the young entrepreneur. In 1884, he and his brother put a record-breaking number of longhorns on the trail: 15 herds of approximately 3,000 each or 45,000 in the year. And before he quit that business in 1886, he estimated that he took or sent over 75 herds up the trail.

Pryor's most successful cattle trade was yet to follow, however, in 1898 at the close of the Spanish-American War. He had sent an agent to Cuba to watch and report back when it was safe to ship cattle. Two weeks after the conflict, he began shipping boats of cattle to Havana, about 7,000 head, which he bought for $15 each and sold for $85.

Pryor was also shrewd in real estate trading and had one deal he liked to tell about. Around 1900 he bought a 100,000-acre ranch for $1.40 per acre, located about 100 miles southwest of San Antonio, where the town of LaPryor is named for him. Three times he sold that ranch "to people who got stuck on it," each time carrying the notes himself and collecting (consecutively) $30,000, $60,000 and $200,000 in down payments. And three times he got the ranch back, when the notes were not paid.

The author of *Prose and Poetry of the Live Stock Industry of the United States*, published in 1905 and one of the great books on the cattle industry, said of Pryor:

> *An intuitive knowledge of human nature possessed by few men. . . .An almost unerring judgement in deciding important business points. . . .His decisions are quick and clear, but he calls for full presentation of the facts, and he seldom revises a decision after it is once made.*

Thus, there is little wonder that Colonel Pryor became a multi-millionaire with holdings across the country in land, banks, insurance and development projects, as well as an admired Association leader.

DWIGHT B. HEARD
President, 1915-1916
Phoenix, Arizona

His ranch, a show place with purebred Herefords and Shorthorns and Thoroughbred horses drew many visitors, including Teddy Roosevelt who came to Arizona to dedicate Roosevelt Dam. Born in Boston of a wealthy family, Heard moved to Phoenix and purchased 8,000 acres that eventually became the southern half of Phoenix. He also was publisher of the *Arizona Republican* newspaper and established the famous Heard Museum in Phoenix.

Supply and Demand Sidetracked

Back at the El Paso Convention in 1916, members seemed to be torn between their patriotism and their fury about the wildly fluctuating market. Some believed the fluctuations were intentionally caused by packers—big packers who were making unprecedented profits. Others expressed doubt about the law of supply and demand. Said Heard:

The 21st National Convention *at Salt Lake City, Utah, in 1918.*

Many experienced men who have given this market situation close attention claim that the good old law of supply and demand has apparently been sidetracked.

To which A.E. de Ricqles of Denver, Chairman of the Special Committee on Markets, added:

Children are taught regarding so-called laws of supply and demand. . .but time taken for the study of these laws is wasted, and under present market conditions they do not apply.

There was much discussion on the cost of production, which might be a better price basis than supply and demand. Costs were higher than prices, they believed, but no one seemed to know the cost of production.

In an attempt to measure and quantify supply, the population ratio of cattle to people was frequently quoted. In 1890, the ratio was 936 head of cattle to 1,000 people; and by 1915, it had dropped to 644 head per 1,000 people. Yet, prices per head had not advanced proportionately, or so they believed. [Cattle prices averaged $40.67 per head in 1915.]

Many experienced men who have given this market situation close attention claim that the good old law of supply and demand has apparently been sidetracked.

—ANLSA President Heard
Speaking at the 1916 National Convention

The war, however, was obscuring their efforts to achieve a balance of suplly and demand.

FOOD ADMINISTRATION: AN EXPERIMENT

Soon after the United States declared war on Germany, April 6, 1917, President Woodrow Wilson appointed Herbert C. Hoover Food Administrator, and appealed to farmers and stockmen to increase the production of food products. The new Association President Pryor pointed out:

Food administration is an experiment in this country. The task is gigantic, the interests involved are exceedingly complex, and it would indeed be a miracle if mistakes were not made.

One mistake made, in the minds of many cattlemen, was the declaration of a "Meatless Day," one day of the week. The opponents argued that

- Beef exports had dwindled to nearly nothing (two percent of gross value, including by-products),
- Beef supplies had stacked up in cold storage,
- Market prices were below the cost of production.

Thus, this kind of rationing did the industry more harm than good.

Food Administration officials attempted to explain that "wheatless day and meatless day have come to be visible symbols by which people pledge themselves to help win the war." Nevertheless, many cattlemen were frustrated, feeling that their prices were not rising in line with the items they purchased and that cattlemen were being asked to carry an unfair burden in the war effort.

For this reason, the Food Administration decided to stimulate production of pork by setting a minimum price on hogs. The Food Administration explained that pork had been singled out because it could be increased much more rapidly than beef and was stored more easily (in salted and smoked form). Also, they reasoned that hogs were easier to support, because one farmer usually owned a hog all of its life, while two, three or four cattlemen might own a steer during its life.

Since the Civil War, it had been accepted as a formula that 60-cent corn meant $6 per cwt. hogs, the price of hogs moving up or down with corn prices. Thus a corn-to-hog ratio of 1-to-10. But when the Food Administration set a minimum price of $15.50 per cwt. for hogs, the ratio became 1-to-13. Officials avowed that this minimum price was higher than the cost of production, and that the higher ratio was used for purposes of stimulation.

Cattlemen angrily protested this discrimination until the Administration lifted the Meatless Day for beef, while continuing it for pork.

A REGULATED MONOPOLY

Cattlemen also complained that packers were continuing to make record profits while producers lost money, which at least was unfair and at most was unpatriotic. Consequently, the Food Administration placed the packers under license, supervised their operations and fixed their profits at 2.5 percent of sales. Said Pryor, with halting satisfaction, *They now are a regulated monopoly.*

Meanwhile, the Market Committee, torn between patriotism and their avowed objective of reining in the "Beef Trust," was continuing its legal and political pursuit of packers. The Beef Trust was the common name given the "Big Five Packers," who were engaged in monopoly and other anti-trust violations. With the aid of Food Administrator Hoover and a few key congressmen, they prevailed on President Wilson in 1917 to order an investigation by the Federal Trade Commission (FTC). Then they went to Congress and obtained a $250,000 appropriation to fund the investigation.

The war, the issue of patriotism and the concern of consumers about high food prices made the timing right. So they pushed relentlessly, even while packers were contending that cooperation and patriotism were more important to the war effort. ["Free markets" became the battle cry of producers, while "cooperation" was the response—almost the motto—of packers.]

IKE T. PRYOR
President, 1917-1918
San Antonio, Texas

Pryor had a colorful career. He was born in poverty, orphaned at age five, moved about from Florida to Alabama to Tennessee and, at age nine, fought in the Civil War. At the age of 18, he moved to Texas and became a trail driver, taking 15 herds "up the trail." He was a shrewd real estate investor, loved by neighbors. The town of La Pryor, Texas, is named for him.

Produce More Food, *was the plea from Food Administrator, Herbert C. Hoover. Appointed by President Woodrow Wilson during World War I, Hoover, in turn appointed an Agricultural Advisory Board of 100, with subcommittees for beef, pork, dairy, wheat, and so on. ANLSA officers and several other key members served on the Board of 100 and gave this work priority. The task of administering food was enormous. Hoover was generally considered to have done a good job, which contributed to his being elected president on 1928.*

FIRST MARKET COMMITTEE

E.L. Burke of Omaha, Nebraska, *headed the first Market Committee, perhaps the most powerful and influential committee in the history of the Association. The Committee was instrumental in getting the Packers and Stockyards Act and in establishing the National Livestock and Meat Board. Burke was considered a bulldog, a persistent worker for reform.*

The real issue, declared E.L. Burke of Omaha, Nebraska, becomes this:

> *Shall four or five very small groups of men with unlimited financial power, control the meat supply of 100 million people, exploiting the producer on the one hand and the consumer on the other?*

Over the next few years Burke would battle stockyards and packers as head of the first Market Committee of the Association. In 1916 he issued an unusually significant report from the Special Committee on Markets, which laid out a strategy for the next several years. The report contained proposals that would surface time and again before the 20th century ended, and prove that marketing of cattle would always remain at the center of the Association's issues.

In the report, Burke listed several possible ways "toward bettering present conditions:"

1. Force buyer competition.
2. Government supervision or regulation.
3. Actions for damages against packers for losses sustained by sellers, when it is proven that anti-trust laws are broken.
4. Establishment of competitive plants.
5. Cooperative marketing.
6. Government investigation of the packing business and subsidiaries.
7. Eliminate packer control of public stockyards.
8. Establish a market paper owned by and edited to producers interest.
9. Curtail production.

The report led Heard to appoint a Market Committee. This Blue Ribbon Committee was made up of the most influential cattlemen of the day: H.A. Jastro of California, former ANSLA president; E.L. Burke of Nebraska; A.E. de Ricqles of Colorado; J.B. Kendrick of Wyoming, later ANLSA president; and I.T. Pryor of Texas, later ANLSA president.

So enthused were the members that within 30 minutes they raised a guaranty fund of $54,000 and placed it at the disposal of the Market Committee, more than double the annual budget ($20,285) of the Association! The committee, with separate funding, then hired Walter L. Fisher, a Washington attorney and former Secretary of Interior, as legal counsel. Fisher would stay with the committee and guide their efforts for the next five years.

The following year, at the 1917 Convention in Cheyenne, Heard praised the Market Committee:

> *In the 20 years of the history of this Association, no more important work has ever been undertaken. . . .They are blazing the trail for an improvement in marketing conditions which will eventually benefit every man and woman engaged in the live stock industry of this country. We have put our hand to the plow. The task is an immense one, but we must run a straight furrow to the very end.*

Over the next four years the task of the Market Committee was a vital one, affecting every producer throughout the country and the financial interests of powerful corporations. As Kendrick said,

> *It was a task, also, that had a very real meaning for every family in the country, for it affected every table.*

In his report to the 1919 Convention, Burke explained how the Committee had formed coalitions with other groups. Besides nearly all farm and livestock organizations, the Committee had gained support from the National Consumers' League, the National League of Women Voters, the American Federation of Labor, the Farmer-Labor Conference and the newly organized American Farm Bureau Federation.

After President Harding signed into law the Packers and Stockyards Act in 1921, the Association and its leaders introduced an era of reconciliation.

He then proposed a plan calling for a National Live Stock and Meat Board which was passed unanimously by the members.

Thus, the Market Committee became—and remains today—one of the strongest committees of the Association.

When World War I ended, packers naturally attempted to get their controls lifted. But the ANLSA Market Committee stepped up its support for the FTC investigation, for which they had supplied much information and testimony.

Other Issues and Resolutions

In the meantime, the Association passed many resolutions, typically 20 to 30 each year: endorsing municipal abattoirs (local packing plants); opposing tax on oleomargarine (a perennial resolution); encouraging import tariffs on livestock and its products; protesting proposed advance in grazing fees on National Forest; eradication of foot-and-mouth disease; and control of contagious abortion.

Then there were other resolutions, which reflected the times and areas of concern: creating one strong national organization of producers; federal control of railroads; representation in Washington; importation of livestock and meat from countries where contagious animal diseases exist (a perennial resolution); endorsing suffrage for women; control of grazing on the public domain; opposition to insurance on livestock for loan security; government help in the control of predators, rodents and poisonous plants; deploring an increase in livestock commission charges; municipal meat markets (to keep retail prices more in line with cattle prices); cooperative livestock sales agencies; and commending the work of the (new) American Farm Bureau Federation (the Farm Bureau).

The Farm Bureau was founded in 1919 with 30 state federations or associations and 300,000 members. *If it makes good,* commented Burke, *this federation is destined to become the great representative agricultural organization in this country.*

Some convention delegates were not happy with the idea of the Farm Bureau. But Burke acknowledged the opposition and added,

> *We have been advised by various people outside our industry, largely bankers, that legislation is not what is wanted; that cooperation is what is needed; that we are making a mistake.*

Public Domain, An Old Subject

Neither war nor monopoly kept the issue of public domain from cattlemen's minds. Frustrated by its failure to find an acceptable solution

> ***The real issue becomes this: Shall four or five very small groups of men, with unlimited financial power, control the meat supply of 100 million people, exploiting the producer on the one hand and the consumer on the other?***
>
> —E.L. Burke
>
> *Chairman, Market Committee, speaking at the 1916 Convention*

to public lands (acceptable to politicians, the public and stockmen), the Association had Clay Tallman, Commissioner of the General Land Office, review the public lands situation at the 1919 convention. The title of his address, "The Public Domain and the Stock Industry, An Old Subject."

But the main thrust of the Association, as set out in Article II of its constitution, would remain:

> *To secure to livestock men the widest, best and most competitive market possible for their products, and to this end to prevent combination and monopolies.*

President Kendrick of Wyoming

When John B. Kendrick became president of the Association in 1919, he was already serving in the United States Senate, after having been governor of Wyoming. This was just one thing that made Kendrick a unique ANLSA president and a man for the times.

Like Pryor before him, Kendrick was orphaned (at age four) and farmed out to various relatives in East Texas. Also like Pryor, he rode the trails to the north and eventually got to Wyoming. He liked the country and the people, married the boss's daughter, and stayed. After his second trip up the trail (a five-month ride with 3,500 head), he began putting together ranches until he had holdings on both sides of the Wyoming-Montana border.

As a young rancher, Kendrick was true grit. In 1887, the editor of the *LUSK HERALD* wrote that he had roped a mountain lion, eight feet from tip to tip. . .and had to drag it to death. On another occasion, Kendrick and a buddy head-and-heel roped a big buffalo bull "just for the hell of it". . .and had a "devil of a time" getting it loose.

This great industry is entitled to an organization that fairly and fully represents the entire industry. . . the producers of cattle, the feeders of cattle, the producers of hogs and the producers of sheep—not only those this side of the {Mississippi} river but throughout the country.

—Thomas E. Wilson

Speaking at the Kansas Livestock Association in 1919

Kendrick entered the political arena at the age of 53, starting as a State Senator, then becoming Governor, then going to the United States Senate (1917-1933) as a Democrat from a Republican state. Members on both sides of the isle relied on him regarding agricultural matters, and Secretary of Agriculture David F. Houston once introduced him as "the livestock section of the United States Senate." As late as 1971, one historian wrote, "The American West has yet to produce his equal."

From the day Kendrick became ANLSA president in 1919, he was the champion of free markets for livestock and a leader in the ongoing battle to regulate packers. He championed free markets declaring:

> *We are out for what is right, and for nothing but what is right, We want a free American market which every day shall register the value of a consignment of livestock as accurately as the scales register its weight.*

LET US COOPERATE

Thomas E. Wilson was president of the Institute of American Meat Packers during these years and was their principal spokesman. It was in March 1919 that he gave a "let us cooperate" speech to the Kansas Livestock Association.

We do not need legislation, pleaded Wilson. *What we need is "cooperation between the producer, the packer and the government.*

This was the speech, some people say, in which Wilson planted the seeds for the National Live Stock and Meat Board, although it was not officially organized for another three years (1922). At that time, however, some said it was another move by Wilson to head off legislation to regulate the packers.

Wilson did not endear himself to ANLSA leaders when he said,

> *One of the great drawbacks in this industry is the failure on the part of producers to properly organize. . . .This great industry is entitled to an organization that fairly and fully represents the entire industry . . .producers of cattle, feeders of cattle, producers of hogs and producers of sheep—not only those this side of the river but throughout the country.*

Of course, this is what the ANLSA had been attempting to do, but the Association had not made much effort "on the other side of the river."

At the 1920 convention in Spokane, Kendrick, drawing on his experience on the Senate floor, waxed eloquent:

> *The past year has been a period of storm and stress for the live stock industry. . . .For a great majority of stockmen, it has been a time of limited profits and unlimited anxiety and worry.*

Then, with drama, he concluded his address:

> *Let us work together that the day may speedily come when over the gate of every great stockyard in the country shall be inscribed the motto: Equal opportunity for all, special privileges for none.*

A DEBATE OF GIANTS

Surprisingly, that feeling was not shared by all members; at least, some did not favor legislation. The opposition would be led by none other than Murdo Mackenzie, who a decade earlier had been the Association's esteemed president. Since then, Mackenzie had been in Brazil, where he built and managed the largest ranch in the world (10 million acres with 250,000 head of cattle). There he also built packing plants and—it was insinuated—had financial dealings with American packers who had large interests in South America. When he returned to the United States, he became associated with Thomas E. Wilson of Wilson & Co. "to foster better relations between producers and packers."

Now, at his first ANLSA convention in nine years, the big Mackenzie asked for the floor. This was to be a debate of giants. Of Mackenzie, Teddy Roosevelt and others had earlier labeled him "the most influential of the western cattle growers." And of Kendrick, more recently, "the greatest man in the West." Pryor, the immediate past president, said in introducing Kendrick, *We believe anything he tells us.*

I want to show you, Mackenzie boomed, *that if those bills are passed and allowed to go to their legitimate end, they will be the means of giving you more trouble than you ever had before in your business.*

Stretching a few points, he argued:

> *I do not believe, gentlemen, that since the constitution of the United States was written such powers have ever before been conferred by Congress on any one man. . . .I am unalterably opposed to any such powers being placed, by law or otherwise, in the Department of Agriculture. That department has as much to do now as it can well attend to; but it seems it will not be satisfied until it has the power to tell us how to feed and pay our men, and how to breed and run out cattle.*

Burke, speaking for the Market Committee, responded to Mackenzie by reading from the Market Committee report;

> *The problem we have been attempting to solve is simple enough. It is nothing less than whether this democracy shall permit a few men of unlimited power and unlimited wealth to stand between the producers of foodstuffs, on the one hand, and the consumers, on the other, and dictate the terms of which each shall live. . . .*

JOHN B. KENDRICK
President, 1919-1921
Sheridan, Wyoming

After driving a herd of cattle from Texas to Wyoming, he met a rancher's daughter, married her, and stayed to became Governor of Wyoming, then United States Senator. While serving in the Senate, he was elected President of ANLSA, reportedly solving the Association's lobbying needs for a while. During that time, Kendrick wrote and pushed through the Packers and Stockyards Act of 1921. *The West is yet to produce his equal,* writes one historian.

John B. Kendrick in Front of the Barn at the OW Ranch on Hanging Woman. *The horse cannot be positively identified. . . ."Kemp" or a Wallop-raised horse named "Puck." The rifle is probably a .40-82 Winchester. The scabbard was made by Meanea of Cheyenne. The bridle bit was known as a Kendrick-Moran, designed by Kendrick and his handyman and made by the Star Bit Company, long out of business. (Recollections from John B. Kendrick's son, Manville Kendrick.)*

The Packers and Stockyards Act

Shocking Report

The results of a Federal Trade Commission (FTC) study, conducted at the urgings of the ANLSA Market Committee, were presented to President Woodrow Wilson. In July 1919, confirming what the cattlemen had long maintained. The public was shocked. The study pointed out that the Big Five packers—Swift, Armour, Morris, Cudahy and Wilson—jointly or separately held controlling interest in 574 companies, minority interest in 95 others and undetermined interest in 93 others, a total of 762 companies. It went on to say that they produce or deal in some 775 commodities, largely food products.

In addition to meat foods, the report said, they produce or deal in such diverse commodities as red meat, poultry and dairy products, fresh tomatoes, banjo strings, leather, cottonseed oil, breakfast foods, curled hair, pepsin and washing powders. Their branch houses take on the character of wholesale grocery stores dealing in various kinds of produce and special lines. They dominate or are factors in cattle loan companies, railways and private car lines, public markets and market newspapers. They are interested in banks, ice, salt, boxes, hides, oleo, fertilizer, soap, glue, ad infinitum.

The conclusion of the FTC report, was in brief: "The power of the Big Five Packers in the United States has been and is being unfairly and illegally used to: manipulate livestock markets. . .restrict interstate and international supplies of foods. . .control prices on dressed meats and other foods. . .defraud both producers and food consumers. . . crush effective competition. . .secure special privileges from railroads, stockyard companies and municipalities . . .profiteer."

The Consent Decree

With this information, the Justice Department threatened to go to a grand jury in New York, an act which would charge the packers with criminal charges for violation of antitrust laws. So the packers proposed a compromise, "The Consent Decree," and the Justice Department accepted it.

At last, cattlemen had won their case! Or so some thought. But not in the minds of the ANLSA President Kendrick and the new Market Committee. The task which had been undertaken in 1916 in El Paso would not be completed, they affirmed, until there was legislation to assure that packers lived up to the Consent Decree. And that meant another prolonged battle.

The Consent Decree

The packers admitted no guilt but did consent to the following:

1. To sell all their holdings in public stockyards.
2. To sell all their interests in stockyard railroads and terminals.
3. To sell all their interests in market newspapers.
4. To dispose of all their interests in public cold storage warehouses.
5. To forever disassociate themselves with the retail meat business.
6. To forever disassociate themselves with . . .wholesale groceries.
7. To forever abandon the use of their branch houses, route cars and auto trucks.
8. To submit perpetually to the jurisdiction of the United States District Court under an injunction forbidding conspiracy or monopoly.

Packers and Stockyards Act

Kendrick reasoned, that legislation was necessary because the Big Five packers were slaughtering more than 82 percent of all cattle killed for interstate commerce; they were handling 95 percent of the fresh beef; and their profits during the past five years had multiplied three and four times. All this at a time when producer profits were diminishing. In 1919 before becoming Association president, Kendrick, as United States Senator, had introduced a bill in Congress which had three simple provisions:

1. License all packing houses,
2. Prohibit ownership of stockyards by packers,
3. Require railroads to furnish refrigerator cars to anyone who requested them.

Packers were resisting legislation by all means: expensive attorneys, million-dollar advertising campaigns, domination of committee hearings with packed rooms and lengthy testimony, and more. On one occasion, some farmers appeared at a congressional committee hearing with written testimony in opposition to the Kendrick Bill and in support of packers. But upon questioning from the chairman, it turned out that they had not read the bill nor could they tell him how much their hotel room in Washington was costing.

W.W. Turney, president of the Cattle Raisers Association of Texas, also talked on organization:

> *There is going around the country today the slogan: 'Let us join hands with the packers.' That is not the place to join hands. God*

(above) **The Largest Office in the World.** *Through this maze of desks in the cavernous Swift & Company offices passed decisions for many of Swift's subsidiary interests which impacted cattlemen throughout the country.*

(left) **Thomas E. Wilson**, *president of Wilson and Company and president of the Institute of American Meat Packers, was the principal spokesman for the packing industry during the years that led to the Packers and Stockyards Act of 1921. He held his own amongst formidable foes in the ANLSA and maintained throughout the battles that the solution to these problems was cooperation within the entire industry. His persistence led to the creation of the National Live Stock and Meat Board.*

knows the packers don't need your help. They can spend $4,000,000 in advertising a year, charge it to legitimate expense, and pay no income tax on it; but if you were called on to furnish your secretary $1,000 for advertising, you would wonder how he was going to waste all that money.

The Association itself was not in agreement over the proposed legislation, with such prominent opponents as former president Mackenzie. Finally, in May 1921, 25 senators met in the Washington office of the new American Farm Bureau Federation and agreed to block adjournment of Congress until the bill was passed. And on August 15, 1921, President Warren G. Harding signed the Packers and Stockyards Act into law. It gave the Secretary of Agriculture supervision over the packers, stockyards, commissionmen, traders, buyers and sellers in the stockyards and in country trading.

Immediately after the act went into force, on November 1, 1921, the livestock exchanges contested its constitutionality. But on May 1, 1922, the United States Supreme Court upheld all provisions of the Act and it has been in force ever since, although with numerous amendments or changes in regulations.

To industry leaders at that time, it was the most important legislation in Association history; and that may be true even to this day. The reasons were threefold:

- the long labors involved (six years),
- the extent of its application (to all segments of the industry),
- its durability (75 years and going).

Some industry leaders might argue today that the Beef Promotion and Research Act of 1985 is of equal importance, but it has yet to stand the test of time.

During the war, packers were put under federal license. Loose as control was, it exerted a real restraining influence and established the valuable precedent of government regulation. . . The fierceness with which the packers attacked the bills, and the great campaign of misrepresentation, are probably without precedent in our legislative annals.

A Conflict of Interest

For the 1921 Convention, the Association was back in El Paso, where five years earlier the first Market Committee was appointed. Reports from Washington were that the proposed legislation was moving forward, but not the Kendrick Bill per se. Opponents had claimed that it would be "a conflict of interest" for the president of the American National Live Stock Association to be writing legislation for the United States Senate. Several other bills were introduced, but it was a House bill, very similar to the Kendrick Bill, that would eventually be passed. No one doubted, then or now, that Kendrick was the "father of the Packers and Stockyards Act."

. . .I am unalterably opposed to any such powers being placed, by law or otherwise, in the Department of Agriculture. That department has as much to do now as it can well attend to; but it seems it will not be satisfied until it has the power to tell us how to feed and pay our men, and how to breed and run out cattle.

—ANLSA past President Mackenzie
Speaking at the 1920 Convention against the proposed Kendrick Bill

In the meantime, the dissension among members, which developed at the previous convention, had lingered and it was hurting the Association. Kendrick was perplexed and said with obvious disappointment:

In light of the 40 years of clamor against the unfair practices and the irregularities at our great market centers, it is impossible to comprehend how anyone can oppose reasonable legislation calculated to bring publicity, and with publicity undoubted confidence, in this vital matter.

Lack of Organization

Then Kendrick, and speakers who followed, talked about organization, in an obvious attempt to regain unity in the Association. Kendrick appealed to members with his speech.

The livestock industry of this country represents a larger amount of material wealth, and less organization, than any other of our great industries. . . .Such organization as it has renders more substantial service, and receives less support, than that of any other industry. You all know and understand the impossibility of securing financial aid to carry on the work of an association that is directed by its executive committee; and yet it is not too much to say that for every dime paid into the treasury of this organization its returns in benefits amount to dollar.

Without hesitation, I declare that we as representatives of the livestock industry ought either to provide for ourselves a strong, forceful organization. . .or we ought to disband entirely any form of association. As it is today, our efforts are futile, and hence are rightly subject to the scorn of our enemies.

The criticism was sometimes harsh from the outside as well as the inside. For example, Fred P. Johnson, secretary and manager of the National Western Stock Show was terribly negative. In the *Denver Daily Record Stockman,* January 8, 1920, he wrote,

National organizations have done very little in a practical way beyond adopting numerous resolutions on every subject under the sun and making various efforts to secure legislation with practically no results.

John Clay, the famous Chicago commission man and former president of the Wyoming Stock Growers Association, was even more critical in his 1924 book, *My Life On The Range:*

The 26th Annual Convention *held in Los Angeles in 1923.*

> *The work, the aim of our various cattle associations, from the St. Louis convention in 1884 to the present time, have in the main been destructive, not constructive. . . .This is not to say that some good has not been done, that many honest men have worked hard to accomplish results, but practically the results have been barren of good.*

Sam H. Cowan, attorney for the Association, pleaded for the members:

> *Go away from this convention united. . .Make your fight on your disagreements within, but stay with your organization.*

Burke gave his usual hard-hitting Market Committee report. After pounding the packers and *their unalterable determination either to rule or to ruin the industry,* he offered this on organization:

> *Past experience shows that men take up cooperation only when they are forced to do so from motives of self-protection. Every other line of endeavor has learned its lesson except the producers of live stock. . .agriculture has been the last to see the light, preferring a starved individuality to a well-fed cooperation.*

The split in the Association undoubtedly was comforting to packers, whose opposition never waned, and was almost enough to defeat the legislation.

FINALLY, A PACKERS AND STOCKYARDS ACT

It did pass. And to the cattlemen's delight, the new Secretary of Agriculture was Henry C. Wallace of Iowa, who for several years had been a member of their own Market and Executive Committees.

THE OLIVE BRANCH

With that victory under their belts, the Association now was receptive to talking "cooperation." The fact that livestock prices were 50 percent below wartime highs, and every producer in the country was said to be losing money, also had the Association leaders groping. In the conclusion of his last address as president of the Association, Kendrick asserted,

> *The solution of our task lies along the line of patient and courageous cooperation on the part of all.*

To demonstrate that the cattlemen held no malice and really were extending "the olive branch" to packers, they invited Thomas E. Wilson, president of the Institute of American Meat Packers, to address the 1922 convention in Colorado Springs.

The interests of the producer and of the packer are so mutually dependent, declared Wilson, *that harmonious cooperation is essential to the continued development of the industry.*

Learning to Increase Demand for Meat

Addressing the 1922 convention, Thomas E. Wilson, president of the Institute of American Meat Packers, ticked off figures that meat consumption per capita had dropped from 181 pounds in 1900 to 154 pounds in 1920, a 15 percent drop in two decades. *A major reason,* he said, *was the propaganda that meat is harmful to the health.*

What can be done about it? Wilson had a plan. He explained,

> *Scientific data to correct adverse propaganda should be collected, compiled and disseminated. . .among dietitians, physicians, hospitals, teachers, home demonstrators, household editors, agricultural colleges and others.*

With the establishment of the National Livestock and Meat Board that same year, producers began an ongoing campaign to understand the demand for beef, address it and adjust the industry to retain market share.

Noting the 15 percent drop in beef consumption over two decades, Wilson declared the need for scientific evidence to correct adverse propaganda. This could only be done through the cooperation of organizations representing all branches of the industry, he believed, and he pledged the support of his organization, the Institute of American Meat Packers.

What a difference a year had made. Wilson received a standing ovation!

Meat Board Proposed

Following the address by Wilson, Burke gave the report of the Market Committee, in which he announced: *The hatchet is buried; and we are ready to go ahead with this great cooperative work.*

Then he detailed a plan for a new organization to be called the National Live Stock and Meat Board, which would be made up of representatives from all areas of the industry. This plan was approved unanimously by the members. Two months later, on March 10, 1922, the National Live Stock and Meat Board was officially organized. It set a new precendent in the industry: build demand by promoting the product. But it would be near the end of the century before the Association took that philosophy on as its main agenda.

TIGHT GATES COLD FINGERS

1984

ARTIST: HAROLD HOLDEN

COMMISSIONED BY THE NATIONAL CATTLEMEN'S ASSOCIATION.

SERIES: 35 BRONZES

"More Sustaining Than Meat!" When Hershey Candy Company printed that slogan on their Hershey bars, the only candy bar at the time, the livestock industry knew it had to start telling its story.

The seeds for a National Live Stock and Meat Board—one of the most successful organizations in the history of the livestock industry—are generally credited to Thomas E. Wilson, president of the Institute of American Meat Packers, and also president of Wilson and Company Packers. His consistent urging for cooperation in the total industry, plus his knowledge of the supply and demand for meat, led others to take up the cause of sound promotion.

In 1919, when the American National Live Stock Association (ANLSA) was seeking federal legislation to curb the "tyrannical monopoly" of the packer trust, Wilson traveled to Hutchinson, Kansas, to address the Kansas Livestock Association (KLA). His mission was to smooth over differences within the industry and his message was, "Let us cooperate."

However, the ANLSA was in no mood to cooperate until they got the Packers and Stockyards Act of 1921 passed. In 1922, however, ANLSA invited Wilson to address their 1922 Convention in Colorado Springs where he reiterated "the need for cooperation" by all segments of the industry.

E.L. Burke, head of the ANLSA Market Committee, presented a detailed plan for a unified meat promotion organization to the Convention. This plan, worked out at a meeting of several organizations the previous November in Chicago, called for a National Live Stock and Meat Board. Although the last livestock organization to do so, the Association finally passed the plan unanimously.

Thus, in 1922 the National Live Stock and Meat Board (NLS&MB, referred to as the Meat Board) was created. Its main goal was to promote all red meats: beef, lamb and pork.

The Meat Board was organized with 17 directors: 11 representing producer organizations, two representing market agencies, two packers and two retailers.

An earlier attempt, initiated by packers, had failed because the packers wanted half of the directors, and the producers had balked. The structure of the new organization gave more clout to the producer sector, which in turn gained the support of individual producers.

Directorships were perceived as rather important. So charter directors, out of the 14 founding organizations, were grandfathered in through the bylaws, in addition to any seats they might earn otherwise. The initial directorships representing beef went to the ANLSA, KLA and TSCRA. The other seats belonged to livestock exchanges, commission firms, packers, retailers, breed associations, general farm organizations, as well as directors from the other meat species.

The first manager of the Meat Board was R.C. Pollock, who served from 1922 until 1960. He was a successful leader and developed the Meat Board into a powerful organization through the early years. He was also especially adroit at acquiring voluntary contributions from producers and matching funds from packers.

The early Meat Board emphasis was on *meat*, since Midwest associations and the Farm Bureau represented producers who were diversified in beef, pork and lamb. Also, most packing plants were multi-species.

The first campaign, in 1923, was "Meat for Health." Despite many new themes, this premise never changed.

When federal meat grading was introduced in 1926, packers objected and finally agreed to try it *only if the Meat Board would coordinate a test*. And for the first few years, the Meat Board paid four graders salaries of $2 per hour to keep the program going.

The Meat Board developed through research all the nutritional information on meat including the amount of various

Customer Satisfaction

First, the customer must want our product. . .and wanting it, must have the confidence in its wholesomeness and consistent quality to buy it. . .then to buy it again and again.

This Guiding Principal Never Changed.

The trilateral approach to marketing meat:

Research
Universities and Independent Scientists.

Education
Students, Meat Cutters, Chefs and Housewives.

Information
Media dissemination.

EDUCATION — INFORMATION — RESEARCH

The Meat Board's Theme Has Never Changed.

elements, and distributed this information to schools and newspapers all over the United States. Some of the earliest research supplied factual information on nutrition that remains valid today. The soundness of Meat Board programs, based on research and nutritional facts, became so highly regarded by the media, health professionals and the public that the approach of nutritional facts based on research became the basis of food nutrition reporting throughout the 20th century.

By 1946, a total of 1,329 nutrition review reports, in which the Meat Board participated, had been published, as well as hundreds of bulletins, posters, booklets for schools and feature articles for food editors. In 1948, for example, 14,076 students from 48 states entered the Meat Board Poster Contest.

Compared with other livestock organizations, the Meat Board was always the best funded. But there was never enough, especially after the Meat Board started paid advertising. So to finance its operations the Meat Board started the first commodity "checkoff" in the United States, although at the time it was called a voluntary deduction. As stated in *Growth of a Force:* published in1988.

> *The work of the Meat Board would be funded by the first "checkoff" in American agriculture—a unique system of deducting funds from the sale of a commodity. Producers were requested to allow voluntary deductions of five cents per carload [25 head of cattle per car]. . .at gathering points—terminal markets, auctions and packing plants—and packers were asked to match that contribution.*

This rate increased to 25 cents per car or one cent per head in 1931, to two cents in 1953, to three cents in 1962. Most of the collections were made at central markets. But the large majority of cattlemen in the west sold cattle direct, not passing through central markets, thus seldom paid the fees. Cattlemen talked beef promotion, but paid little.

First year income to the Meat Board (fiscal 1923), was $31,228. Then it grew steadily, reaching $100,000 in 1931 (a depression year), $1 million in 1956, $2 million in 1972 and $5 million in 1985.

But internal problems developed to threaten the future of this successful organization. In the mid-1950s, a National Meat Promotion Committee was appointed "to coordinate beef, pork and lamb promotions." In the midst of a depressed market and severe drought, cattlemen were less than pleased with this multi-species approach and countered by forming the National Beef Council which sought a legislated checkoff.

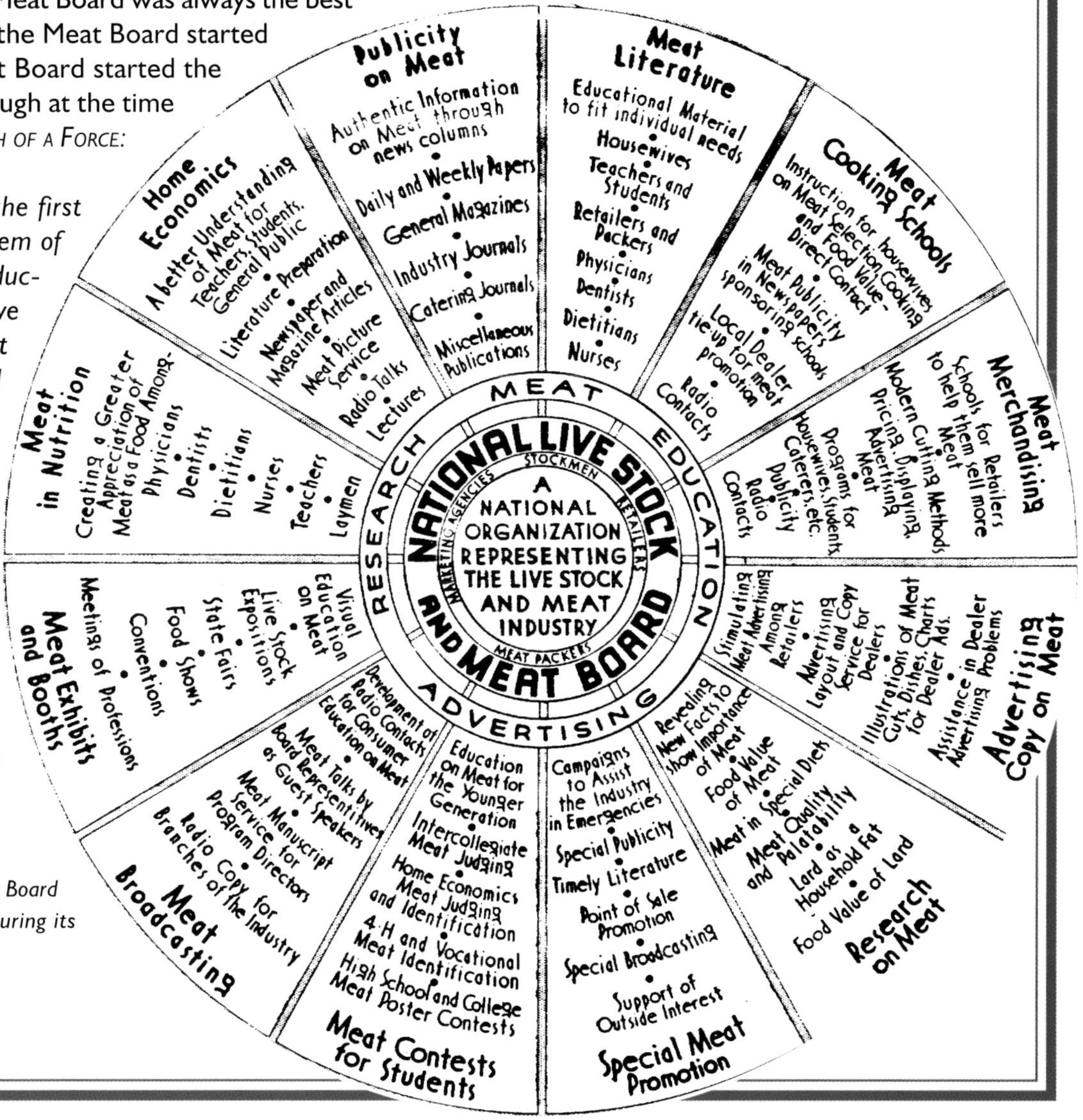

Proposed organization chart *for the National Live Stock and Meat Board prior to its inception in 1922. Meat Board programs changd little during its 74-year history.*

Cooking School in 1929 *sponsored by the* Chicago Daily News *with assistance from the Meat Board. This crowd of 15,000 filled a Chicago stadium. Max Cullen from the Meat Board put on a meat-cutting demonstration. "From the stage," he said, "it looked like 100,000 people." Similar schools, lectures and demonstrations were conducted all across the nation.*

Conference on Effect of Feed on Quality and Palatability of Meat Called By National Live Stock and Meat Board

Quality of meat *was an early concern and the Meat Board wasted no time in taking on that issue. In 1924, the Meat Board called this Conference on Effect of Feed on Quality and Palatability of Meat.*

The Meat Board and the American Farm Bureau killed the legislation, fearing a legislated checkoff would interfere with the voluntary checkoff financing the Meat Board.

While the NBC was struggling to stay alive, they were making the point that cattlemen wanted to promote *beef*, not *meat*. So the Meat Board appointed a Program and Policy Study Committee, chaired by John M. Marble of California and Cornell University economist Dr. Herrell DeGraff. Among their recommendations was that the Meat Board be divided into species committees: a Beef Committee, a Pork Committee and a Lamb Committee. (*See pages 136-141.*)

The Meat Board continued to struggle financially, until 1973 when it received a $200,000 grant from the Texas Cattle Feeders Association and officers of the Meat Board agreed that grant turned the organization around.

Then came the $1-per-head beef checkoff passed in 1986, and the Meat Board income shot to more than $60 million, 90 percent of which was beef dollars.

In January 1996, the Meat Board's pork and lamb divisions were spun off and Beef Industry Council's functions were woven into the new National Cattlemen's Beef Association. Thus, in 74 years, beef research, education and promotion went full circle—back to the cattlemen's Association that had help start it.

For the other side of the picture look to the Hindu and the Chinaman.

But after all, what better argument for meat is there than a thick steak, done to that perfect turn which brings out little plashes of the rich juice; or mayhap smothered in onions or garnished with Creole sauce? A substitute for that? Hardly! Nor is there any for a big, juicy roast, flanked on each side by well-browned potatoes and with a tureen of gravy handy. When a man's hungry he wants something that sticks to his ribs. And meat does that better than anything that the human race has found in several million years of pretty ardent searching. Meat is a man's food.

Additional copies of this booklet may be obtained upon request from the National Live Stock and Meat Board, 1665 Old Colony Building, Chicago, Ill.

Meat—

A Man's Food

Issued by the
NATIONAL LIVE STOCK AND MEAT BOARD
CHICAGO, ILL.

The best source of iron is beef *so concluded Meat Board—sponsored research at Pennsylvania State College, 1924 to 1926. Research showed that meat organs were the best source of iron and that beef was a better source than pork or lamb. Previously retailers had given liver away; now it had value.*

NOTHING TAKES THE PLACE OF
MEAT
NATIONAL LIVE STOCK AND MEAT BOARD
GREATEST KNOWN SOURCE OF STRENGTH

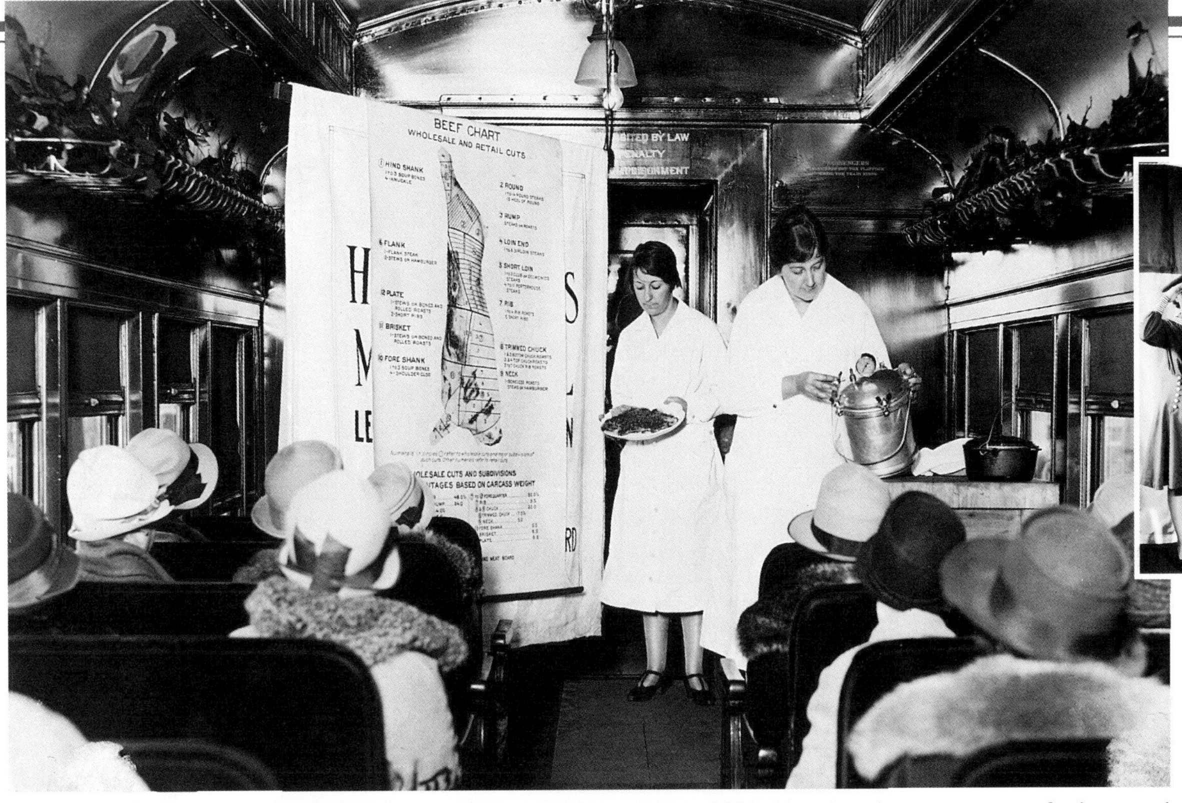

Train Demonstrations, A Creative Way to Spread Information in 1926. *Meat Board nutritionists give food care and preparation lessons to a captive audience. But schools and newspapers were the main recipients of Meat Board information.*

Bringing Good Nutrition to the Troops. *During World War II, as part of its education program, the Meat Board conducted thousands of schools for the military on how to preserve and prepare meat.*

Meat Board Chief Executives

R.C. Pollock 1922-1954

Carl F. Neumann 1954-1968

David H. Stroud 1969-1979

John H. Huston 1980-1996

Meat Board Chairmen

Howard Leonard	1923-1924
D.A. Millett	1924-1927
J.H. Mercer	1927-1929
Charles D. Carey	1929-1934
Thomas E. Wilson	1934-1939
Albert K. Mitchell	1939-1942
H.W. Farr	1942-1945
J.W. Rath	1945-1947
Will J. Miller	1947-1949
F.G. Ketner	1949-1951
Jay Taylor	1951-1953
G.N. Winder	1953-1955
J.F. Krey	1955-1957
R.J. Riddell	1957-1959
A.G. Pickett	1959-1961
John M. Marble	1961-1962
Norman Moser	1962
James B. Nance	1962-1966
C.O. Emrich	1966-1968
Gene Gunter	1968-1970
Dolph Briscoe, Jr.	1970-1972
John A. Copeland	1972-1974
Earl E. Harriss	1974-1976
J. Merrill Anderson	1976-1978
A. Marie Tyler	1978-1980
Richard A. Welding	1980-1981
Virgil M. Rosendale	1981-1982
Robert M. Carter	1982-1983
James A. Mullins	1983-1984
Roy B. Keppy	1984-1985
Hilmar G. Moore	1985-1986
J. Richard Pringle	1986-1987
Ralph R. Howe	1987-1988
Donald D. Jackson	1988-1990
Leon L. Locke	1990-1991
Robert D. Norris	1991-1992
Robert N. Rebholtz	1992-1993
Polly Owen	1993-1994
Jim Hauge	1994-1996

Alexandre Hogue DROUGHT STRICKEN AREA

Survival

In the morning the dust hung like fog, and the sun was as red as ripe new blood. All day the dust sifted down from the sky, and the next day it sifted down. An even blanket covered the earth. It settled on the corn, piled up on the tops of the fenceposts, piled up on the wires; it settled on the roofs, blanketed the weeds and trees.

—John Steinbeck *The Grapes of Wrath*

CHAPTER FIVE

Between The Wars

Between the wars was an era of bootlegging, Babe Ruth, assembly-line Fords, stock market collapse, New Deal and the meteoric rise of Hitler and Nazism. For cattlemen, it also was an era of record low prices, the introduction of beef grading, Dust Bowl, Great Depression, the Agricultural Adjustment Act and many other new government programs. For the Association, it was an era of struggle, budget cutting, poor attendance at conventions and generally restricted activities. As one past president said, *It's difficult to have a great Association on an annual budget of $16,000 to $29,000.* Yet there were cattle industry leaders who saw the necessity for a national organization, especially as the issues became more national in scope. They doggedly held the organization together.

The Entire Cattle Industry Went Broke

The two decades, 1920s and 1930s, were the worst in cattle history. Underlying the hard times and frustrations of those years was the frequent problem of low, low prices.

Cattlemen, as well as farmers, had responded to the government's request during World War I to "produce, produce" and increased cattle numbers and food production. But six months after the armistice was signed, the market could not handle the large volume of production. Meat exports had practically shut down; Europe was broke and United States consumers had less money to spend on beef.

In May 1920, there was another panic, the second or third in the past 40 years. Financial institutions were calling notes and forcing liquidation; cattlemen were begging and praying for credit. Cattle prices were cut in half from the

TIMELINE

1926 Admiral Byrd flies to North Pole.

1927 Charles Lindbergh makes the first solo transatlantic flight.

Babe Ruth hits 60 home runs.

1928 Philo T. Farnsworth demonstrates first television.

George Eastman demonstrates first color motion pictures.

Future Farmers of America organize.

1929 Herbert Hoover becomes 31st president.

Stock market prices crash on October 29 (Black Tuesday).

1930 Over 1,300 banks closed.

1931 Bank failures reach 2,294 as unemployment reaches 9 million.

Al Capone sent to prison for tax evasion.

1932 Drought in the Great Plains leads to the Dust Bowl.

1933 Franklin D. Roosevelt becomes 32nd president.

Federal Deposit Insurance Corporation (FDIC) established.

Prohibition repealed.

Adolf Hitler named German Chancellor.

1934 Drought worsens in Great Plains, creates Dust Bowl. Topsoil from farms in Southern Great Plains blows as far as Atlantic Coast.

1935 Social Security Act reserves funds for pensions and unemployment.

1936 Jesse Owens earns four Olympic gold medals in Berlin.

1937 Amelia Earhart sets out to circle the globe, is lost over Pacific Ocean.

German dirigible "Hindenburg" explodes and burns at Lakehurst, NJ.

Spam introduced by George F. Hormel.

1938 Superman stars in the first issue of Action Comics.

ISSUES

Transportation
•
Freight Rates
•
Credit and Financing
•
Agricultural Marketing Act
•
Tariffs
•
Taylor Grazing Act
•
Meat Grading
•
Survival

CATTLE PRICES SUFFER DEVASTING PRICE SWINGS IN THE 1920S

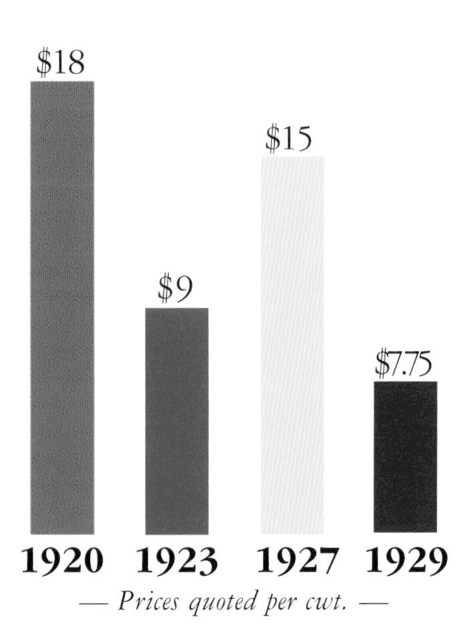

BEN LILY

TRAPPER, MOUNTAINEER, CONVENTION SPEAKER

The Association has had many renowned speakers, from generals to astronauts, but none as captivating as Ben Lily when he addressed the 1928 Convention in El Paso.

Lily hunted bears and lions in New Mexico and Arizona, for which ranchers paid him up to $100. Some years he made several thousand dollars. His career began in the swamps of New Orleans, where he once hunted bear with Teddy Roosevelt, who mentions Ben in his autobiography. But Ben went West, "where the 'bars' are bigger."

Lily traveled light, not even a blanket, carrying only what he needed to accompany the meat he shot for his dogs and himself. When given a room at the old Shelton Hotel in El Paso for the Convention, he pulled off the bed covers and slept on the floor as if laying under a pile of pine needles.

Vic Culbertson, manager of the GOS Ranch, for whom Lily had hunted, and the 1929-1930 president of ANLSA, brought Ben to El Paso. Lily's speech to the Convention was believed to be his only public speech of significance. His topic, "What I Know About Bears and Lions."

wartime high of $18 per cwt. and feeders were losing $50 to $80 per head "in cold cash." The entire cattle industry was broke.

Frank J. Hagenbarth, the second president of the Association and now a "senior statesman," was called on at the 1923 Convention in Los Angeles to analyze the situation and "lift the spirits." Hagenbarth was also president of the National Wool Growers Association (for 21 consecutive years) but continued as a sizable cattleman with several thousand head in Utah, Texas and Kansas.

After recounting similar price busts in 1882-1885, 1893-1896 and 1904-1906, Hagenbarth acknowledged *new clouds over the landscape, creating gloom and misery*. But he assured fellow cattlemen that *the sun is going to shine again. . .if you can only hold on.*

It was 1927 and 1928 before the sun broke through and prices again reached a profitable level. They increased to $15 per cwt., enough to cause talk of new boom times, and even saw threats of beef boycotts in eastern cities. Unbridled buying of stocks on the New York Stock Exchange set new records and set the stage for a crash that would be felt around the world.

Cattle prices took another nose-dive in late 1929, following the general economy, and continued the downward, devastating slide. By 1931, top cattle were selling for $7.75 per cwt. and cows for $5.75, going on down to $2 for plain cows in 1933.

Searching for hope, Henry G. Boice of Tucson, Arizona, the 1931 president of the Association, said, *The statistical position of the beef cattle industry is favorable. Beef cattle numbers declined from 34 million in 1900 to 24 million in 1930. Beef cattle per 100 human population declined from 45 head to 20 head.*

But that was not the whole story. There were eight million more dairy cattle than beef cattle in 1930, and dairy associations were urging a 10 percent reduction. That meant a glut of dairy beef, a situation that would haunt beef producers several times in the last half of the 20th century. In addition, in 1929 pork had overtaken beef in total production: 72 pounds of pork per capita, compared to 51 pounds beef.

Transportation the Top Issue

During the first 35 years of the Association's existence, no subject got more attention than transportation, rivaled only by the public domain.

At the death of T.W. Tomlinson, the Association hired F.E. (Ferd) Mollin as Executive Secretary, a cattle feeder in Nebraska who had been associated with the Omaha Stock Yards. To continue their fight with the railroads, the Association also hired Charles E. Blaine, a Phoenix attorney, as traffic counsel. Blaine loved to blast the railroads, and did so frequently to the delight of cattlemen. He worked on a contingency, a share of what he saved individual cattlemen who had been overcharged by the railroads.

By 1933, the depression was well underway; cattle prices sank to disaster levels and cattlemen were looking for culprits. Lo, the railroads, claiming lost business was threatening their existence, asked for a 15 percent rate hike!

FRED H. BIXBY
President 1922-1925
Long Beach, California

"We are a militant, fighting, non-partisan, non-political, non-compromising body of cattlemen," he declared, after serving four years as President. He also boasted that the ANLSA was "the largest Association in the United States," without offering proof. A jolly rancher, farmer, feeder, packer and banker, he frequently led the call at conventions for donations or pledges to "keep the Association going one more year."

CHARLES M. O'DONEL
President 1926
Bell Ranch, New Mexico

An Irishman, educated in Britain and France, who served in the Queen's forces and fought in South Africa, O'Donel came to the United States in 1883 and became manager of the large Bell Ranch. He was the first of two Bell Ranch managers to become President of ANLSA. Due to poor health, he served only one year. At the Bell Ranch, he used only purebred bulls, first Shorthorns then Herefords, until he build one of the most famous Hereford herds in the Southwest.

Trails, Trains, Trailers & Trucks

Of the many changes in the cattle business, few have been more visible or had more impact than transportation. The success of this industry from the very beginning lay in its ability to reach its market. Cattle were first shipped as a food source for the early explorers; but as early as 1519, Cortez recognized the benefit of shipping cattle to the newly conquered Yucatan Peninsula where he set up cattle ranching. From that point forward in North America, the industry has found ways to get its cattle to market.

An estimated 10 million cattle went "up the trail" between 1840 and 1890. Cattle went mostly from Texas to the North and West, some to stock free ranges, but most to reach railheads.

By the beginning of the Civil War, railroads had reached Chicago and the Chicago Stockyards opened at the end of the War in 1865. Packers soon followed: Armour, Swift, Morris, Cudahy, Wilson and others quickly made Chicago the "Meat Packing Capital of the World" and the largest cattle market in the world.

As new iron rails punched their way across Missouri, Kansas and Nebraska, with holding pens and loading chutes along the way, they became the destination for hundreds of trail drives. From there, the cattle could ride the rails to Chicago or population centers further east.

In 1869, the East met West when Union Pacific tracks connected with Central Pacific tracks in northern Utah. It was celebrated as the "biggest industrial event to date," and the United States truly became one nation. It also signaled the "beginning of the end" for big trail drives, which phased out around 1890. Railroads spidered out across the country and large packing plants expanded to build near major railroad networks, leading to the establishment of central, or terminal, markets in Chicago, St. Louis, Kansas City, Omaha, Denver, Fort Worth and a dozen more not quite so large.

In 1911 at the Indianapolis market, livestock were first delivered to market by truck. At first these small, single-axle trucks did not offer much threat to the big railroads and terminal markets, but this was the quiet beginning of another revolution in the industry. By the late 1920s, semi-trailer trucks were introduced, which permitted bigger loads, longer hauls and lower rates.Trucks could transport cattle directly from the ranch to market, and the focus of marketing cattle began to change again. By World War II, railroads began to feel the pinch.

In the meantime, some innovative farmers and ranchers built two-wheel trailers to pull with their automobiles. Then came then pickups and, in 1949, "gooseneck" trailers.

The first public livestock auction opened in 1904 at Union, Iowa. It was a new kind of market that became common in the 1930s and 1940s. By 1952, there were 2,500 public auctions, one in nearly every county, and terminal markets declined. Trucks and local auctions allowed smaller farmers to reach a marketplace with smaller numbers of cattle, but a good source of cash. Larger producers turned to the development of larger trucks.

Trucks and trailers put cattle trains out of business and gave a big boost to auction markets. The last known commercial shipment of cattle by rail was in 1980, from Yampa to Denver. In the1970s, the USDA attempted research to revive rail shipments from Florida to Texas, but it was too late. Trucks and trailers, and the convenience they offered, were here to stay.

Transportation Timeline

1519 Hernando Cortes brings first cattle to North American continent.

1650 American colonies begin exporting cattle by ship.

1779 First cattle trail in North America, from San Antonio, Texas, to the Louisiana Territory.

1805 First recorded Northern cattle drive from Circleville, Ohio. Western farmers seek livestock markets in populous East.

1852 Railroads reach Chicago from East, adding to the westward spread of livestock raising and feeding. Five different railroads establish their own stockyards there.

1865 Union Stockyards in Chicago become hub of livestock industry.

1867 Kansas Pacific Railroad reached Abilene, Kansas, establishing gateway for Texas trail herds to reach eastern consumer markets. Cattle drives begin. First shipment of cattle from Abilene to Chicago.

1875 Chilled beef shipped from New York to Europe in refrigerated ships, followed by a frozen shipment to England the following year.

1904 Caterpillar truck invented.

1911 First delivery of livestock by truck in Indianapolis.

1960 Transportation shifts from rail to truck; slaughter operations built near feedyards and moved from centralized city stockyards.

102
102

The first truck consignment of livestock *to a terminal reached the Indianapolis market on July 25, 1911. By 1932, in some areas of the country, trucks were hauling a third of the cattle and half of the hogs to major markets. Trailers like these were also helping change the marketing system.*

Blaine seized the opportunity and publicly blamed the cattlemen's losses not on low prices but on (1) the [worldwide] depression, (2) high freight rates, and (3) exorbitant salaries to numerous railroad executives on Wall Street, some "as high as $135,000 per year."

> ***Certainly a problem exists in beef production. . .The cattle industry as a whole carries a load which no other industry has succeeded in bearing.***
>
> —Willard C. White
>
> *Executive Vice President of Armour and Company*
>
> *Speaking at the 1929 Convention*

Equally provoking to the Association, the railroads were attempting to block the emerging truck industry, considered a boon to cattlemen. After all, trucks were offering the first competition ever for the monopolistic railroads; some cattlemen thought trucks were about to revolutionize the way cattle were marketed.

Texas had a new law, passed in 1931 with the backing of railroads, known as the 7,000-Pound Load Law. In the name of "safety," it provided that no truck operating upon the highways could carry a load in excess of 7,000 pounds, unless the truck was engaged in transporting commodities from or to the nearest railroad station, in which case it may handle 14,000 pounds. The railroads were seeking similar laws in other states; it was an easy way to combat competition from the new trucking industry. A loaded rail car carried a minimum of 36,600 pounds, so the bulk of the transportation was still with the rails.

With the support of the Association and cattlemen in general, trucks won the battle. Trucks, along with two-wheel trailers, revolutionized livestock marketing and made it possible for local livestock auction markets to function throughout the United States.

Revolution In Marketing

The first public livestock auction market opened for business in 1904 in Union, Iowa. By 1952, there were 2,500 such markets in the country and terminal markets were on the decline.

With the state of the economy sinking from bad to worse, adequate credit became a crucial issue for cattlemen and for the Association. President Warren G. Harding, a Republican, felt that the government was in part responsible for getting cattlemen into their over-supply situation following World War I. So as an emergency measure to partially absorb the shock of deflation, the War Finance Corporation advanced approximately $90 million on livestock. But the Association lobbied for more permanent action. That action came in 1933 with the Intermediate Credit Act, which established the Intermediate Credit System in connection with the 12 Federal Land Banks, and literally helped save the entire industry.

The marketing system, from cattleman to consumer, was another huge problem for the Association. Orderly marketing was needed. Most cattle were marketed through the big terminal markets, and most of them in clumps on Mondays and Tuesdays.

Many a headache was brewed thinking up ways to bring about orderly marketing, but most proposed schemes were rejected. Likewise, suggestions to avoid the congestion at bigger terminals usually fell on deaf ears. It was said that many cattlemen took enough pride in selling on the big markets, and often traveling there with their cattle, that they would take $1 per cwt. less in places like Chicago, Kansas City or Fort Worth than in smaller markets.

LUCAS C. BRITE
President 1927-1928
Marfa, Texas

After trailing a herd of cattle to the Big Bend area of Texas, Brite fell in love with the country, stayed, and put together a 128,000-acre ranch with 3,000 registered Herefords. "There are three parts to live stock husbandry," he preached, "breeding, feeding and marketing." In 1921, he bought a movie camera, made movies of his cattle, thus helping "Brite Bulls" become popular throughout the Southwest. On the ranch, he built a tabernacle for annual "Brite Camp Meetings," and endowed the Brite College of the Bible at Texas Christian University in Fort Worth.

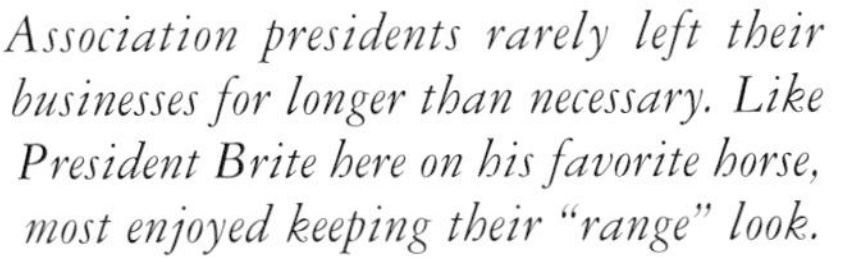

Association presidents rarely left their businesses for longer than necessary. Like President Brite here on his favorite horse, most enjoyed keeping their "range" look.

L. C. Brite, one of the best known cattlemen of the Southwest, is here shown making moving pictures on his ranch near Marfa, Texas. Mr. Brite is taking pictures of the year's work on the ranch, which will be spliced together and exhibited as an advertisement of his cattle and a true pictorial of everyday life on a big Texas ranch.

BEHIND THE SCENES

FRANK E. "FERD" MOLLIN

EXECUTIVE SECRETARY

1929-1955

For 26 years, longer than any other executive, Ferd Mollin led the Association through the most difficult economic times of the century. Not only did it survive, but it grew during the last 10 years of his tenure to 29 state and 120 local affiliate cattle organizations representing 150,000 cattlemen.

Born in Genoa, Nebraska, in 1887, he attended high school and business school in Lincoln. In his 58-year career he held only two jobs. His first was for Kent & Burke, cattle feeders at Genoa, later headquartered in Omaha. There he was trained by Edward L. Burke, the fireball chairman of the old Market Committee of ANLSA. In 22 years, Mollin rose to general manager of the firm's extensive feeding operations and eight ranches. Then he went to ANLSA.

During those lean years, Mollin ran the Association practically single handed, handling membership, conventions, lobbying and editorials. His style was direct and sometimes caustic. In 1933, for example, he wrote and duplicated copies of a speech to be delivered to the Institute of American Meat Packers in Chicago. It was so offensive to the host that he was forced to withdraw the copies. One of the things he had planned to say:

> *For 20 years, the distributor has added again and again to the toll taken out of the farm product on its way to the consumer. Is it any wonder that today agriculture is prostrate and millions of potential consumers hungry?*

In Washington, he gained the reputation of "against everything." Whether that was his own personality or whether he merely reflected the attitude and stance of his employers, he was well admired for his tenacity by the cattlemen he represented. ANSLA Past President Henry G. Boice once said: "Ferd Mollin led the fight against the ratification of the Argentine Sanitation Convention, and he won. And President Roosevelt lost."

In 1957, he was inducted into the Saddle and Sirloin Portrait Gallery, one of only three Association officials to be so honored.

The Association regularly attacked the commission rates at the major terminal markets and tried, with little success, to get them lowered through legislation or through the Packers and Stockyards Administration. They also charged that the terminal markets were structured more for buyers than for sellers, and they accused the speculators at terminals of being "leeches," claiming that as many as three or four speculators sometimes would take ownership, meaning three or four fills, and profit on cattle between the rancher and feeder.

As a result of these activities, the Association regularly passed resolutions in support of direct marketing. California had a direct marketing plan, direct from rancher to feeder or rancher to packer, that operated successfully for several years and was endorsed for just as many years by the Association. But the idea never caught on elsewhere for very long.

FEDERAL FARM BOARD

When President Herbert Hoover, the former Food Administrator during World War I, took office in 1929, he made credit and marketing the cornerstones of his farm policy. One of the early bills he signed was the Agricultural Marketing Act of 1929, which created a Federal Farm Board and appropriated $500 million for the Board to loan to producer-owned cooperatives. President Hoover called it, "the most important measure ever passed by Congress in aid of a single industry."

Although historians do not generally record Hoover as a friend of agriculture, Association leaders applauded his efforts. Further disproving this impression, in 1930 L.C. Brite wrote of Hoover: *He has probably gone further in extending a helping hand to the farmer and ranchman than any of his predecessors.*

Meat Grading Introduced

In 1924, at the request of two government agencies that purchased meat, the United States Shipping Board and the Veterans Bureau hospitals, the USDA published tentative standards for grading. The editor of *Breeders Gazette*, Alvin H. Sanders, became enthused and wrote that

> *Beef from well fattened cattle of excellent conformation and quality should be marketed as Blue Ribbon Beef.*

That editorial prompted 250 prominent cattle breeders and feeders to meet in Kansas City in 1926 to discuss the advisability of grading and stamping the better quality beef as Prime and Choice and to organize the National Better Beef Association to promote and finance grading and stamping. Oakleigh Thorne of New York was elected chairman.

Thorne told the ANLSA convention in 1927.

> *The major problem is whether it should be voluntary or compulsory. Also, there is the proposition of whether it should be done by an employee of the packing plant or by an official of the United States government.*

Major packers opposed government grading and introduced their own house grades, like Swift Premium, Armour Star, Wilson Certified and Cudahy Puritan. But there was *nothing standard about house grades*, Association leaders argued, *except that was the best beef that a given packer had in a given plant on a given day.* Consequently the Association supported government grading.

Later the packers agreed to go along, if the National Live Stock and Meat Board would coordinate the program. The Meat Board agreed and for a few years and paid the salaries of four inspectors.

After World War II, independent packers forced the majors to give up their house brands and grading began to increase, always with the support of the Association. By 1996, 81 percent of the total slaughter was graded.

O.M. Plummer

Truth in Meats

O.M. Plummer, early beef promoter of Portland, Oregon, was introduced at the 1927 convention in Salt Lake City as "a prophet in the industry," after which he gave a rousing speech. *People are entitled to know what they are buying—before they eat it,* he declared. Also, he implored fellow cattlemen: *Never refer to 'tough beef,' it is just 'less tender.'*

Later, he proposed that women be enlisted to help promote beef, perhaps the first person to do so. *A women's auxiliary,* he recommended, *composed of the wives of livestock people.* But he possibly got carried away when he declared, *This passing fad for slenderness in women has been found to be very dangerous to health, and medical men now urge more plumpness, which means more meat.*

Nevertheless, Plummer's slogan, "Truth In Meats," was used to promote a new concept to assure quality meat.

Drought Victim. *Powder River County, Montana, 1934. High prices and the push for production brought on by World War I encouraged the over cultivation of the arid Great Plains of the West. However, farm prices fell severely once the War was over and cultivation of the Plains abruptly halted. Huge areas of land lay idle, stripped of its grass cover from cultivation and exposed to all the elements of nature. With the onset of drought in 1930, some 50 million acres turned into a virtual desert. In 1934 a great dust storm rolled over the parched land blowing eastward over 300 million tons of precious topsoil. Ships as far as three hundred miles at sea in the Atlantic Ocean were touched by the dust. Cattle that had been kept alive in the drought by ranchers carrying water to them and providing what little feed could be found choked to death in the dust. Some quarter of a million farmers and ranchers were wiped out.*

The major thrust of the Farm Board was cooperative marketing. Thus the National Live Stock Marketing Association was organized in 1930 and soon had 19 cooperative associations operating on all the principal markets of the country. By 1933, the number of member associations had increased to 24, serving 300,000 producers in 38 states. They in turn established subsidiaries to handle financing, which became known as the present National Live Stock Producers Association and which has been supported throughout its history by the Association. In 1994, 13 of these marketing associations and six credit corporations continued to operate and help a large number of people.

...there has unconsciously developed an idea that the agricultural producers are subjects for charity. . . I hope that we, as livestock producers, in the years to come can look the world squarely in the face, with a consciousness that, even though the depression left our business bent and sometimes broken, our character is still untarnished."

—ANLSA President Henry Boice
At the 1931 Convention

The Federal Farm Board, however, was discontinued in 1933 by President Franklin Roosevelt, who offered a "New Deal."

PROTECTIONISM FOR CATTLEMEN, TOO

The 1920s was an era of protectionism in the United States. Some folks blamed protectionism for part of the economic ills; others said protectionism was a response to economic hard times. Whatever the reason, the Association fought several years for a protective tariff, "the same protection given to other industries."

The Emergency Tariff Act of 1921 put an import duty of 30 percent ad valorem on live cattle, two cents per pound on fresh and frozen meat and 25 percent on prepared meats, with no tariff on hides. The Association screamed "unfair," particularly regarding hides, but the more permanent Tariff Act of 1922 was no different.

Cattlemen protested unfair competition with foreign beef, citing a University of Wyoming study showing the cost to produce and market a steer in that state to be $9.33 per cwt., compared with $5.33 in Argentina. *To leave the livestock industry unprotecte . . .is unjust and un-American,* declared Association President Brite in 1929.

The following year, the long-sought increase in tariffs finally became law. It increased the duty on cattle to three cents per pound, fresh beef to six cents per pound and hides to 10 percent ad valorem. A legislative victory for the Association, yes, but not enough to ease the financial pain.

Marketing System Challenged

Association leaders began to challenge the whole marketing chain—from producer to consumer—calling it "unnecessarily expensive, unwieldy and unsound."

Some packers agreed. Speaking at the 1929 convention in San Francisco, Willard C. White, executive vice president of Armour and Company, suggested a reorganization of production and marketing methods to reduce the amount of rehandling:

> *There are 14 profits at a minimum and 25 at a maximum that must be collected under our system. Certainly a problem exists in beef production. . .the cattle industry as a whole carries a load which no other industry has succeeded in bearing.*

Even the chain stores, a new phenomenon in America in the late 1920s and early 1930s, were attacked. They were accused of handling low grades of meat, due to an emphasis on price rather than quality. They were also accused of defrauding consumers by offering some name brands at a discount and making it up by charging the same customer higher prices for other items.

The Association even went so far as to ask that the 1919 Consent Decree be modified to allow Swift and Armour back in the retail business to compete with the emerging chain stores. The rationale was that packers might sell beef cheaper, thus move more volume. A federal judge denied this request in 1931, but he did allow Swift and Armour to re-enter the food manufacturing and distribution business.

One of the more positive developments of this era was a new concern for "the consumer perception of beef." In 1927, the industry picked up on a new slogan, "Truth In Meats," originated by O. M. Plummer, the enthusiastic manager of the Pacific International Live Stock Exposition at Portland, Oregon.

Challenge of Survival

The greatest challenge between the wars both for cattlemen and for the Association was to "just survive." They had reason to suspect they were into a depression, not merely another dip in cattle prices, when the New York stock market crashed on Thursday, October 29, 1929. The following Tuesday, there was a panic, causing a record 16 million shares of stock to be sold.

By 1933, unemployment had reached 24.9 percent of the work force; average annual income dropped to $376 [on farms to $74 per year]; and the people simply did not have money to buy beef. During the same four years, cattle numbers increased 30 percent, to a record 74,369,000 head, due to lack of market, and prices dropped 70 percent, averaging $17.78 per head.

VICTOR CULBERSON
President 1929-1930
Silver City, New Mexico

Born in Georgia, grew up in Texas, and ran away from home at 13, he took odd jobs such as railroad crew water boy, waiter, miner and scout for troops fighting Indians. While working for a mine owned by G.O. Smith, he induced Mr. Smith to lease 150 cows, with which he built and managed the well-known GOS Ranch in New Mexico. As president he called for rebuilding the nation's cattle population, after it had dipped to only 11 million head.

HENRY G. BOICE
President 1931
Tucson, Arizona

Born in Missouri, he grew up on the XIT Ranch in Texas. After attending school in Los Angeles, he became president and general manager of Chiricahua Cattle Company, Arizona's largest cattle company. It ranged cattle on Indian reservations, national forests and state land, as well as company land. Back in Missouri, Boice's grandfather travelled to England and returned with Anxiety 4th, the Hereford bull that became famous throughout America.

Family Influences the Agricultural Sector. *The only father-son secretaries of agriculture, the Wallaces strongly influenced the agricultural situation between the wars. Henry C. Wallace served as Secretary of Agriculture (1921-1924), and his son, Henry A. Wallace, was apointed Secretary of Agriculture in 1933. Henry C. Wallace had served on the ANSLA Executive Committe and the Market Committee, the only such member ever to become a Secretary of Agriculture.*

With Roosevelt's backing, Henry A. Wallace was a "New Dealer" and one of his first programs was the Agricultural Adjustment Act. He had been editor of the family magazine, WALLACE'S FARMER, and founder of Pioneer Hybrid Corn Company; he would later serve as Vice President of the United States (1941-1945) and as a presidential nominee of the Progressive Party (1945). In 1934, Don Murphy, Editor of WALLACE'S FARMER, asked his longtime friend, Henry A. Wallace, "We have all these programs to help the cotton farmers and the grain farmers, how abou the cattlemen?" To which Wallace replied, "Oh hell, they're all Republicans anyway." {Henry A. had been a Republican, until he was appointed Secretary of Agriculture by FDR.}

Henry A. Wallace, standing before a portrait of his father Henry C. Wallace.

Henry Boice, the 1931 president, was an articulate and discerning president of the Association. In his final address to the assembled cattlemen in San Antonio, Boice expressed deep concern about the mental and moral toll that the depression was beginning to have on cattlemen:

> *In times like these, it behooves all of us to stop and analyze the effects of present circumstances and changing conditions upon the character of each of us. There has been so much said about the need for assistance by the agricultural producers that there has. . .developed an idea that the agricultural producers are subjects for charity. . .I hope that we, as livestock producers . . .can look the world squarely in the face, with a consciousness that, even though the depression left our business bent and sometimes broken, our character is still untarnished.*

President Franklin D. Roosevelt took office in 1933 and immediately initiated a multitude of "New Deal" programs. He appointed as Secretary of Agriculture Henry A. Wallace of Iowa.

National Convention *in Rapid City, South Dakota, 1935. At the NCBA Midyear Meeting in 1997, Ralph D. Jones of South Dakota pointed out that the two gentlemen directly center in photograph were his two grandfathers: Tom Jones, president of the South Dakota Stock Growers Association and Tom Berry, Governor of South Dakota.*

THE NEW DEAL

The Agricultural Adjustment Act (AAA) was the first attempt by government at supply management. It paid farmers to reduce acreage and to store commodities on the farm, and it established price supports based on a new concept, parity. Parity was a method of measuring agricultural equality; it was based on 1910-1914 prices and required a program of price supports to achieve parity. But first would come the need to declare beef a basic commodity.

Early in 1933, as Congress debated the AAA, most cattlemen opposed all efforts to have cattle included as "a basic commodity," which would have made them eligible for production controls and price supports. That would strain their time-honored spirit of free enterprise and self-reliance. Cotton, wheat, corn, rice, tobacco, hogs and milk already had been declared basic commodities. Rye, barley, flax, grain sorghum and peanuts would be added later.

But as the year wore on, the Plains states became engulfed in the fiercest drought in all history. Dust storms were so bad that some towns burned lights by day. Grasshoppers and rodents devoured feed supplies. Water holes gave up and wells quit. Many cattlemen hauled water, by wagon, trailer or truck, but they could not keep ahead of the thin and thirsty cattle. Cattle were dying by the thousands and cattlemen began to reconsider their philosophical stance.

The 1934 convention, long to be remembered and considered the most controversial convention ever, was held in Albuquerque, New Mexico. In spite of hard times, attendance was the largest in recent years.

CHARLES E. COLLINS
President 1932-1935
Kit Carson, Colorado

"The grand old man of the livestock industry," he was called. Forceful and well informed, he served as President four years, holding the Association together during The Great Depression. He started out in the industry helping his father trail cattle, living both in Mexico and Kansas. In 1907, he bought his first ranch in eastern Colorado and built it to 100,000 acres. Not only a rancher, he was also a state senator, bank president and president of the Franklin Blackleg Serum Co., which he helped found. He also was the father of the 1956 president of ANCA.

Beef Becomes a Commodity. *Two influential Texans, Senator Tom Connally (right) of Marlin, Texas, chairman of the Senate Foreign Relations Committee, along with Texas Representative Marvin Jones (left) of Amarillo, chairman of the House Agriculture Committee, authored the Jones-Connally Bill to make beef a basic commodity.*

Intent: To make cattlemen eligible for government help during the Great Depression. This bill—introduced in Congress, but not acted on—was a very hot topic at the 1934 ANLSA Convention in Albuquerque. It was so controversial that the president refused to let members vote on it.

Immediately after adjournment of the 1934 Convention, with the instigation of the Texas and Southwestern Cattle Raisers, the bill passed quickly. As in many times throughout the history of the Association, when push came to shove, the TSCRA were the real power houses.

The Day They Shot Our Cattle

The government purchased 8.3 million cattle—*and shot most—reducing the cattle population in the United States 11 percent in eight months.*

Shoot our cattle?! The cattle we had raised, petted, fed and named? That was a disturbing thought for a 10-year-old East Texas boy, who had learned to love cattle. We had about 30 head, more than most farmers in our cotton-growing community.

But the economic times in 1934 were equally disturbing to my parents. The Great Depression was well underway; the banks had closed in 1931, causing my family, along with thousands of others, to lose all of our savings. We were three years into the drought; the creeks and local ponds had dried up. We were hauling water—drawn by hand from a neighbor's well—in barrels on a wagon, but the cattle never seemed to get enough.

Obviously, the cattle should be sold. Everybody wanted to sell. But there was absolutely no market. Cattle were already dying from starvation or from bogging in the creeks.

President Roosevelt's "New Deal" programs were already offering relief to farmers who would plow up cotton (which we did), or kill little pigs. However, cattle industry leaders were holding out. They had too much pride and self-determination to accept government help. But when you run out of stock water, pride and self-determination tend to wither.

Finally, in June 1934, Congress approved cattle as a basic commodity and allocated $63 million for a purchase-and-slaughter program. Cattle in good shape would be purchased, slaughtered locally, canned by people on work-relief and the meat given to the poor. Cattle that were too thin, as ours were, would be condemned and shot on the spot.

For several weeks, Dad and Mom agonized over whether to have our cattle shot. Dad pointed out that for condemned cattle the government was offering $12 per head for those over 2 years of age, $10 for yearlings, and $4 for calves. "Pretty good, considering these times!" Furthermore, the price included a benefit program for producers with mortgaged cattle; bankers would not be allowed to get more than half the payment.

For cattle not condemned, the price was much better: $12 to $20 for those over 2 years, $10 to $15 for yearlings and $4 to $8 for calves.

The longer we waited, the poorer the cattle became and hauling water was becoming "less noble," and less effective. So my dad gave in.

Two government agents carrying high-powered rifles arrived one afternoon; we had all our cattle penned in a lot right behind our house; and the big man simply asked, "Which ones?"

Dad would point to one, starting with the weakest, and they would shoot. After about 12 were shot, it became harder for my dad to point. In less than an hour, the men left, leaving 18 dead. Neighbors came and took two of the fatter calves to dress that night. The next day, we drug the remaining dead ones with teams to the back of the pasture, where the buzzards and coyotes took over.

A lot of other cattlemen went through similar experiences. Within eight months, the government purchased 8.3 million head, reducing the national cattle population by 11 percent. The average price paid was $13.50 per head.

From the Personal Experience of Charles E. Ball

An estimated 1,500 members and visitors overtaxed the hotels; railroads brought in Pullman cars to handle the overflow. Some cattlemen claimed they had to borrow money for a train ticket. But the word was out: the issue of cattle becoming a basic commodity was to be debated. Simple as it sounded, it was an emotional issue, touching the heart, the soul and the pocketbook of every cattleman.

The debate in the country had begun the year before. An emergency meeting had been called in Denver in November 1933 to discuss the deteriorating situation. President Charles E. Collins appointed a Committee of Five—C. J. Abbott of Nebraska, Dolph Briscoe, Sr. of Texas, Elmer Brock of Wyoming, Hubbard Russell of California and himself—to study the alternatives and make recommendations at the Albuquerque convention.

By convention time, the committee had met several times and agreed on their recommendation: "Refer the matter back to each state organization for their individual action."

"Cop-out!" shouted members who had traveled across the country and had "come to vote." A Mr. Delaney argued, *It is a national problem, it is national legislation and the American National should take a position. . . .I don't believe in coming down here and resolving ourselves into a debating body, with no decision.*

Dolph Briscoe, spokesman for the Committee of Five, explained that Association members were equally divided and that a vote would surely split the organization. But that didn't satisfy men like Dan Caseman of Kansas, who expressed the sentiments of many cattlemen in cattlemen's fashion: *You are impairing your intellectual integrity and your*

Biggest Cattle Deal

The Emergency Cattle Purchase Program was to solve at least three problems:

1. Reduce inventory and boost prices for cattlemen.
2. Unemployed in rural communities would get jobs to process and can the meat.
3. The poor would receive the canned meat.

Thus, all three groups would benefit. But it did not turn out that way. Many of the cattle were so emaciated they were condemned as unfit for human consumption; the unemployed were inexperienced and often did a poor job of canning; and the poor would sometimes not eat the questionable meat. So most of the cattle were shot on the spot, then buried or left for the coyotes and buzzards to devour.

During the next eight months, the government purchased 8.3 million head, reducing the United States cattle population 11 percent. The price ranged from $4 for calves to $20 for fatter cows, for an average of $13.50 per head. Among the states supplying the larger numbers were Texas 1,908,570, North Dakota 977,120, South Dakota 912,846, New Mexico 544,922, Kansas 521,056 and Missouri 511,588.

While it was the biggest cattle deal ever, it remained controversial for years. J. Evetts Haley, rancher and historian from Canyon, Texas, wrote in an article, "Cattle Business and Monkey Business," that participating ranchers "surrendered their birthright for a herd of canner cows." Yet others said, "Most ranchers wanted aid of some kind, not rugged individualism."

In any case, by 1935, drought, dust and government purchases had ended the problem of overproduction. Most critics would concede that this program removed many nondescript animals of poor breeding and raised the average quality of the remaining seed herds.

Thousands of government cattle *held in pens at the Fort Worth Stock Yards awaiting shipment to ranges in other states or to slaughter and canning plants. These cattle show every color, sex, age, growth and condition of every beef and dairy breed known. From* THE CATTLEMEN*, October 1934.*

moral integrity when you take this bribe. . .I refuse to be subsidized . . .To hell with their money!

That was *the* philosophical problem many cattlemen had with government help. But there was a bigger practical problem. The Association's constitution and bylaws called for a weighted vote, one vote for each $5 in dues by an individual or an affiliated association, but there were no records for how much each had paid. Because the Association never raised enough dues money for expenses, pledges were solicited at the end of each convention. Several members and state associations would pledge amounts ranging from $100 up to $1,000, but not all pledges made were paid. Consequently, President Collins explained that a "constitutional vote" would be almost impossible and certainly split the Association. President Collins refused to let the issue come to a vote. So the highly-charged convention ended anti-climatically.

That was not the end, however. Immediately after adjournment, Dolph Briscoe, president of the Texas and Southwestern Cattle Raisers Association (TSCRA), called a rump meeting of Texans present. Jay Taylor of Amarillo moved that they support the Jones-Connally bill to make cattle a basic commodity, and it passed 40 to five. The Texas group sent telegrams to Texas congressmen and senators about their vote and the bill quickly passed, appropriating $63 million for cattle purchases by the Federal Surplus Relief Corporation. The total aid figure was later boosted to $525 million. On June 1, 1934, the Emergency Cattle Purchase Program began.

The New Deal introduced many other programs and agencies, a number of which prevail today, and still impact cattlemen. The proliferation and potential permanency of such agencies was an omen that concerned cattlemen greatly.

For the western states, the most significant New Deal program was the Taylor Grazing Act of 1934 which contained a provision for grazing fees and some security for ranchers using federal lands. Throughout the 36 years of the Association, there had been numerous speeches and resolutions on the public domain, but never an accord among producers and no action by Congress. Many of the proposals called for ceding unappropriated federal land to the states where they were located. Will C. Barnes, first secretary of the American Stock Growers Association, forester and writer, recorded this in the *AMERICAN CATTLE PRODUCER*, October 1934:

> *Just to refresh our memories and get the record straight: The first time the lease-law matter was before any large association was at Denver in 1889. . .My notes show that this question has come up at practically every meeting of the National from that time to this, the vote generally being about 50-50. Meanwhile the area known officially as the 'unallotted, unappropriated public lands of the United States has dwindled from over 500 million to less than 200 million acres of badly over-grazed and eroded public land—hardly worth fighting over.*

In addition, the eastern politicians opposed "giving away assets that belonged to the government and to all the people." So controversial had been the issue, it took the strong arm of President Franklin D. Roosevelt to get any action by Congress.

Not all Association members were happy with the "solution" that the Taylor Grazing Act afforded, but at least it was a move off dead center. President Roosevelt placated them by appointing one of their most colorful members, Ferry Carpenter of Hayden, Colorado, as the first grazing administrator. But he did not last long. After exerting his rancher independence and failing to adapt to the bureaucracy, he became crosswise with Secretary of Interior Harold Ickes and was forced to resign in 1938.

ALBERT K. MITCHELL
President 1936-1937
Albert, New Mexico

"Everybody knew Albert, or felt they did," says a distant rancher who never met him. An esteemed leader, he served as president or chairman of numerous livestock organizations, including the American Hereford Association, American Quarter Horse Association, National Live Stock and Meat Board and Cowboy Hall of Fame, and winner of the prestigous Golden Spur Award. He was also a state representative and on the Republican National Committee. He was the second of two managers of the large Bell Ranch to become President of ANLSA, and he ran his own family ranch, The Tequesquite, as well.

EXPERIMENTING WITH BUREAUCRATS

During most of the 1930s, the Association spent much of its energy resisting and refuting bureaucratic experimentation and expansion under the New Deal. *There has been a lot of idle chatter about the redistribution of wealth*, said President Charles E. Collins at the 1935 convention in Rapid City, South Dakota, *It seems to have been the opinion of the President and the 'brain trust' that through legislation they could make all people prosperous. . .It just can't be done!*

Again, at the 1936 convention in Phoenix, President Collins addressed the "broader questions" facing cattlemen. *I am still at a loss to understand what are the hopes and objectives of the adjustment administrators,"* he stated. *"Apparently, it's that no one engaged in the business will ever go broke or lose money.*

"New Mexico's busiest man." *Albert Mitchell flew his own plane—rare in that day—to save time.*

The Taylor Grazing Act

Grazing public lands was wrought with confusion; it was a source of continuous conflict for ranchers and contributed to overgrazing and damage to the land. The accepted custom, which traced back to the Mexican Mesta in the 1500s, was that one rancher would not infringe on another's range as long as it was stocked. But if he took off his stock, because of drought or to save forage for the winter, another rancher or nomadic sheep herder could move in. Security of tenure was the biggest desire of ranchers, which they agreed could best be provided through private ownership. But the East and West could not agree politically on the several bills that were introduced periodically in Congress for the dispersal of public lands.

The first stability of sorts came with the Taylor Grazing Act of 1934, written by Rep. Edward T. Taylor (D-CO). This Act brought some security to the rancher, and effectively ended homesteading and the open range.

The Act provided for the Department of Interior to:

1. Administer 173 million acres of unappropriated land;
2. Establish grazing districts;
3. Charge "a reasonable fee" for the right to run animals thereon.

It also allowed ranchers to lease land for 10 years as well as preserve privileges and customs.

Under the Act some 30 grazing districts (three to nine million acres each) were established. Ranchers were granted controlled grazing privileges, but no property rights to the land. There were no grazing fees the first year and Harold Ickes, long-time Secretary of Interior, promised that future grazing fees would be based on the cost of administration. In 1935 when the first fees were charged, that cost was $150,000; in 1995, it was $1.1 billion.

Representative Edward T. Taylor, *a Democrat from Colorado, sought to bring stability into the chaos and confusion of public lands grazing by authoring the Taylor Grazing Act of 1934. This Act regulated the grazing of public lands until it was combined with the Bureau of Land Management.*

The Association thought this would be workable, especially after Secretary Ickes selected Farrington (Ferry) Carpenter as first director of the Grazing Service. Carpenter, a likable Colorado rancher, attorney, state legislator and member of the Association, told Ickes the only way the Grazing Act ever would succeed was to have rancher input and cooperation. So Carpenter set up local advisory boards, elected by ranchers, for each district. Ranchers liked this procedure, because they had a voice in management decisions.

But Ferry Carpenter was no bureaucrat. He only knew how to get things done out West. After being reprimanded by Ickes (for relying too much on advisory boards and too little on Interior staff), he was forced to resign in 1938.

By 1946, the Grazing Service was becoming too aggressive, which provoked Congress to cut its appropriations in half, from $1.7 million to $802,000. The cut forced a major reduction in employees, and the Grazing Service couldn't survive. In 1947, it was combined with the General Land Office into the Bureau of Land Management (BLM).

Drawing on a quote from President Cleveland in 1887, he continued: *It is not the function of government to support the people, but the people must support the government.*

We are always going to have good and bad times, as we always have had, added Collins, *for one breeds the other.*

The cattlemen felt somewhat allayed when in 1936 the Supreme Court ruled that the AAA program was unconstitutional, stating that the constitution gave the federal government no right to regulate agricultural production. The government already had collected $200 million in processing taxes through packers, which the Court ordered

FIRST GRAZING ADMINISTRATOR—FERRY CARPENTER

You never had to wonder where Ferry stood, he was quick to tell you, said a friend of Farrington R. (Ferry) Carpenter, the first grazing administrator of public lands hired under the 1934 Taylor Grazing Act. *That's one reason ranchers liked him and one reason the bureaucrats loathed him.*

For example, when Ferry told a group of Nevada ranchers that *trying to speed up a bureaucrat is just like throwing sand in the gears—it just stops him cold,* he was reprimanded by Secretary of Interior Harold Ickes.

I kept getting fired regularly every time I opened my mouth, said Carpenter later, *but I wasn't fired for keeps until 1938, and by that time I was glad to go home.*

Born in Illinois in 1886, he was sent to New Mexico at age 13 for his health. But he went back East to Princeton for college and later to Harvard for a law degree. In between, at age 21, he homesteaded 160 acres on the western slope of Colorado at Hayden, Colorado, and stayed there (except for occasional duty in Denver or Washington) until he died at 94. He sometimes poked fun at himself as "a Harvard squatter."

As administrator of the 1934 Taylor Grazing Act, Ferry Carpenter once strode to the podium and faced drought- and depression-plagued members of the Wyoming Stock Growers Association. USDA Secretary Henry A. Wallace had just finished addressing the assembly and the dearth of applause, dour expressions and shaking heads made it amply evident that many did not like what they had seen and heard. *Luckily,* said one, *Wallace had to rush to catch a train, or the people would have vented their anger on him.*

Ferry's cheerful voice and buoyant expression quickly lightened that mood. His short, punchy stories and pertinent and authoritative information regarding implementation of the Taylor Grazing Act changed the atmosphere of the entire convention. "What a wonderful Talk!" men and women from throughout the state declared. Oddly, few could recollect anything he had said.

After Carpenter left government service, he later gained national fame with his rhetoric and oratory tales. Local folks lovingly called him "the yarnin' champ of Yampa Valley" and, in 1952, *THE SATURDAY EVENING Post* featured him as "America's Most Unusual Storyteller."

But as a rancher, small town lawyer and "two-bit notary" in Hayden, Colorado, he bought up several deserted homesteads and put together a sizable ranch which he stocked with registered Herefords. In the 1950s, he became an outspoken prophet of performance testing and was elected President of Performance Registry International. In addition, he was elected or appointed to a number of county, district and state offices.

Not only was Carpenter plain spoken, he was articulate, intelligent, witty, a spell-binding speaker and well-respected. Hence, on a number of occasions, he was an effective ANLSA and ANCA spokesman, but never an officer.

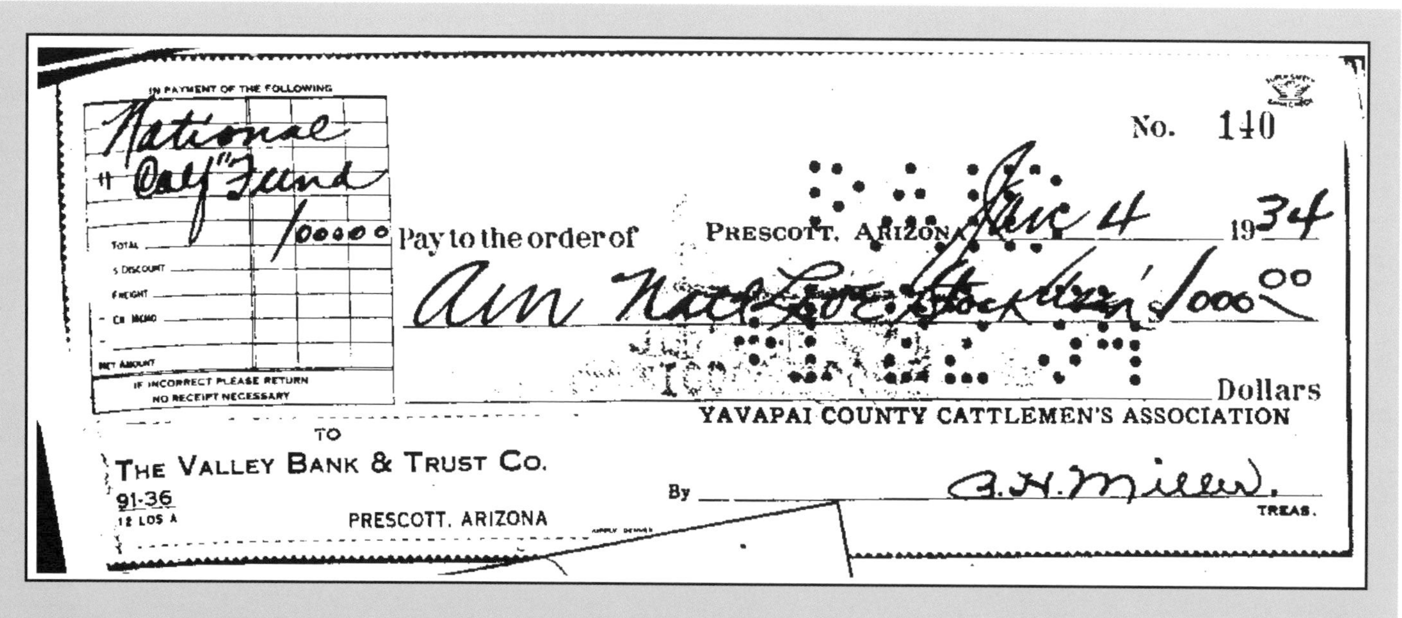

Financing the Association Has Never Been Easy. *Yavapai County Cattlemen's Association in Arizona started the idea of having members donate calves which were then sold with proceeds going to ANLSA. In 1934, Yavapai presented the Association with a $1,000 check, and has done so every year since.*

Between the wars, the Association operated on $16,000 to $29,000 of income a year, although the announced budget usually was above that. The bylaws "suggested" a dues rate of one-half cent per head with a minimum of $5 per year for individuals and a minimum of $50 for affiliated associations. But dues income consistently fell far short of expenditures.

During the 1920s and early 1930s, the jovial Fred Bixby from Long Beach, California, (president 1922-1925) typically would take the floor near the close of the convention and make his pitch for pledges.

For the past three days, you have heard the good things that our Association is doing, he would begin. *Now it's time for you and me to decide, do we want an Association to represent us next year? If so, we must have $20,000. I'll begin by pledging $500.*

Then someone would goad him, *Last year, you gave $1,000, Fred.*

Alright, he would reply, *I'll give $1,000 again if you'll give $500.*

And so it went, with big ranchers pledging $500 down to $10, for a total, usually, of $14,000 to $18,000. Unfortunately, not all pledges were collected. When the collections fell short, Bixby was known to loan the Association money. Even so, the chief executive some months was not paid. During the 1930s, another method evolved for supplementing dues income: calf sales, an idea started by the Yavapai County Cattlemen's Association in Arizona.

The ANLSA also changed its bylaws in 1934 and increased dues from 1/2 cent per head to "a suggested" one cent per head. But at the same time, minimum dues for individuals were reduced from $5 to $1.50 per year.

With money so scarce, the Association and members drove hard bargains during that era. At the 1936 convention in Phoenix, they obtained special rates at the deluxe Westward Ho Hotel: $3 for rooms with single beds, $4 for double beds and $5 for twin beds.

returned. Many cattlemen claimed an interest in that rebate, although the packers maintained they had not collected it from producers. Instead, they claimed to be losing money during the two years that the processing taxes were collected, a comment which prompted Albert K. Mitchell, president of the Association in 1936-37, to quip, *The packing industry is the most successful one I ever knew which operates constantly in the red.*

Amid the philosophical and political protests, there was little denying that the New Deal had turned the economy around, although many of its emergency and temporary programs became permanent. This caused some cattlemen, then and now, to conclude that the cure was worse than the ailment.

But the political powers at that time pointed out that by 1938 farmers and ranchers were living materially higher than under the previous administration. According to the Bureau of Census, of every 10 farms: seven had automobiles, six had radios, four were lighted with electricity, four had telephones, three had running water in the house, three had tractors and two had a motor truck.

Cattle prices improved also, from an average of $11.40 per head in 1934 to $24.10 in 1938, only to cause meat boycotts in New York, Los Angeles and other cities. The boycotts were led, according to an editorial in the *AMERICAN CATTLE PRODUCER*, by "malcontents, non-workers, plain shirkers." And the editorial added, *Regretfully, it must be stated that a few women who should have known better, no doubt seeking a thrill, also became involved.*

Unfazed through the first eight years of the New Deal, the Association still maintained in 1940 that the Number One Public Problem was "economy in government." Outlays by the federal government during the 1930s tripled to $9.5 billion and the federal debt almost tripled to $48 billion, creating a pattern that would continue over the next fifty years.

At the Denver convention in 1940, 26 resolutions were passed, most of them opposing New Deal programs and at least one of which would be appropriate today:

> *WHEREAS, spending exceeds revenues, taxes grow and are becoming staggering, national debt approaches the limit, deficits mean disaster, and much of federal appropriations comes from selfish groups; THEREFORE, Americans must place welfare of country first and combat pressure upon Congress for expenditures not vital to the public welfare.*

As the 1930s ended, a new World War was casting dark shadows over Europe. Thence, Association priorities shifted from its political and economic concerns to patriotic goals such as feeding the armed forces and "the preservation of freedom in and for our nation."

HUBBARD RUSSELL
President 1938-1939
Los Angeles, California

A dominant personality, he was a moving force in the ANLSA in the 1930s and 1940s. Russell Brothers (Hub, Joe and Harvey) operated about 50,000 acres north of Los Angeles and built the largest purebred herd of Herefords in the West. They drove herds down the main streets of Los Angeles, after midnight, as required by city ordinance, to market or move to another ranch. In 1924, when foot-and-mouth disease erupted in Los Angeles, they were forced to drive 3,500 head into a trench to be shot and buried.

A New Breed of Presidents. *Hub Russell (left) in his first automobile, a 1900 Oldsmobile, and (above) on his showhorse in a 1905 parade. Like his predecessor, Albert Mitchell, Russell was modern in every sense. He also had a strong feeling of where the industry had been and where it needed to go. Although many presidents would come from California, none other would come from such an "urban" area.*

Let's give him
Enough and On Time
Norman
Rockwell

Norman Rockwell

Feeding The World

American farmers and cattlemen discovered they could feed an army on the march from across two oceans, and they also found they could feed the world. The rural areas made the necessary sacrifices and produced the food Uncle Sam asked for. In return, they lost much of their younger generation, not only to the ravages of war but as well to the urban centers and promises of a new prosperity that would not come from the land and animals.

CHAPTER SIX

Wartime Effort & Sacrifice

December 7, 1941. President Franklin D. Roosevelt called it *a day which shall live in infamy!* It was a day that transformed the country, the world and ultimately the American National Live Stock Association. The four years that followed revealed the terrible and the wonderful, the worst of times and the best of times.

Addressing the 45th Annual Convention in Salt Lake City, 30 days after Pearl Harbor, a solemn ANLSA President J. Elmer Brock declared:

> *The treacherous and unprovoked attack on this nation on December 7 {made us} a united people in a matter of hours. Political differences were shelved and we presented a solid front. . . .Our industry now has added importance and must assume increased responsibilities. We {the Association} should make ourselves felt as a stabilizing influence in this hour of confusion and stress.*

Following that patriotic address, the first item of business at the 1942 Convention was the unanimous approval of a telegram to President Roosevelt. It pledged the range men and women of the western states to gladly make the necessary sacrifices to assure a beef supply for the nation and to assure victory in order that we may preserve liberty and freedom for our nation.

That was a major commitment, one that indeed would include "necessary sacrifices" and unforeseen frustrations over the newly imposed wartime programs. Price controls quickly became the Number One issue, and would remain a pestilent issue that would preoccupy the Association for the next five years.

Price Controls

Soon after war was declared, discussions about price controls arose. The Office of Price Administration (OPA) was activated and by 1943 price ceilings

TIMELINE

1939 Germany invades Poland (World War II begins).

DDT gains widespread use.

Television first publicly broadcast.

1940 France surrenders to Germany.

1941 Japan bombs Pearl Harbor; United States enters WW II.

First commercial television broadcast.

1942 Glenn Miller receives the first gold record for a million sales of "Chattanooga Choo Choo."

1943 Rationing of sugar, gasoline, meat and other items begins.

Roosevelt orders freeze on all wages and prices.

Cattle tick fever eradicated in United States.

1944 D-day: Allies land at Normandy in largest amphibious invasion ever.

Rome falls to the Allies.

United States black market in scarce consumer goods is estimated at over $1 billion a year.

1945 FDR dies, making Harry S. Truman 33rd president.

Atomic bombs dropped on Hiroshima and Nagasaki, Japan.

Germany surrenders May 7. Japan surrenders August 14. WW II ends.

United Nations organized.

1946 Winston Churchill refers to "iron curtain," behind which Soviet Union is organizing governments of central and eastern Europe.

Price controls removed, resulting in higher prices and mass strikes for higher wages.

1947 Jackie Robinson becomes first Black American in major league baseball.

Over $13 billion in aid sent to help rebuild Europe.

Researchers at Bell Labs build first transistor.

ISSUES

Big Government
•
Price Controls
•
Rationing
•
The Black Market
•
Fresh Beef Imports
•
Tax Issues
•
Supply & Demand

were set on meat, as on many other consumer items—butter, sugar, shoes, gasoline and more. Hence, the controversy and confusion over controls began, made worse by the blossoming of new agencies.

One example of the confusion for cattlemen and farmers was the conflict between the War Food Administration (WFA) and the OPA. The WFA, headed by Secretary of Agriculture Claude Wickard (a farmer from Indiana), was friendly to agriculture and committed to increased production. The OPA, on the other hand, was to keep prices down, thus restricting production.

Another example of absurd policy resulted when a 1942 bill boosted support prices to 90 percent of parity on nearly all major farm products. Grain production shot up, necessitating production controls throughout much of the war and for sometime afterwards. In fact, some farmers were being fined 42 cents per bushel for producing wheat in excess of their quotas. At the very same time their neighbors were subsidized 49 cents per bushel to buy government feed wheat imported from Canada (to increase beef production).

A year later, the OPA "rolled back" the wholesale price ceiling about two cents per pound on beef to ease pressure on consumers, but then paid packers an equivalent subsidy to prevent the rollback from affecting farm prices.

Although Association leaders knew, as did many government leaders, that food price controls in the past had never worked satisfactorily, they felt a wartime duty to try and develop a system of controls that would be fair to consumers, processors and producers alike, without impairing production. That was a tricky, if not impossible, task.

ANLSA President Frank S. Boice spent much time in Washington working with other farm groups and the OPA, as did Secretary F.E. (Ferd) Mollin. As members of the Joint Livestock Committee, which had representatives from 93 organizations, they made an early attempt to devise a program of controls to include:

1. Dollars and cents ceilings on meat at the wholesale and retail levels.
2. Licensing of slaughterers. (Any violation of the ceiling would cause the slaughterer to lose its license to sell to the government, who at that time was the largest buyer.)
3. A set-aside of 30 percent for military and government requirements, leaving 70 percent of meat production for civilians.
4. Rationing to consumers through the use of coupons.

The initial ceiling on dressed beef was "not to exceed March 1942 prices." For live cattle, that translated into an average of about $10 per cwt., and was later raised to a top of $18 per cwt.

At the 1943 Convention, Boice made a halfhearted attempt to rationalize this program:

> *Let us admit frankly that most of these controls are necessary if disastrous inflation is to be avoided. Inflation threatens as a result of fewer and fewer things to buy and more and more money in the hands of the consuming public with which to buy.*

ALPHABET SOUP

With the war came numerous government agencies to control and administer the war efforts. The government programs of the previous decade had not always been popular with the cattlemen, who were glad when many of them were dissolved. Now government-shy cattlemen were again confused by the hastily put together and often overlapping war agencies that would impact their business while the nation was at war. The confusion was made worse by the onslaught of acronyms that would quickly become a part of their daily language.

OPA Office of Price Administration
WFA War Food Administration
OES Office for Economic Stability
OWM Office of War Mobilization
OPM Office of Production Management

NATIONAL INCOME DOUBLED

By February 1943, industrial wages had increased 70.6 percent (over January 1939) and defense workers were experiencing the new phenomenon of time-and-a-half wages for overtime. Higher wages, combined with a 40 percent increase in the industrial labor force, resulted in the national income doubling! Inflationary forces were tremendous.

Like most consumer goods, meat supplies were limited. Cattle numbers were increasing at a rate of over four percent per year. Compared with most expansion periods, this was a large increase, but not enough to satisfy the growing appetite of defense workers for beef.

Despite the Association's ongoing campaign to avoid price ceilings put on live cattle. Price ceilings did occur. The packers had pushed for a price ceiling; they already had a subsidy for beef, but they wanted to shift that monkey to the back of producers. Cattlemen knew a price ceiling would be a nightmare, given the wide variation in cattle types, weights, grades, and so forth. In addition, the ANLSA and other associations argued that a price ceiling on live cattle would be an obstacle to increased production, which the government was urging. The 1943 beef goal was to produce 16 percent more meat than in 1942, but there were already obstacles to reaching that ambitious goal: shortages of manpower, transportation, machinery, tires, gasoline, windmills, fencing materials, horseshoes and various supplies.

Not the least of the obstacles, or "necessary sacrifices," was the number of young men, many coming from farms and ranches, who had volunteered or were drafted into military service. At the height of the war, there were 12,454,000 men and women in uniform. Millions more from farms and ranches moved to the cities to work in shipyards, aircraft factories and other defense plants for wages never before dreamed of. There was little help left to accomplish the high goals of beef production. In addition, short supplies,

J. ELMER BROCK
President 1940-1941
Kaycee, Wyoming

Brock was born in Missouri, attended high school in Wyoming, business college in Nebraska, and then settled in Wyoming. He was remembered as a "far-sighted and many-sided" man, known to his colleagues as an independent thinker, diplomat and practical economist. He was also candid and had a fiery disposition. "There are 59 federal land management agencies controlling our public lands," he snorted in one speech, "and the Forest Service is the worst." A fighter for private ownership of public lands, he frequently slammed "the federal over-lordship." As president when the United States entered World War II, he pledged the Association's support and extolled patriotism among members.

GOVERNMENT BY BUREAUCRACY

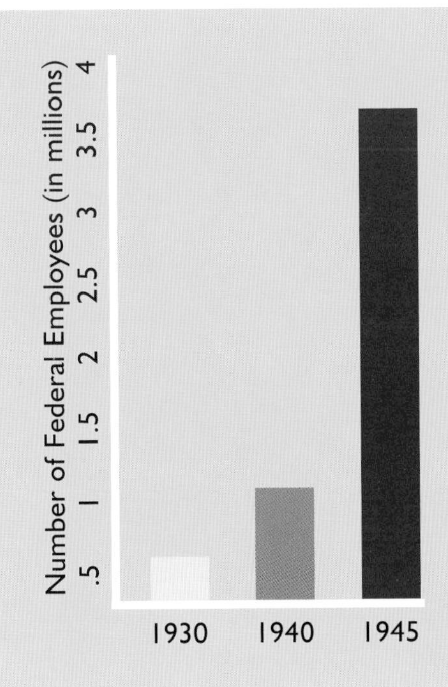

Few topics have received more attention by this Association over the century than "the ever-growing government." The cattle business had grown largely without government assistance and the basic independent nature of the cattleman himself caused him to spurn any suggestion of government interference. Consequently the onslaught of government programs in the 1930s followed quickly by wartime controls caused great concern in the Association.

The May 1947 *AMERICAN CATTLE PRODUCER* editorial, "Government By Bureaucracy," summarized those feelings.

> *Few of our citizens realize the tremendous growth of, and concentration of power in, the federal bureaus which in the past 15 years have filled Washington to overflowing and sprawled out into many of the other principal cities of this country. In 1930, there were 580,494 federal employees in the executive department of the government; in 1940 there were 1,001,581; and in 1945 there were 3,675,768. It now begins to appear that Congress, with unparalleled generosity in setting up new departments and expanding old ones and giving them almost unlimited appropriations, has created a bureaucracy which, judging by recent events, is even more powerful than Congress itself. In 1932, there were 521 agencies; today there are 1,141. . . .In the past 17 years the public indebtedness has risen from around $16 billion to $260 billion.*

Goosenecks Bring Markets Close to Home. *Ranchers watched, marveled at the idea, but were reluctant to buy. That was the reaction to a new oddity in the industry called "The Gooseneck," first manufactured in 1946 by W.H. Batchler, a rancher at Graham, Texas. The United States Patent Office denied Batchler a patent, since he had borrowed the concept from a Russian sleigh. But within 10 to 20 years, ranchers recognized its added maneuverability and stability and it became the stock trailer of choice, virtually replacing the bob-tailed truck. As a versatile vehicle for hauling livestock to local auction barns, the gooseneck contributed substantially to the further decentralization of the cattle markets.*

Auction Market at the Beginning of World War II. *The use of trucks and trailers as well as the breakup of packing houses and central markets made a market like this one in San Angelo, Texas, the center of the cattle business in local areas. This decentralization also helped fuel the black market that grew up during the War years. With so many small operators there was ample room for slipping through the regulations.*

record-high incomes, price controls and rationing became the elements for a black market that would strain the resolve of patriotic citizens.

> ***{we will} gladly make the necessary sacrifices to assure a beef supply for the nation and to assure victory in order that we may preserve liberty and freedom for our nation.***
>
> *—Telegram from the 1942 Convention to President Roosevelt pledging the Association's support*

During the 1944 Convention in Denver, at the height of World War II, outgoing President Boice expressed his mixture of pride and hope, confusion, doubt and frustration with the way the government was handling matters:

> *We are proud of the accomplishments of our fighting forces in all quarters of the globe. But here at home. . .there is doubt everywhere; doubt concerning the wisdom of and the necessity for many of the things that are being done by government; doubt of the sincerity of many of our leaders; and doubt concerning the kind of nation we are building for ourselves in the future.*

Black Market Chaos

Boice was particularly concerned about the black market and the new subsidy for beef that was being paid to packers. The subsidy, varying from \$0.50 to \$1.40 per cwt. depending on quality and location, was

RATIONING

The best known attempt by OPA to control the food supply was the use of ration stamps. Each man, woman and child was entitled to stamps and, once a month, a representative of the family went to the court house and stood in line for their books of ration stamps.

In addition to the red, green and gray ration stamps, a point system was superimposed that related to type or quality of product. So shoppers always asked, "How many points per pound?" Cents per pound were incidental.

Non-food items were rationed also and consumers found innovative ways to deal with shortages. Victory suits for men, for example, consisted of one pair of cuffless pants and a short jacket with narrow lapels. OPA decreed that women's dresses had to end one inch above the knee and swim suits had to be two-piece. Silk was needed for parachutes, so women substituted leg makeup for hosiery. Patched clothing became the fashion fad and consumers found ways to "use it up, wear it out, make it do or do without."

Victory gardens were planted in backyards, front yards, flower beds and on vacant lots. Officials estimated that one third of the vegetables eaten in 1943 came from victory gardens.

Food rationing, and the accompanying price controls, was accepted by patriotic consumers for two or three years as a "wartime sacrifice." But the inconvenience, the waiting in lines, the inequities and the publicized abuses caused more and more to turn to the "gray market."

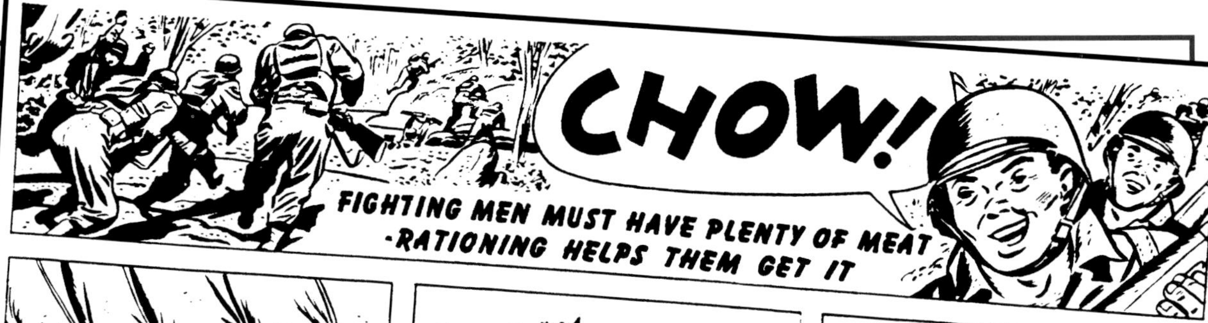

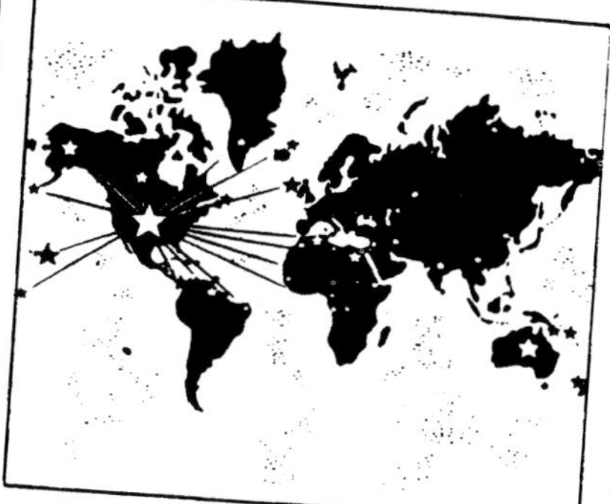

Distributed by the Live Stock and Meat Board in May 1943.

War Won on Imports

The Argentine Sanitary Treaty is now dead. It was withdrawn from a congressional committee a few days ago. Proposed in May 1935. . .it has been resting in committee all this time. The treaty intended that we import meat from zones in Argentina that were supposedly to be found free of foot-and-mouth disease. An embargo written in the tariff law forbade this. . . .The American National Live Stock Association. . .led the fight against its ratification.

So began an editorial in the May 1947 *American Cattle Producer*. The Association considered the defeat one of its more significant victories. Once again, Senator Tom Connally (D-TX), Chairman of the Senate Foreign Relations Committee, had proven a formidable ally of the cattlemen. With Senator Alva Adams (D-CO), they had kept this treaty pigeon holed in the Senate Foreign Relations Committee for 12 years, over the protests of President Roosevelt and Secretary of State Cordell Hull. President Truman finally killed it.

The Association objected officially because of foot and mouth disease in Argentina, claiming it was purely a sanitary issue. Some proponents, however, called it "a non-tariff barrier."

[In 1994, under GATT agreements, the NCA and the United States relented to fresh meat imports and agreed to "regionalization." Technology for detection and control of foot-and-mouth disease had greatly improved; also American cattlemen were exporting more beef and were supportive of two-way trade.]

Senator Alben Barkley *(D-KY) longtime Senate Majority Leader, later to become Vice President under Truman, spars with Senator Alva Adams (D-CO). The Washington Star, April 1941.*

Secretary of Agriculture Claude R. Wickard *was the first to sign up for the Food for Freedom campaign. A farmer himself from Indiana, Wickard encouraged high production during the war years and increased his own production of hogs in 1940 to 750, a record for his 330-acre farm, along with his production of Milking Shorthorns and corn. Here he is keeping in contact with Washington on a party line while keeping an eye on his Carroll County, Indiana, farm.*

intended to "reduce the price to consumers and encourage production by producers." But neither consumers nor producers were feeling any benefits.

Toward the end of the war, the Association appealed to Congress for an increase in the price ceiling for live cattle—by then up to $18 per cwt.—because of their increased costs for labor, corn and other feedstuffs. Instead, they got a subsidy $2 per cwt. on live slaughter which they had resisted for four years.

In their testimony, Association leaders pointed out that cattlemen, at the request of government, had increased cattle numbers significantly, from 65 million head in 1938 to 85 million in 1944. Also, they showed that producers had produced meat in 1942 at a record rate of 20 tons per minute. [Fifty years later in 1992, cattlemen were producing beef at the rate of only 21 tons per minute; cattle and hog producers together were producing meat at 37 tons per minute.]

As newly affluent civilians clamored for more and more beef, some packers began bidding up the price of live cattle and selling it on the black market. So did retailers, usually purchasing from smaller non-certified packers or "shade tree" slaughterers on whom no records were available and whose sanitation was questioned. Consequently, with consumers, retailers and slaughterers willing to deal in the black market, enforcement of the ceilings became nearly impossible. By the end of the war, the black market had become so common and so accepted that it was called a "gray market."

Although loyal to the war effort for several years, most people had tired of the price controls. ANLSA President A. D. Brownfield, succinctly summed up cattlemen's lack of patience with controls at the 1945 Convention in Denver:

> *Prudence and not politics should be used in eliminating it as quickly as possible. Control has been hard to accept by a group of freeborn citizens accustomed to the wide-open spaces and building their own security in their own way.*

Nevertheless, the OPA, like many government programs, was slow to die, and the black market grew in the 10-month period following the war before controls were lifted. At 1946 Congressional hearings, one year after the war ended, Association spokesmen testified that a combination of price- supported corn and ceilings on meat were causing farmers to cut short their feeding periods and, thus, limit beef pro-

FRANK S. BOICE
President 1942-1943
Sonoita, Arizona

A brother of the 1931 ANLSA president, he helped devise a program of controls during WW II. Not a believer in controls he became convinced they were necessary to avoid disastrous inflation. In an emotional speech during the 1944 Convention, he expressed "a mixture of pride and hope, confusion, doubt and frustration... concerning the kind of nation we are building for ourselves in the future." For his services, Boice was elected to the Cowboy Hall of Fame in 1958.

The Association always *put forth an impressive group of cattlemen. During the War, many members spent long hours in Washington fighting the battles over price controls, grazing fees, and tariffs. One of the Association's greatest successes in that period was their defeat of the ratification of the Argentina Sanitary Treaty of 1935.*

No More Controls

Four years of experience with government controls, culminating in the present scandalous situation, shows conclusively the impossibility of controlling livestock and meat prices and meat distribution through government laws. Controls should be removed.

—Senate Committee Report, 1946

Once again price controls had not worked. After the war was over, farmers held back livestock in hope of higher prices, creating even greater pressure on supplies. The Congress ended OPA and a flood of livestock rushed through to people who had been on short rations and longing for red meat. Supply and demand was back in operation and the public's demand for beef was there.

Des Moines Register, July 4, 1946. Ding's Cartoons by Jay N. Darling (Ding), published in 1960 by Pioneer Hi-Bred Corn Company.

duction. Packers testified that 1,000 butcher shops in New York City had closed due to the black market situation because they were buying on the black market and selling under the OPA ceiling. Retailers testified that the OPA law had made crooks out of legitimate retailers and consumers, and had caused lack of respect for all laws.

Back to Supply and Demand

Following these hearings, the Senate Committee on Agriculture and Forestry issued a revealing report that confirmed many of the complaints being voiced:

1. Livestock and meat controls have completely broken down to most levels;
2. Most meat is being sold at black market prices;
3. In spite of an excessive inventory of cattle, there are still severe shortages of meat in some places because of black markets;
4. The price freeze had forced many slaughterers to go out of business;
5. The black market is imperiling the nation's health, causing economic loss and creating disrespect for all laws.

Thus, the Senate Committee on Agriculture confirmed what historians (and some cattlemen) had known for years regarding the folly of government food controls: they do not work.

In 1922, Mary G. Lacy, a USDA librarian, gave a scholarly address, "Food Control During Forty-Six Centuries," concluding:

> *The history of government limitation of price seems to teach one clear lesson: in attempting to ease the burdens of the people in a time of high prices by artificially setting a limit to them, the people are not relieved but only exchange one set of ills for another which is greater.*

So the OPA finally fell on June 30, 1946. And the Association was pleased. *The American Cattle Producer* reported the following month: *Cattlemen are eager for a re-acquaintance with supply and demand and their own enterprise and business acumen.*

Non-War Battles

Amid the patriotism and sacrifices of World War II, other constructive efforts by the Association were either overlooked or paled by the frustrations of price controls. War only intensified the battles cattlemen were having over the Reciprocal Trade Act, originally passed in 1934. The Association protested the "almost unlimited authority" of the President to lower tariffs without Senate approval. President Roosevelt, using authority first granted or usurped during the Great Depression then again during World War II, had made many trade agreements since the law passed, none to the benefit of American producers.

The Association had been successful in preventing ratification of the Argentine Sanitary Treaty of 1935, through which the State Department had agreed to fresh beef imports from Argentina.

The war also did not stop the skirmishes between cattlemen and the Department of Interior over increased grazing fees, even after the government had clamped on price controls. In November 1944,

A.D. BROWNFIELD
President 1944-1945
Deming, New Mexico

Born in Brownfield, Texas, a town named for his father, young "Dee" moved to New Mexico in 1915, where he produced fine Herefords. He helped organize the Production Credit Association, helped establish the New Mexico Agricultural Experiment Station, served in the state legislature, was President of the New Mexico Cattle Growers Association and one of the first directors of the Cowboy Hall of Fame. He felt his greatest accomplishment was to help write the Taylor Grazing Act and the Federal Range Code.

UNCLE SAM WILSON OF TROY SUPPLIED BEEF TO THE UNITED STATES
ARMY DURING THE WAR OF 1812 - STAMPING HIS BARRELS WITH THE LETTERS 'U.S.'-
THIS BEEF BECAME KNOWN TO THE ARMY AS 'UNCLE SAM'S' AND THIS FAMILIAR
APPELLATION WAS THEREAFTER BESTOWED ON OUR OWN GOVERNMENT * * *

America's Most Famous Packer. *Samuel Wilson, born in 1789, ran a successful cattle slaughtering business in Troy, New York, employing as many as 100 men and processing 1000 cattle a week. Widely known for his kindness and benevolence, Wilson was called "Uncle Sam" by friends and neighbors. When the War of 1812 broke out, Wilson won a contract for corned beef "packed in full round barrels of white oak" for the soldiers. There was competition for the army beef business, but because Wilson had a reputation for superior quality, "U.S." was stamped on each barrel and package for the army. The meat was referred to as "Uncle Sam's beef" and jokingly as "Uncle Sam's pork."*

Because "U.S." also stood for United States, the term and persona of "Uncle Sam" spread to anything that belonged to the federal government.

Cartoonists picked up the idea by the time of Wilson's death in 1854 and were drawing their conceptions of "Uncle Sam." Cartoonist Thomas Nast added a pointed beard and starry vest to the figure with striped trousers and top hat, and this representation gained wide popularity in the 1860s and 1870s.

A century later, on September 15, 1961, the 87th Congress officially recognized Samuel Wilson as the progenitor of the nation's symbol, "Uncle Sam."

Uncle Sam Wilson is depicted here in a mural entitled "Origin of Uncle Sam," one of a series of military paintings for the Hotel Hendrick Hudson in Troy, New York, was painted by artist George Gray in 1937.

National Livestock Tax Committee

Before the Association became influential and affluent, there was a tendency, when a problem arose, for a group of ranchers to get together and go their own way. Such was the case in August 1943, when representatives of the ANLSA and the National Wool Growers, along with some state and breed associations, met in Amarillo to organize the National Livestock Tax Committee (NLTC).

Prior to World War II, smaller cattlemen had not paid enough taxes to worry about, but the war changed that. Cattlemen began to have problems with the IRS, and the NLTC became their voice.

Though the Association participated in setting up the Committee, it was organized and financed privately. The Committee made decisions, hired lawyers and CPAs and raised funds to pay their bills. There were always close association ties, with Frank S. Boice as the first chairman and Ferd Mollin its Secretary-Treasurer.

The Tax Committee was run by a steering committee who hired four well-known accountants from across America.

The first NLTC objective was to obtain IRS approval of the "unit livestock price method" a simplified method of valuing inventory of breeding animals, sometimes called the "constant cost" method.

The second objective was to treat profits realized from the sale of breeding animals as capital gains and be taxed accordingly. Both objectives were achieved in 1944.

The method was simple: a constant cost was assigned to an animal, such as $500 for bulls or $200 for cows, then the animal given a four to eight-year life and depreciated. Depreciation was written off as an expense, while salvage value fell under capital gains.

Some cattlemen had used this method since the income tax law in 1913, but it was not recognized in all IRS districts. Thus, cattlemen were subjected to non-uniform tax practices and penalties.

This method also impacted the industry by encouraged investment in cattle by wealthy individuals looking for tax loopholes, which contributed to the industry over the next three decades. It also later contributed to the succes of the dairy industry.

For the next 35 years the National Livestock Tax Committee fought and won many battles for livestock producers, in conjunction with ANCA's tax committee. In 1978 after NCA was created, the NLTC was then dissolved to avoid duplication of effort.

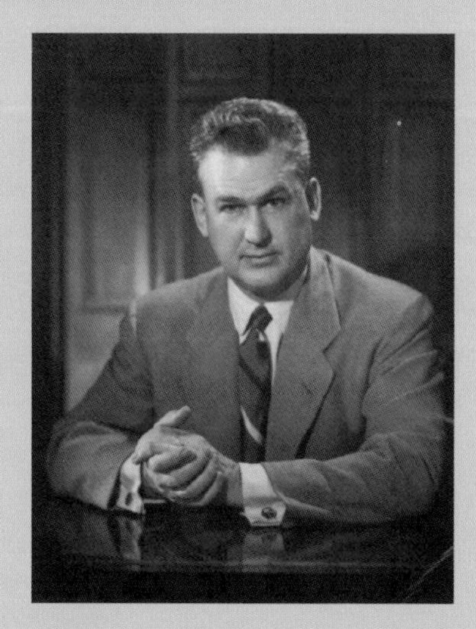

The Spark Plug of the NLTC. *Denver attorney Stephen H. Hart was considered a great gentleman and an outstanding lawyer. He often did work without pay or waited two or three years for his money.*

the Department of Interior proposed to increase fees from five cents to 15 cents per animal unit per month on 142 million acres under the Taylor Grazing Act. The Association protested and prevailed

> ***Cattlemen are eager for a reacquaintance with supply and demand and their own enterprise and business acumen.***
>
> —*The American Cattle Producer*, June 30, 1946

even though the Grazing Director argued (unsuccessfully) that the Act called for "a reasonable fee," and he did not think five cents was reasonable.

Tax Problems

Income tax battles with the IRS also flared. In August 1943, representatives of the ANLSA and the National Wool Growers, along with some state affiliates and some breed associations, met in Amarillo to organize an independent organization, the National Livestock Tax Committee (NLTC).

During the war and the decade that followed, seeds were planted that would change the industry and the Association. The Association still represented primarily the 18 western grazing states and frequently was chastised in Washington, for claiming to represent "the nation's cattlemen." That, too, would change with reconstruction and new expansion of the cattle industry.

The Longest Issue

At the first convention of the National Live Stock Association in 1898, Governor William A. Richards of Wyoming dramatized the problem of the public domain as the greatest *importance to the people since the federation of states* and assured it as a priority issue for the brand new Association. Since then, the problem of public lands has been a simmering—sometimes boiling—issue at every convention.

In Congress, public lands ranchers occasionally scored a victory. But in general it has been "one step forward and two steps backward." Not only have they failed to win over Congress in the last hundred years, they often found their cause to be divisive within their own Association. But it was a livelihood and way-of-life issue, which called for persistence.

Governor Richards proposed what seemed a logical solution: cede the unclaimed land to the states, which in turn could sell or lease the grazing land to ranchers and use the proceeds to build dams and develop irrigation projects. This approach seemed fair; it was essentially the same offer given to the original 13 colonies and states east of the 100th meridian. Richards concluded emphatically:

> *The time has arrived when the United States should retire from the public lands business!*

For a hundred years the issue has remained in gridlock. The close-minded response back East, where most of the voters resided, always was the same: *That land belongs to the public—to every man, woman and child in America.*

The stakes were, and are, enormous. The federal government owns nearly one-fourth of the 1.9 billion acres in the continental United States and half of the 11 western states. In 1995, the Bureau of Land Management (BLM) of the Interior Department managed 191 million acres and the Forest Service of the Agriculture Department managed 160 million acres.

The public domain problem in the West began in 1862, with passage of the Homestead Act, offering 160 acres to persons willing to stay on the land. Its purpose was to help settle the West Subsequent homestead acts, five in total, increased the acreage from 160 to 320 acres, then to 640 acres, but that was still too little in most cases to make a living on it in the West.

But many tried. By 1930, there were 596,400 claims for 103,889,244 acres. At the same time, ranchers were claiming preemptive "range rights" to the land, by virtue of having occupied and used it. But there were no legal rights.

After barbed wire became available, big ranchers used it to block passage through their "country;" and homesteaders used it to protect their crops from ranchers' cattle. This did not contribute to "neighborliness," but instead to numerous fence cuttings and occasional shootings.

Back in Washington, the Interior Department, with responsibility for administering the homestead acts, helped push through anti-fencing legislation in 1885. Using this legislation, several presidents and Interior secretaries between 1885 and 1933 ordered the removal of all illegal fences belonging to ranchers. On one occasion, military force was used to remove fences in Wyoming.

Shortly after the turn of the century, the Departments of Interior and Agriculture were competing for jurisdiction of the unappropriated forest lands, and fencing became a bargaining tool. The Interior Secretary riled ranchers by banning grazing from 1898 to 1901. So Agriculture's Forestry Bureau seized this opportunity to offer grazing, plus the right to maintain fences, if the ANLSA would supp*ort the transfer of forest lands.*

The Association obliged. So in 1905, 85.6 million acres were transferred from Interior to the Bureau of Forestry, which in 1907 became the Forest Service. A year later, in 1906, the Bureau of Forestry started charging ranchers a fee for grazing, and in a few years, the ranchers' loyalty (or tolerance) shifted back to Interior. In the decades that followed, their dislikes shifted back and forth, depending on which set of bureaucrats were reducing rates or raising fees.

Help Wanted

Government Agency seeks 27,000 self-starters with a passion for the outdoors to help manage 270 million acres of public land. Must be on call 24 hours a day, 365 days a year. Extensive knowledge in the following areas a must:

- Rangeland Management
- Wildlife Biology
- Riparian Area Development
- Animal Husbandry
- Livestock and Agricultural Production
- Erosion Prevention
- Law
- Accounting
- Meteorology
- Hydrology
- Economics

Additional prerequisites include a knack for coordinating "multiple uses" of federal lands for hunting, fishing and other recreational activities on a limited budget.

Salary: No compensation. Successful candidates will need to collectively generate millions of dollars for the U.S. Treasury.

In the event S.1459 does not pass, direct all resumes to local unemployment offices.

Help Wanted to Pass the Public Rangelands Management Act. *NCBA used this poster at a news conference in Washington, DC, on July 11, 1996, when nearly three dozen ranchers visited around 200 offices of House and Senate members to lobby for passage of the Act. Eastern state ranchers paired with western ranchers to visit otherwise inaccessible congressmen. While the Act passed in the Senate, it was stalled and never made it to vote in the House.*

The open range and all its problems continued into the 1930s, when the Interior Department and the emerging conservation groups blamed big ranchers for the overgrazing and erosion on public lands. The reason for overgrazing, in most cases, was that a rancher could secure tenure only when his claim was stocked.

The accepted custom, which traced back to the Mexican Mesta in the 1500s, was that one rancher would not infringe on another's range as long as it was stocked. But if he took the stock off, because of drought or to save forage for the winter, another rancher or nomadic sheep herder could move in. Thus, the tendency was to stock for normal or good years, which resulted in overgrazing during droughts. It was a point of great frustration especially for ranchers who wished to maintain the land in good grazing condition. Security of tenure was the biggest desire of ranchers and could be best attained through private ownership. But the East and West could not agree on the several bills that were introduced from time to time in Congress.

The first stability of sorts came with the Taylor Grazing Act of 1934 which ended homesteading and the open range and set up the Grazing Service (See Chapter 5). The Grazing Service, under the capable leadership of the popular Ferry Carpenter, a member of the Association, was widely accepted by ranchers. However, with cuts in appropriations, the Grazing Service was combined in 1947 with the General Land Office into the Bureau of Land Management (BLM).

Will C. Barnes: Rancher and Government Inspector. *In 1906, Gifford Pinchot, Chief of the Forest Service, asked Barnes to come to Washington as a grazing inspector and Forest Service liaison with western ranchers. He held that position until retirement in 1930. He was a cattleman turned bureaucrat, and certainly that was to the cattlemen's advantage. Few members of the Association were more colorful than Will C. Barnes: soldier, rancher, association officer, legislator, forester, writer and public servant. He was appointed to the Arizona Livestock Sanitary Board in 1887, became Secretary of the New Mexico Cattle Growers Association and served as the first Secretary of the splinter group, American Stock Growers Association, until it merged with the National in 1906. He started a campaign for government funding to preserve the American Longhorn, which was facing extinction, and in 1928, Congress appropriated a maximum of $3,000 "to purchase and maintain a herd of longhorned or Spanish breed of cattle for the Wichita National Forest in Oklahoma."*

"Seize the moment!" advised ranchers who saw this as an opportune moment to finally privatize the public lands. So ANLSA and the National Wool Growers Association formed a Joint Livestock Committee on Public Lands and conducted a national campaign based on "fairness and right."

J. Elmer Brock of Wyoming, a past president of ANLSA and a fervent fighter for public lands, was vice chairman of the Committee. When conservationists and the eastern press rushed to support the Interior Department, Brock became adamant in his speeches.

> *Federal ownership or control of land is a form of Communism. We want equal rights with the original states. . . .The effete East argues that these public lands belong to all of us. They do not!*

His legal argument was that Congress intended eventual privatization when it wrote in the Taylor Grazing Act "pending final disposition" of public lands.

But not all ranchers wanted privatization. Some preferred to lease land, rather than own it and pay taxes. Some advisory boards had even contributed $150,000 to pay the salaries of local Grazing Service employees.

Nevada's Trouble with Public Lands

Nevada is a good example of the kinds of problems spawned by public lands. In Nevada, where public lands account for 87 percent of the total area—more than in any other state—the conflicts have been endless.

In the early part of the century, the amount of land owned by the government put an undue tax burden on the remaining private lands, most of which was owned by ranchers.

While serving in the state legislature 1929 to 1930, William F. Dressler, a rancher in Douglas County, and father of ANCA President Fred Dressler (1960-1961), was instrumental in passing legalized gambling after two decades of absence. Gambling was one way to stimulate the state's economy and keep property taxes from skyrocketing.

That decision resulted in a flood of unfavorable publicity throughout the United States. However, in 1995, Nevada gambling provided $539 million in state taxes and later with a sales tax added have kept property taxes reasonable—in the lower one-third of the 50 states.

Counting Cattle. *Forest officers counting cattle entering Bridger National Forest. Photo taken in 1914 by Will C. Barnes, who helped organize the American Stock Growers Association in 1905 before joining Forest Service.*

It was a losing battle anyway. The eastern press, urged on by the Interior Department, Forest Service and conservation groups, continued to berate ranchers as "greedy land grabbers" who abused the public lands. And nothing happened toward privatization.

The next push for privatizing public lands came in the 1980s, by Republican President Ronald Reagan and his Secretary of Interior James Watt. But byy this time, the conservationists and environmentalists were well organized, financed and more vocal than ever. So again, nothing happened.

Meanwhile, grazing fees, as determined by bureaucrats and politicians, were a recurring point of contention between permittees and agencies. BLM fees, which started in 1936 at five cents per AUM were significantly lower than Forest Service fees, until 1970 when both jumped 200 to 300 percent. It was 1974 before BLM fees reached $1 per Animal Unit/Month (AUM), and in 1980 they peaked at $2.36. Under congressional pressure, a uniform formula was established so permittees paid both agencies from the same basis. In 1995, both BLM and Forest Service fees were $1.61 per AUM. Now, using a formula derived from current cattle prices, fees dropped in 1997 to $1.35 per AUM.

Combined costs of federal grazing in 1992, as reported by the two agencies, were $73 million, while grazing fees brought in $27 million. Quoting such shortfalls through the years, politicians and others have repeatedly pushed for much higher fees. Cost of federal grazing by the government is largely costs for administration and surveillance of the land, and in some area water development.

On the other hand, permittees, claiming that operating costs on public lands are

The Public Lands Council

When President John F. Kennedy appointed Stewart Udall as Secretary of Interior (1961-1968), public lands permittees became nervous. Udall made no bones about his feelings: grazing fees were too low and stockmen had too much influence in public lands policy.

The "influence" to which he objected dated to the Taylor Grazing Act of 1934, which at the time cattlemen thought would make ranching on public lands tolerable. Prior to 1934, ranchers claimed that government officials did not even know where the public lands were located, much less their capabilities.

So Ferry Carpenter, a Colorado rancher who became the first director of the Grazing Service from 1934 to 1938, set up local advisory boards of stockmen, elected by their peers, to help locate the boundaries of grazing districts and to adjudicate the range under the new law.

Ranchers liked this, as did Interior officials. So the Grazing Service in 1940 called a meeting of 18 stockmen, one cattleman and one sheepman from each of the nine Taylor Grazing regions, to consider revisions in the Federal Range Code. At this meeting, the graziers organized themselves into an organization called the National Advisory Board Council.

In 1949, however, Secretary of Interior Julius Krug declared the National Advisory Board Council to be an instrument of his department. Stockmen did not object much, even though the Secretary added three wildlife representatives to the Council. Little did they suspect, this was the beginning of their diminishing influence.

Some 15 years later, Council members were added to represent forestry, mining, oil and gas, county government, urban residents, recreation and other multiple-use advocates.

Subsequent reorganizations of the National Council left stockmen feeling "more diluted." At the same time, cattlemen were painfully aware that the public lands was a divisive issue within ANCA, and that some members resented the time devoted to it by the Association.

So in 1968, stockmen put together another private organization, the Public Lands Council (PLC). Harry Lee of New Mexico was the first president; Dave Rice, executive of the Colorado Cattlemen's Association, was the first secretary (for 22 years); and Joe Tudor, a former attorney for Interior and an expert on the Taylor Grazing Act, was the first counsel. Each of the 14 public lands states (presently 13, because New Mexico pulled out in 1994) had four voting delegates, including one on the Board of Directors.

To finance the new organization, the Council asked all permittees to pay an assessment of five cents per permitted animal unit month (AUM), although not all did. In addition, they solicited financial and staff help from ANCA, the National Sheep Industry Association and the National Grasslands Association.

By 1994, the PLC had a staff of three and an annual budget of $220,000. While maintaining autonomy, PLC shares offices with NCBA in Washington and is linked to the NCBA Federal Lands Committee.

higher than on private lands, have so far defeated efforts for higher grazing fees. The longest issue had also become a partisan issue, in addition to a complicated economic issue. As Senator Orin Hatch (R-UT) lamented in 1993, *Every time we get a Democratic president, there's an assault on the West.*

But ranchers and the Association continue to persist. Not only has public lands been the longest issue, past officers say it has also been one of the most nagging and divisive issues for the Association. The emotion involved has far overstated its importance in relation to the total industry. Of a total 1.2 million cattle operations in the United States, less than 24,000 ranchers have federal grazing permits. Only about three percent of the nation's cattle graze on public lands.

Ranchers Pay for the Use of Federal Lands. *Not only do permittees pay fees for use of the land, but they must also maintain fences, and in some cases build and maintain water areas—a capital investment on property that does not belong to them. With permits given for only 10 years, most ranchers expense the costs for grazing federal lands.*

Handling Stock in Beaverhead National Forest. *Cattle en route to summer grazing range on the upper Ruby River.*

Good Environmental Practices Benefit All Parties. *NCA started another national campaign in the 1990s to gain public support, claiming ranchers are the "original environmentalists." They maintained that ranchers more than anyone work to improve the natural resources at their disposal. And they have worked diligently together with the BLM and Forest Service to establish correct grazing periods conducive to the local environment.*

THE HAMBURGER

People in the great lakes region of Illinois, Indiana, Michigan, Ohio and Wisconsin consume more burgers than people in any other region in America.

HISTORY OF THE HAMBURGER

The life of the hamburger is fraught with controversy: Who invented it? Who has the best burger? Who offers the most meat? Better with catsup or mustard?

Only since World War II has the hamburger been popular enough to matter. But now that Americans eat over 5 billion burgers a year, 40 to 50 percent of American beef production goes into ground beef. Between 25 and 30 percent of the meat from a fed steer, 90 percent of a cull cow and nearly all imported beef goes into ground beef. And most of that ends up in hamburgers.

But it has not always been this way. During the first half of the 20th century, there was almost no place for meat from cull cows to go. So during droughts or periods of forced liquidation, the cattle cycle was exacerbated and price swings were severe. The hamburger phenomenon changed the beef market forever.

The hamburger as we know it is as old as the Association. And at least five people claimed to have "invented" it:

Fletcher Davis of Athens, Texas, was serving ground beef between two slices of homemade bread in the 1880s. Friends thought it so unique that they sent him to the 1904 St. Louis World's Fair, where he "introduced hamburger to the world."

Frank Menches, a concessionaire at the Summit County Fair (Akron, Ohio) in 1892, also claimed the hamburger. When he ran out of pork sausage, he substituted beef and his customers liked it.

Other claimants were Charlie Nagreen of Seymour, Wisconsin, in 1885, and Louis Lassen of New Haven, Connecticut, in 1900.

Actually the hamburger idea is very old. Jeffrey Tennyson, author of *Hamburger Heaven*, determined that the idea came from the various tribes of Tartary, nomadic horseman who roamed the Baltic provinces of Russia. They developed a fondness for raw beef, today known as "steak tartare." The Tartars introduced it to their German trading partners from the port city of Hamburg who fried the meat and seasoned it with onions. Later, German immigrants coming to America brought the recipe with them. From that time forward, though, the hamburger became uniquely American. In fact, when President Lyndon Johnson sent a trade team headed by former ANCA President Jay Taylor to Germany, Taylor concluded that the Germans in Hamburg had no clue what a hamburger was, but liked them when served.

55 percent of burgers are ordered for lunch.

Five billion hamburgers and cheeseburgers were served in restaurants in 1994, up 2.7% from 1993.

McDonald's has close to 15,000 restaurants in 84 countries. One McDonald's opens every 8 hours
(1995 statistic)

Favorite Toppings:
- **41% include catsup**
- **26% include cheese**
- **26% include mustard**
- **20% include onion**
- **16% include mayonnaise**
- **16% include lettuce**
- **14% include tomato**
- **13% include pickles**

People who eat burgers go out for one about three times every two weeks.

Hamburgers and cheeseburgers comprise 75.6% of beef served away from home.

Top 10 Burger Legends

Chain	1995 sales (*$ in billions*)
McDonald's	15.80
Burger King	7.83
Wendy's	4.15
Hardee's	3.52
Jack in the Box	1.08
Sonic Drive-In	.88
Carl's Jr	.56
Whataburger	.41
Rally's	.37
White Castle	.32

SAM
FUZ© 97
KEITH McLENDON

Martin Johnson Heade EVENING, LAKE ALTO

A New Generation

After World War II, the organized cattle industry stretched eastward, crossing the Mississippi and moving into uncharted territory just as the industry had done a century before with trail drives that opened the western and plains states. But the industry met there with established cattlemen. Florida had been in the cattle business since 1520, Mississippi and Louisiana since 1700. It was a different business, with different concerns, but the industry would now, at long last, truly represent cattlemen across the nation.

CHAPTER SEVEN

Reconstruction & Expansion

The decade after World War II brought unprecedented changes to the country, including far reaching changes in the cattle industry. There was reconstruction, expansion, boom and bust. When the American National Live Stock Association celebrated its 50th Anniversary in 1947 in Phoenix, members felt good about the country's recent victory in war and their new freedom from price controls and rationing. A record-setting turnout of 2,000 members from 25 states came to the Convention. They also felt free, if not duty-bound by tradition, to renew some pre-war attacks on the government.

A few of the latent topics that they brought to the fore, and continued to keep there for several years, included public lands, tariffs, government spending, and foot-and-mouth disease.

Public Domain

Public lands had been the subject for tirades and resolutions at nearly every convention. Now Association leaders were saying that the Taylor Grazing Act of 1934 was intended only as a stop-gap, "pending final disposition," and that it was now time to legislate equitable disposition of the public domain and give right of purchase to users. The Public Lands Committee recommended that the price per acre be determined by formula: animal units per section times seven cents. The purchaser would put down 10 percent of the total amount and pay the remainder over 30 years with 11.5 percent interest. Similar proposals during the past half-century had fallen on deaf ears in Washington, as did this one.

The United States Forest Service, earlier endorsed by stockmen year after year, was now termed "a detriment to our form of government in causing widespread dissatisfaction among forest permittees." A congressional investigation was demanded that would show the need for legislation to remove the evils and insure fair adjudication of grievances.

TIMELINE

1948 Polaroid creates 60-second camera.

Vitamin B-12 discovered—leads to discovery that antibiotics added to feeds increases animal growth.

Berlin airlift: U.S. flies supplies to Allied-controlled Berlin.

1949 Walt Kelly's satirical comic strip character Pogo exclaims "We have met the enemy and he is us."

1950 Diners Club credit card encourages buy now pay later philosophy.

Diethylstilbestrol (DES), the first important growth hormone, approved for use in food animals.

Korean conflict begins.

1951 American National Live Stock Association changes name to American National Cattlemen's Association.

1952 First freezing of bull semen for A.I.

CowBelles, women's auxilliary of ANCA, created to promote beef.

Dwight D. Eisenhower elected 34th president.

1953 Discovery of DNA structure.

Joseph Stalin dies after 29 years as dictator of the Soviet Union.

Korean armistice signed.

1954 Social Security extended to farmers.

Salk vaccine defeats polio.

Marlboro creates "The Marlboro Man" to promote cigarette sales.

1955 U.S. military advisors sent to train South Vietnamese army.

Martin Luther King Jr. leads boycott of Montgomery bus lines.

1956 Soil Bank created: pays farmers to remove cropland from production.

Videotape recorder introduced.

1957 Soviet Union orbits first satellite.

First atomic power plant goes online at Shippingport, PA.

1958 Nikita Krushchev takes over as premier of the Soviet Union.

ISSUES

Tariffs and Trade
•
The Brannan Plan
•
Beef Promotion
•
Bust of 1953
•
First Real Facts About Beef
•
Expansion of Industry
•
Grading

ANLSA President William B. Wright chided the Forest Service at the Golden Anniversary Convention:

The stockman knows from his reading of the bible that, according to the Book of Genesis, in the beginning God created heaven and earth. On the third day God created grass. On the sixth day, grass was in such abundance that He created cattle. But before the sixth day was over, God created man to beneficially utilize his creations.

The Book of Genesis doesn't mention the Forest Service.

Only western congressmen listened with empathy to these demands of stockmen, and they were in the minority. Eastern congressmen and some emerging environmentalists maintained that public lands belonged to all citizens and were not for sale.

The persistent public lands issue and the unrelenting resolutions initiated by users have at times been divisive within the Association. Several past presidents, off the record, have expressed disgust with recurring public lands issues and questioned why the Association should spend so much time on them. After World War II, many Association leaders believed, at least privately, that they were fighting a losing battle on the public lands front. But they continued to go along with the debate to avoid a rift.

Fighting Tariffs

Cattlemen had always maintained a protectionist approach to restrict imported items. Following World War II, however, aid programs such as Lend Lease and The Marshall Plan placed great demand on products from the United States. Unsuccessful in fighting the "Trade Not Aid" philosophy of the times, cattlemen were eventually forced to consider some form of tariffs to maintain any reasonable balance of trade.

Cattlemen Fight Growth of Government

Association leaders thought it was time to cut back big government and missed few opportunities to say so, whether in speeches, resolutions or in their monthly magazine, *American Cattle Producer.*

In 1947, the articulate Wright observed, *We are still riding the foam of synthetic prosperity produced by deficit financing and augmented by the impacts of war.*

He then gave three pithy reasons why cattlemen never have supported any legislation designed to raid the federal treasury:

1. The cowman is an individualist and does not like to be regimented.
2. He is self-reliant, endowed with fortitude, ingenuity and industry.
3. He is not gullible.

Six years later, at the 1953 Convention, ANCA President Sam Hyatt expressed similar concern:

> *When you compare the estimated 1953 taxes of $69 billion with the tax take of $5 billion in 1939 and $7 billion in 194l, it is unbelievable such an increase could happen in that short span of years.*

Yet another six years later, at the 1959 Convention in Omaha, the lead resolution asked Congress to spend within the budget and to *face up to the fact that we have already gone a long way toward ruinous inflation.*

Neither did cattlemen relish the trend in income taxes. In 1939, federal income taxes averaged 1.2 percent of personal income. By 1945, the proportion had risen to 11.2 percent, with the maximum rate on income above $200,000 at 94 percent.

The Brannan Plan

Since 1950 was an election year, the public and congressional debate centered around the Agricultural Act of 1949, better known as the "Brannan Plan" after Secretary of Agriculture Charles F. Brannan. In a nutshell, the aim of the Brannan Plan was to keep

Trade Not Aid But Not for Cattle

For most of its history, the United States has been a protectionist nation utilizing a duty or tax to restrict imported items. In general, Republicans from the West have advocated higher protective tariffs, while Democrats from the East have supported lower tariffs and more imports.

The first tariff was a nine percent duty imposed in 1789. Protective tariffs reached their peak in the Tariff Act of 1930. This Act was widely criticized later as having exacerbated the fall in world trade and contributed to the Great Depression.

In 1934, the Reciprocal Trade Agreements Act authorized the President to negotiate reductions in tariffs up to 50 percent. This Act was extended several times; and Presidents Roosevelt and Truman used it entering into 25 bilateral trade agreements with foreign countries. By 1951 our tariff on dutiable products had dropped to about 12.5 percent—the lowest since 1789.

After the war, the United States was called upon to supply food, clothing, fuel, agricultural implements and industrial machinery to war-shattered Europe and Japan, along with other countries we had supplied before the war. For a period, we also had aid programs such as Lend Lease and The Marshall Plan, creating even greater demand for our products. Because our exports were greatly exceeding our imports, the country and even the Association became concerned about the "dollar gap."

In 1947 the United States and nearly 40 other countries entered into a pact called the General Agreement on Tariffs and Trade (GATT); but the Association did not support GATT until four decades later. Secretary Mollin cautioned members at the 1955 Convention in Reno:

> *GATT imposes a grave threat to our economy as it recognizes an authority higher than our own Congress in dealing with the economy of this and other countries.*

In the 1950s, the phrase "Trade Not Aid" became a popular topic for editorial writers and other free traders. The only way to get more trade was to increase imports; the only way to do this was to lower tariffs. Consumers liked the approach, but not cattlemen.

The "Trade Not Aid" policy prevailed, however, leaving Association leaders and other protectionists no alternative except to explore non-tariff barriers; thus the concept of import quotas was advanced. A resolution at the 1956 convention in New Orleans asked that quotas be set on livestock and livestock products to limit imports to the number of pounds exported in 1955. However, no relief came. By 1959, imports had reached a record eight percent of domestic production. Economists estimated the imports were costing United States producers $1.50 per cwt. for live cattle and depressing the market. But it was not until 1964 that the Association was able to get a law to limit imports.

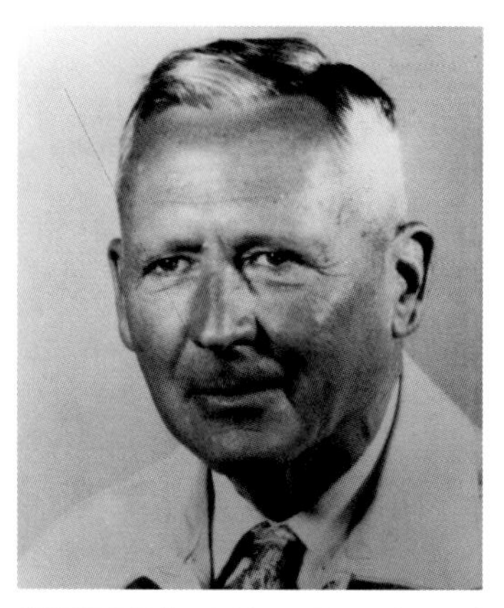

WILLIAM B. WRIGHT
President 1946-1947
Deeth, Nevada

With a sharp tongue, he attacked the BLM and Forest Service. "Wording in the Taylor Grazing Act," he argued, "meant equitable disposition of the public domain to permittees." He also opposed deficit spending, internationalism and free trade, and the "lack of understanding by the public of their dependence upon cattlemen." He fought to contain foot-and-mouth disease in Mexico.

ARTHUR A. SMITH
President 1948-1949
Sterling, Colorado

First rebuffed as a "half-breed," being a cattle feeder, Smith was later accepted and loved. Born in Ohio, he ranched in Wyoming, homesteaded in Idaho, and settled northeast of Sterling, CO, where he was the largest early feeder of wet beet pulp. He became president of the Colorado Livestock PCA and director of two banks. He opposed price controls, worked for an industry public relations plan and was the first to suggest ANLSA buy their own building in Denver.

AMERICAN CATTLE PRODUCER, June 1949

food prices low for consumers, farm prices high through direct payments, with taxpayers making up the difference. As they had consistently been in the past, cattlemen were still against subsidies and opposed the plan.

THE MOST DREADED ANIMAL PLAGUE

Throughout the first half of this century, nothing aroused the emotions of cattlemen or sparked unity as did foot-and-mouth disease. Association leaders played it to the hilt, often implying that the disease could wipe out our $10 billion cattle industry. It was serious, but United States cattlemen had already survived eight outbreaks in this country.

In 1935 the United States entered into the Argentine Sanitary Treaty (part of the free trade movement), which the Association hotly contested from the beginning and kept from being ratified. Following alarm about a foot-and-mouth epidemic in Mexico, President Harry Truman finally agreed to kill the Treaty. A massive campaign to eradicate the disease then began, and eradication was finally achieved in 1952. (*See pages 234 to 237.*)

THE YEAR OF PUBLIC RELATIONS

Cattlemen caught a lot of flack in 1948 from consumers, labor unions and newspaper columnists. Prices had risen 75 percent during the previous three years and were predicted to go higher. This influenced President Truman—not insensitive to political heat—to ask for standby price controls again, even after declaring in November 1946 that controls would do the nation's economy more harm than good.

Several other things caused the Association to feel it was getting a bad rap from the press. It was credited with blocking meat imports from Argentina; accused of misleading the public regarding public lands; and charged with not representing rank and file cattlemen.

We most certainly do represent all cattlemen, retorted ANCA President Smith. *In 1948, we had as members 18 affiliated state associations, 100 local or regional associations and 3,500 individual cattlemen.*

Outgoing ANLSA President Wright cited *public relations. . .of more importance than any other single item today to our industry.* Thus, the Association proclaimed 1949 as "The Year of Public Relations."

As the commitment to public relations grew, Lyle Liggett was hired in 1953 from the University of Denver as the first director of information and public relations. He led a classic public relations program,

NEEDED: A SECRETARY *FOR* CATTLE

CATTLEMEN FIGHT THE "BRANNAN PLAN"

The Agricultural Act of 1949 tried once again to confine cattlemen within a structure of price and production controls. The author of this Act was Charles F. Brannan, Secretary of Agriculture from 1948 to 1953 under President Truman. An attorney by training, Brannan followed strictly the policies of Presidents Roosevelt and Truman in seeking price and production controls similar to wartime and immediate post-war periods when needs were different. Price supports were a popular plan of eastern politicians to supply cheap food to the big populations of eastern cities. The government maintained that by supporting crop production, it would keep the farmer in business and food prices reasonable.

Brannan's program was pushed by the National Farmers Union, for whom he later went to work, and other farming groups that had benefited from subsidies. But the cattlemen would have nothing of it. With the feeling that once accepted, subsidies were hard to get rid of, the cattlemen voiced their preference to live in an independent and self-sustaining way.

In testifying against the Act, ANLSA President Smith reaffirmed: *The historic position of the ANLSA opposes subsidies and controls.* Also in testimony, ANLSA President Bamert asked: *What possible excuse is there for subsidizing every consumer in this country?*

The Brannan Plan per se died in Congress, but direct payments to farmers to attain 90 percent of parity continued for several years.

There were cattlemen who did, however, support the plan. In 1953 at Dalhart, Texas, some 500 angry cattlemen met and organized the United Livestock Producers Association. Leader Eck Brown blasted ANCA: *Existing livestock associations don't represent the real sentiment of cattlemen. If we don't get supports at 90 to 100 percent of parity, we're breeding another depression.*

ANCA did not buy into this sentiment. At the 1954 Convention in Colorado Springs, ANCA President Hyatt reasoned: *We've had some awful good times in the cattle business. Now that we've had a bump, are we going to get weak-kneed and go on the dole? I say let's stand on our own and put some sense into the farm program.* Members there from 23 states agreed and voted unanimously to reject price supports.

Ezra Taft Benson, new secretary of agriculture, congratulated cattlemen at the Convention for rejecting price supports. *You faced up to the situation with real courage. Despite drought and declining prices, you didn't ask the government for help.*

For every 4 people sitting down to a meal in 1950 there will be another person at the table in 1975
AGRICULTURE'S JOB IS TO FILL THE 5th PLATE

Charles F. Brannan
Secretary of Agriculture 1948-1953

(top) **The Fifth Plate** *was one of Brannan's themes. Because the population was expected to increase 25 percent by 1975, support prices "were needed to assure a food supply." But that has never been the case. When 1975 arrived and the population exceeded 213 million, farmers produced surplus food, again true in 1995 (pop. 252 million), and yet again in 1997 (pop. 270 million).*

*(below)***This Editorial Cartoon** *depicted cattlemen's sentiments towards the Brannan Plan.*

Second Agricultural Revolution

The two decades following World War II saw more changes, especially in agriculture and the cattle business, than anyone could remember. Beef consumption in 1947 was the highest in 40 years, at 115 pounds per capita (carcass basis). Prices were 125 percent above 1941 prices and by 1949 they were 210 percent higher. Cattlemen just could not satisfy the new demand for beef.

During the same years, the South was undergoing the "Second Agricultural Revolution," as USDA historian Wayne D. Rasmussen called it. The First Agricultural Revolution had taken place following the Civil War when a combination of strong demand, high prices and labor shortage convinced many farmers to switch from hand power and hand tools to horse power and horse-drawn machines. From 1860 to 1918, the number of horses and mules increased from 8,878,000 to 26,723,000.

But now the Second Agricultural Revolution was seeing a switch from animal to mechanical power. Farmers were slow to switch from animal power because they already had horses and mules and they could grow their own feed at virtually no cost. A tractor required a significant investment and ongoing costs for fuel. But the number of tractors grew steadily, from 920,000 in 1930, to 3,394,000 in 1950, to 4,600,000 in 1987.

In addition to mechanization, there came a veritable explosion of technology. Everything changed: improved seeds (often hybrids); fertilizer; chemicals to control weeds, insects and diseases; widespread conservation practices; bigger tractors; improved breeding and feeding techniques for livestock; and much more. By 1960 each farmer was producing enough food and fiber for himself and 46 others; and by 1995, enough for himself and 129 others.

New Technology for New Times. *Equipment such as this 1951 John Deere tractor and a New Ideal picker changed the face of agricIture.*

using newspapers, magazines, radio, television, speeches before civic groups, window displays and billboards. Two films were produced, *All Flesh Is Grass* and *Land of Our Fathers*. Also, the Association sponsored a book, *Hell On Horses and Women*, written by Alice Marriott and published by the University of Oklahoma Press in 1953. The cattle business *can be hard and truly hell for the women who live it*, Marriott wrote, *but it can also come about as close to Heaven as any life a woman can live today.*

It was an ambitious program with a shoestring budget, highly dependent upon volunteer effort.

Korean War, More Price Controls

War, inflation or bad drought, any one alone was enough to derail a public relations program. And they all happened during the early 1950s.

In January 1951, while the ANLSA was meeting in San Francisco, four Chinese Communist armies overpowered United Nations forces in South Korea and moved into Seoul. The United Nations called the Korean conflict "a police action," even though United Nations forces suffered 451,727 casualties, including 33,629 United States military men killed.

ANLSA President Bamert told the 1951 Convention that the industry had a duty to keep production high. At the same time, he cautioned government officials in Washington that the rumored price controls would lower production: *the only long-term solution to high prices is high prices, which will increase production.*

Nevertheless, in response to the urging of labor unions and others, the announcement came on April 28, 1951, that live cattle prices would be rolled back 10 percent, to be followed by two additional rollbacks of 4.5 percent each in August and October. Michael DiSalle, administrator of the Office of Price Stabilization (OPS), proclaimed, *this would save housewives $700 million in the cost of beef.* But Bamert and ANLSA knew better; the savings, if any, would come out of cattlemen's pocketbooks.

They pleaded to Congress that a rollback would not save consumers anything; the black market would take over, as it had in World War II. Prices would rise in the short run, causing a reduction in beef production, thus bringing higher prices for the long run. As predicted, it came to pass: rollback, black market, higher beef prices. If there were to be control of meat prices, there should also be control on wages.

So Bamert squared off against DiSalle, a former police chief in New York City. Looking back 42 years later in 1993, Bamert said with a grin, *It was a perfect issue for a president of a national association, one that would arouse the ire and gain the support of all producers.*

President Truman came to the aid of DiSalle, his political crony from New York. He supported not only price controls but also slaughtering quotas on packers as well as the licensing of all cattle buyers. Labor leaders also supported DiSalle.

Bamert put together a coalition of Association leaders representing farmers, ranchers, grain producers, packers, among others, and got the ear of Congress. He persistently preached, *Price controls never have and never will work for cattle and meat. There are just too many grades of animals, too many weights, too many handlers. . . .Government attempts to lower meat prices by controls always have had the opposite effect.* As a result, the two proposed rollbacks of 4.5 percent each never materialized.

LOREN C. BAMERT
PRESIDENT 1950-1951
IONE, CALIFORNIA

The youngest president to serve, he was elected at age 38. Ten years before he was President of the California Cattlemen's Association. He was known for his fights against Korean War era price controls. "The politicians knew price controls wouldn't work," he said, "but claimed they had to do it politically. The politicians won, but it was a mess." In his term the Association changed its name to American National Cattlemen's Association.

1949 The Year of Public Relations. *Public Relations and the promotion of beef had become the new challenge of the Association. But selling the industry on selling itself was the first obstacle to overcome. Cattlemen felt good about the "Eat More Beef" signs along highways that ran through their ranches, although skeptics believed that they were preaching to the choir. Still, such efforts were a positive first step in a new direction for the industry and the Association. Promoting beef would eventually become the very heart of the Association's work.*

SAM C. HYATT
PRESIDENT 1952-1953
HYATTVILLE, WYOMING

"Free markets make free men," declared Hyatt, as he fought price controls and supports. During the Korean War, cattle prices escalated nearly 50 percent, causing over-expansion, then tumbled nearly 50 percent, triggering a call for supports during the "Great Cattle Bust of 1953." Hyatt, was well known and respected in Washington where he spent 40 days in 1953. He served on numerous state and national commissions and advisory committees.

ATTACK THE BUREAUCRATS

Other livestock leaders were assisting Bamert in the fight against controls, of course, especially Executive Secretary F.E. Mollin. Mollin's style was often caustic and abrupt, but he prevailed and was largely considered the driving force behind the Association. Because train trips to Washington often took two or three days (one way) and were expensive for hard-pressed cattlemen, Mollin became the primary spokesman for the Association and probably received undeserved criticism.

While his acrid attacks on bureaucrats sometimes drew applause from rustic ranchers, they gained him and the Association a reputation in Washington of being "against everything." Such criticism prompted him to write an editorial in the *AMERICAN CATTLE PRODUCER* to defend his "negativism," insisting that his statements reflected the policy of ANCA and the conservative nature of western cattlemen. Which of course they did.

CATTLE BUST OF 1953

During the Korean War (1950-1953), cattlemen saw escalating prices—up nearly 50 percent—and over-expanded herds. 1952 beef cattle numbers were up 12.4 percent over the record of the previous year, bringing total numbers to an all-time high of 88,062,000. Then, prices tumbled nearly 50 percent.

Next came a devastating drought throughout the Great Plains that rivaled the historic drought of the thirties. The drought exacerbated the over-supply situation further and led to the "Great Cattle Bust of 1953."

A Tall Man Who Wore a Big Hat. *Sam Hyatt, epitomized the rugged western cattleman who had dominated the Association since its inception. But he was one of the last of that breed. The Association was changing and expanding into new areas of pursuit.*

HOW BAD THE DROUGHT? AND THE BUST?

Many Southwestern ranchers tried to keep their basic breeding herds intact by moving them to Arkansas, Louisiana and Mississippi. Some burned prickly pear for feed to keep their remaining cattle alive.

Near San Angelo, Texas, Lake Concho caught on fire and burned for weeks. Water dried up, the soft peat in the lake bed caught on fire, and fire trucks could not traverse the spongy peat to extinguish the smoldering peat. Complicating the parched ranges and dried-up water holes, grasshoppers swept across five million acres of western range, reportedly eating everything but the fence posts.

Average cattle prices in 1952 were $179 per head; in 1955, they were $88 per head. Pressure on individual cattlemen was tremendous.

One customer of a South Texas feedyard—an extreme example—had two pens of overly-heavy Mexican steers, weighing 1,400 to 1,500 pounds. In early 1953, he turned down a packer bid of $18 per cwt. Two weeks later, he turned down $16; a week later he turned down $14; and a week after that he committed suicide by jumping out of a Fort Worth hotel window.

> ***We've had some awful good times in the cattle business. Now that we've had a bump, are we going to get weak-kneed and go on the dole? I say let's stand on our own and put some sense into the farm program.***
>
> —ANCA President Hyatt speaking at the 1954 Convention

After President Dwight Eisenhower and Secretary of Agriculture Ezra Taft Benson flew to the Southwest to view the drought disaster. They offered cattlemen a slew of government relief programs: low-priced government feed, extended and guaranteed government loans, emergency freight rates for feed, stepped-up government purchases of beef, and more. With wounded pride but flat wallets, many ranchers, and the Association, accepted the government aid with gratitude, just a few years after they had so gallantly fought the battle against subsidies.

Fact Finding Committee

As the "Great Cattle Bust of 1953" lingered on for four years, the ANCA Market Committee became concerned and, in 1957, requested a Fact Finding Committee to investigate and report on the economic factors that influence the marketing and production of livestock.

This would become the most important and far-reaching study in the history of the Association and would define the demand for beef for years to come. The major finding that came out of this study was that the rise in beef demand was the phenomenum of the hamburger.

Self-Help Beef Promotion

Unfortunately, the drought and declining prices persisted. So when Jay Taylor of Amarillo, Texas, became president in 1954, he proposed a self-help way out of the quagmire—beef promotion. With a background in industry [before ranching he was executive vice president of the Halliburton Company], Taylor was known as a super salesman and purveyor of goodwill. While president, he set an unmatched travel pace. He spoke in 47 states and at the end of his two-year term cracked, *I just couldn't gather enough cattlemen in Vermont that would listen to me.*

Taylor soon became known as "Mr. Beef Promotion," and his enthusiasm was obvious. In his 1955 presidential address, for example, he said:

> *There are 10,000 new babies born every day, and nutritionists have proven that these babies should start eating beef at six weeks of age and continue to eat beef every day of their lives. We must work even harder to let every mother know the value of beef as the best daily source of protein.*

In another speech, he proposed the goal of doubling beef consumption in 10 years, which would have been a feat that producers would have had difficulty supplying, even if consumers had demanded it.

Taylor, an influential Democrat [most ANLSA and ANCA presidents were Republicans] and purebred Hereford breeder, had much in common with his friend President Lyndon B. Johnson, who also raised purebred Herefords. There friendship provided a helping hand to cattlemen for many years.

National Beef Council

Two years before becoming president of ANCA, Taylor had been chairman of the National Live Stock and Meat Board. Only one other, Albert K. Mitchell of New Mexico, had been the chief elected officer of both national organizations. Taylor served as president of ANCA in 1936-1937 and chairman of the Meat Board in 1939-1942.

During the disaster of the early fifties, Taylor became displeased with the Meat Board's reluctance to promote beef. The Meat Board (*See page 70 to 73.*), a multi-species organization, was committed to promoting all red meat, not just beef. So in 1955 while president of ANCA, Taylor initiated the National Beef Council (NBC) and led the effort for a

The Fact Finding Committee

In 1957 the Association took one of the most visionary steps it had ever taken. In an effort to understand the demand for beef and therefore produce accordingly, the Association appointed a Fact Finding Committee made up of some of the best known minds in the business. They in turn hired Dr. Herrell DeGraff of Cornell University to tackle this issue.

The Committee and DeGraff researched for three years, issuing a number of telling reports and speeches. For the first time, the industry placed priority on consumer preferences, and this study became the forerunner of several similar studies in the decades to follow.

John M. Marble *of Carmel Valley, California, served as chairman of the Fact Finding Committee. He was joined on the Committee by some of the strongest Association leaders: Tobin Armstrong of Armstrong, Texas; Martin Domke of Greeley, Colorado; L. R. Houck of Gettysburg, South Dakota; Albert K. Mitchell of Albert, New Mexico; and Milford Vaught of Bruneau, Idaho.*

The final report, entitled *Beef Production and Distribution*, by Herrell DeGraff, a 252-page hardback book, was published in 1960 by the University of Oklahoma Press.

In spite of depressed prices, consumers still complained about prices. DeGraff found that between 1936 and 1955 there had been a real increase in demand for beef, in relation to chicken and pork, for three main reasons:

1. The rising social acceptance of hamburgers. Hamburger provided a market for cow meat and less desirable cuts previously discarded so that more available beef could be used to fill this demand without hurting the constant demand for the higher quality cuts.
2. Greater individual purchasing power: more people could afford their favorite meat, even at higher prices.
3. Refrigeration on the farm, which increased rural consumption.

According to DeGraff, other factors also helped boost the demand for beef:

- Young Slaughter cattle. Other than culled breeding stock, slaughter cattle had been compressed into a narrow bracket of slaughter age (typically 18 to 24 months). As a result, the cattle were more uniform in age and produced more desirable beef.
- Fed Cattle. A great majority of animals entering the block beef supply had been through a feedyard. In the feedlots the cattle were fed uniformly and produced not only a more uniform quality of meat, but also a more consistent supply to consumers.

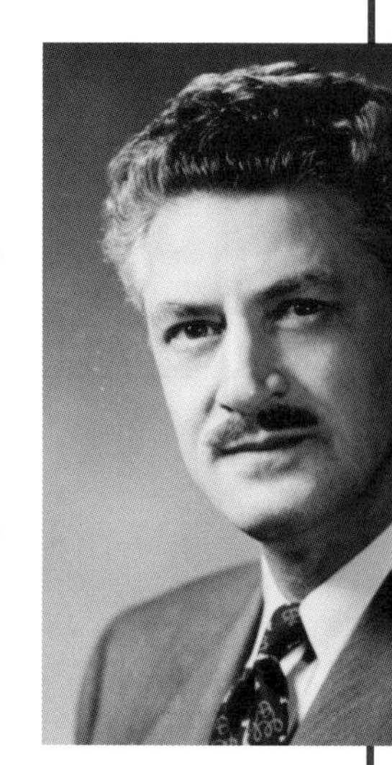

Dr. Herrell DeGraff, *a highly regarded agricultural economist at Cornell University, was hired by the Fact Finding Committee to research consumer preferences and demand for beef. His report, known as "The DeGraff Report," was the industry's first effort to understand the consumer. He later became executive director of the American Meat Institute. In that position he helped moved the industry forward by encouraging cooperation between packers and cattlemen.*

The Fact Finding Committee did, however, also find some points of consumer dissatisfaction:

- Beef was less tender than desired.
- There was a wide variation of tenderness throughout all grades.
- Much of the beef was too fat. Consumers liked the taste of the internal fat (marbling) but not the waste of external fat.

Cattlemen would hear these "points of dissatisfaction" again and again in consumer studies throughout the century.

But the new popularity of hamburger had the most major and lasting impact on the cattle industry, rivaled only somewhat by the post-war explosion of supermarkets and chain stores. It continued to gain in consumer favor, primarily because hamburger changed from a catch-all item to a quality, specification product. Hamburger standardization would become the cornerstone of one of the most successful business arenas ever, that of "fast food ."

The Cattle Bust of 1953 *had occurred. Prices were down, drought had striken the land. Despite growth eastward, Association revenue was down. However, there was hope for the future. Disregarding the reduced income, the Association conducted a building fund drive; they raised $125,000 and moved into a new headquarters building in 1955.*

national legislated checkoff. Seven checkoff bills were eventually introduced in Congress, but they were opposed by the Meat Board and the American Farm Bureau Federation, both of which favored generic red meat promotion.

An organizational split in the beef industry ensued. NBC attempted to make it on voluntary contributions, while the Meat Board continued to collect from producers through market agencies. By 1956, 17 state beef councils had been formed in support of the NBC; but the emotional and financial drain was too great for the leaders or the members. In 1963 the groups compromised and formed the Beef Industry Council (BIC) of the National Live Stock and Meat Board, which assumed the lead in national beef promotion.

Another lasting development in beef promotion during this era was the official organization in 1952 of the American National CowBelles. The women of the industry now had an outlet for their energies

> ***Cattle feeding in the West is becoming a force we can't ignore.***
>
> —ANCA President Taylor
>
> *Commenting on feeders being allowed ANCA membership at the 1955 Convention*

in promoting beef. They knew that they would have far better luck speaking to the average housewife than would the cattlemen, and it was after all the housewife who bought and served the meat.

CHANGES TO BEHOLD

The industry was experiencing many other changes after the war, some led by the Association, some in spite of the Association. Supermarkets, which started popping up in every city, were targeted for criticism, "because the chains undercut independent meat market prices, thus forcing down the price of beef and cattle." [Some supermarkets were chains, some were independents; but critics often lopped them together.] In fact, supermarkets eventually accounted for substantial gains in marketing beef.

JAY TAYLOR
President 1954-1955
Amarillo, Texas

"Mr. Beef Promotion" they called him. Taylor was one of only two association presidents to serve as Chairman of the Meat Board. An affable and colorful character, he founded the National Beef Council, later the BIC of the Meat Board. He was an advisor to four presidents and served on innumerable commissions and national corporate boards.

DON C. COLLINS
President 1956-1957
Kit Carson, Colorado

The only father-son team to serve as presidents of this Association, Don followed his father, Charlie, 23 years later. He was a tall, quiet man known for his integrity, ability and pleasantness as well as for his articulate, home-spun, down-to-earth speeches. Before becoming President, he had served 10 years as a Colorado state senator, where he served on the five most important committees. A shrewd businessman, he was also a bank president as well as president of Franklin Serum Company.

Cattle Boom in Dixie

At the same time the South was undergoing a Second Agricultural Revolution, the boom in cattle numbers captured the attention of the nation. Farmers and would-be cattlemen moved from the Midwest and elsewhere to take advantage of the climate and the new opportunities in the South: cheap labor, improved grasses and clovers, fertilizer and improved breeding.

Within 10 years, the total area in southern pastures increased 11 percent and production per acre increased 50 to 500 percent. The acreage in improved pasture increased 263 percent in South Carolina, 222 percent in North Carolina, 149 percent in Mississippi.

The queen of the new plants, Coastal Bermuda, was a hybrid released in 1943 by Dr. Glenn Burton of the USDA Experiment Station at Tifton, Georgia. By 1992, Coastal Bermuda was planted on approximately 12 million acres. During the same period, Kentucky 31 fescue was covering the Upper South states.

While the Nation's cattle numbers increased by 45 percent from 1950 to 1970, the Southeast grew by 225 percent.

Purebred bulls in great numbers poured into the South; performance testing became common; and feeder calf sales became popular. Most of the better feeder calves went to Midwestern feedlots, while the more common ones went west.

During the 1950s, the trend to compact, quick-maturing cattle led to a bigger problem for many purebred herds. The result was that dwarfism became a threat, especially in the Hereford breed, and to a lesser degree in Angus on other breeds. For fear of spreading the defective genes, markets for the western bulls declined drastically, but when these bulls carrying dwarf genes were mated to native southern cows, dwarfism did not carry through. Westerners seized the opportunity and shipped thousands of dwarf-carrier bulls into the South, thus contributing to the rapid upgrading of the southern herds. Many breeders destroyed their dwarf-carriers and in a few years cleared up the problem.

In 1953, a clandestine and controversal effort was made to upgrade herds. Sixty head of Charolais cattle were smuggled from Mexico into Texas, then into Louisiana. The Association and oth-

(above) **A New and Different Membership.** *Don Collins (left), western cattleman and ANCA president chats with Ben Hill Griffen, Jr. (right), a major player in the Florida cattle and citrus industries. Association leaders soon blossomed in the South, as did cattle numbers.*

(right) **The Miami Convention in 1950** *was the first held east of the Mississippi. Western members saw a promising land where cattle fed on orange pulp, lived in swamps and were still a profitable investment.*

***Woods or Florida Cracker cows**. These tough cattle, descended from Andalusian "Black Cows," had produced both the fighting bulls of Spain and the hearty longhorns. They had roamed the pastures and swamps of Florida for four hundred years. Their strong genetic background thwarted dwarfism, like most other southern cattle, and provided the base for an upgraded cattle industry in Florida.*

The favored short, fat steer *was the trend of the 1950s, but that trend damaged many purebred herds with dwarfism. This 1948 woodcut shows the type of steer winning the judging.*

ers protested, calling on law enforcement either to destroy the animals or return them to Mexico. The cattle were returned and two of the three smugglers sent to jail.

The South was happy to become a part of the national organization. Florida was the first to join the Association in 1944, followed by Louisiana, the only state affiliates from the South for several years. By 1958 eight states east of the Mississippi had joined.

The Association, eager to accommodate the emerging South, opted to hold its 1950 Convention in Miami, and the 1956 Convention in New Orleans.

In 1962, they met again in Florida, this time in Tampa. Tampa was short on hotels and it was said that some cowboys rented cabins in docked cruise ships and joked about their "bonus cruise." And there the Association elected its first president from east of the Mississippi: Cushman Radebaugh of Orlando, Florida.

Pan American takes off from Miami on the 1950 post-convention tour. *Both a new location and a new departure point, Miami opened new doors to cattlemen, and brought the world, and markets, closer to the western ranges.*

ANCA Members Visit Secretary of Agriculture Ezra Taft Benson. *Benson, from Utah, understood cattlemen's issues and was the first Secretary in over two decades to push for free markets, rather than price and production controls. Thus cattlemen felt a sense of security and expanded the industry during the Eisenhower years. (l to r) Ernest Hamm, South Dakota; Charlie Wetzler, Arizona; ANCA President Fred Dressler, Nevada; Louis Harrell, Arizona; Cushman Radebaugh, Florida; Robert Lister, Oregon; and Bill McMillan.*

New Independent Packers

For the first half of the 20th century, the major packers were located at the terminal markets, which were served by railroads, and which, prior to 1920, had economic ties to packers. But the new independents had no such ties. They could foresee the demise of terminal markets, which had been the hubs of cattle commerce for a century, and they had trucks to transport their product. So they built new, modern plants in the country near fed cattle supplies. During the 1980s the last of the old-line packers quit slaughtering. In their heyday of the 1920s and 1930s, up to 80 terminals marketed over 20 million cattle a year. But by 1990, the number had diminished to nine terminals; there they marketed under one million cattle.

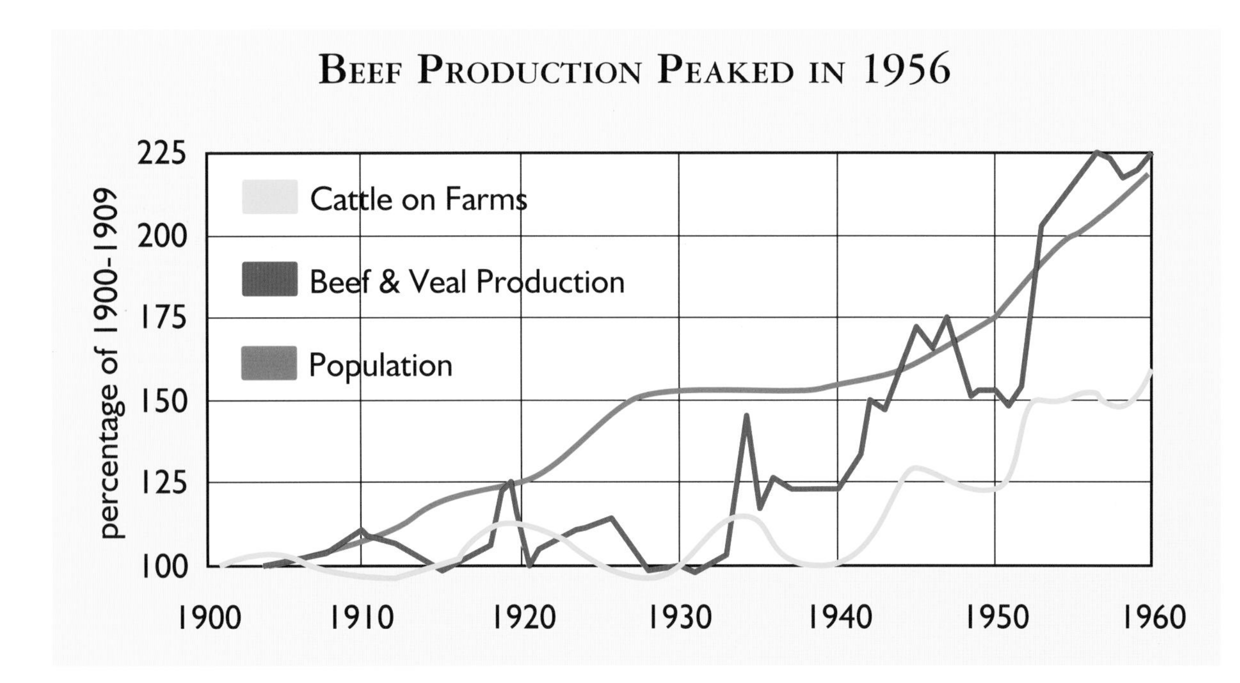

Not only were terminal markets pressured by the growth of smaller, efficient plants, but they carried the further burden of unions. Many had a "master contract" with labor which forced artificial high costs at markets; also, if one plant went on strike, all plants went on strike. The independents initially had no union worries.

BEHIND THE SCENES

RADFORD S. HALL
EXECUTIVE SECRETARY
1956-1958

After serving as Assistant Executive Secretary for 11 years, "Rad" Hall advanced to Executive Secretary when his boss, F.E. Mollin, retired in early 1956.

Before joining ANLSA in 1945, he had spent eight years as livestock editor and advertising manager of *RECORD STOCKMAN* in Denver, where he married the daughter of the editor. Prior to that, he had worked for Swift & Company in Denver.

Hall was born in Trenton, Nebraska, in 1906 and attended the University of Colorado, where he majored in Business Administration. From 1940 to 1945, he served as secretary of the Colorado Hereford Breeders Association and became an honorary life member; he was also Chairman of the Natural Resources Council.

In early 1958, he died suddenly, after only two years as Executive Secretary of ANCA. His successor was David O. Appleton, editor of the *AMERICAN CATTLE PRODUCER* magazine, who served as acting executive secretary for a short time until a permanent replacement was found.

Under the tenure of Rad Hall, the Association added Affiliates and Expanded to the East. *By 1958, Hall reported a total of 141 local, county, state and breed affiliates and approximately 3,000 individual members (a reduction from six years earlier). This included 28 state associations, with eight, for the first time, from east of the Mississippi, and four breed associations (Hereford, Angus, Shorthorn and Brahman).*

Dan Collins and Rad Hall *showing artwork for 1957 Phoenix Convention.*

Local auction markets, which peaked in numbers to 2,500 auctions barns in 1952, became an asset to the beef business, providing a pipeline of supply inexpensively. The convenience of hauling cattle to a local market by truck or trailer had quietly turned cattlemen away from the terminals.

PERMANENT PRESENCE IN WASHINGTON

From the Association's inception, its leaders had felt the need for protection from the government in Washington. Professional help, however, could not be afforded with a shoestring budget. F.E. Mollin, during his 26 years as executive secretary, was the principal spokesman. But his particular approach to treating government as an adversary were not those of a true "lobbyist."

The Supermarket and Chain Store
The Issue is Convenience

The chain store idea developed about 1930 in the large cities of the eastern seaboard and the large west coast cities. Some of the leaders were First National in Boston, A&P in Philadelphia and Safeway in Oakland, California.

Grocery stores and meat markets had been operating as separate businesses. Many stores delivered to homes and did a credit business. Delinquent accounts were hard to collect.

Meat markets with butchers who cut beef to order for a customer had been the final step in the beef production chain. It was a labor-intensive and inefficient service. The growing populations in the urban areas needed quicker service, and the supermarket concept, both independent supermarkets and supermarket chains, became immediately popular. By the time World War II ended, the idea of multiple stores with the same merchandise scattered throughout the large cities and in smaller towns had developed and prospered. Local newspaper advertising of weekly specials attracted attention of the public for the first time.

The stores soon realized that most items in the store, such as canned goods, the staples and other products were the same in everyone's store. They needed a specialty to attract customers. The meat counter was it. Beef was the most popular meat and so the chains promoted beef and actually made the business grow and prosper. Refrigeration had vastly improved during the war effort and beautiful new refrigerated meat cases were available to coax the customers to buy beef. The mea counters lent themselves to special sale signs and promotions.

The new meat counters displaying all kinds of meat and poultry in refrigerated counters [there were no frozen food counters at the time.] appealed to the customers. They could see what they were getting. They did not have to wait while the butcher cut it.

But to do this, supermarkets had to have uniform quality and size of beef carcasses. They became the big pressure for improved government beef grading.

The new large stores that sold uniform cuts of meat at the same price in many stores had to send their butchers to meat cutting classes so that they all learned to cut and trim the beef the same way.

New chains developed all over the country. The organized into buying cooperatives to compete with high volume chains. Competition became very keen, but beef remained in popular demand.

As stores sold in large volumes with specials at all levels, cattle producers began to think that this was hurting their prices. Western cattle producers, far removed from the volume and needs of the urban areas, had difficulty in understanding that these stores were really their customers. But, when prices were low, cattlemen found it easy to blame supermarkets, and over the years at different times, cattlemen filed lawsuits claiming price fixing.

But the new chain stores and super markets were great marketers, and were a main reason beef grew in popularity. Their advertising and their quality control is what caused the large increase in beef consumption. By 1993 chain stores accounted for 22 percent of all grocery stores handling 75 percent of the dollar sales.

Beef Brought in Customers. *In stiff competition, beef was often used as a special item to draw customers. Many chains used beef as its "loss leader," while others, such as the Winn-Dixie Stores headquartered in Jacksonville, Florida, operate throughout the southeast with the slogan "The Beef People."*

Meat Grading
The Issue is Consistency

Grading and Stamping Prime and Choice Beef Carcasses

Under Supervision of

Bureau of Agricultural Economics
U. S. Department of Agriculture

POSTERS ARE FREE—SENT ON REQUEST

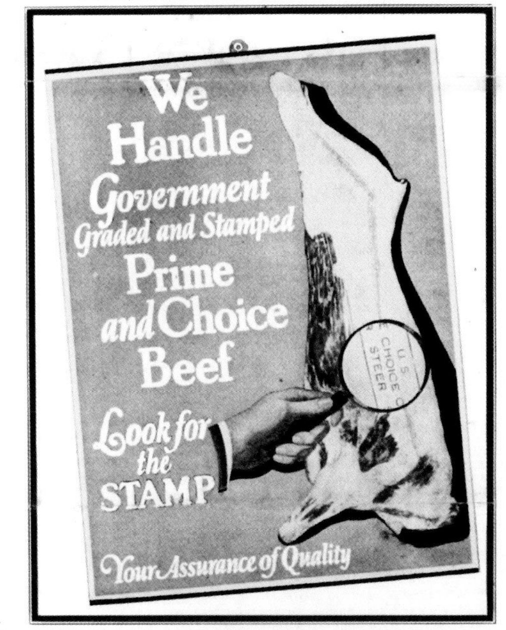

We
Handle
Government
Graded and Stamped
Prime
and Choice
Beef
Look for
the
STAMP
Your Assurance of Quality

Above is a small black and white reproduction of the attractive poster to be furnished those handling graded and stamped beef. The poster itself is 18x24 inches in size and is printed in four colors. The carcass is reproduced in natural colors.

6-14-27

BULLETIN NO. 2
Issued By
NATIONAL LIVE STOCK AND MEAT BOARD
Department, Better Beef Association
407 South Dearborn Street :: :: :: CHICAGO, ILLINOIS

Bulletin was issued on June 14, 1927.

The chain stores had one large problem with beef: lack of consistency. Getting beef in carload lots of uniform, consistent quality was next to impossible. The hotel and restaurant people also needed to prove quality to customers. So these groups turned to government grading.

Government grading and stamping was first offered by USDA in 1927. But for several years, packers agreed to it only if the National Live Stock and Meat Board would coordinate it. The Meat Board agreed and for a few years even paid the salaries of four inspectors.

However, big national packers dominated the industry until after World War II, and they preferred their own private brands such as Swift's Premium, Armour's Star and Wilson Certified.

As a consequence, federal grading was not widely used until World War II when price controls were applied and federal grading became mandatory. After the war, the big packers went back to their house grades. Smaller regional packers saw this as an opportunity and offered federally graded beef. So the big packers reluctantly followed suit.

There were conflicting opinions in the marketplace. Packers wanted more yield with slaughter, which required fatter cattle, while consumers wanted less fat.

Faced with this dilemma, the Association hired Dr. Robert Bray from the University of Wisconsin, as a consultant in 1962. Together with Dr. Earnest Briskey, he prepared "A Special Study of the Beef Grade Standards for the American National Cattlemen's Association," in which he endorsed the yield grading system proposed by USDA.

In 1956 the Livestock Division of the Standardization Branch, USDA, initiated a study that led to yield grading, which had come up with 10 catgories of yield. In 1963, this number was narrowed to six categories, then in 1965 to five. YG-1 would be the most lean and most desirable, YG-5 would have the most fat and be least desirable. Thus dual grading was first offered on a voluntary basis in 1965, was coupled with quality grading in 1975, then was uncoupled in 1989.

Through the years, there have been a dozen changes in the grading system, often at the urging of the Association, and the amount of beef graded has gradually increased: from eight percent of total slaughter in 1940, to 29 percent in 1947, to 81 percent in 1996.

1927 Beef Grades	1997 Beef Grades
1) Prime	1) Prime
2) Choice	2) Choice
3) Good	3) Select
4) Medium	4) Standard
5) Common	5) Common
6) Cutter	6) Utility
7) Low Cutter	7) Cutter

Anything below Select is usually ranked "No Grade."

Percentage of All Beef Graded, 1995

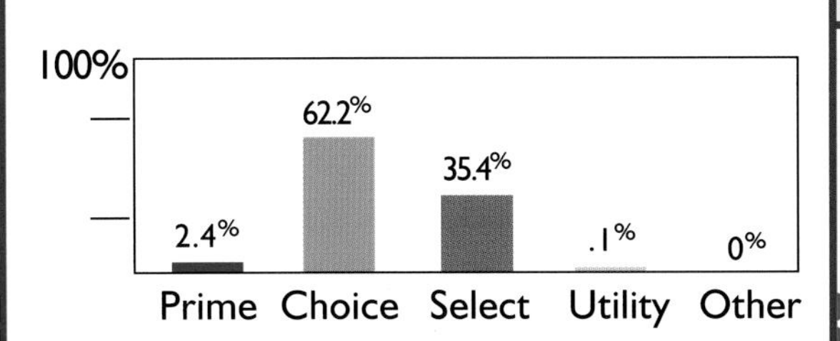

Father and Son Presidents

The Collins Family

Only once in its 100-year history did the Association elect a father and son as presidents. Both were outstanding leaders and their dedication is a shining example of the many families who have supported the Association generation after generation. In 1997 the fifth generation of this family are still enthusiastic members and cattlemen.

Charles E. Collins
ANLSA President 1932-1935

Born in Topeka, Kansas, in 1869, Charles Collins entered the cattle business as a trail hand when his father sent him at 16 to Mexico to help herd his cattle. At 20 he went into the cattle business himself in the new Oklahoma Territory.

Charles co-founded the Franklin Serum Company, the first animal pharmaceutical company, which manufactured blackleg vaccine, and served as its President until his death. He was followed by his son Don who served as president until the company was sold in 1963.

Charles also founded the Kit Carson State Bank. Throughout the Depression this bank never closed its doors.

Modern in outlook, he always carried a barometer with him; when it dropped, he alerted his ranch hands to protect the stock from the forthcoming storm.

At the height of the Depression in 1934 he was elected president of ANLSA and served for four consecutive terms. He helped organize the Federal Credit Association which he felt "helped people to help themselves." But he opposed most New Deal programs which he considered not in the best interest of the individual or the industry.

In 1942 at the age of 73 he was elected to the Colorado State Senate and died while serving his second term in 1944.

Charley was a true individualist: colorful, tough, salty, progressive and respected. He was also direct. While President of ANLSA, he received a telegram from Secretary of Agriculture Henry A. Wallace asking him to submit a national plan for the cattle industry. After thinking about it a little while, he wired back: *If anyone is going to write a cattle plan, it had better be some idiot who does not know a thing about the industry.*

In 1907, Charles, with his wife and five-year old son, Don, settled on the plains near Kit Carson, Colorado, and founded the Collins ranch. He mastered dry land farming and ran steers until 1915 when he brought purebred Herefords to southeastern Colorado.

Don C. Collins
ANCA President 1956-1957

Don Collins followed in his father's footsteps in further developing the ranch, raising Herefords, and as president of the Franklin Serum Company.

He was also Republican State Senator for 10 years, including senate president pro tem. Upon election as president of

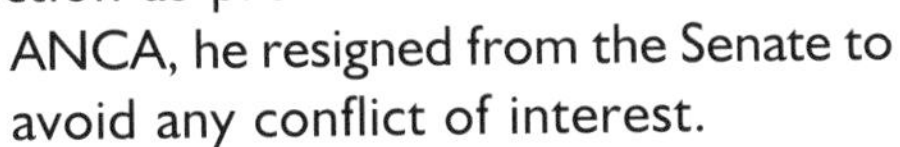

ANCA, he resigned from the Senate to avoid any conflict of interest.

Don Collins saw the Association's expansion into the eastern and southern states, its new look at promotion of its product, and new "revolution" of technology and information that would paint a very different picture for the industry during the last half of the 20th century.

ANCA's First Family in 1956. *Mrs. Don Collins (Blanche Brown), Don Collins, and daughter Polly Collins. Polly Collins was one of the first women to receive a degree in Animal Husbandry from Colorado A&M College. Polly and her husband, Rogers Johnson, managed the Collins Ranch until his death in 1993. Johnson served as the first chairman of the NCA Private Lands sub-committee, and in 1992 received the Cattle Businessman Award from the National Cattlemen's Foundation. One of their four sons, Toby, now manages the Collins Ranch.*

Meanwhile, the Texas and Southwestern Cattle Raisers Association (TSCRA) filled the gap with their attorney, Judge Joe G. Montague, who also spoke for ANCA.

That would all change after 1970 when C.W. (Bill) McMillan moved to Washington and became the executive vice president.

Financing the Association

In 1948, individual dues were two cents per head, $5 minimum.

In 1958, Executive Secretary Rad Hall reported that ANCA income had dropped every year since 1952 and that they had remained in the black only because volunteers had done most of the work and paid their own expenses. To keep going, dues were increased to seven cents per head with a minimum of $10 per year.

The Quintessential Lobbyist. *Judge Joe G. Montague, "The colorful judge in the black hat," was the watchdog of the cattle industry in Washington for 23 years. Six feet tall and 220 pounds, he emulated the cattleman when he walked down the street, through a hotel lobby, or down the halls of the nation's capitol. Already representing Texas cattlemen, he became the de facto lobbyist for ANLSA, later ANCA. A charismatic, cigar-smoking guy who personified the popular image of a lobbyist, Montague knew his way around Capitol Hill.*

He was also a firm believer in government by law rather than by proclamation, a philosophy cattlemen wished expressed to the post-war government in Washington. Mollin and Association leaders followed his lead and the informal arrangement worked well.

Here he is shown with one of the influential Texas cattlemen of the era, Bob Kleberg, Kingsville, TX.

A Champion of Beef Promotion. *Claude E. Olson, Ludlow, SD, was not only an enthusiastic supporter of youth programs, he was an avid promoter of beef. As president of the National Beef Council before its merger into the BIC in 1962, he filed suit against the USDA, major livestock exchanges, packers, the meat Board and others for blocking the 10-cent-per-head checkoff for beef promotion. There were seven bills introduced in Congress for a legislated checkoff during the period of the National Beef Council. None were passed.*

EXECUTIVE BUST

ARTIST: JERRY PALEN

BRONZE COMMISSIONED BY THE NATIONAL CATTLEMEN'S ASSOCIATION AND GIVEN TO RETIRING EXECUTIVES OF STATE AFFILIATE ORGANIZATIONS.

In the mid-1950s, the National Live-stock and Meat Board appointed a National Meat Promotion Committee "to coordinate beef, pork and lamb promotions." This program did not set well with cattlemen, who were suffering from the second worst drought in the century and a severely depressed cattle market.

When Jay Taylor of Texas became president of ANCA in 1954, he and other leaders called on the National Live Stock and Meat Board to step up beef promotion. But they were unsuccessful, even though Taylor had been Chairman of the Meat Board only two years earlier (1951-1953). The Meat Board held to its multi-species approach of promoting all red meat, not just beef. (*See pages 70 to 73.*)

At this point, disgruntled cattlemen decided to form the National Beef Council (NBC) to be financed by a national legislated checkoff.

Taylor was a great beef promoter and was impressed with the work of the newly formed state beef councils. He brought R.C. Pollock, general manager of the Meat Board, to the convention to talk about the potential of promotion with the new tool, television. Inspired by Pollack, attendees enthusiastically picked up beef promotion.

The NBC never did get a legislated checkoff. But although poorly funded, the NBC did get its message across to promote beef on its own. The Meat Board responded by appointing a Program and Policy Study Committee headed by John Marble and directed by Cornell University economist Harrell DeGraffe. Among their recommendations was that the Meat Board be divided into a Beef Committee, a Lamb Committee and a Pork Committee. This recommendation opened the door for a merger of the Beef Committee of the Meat Board and the NBC.

The Meat Board and the NCB then asked John B. Armstrong, head of the Alabama Beef Council, to chair a unified Beef Promotion Committee and seek a compromise. In 1963, under his leadership, the Beef Industry Council (BIC) of the National Live Stock and Meat Board was formed with Armstrong as its first chairman (1963-1969) and Donald E. Walker as secretary and staff executive.

Armstrong recalled that all was not peaceful in the beginning.

> *Members from both sides came to the same table but the hard feelings persisted. They would bicker about minutes of the last meeting—whether they did or did not reflect what really was said. So I ordered a mike to be put in front of each member to record everything said. It was amazing how that caused the more vocal ones to shut up.*

From its inception the BIC stood apart at the Meat Board, serving both as the national promotion arm of the beef industry and the headquarters of the federation of state beef councils.

The first-year budget was $40,000. Thirty years later, with checkoff funds, the budget was over $24 million. But in the early years, budgets never exceeded $100,000. The BIC was quick to find partners in its endeavors, however. That approach has remained part of its philosophy since. In its first year alone (1963), the BIC joined with the American Dairy Association on a "Buttered Barbecued Steak" promotion and the American National CowBelles in promoting "Beef for Father's Day." Also in 1963, a downer year in the cattle market, the BIC began its first television advertising.

During the 1960s, the state beef council movement begun in the 1950s continued to grow. By 1970, nine states had

Past Chairmen of the BIC

John B. Amstrong	1963-1969
William R. Brannan	1969-1970
J.C. Holbert	1970-1973
Peter E. Marble	1973-1974
Melvin O. Kuska	1974-1977
William G. Amstein, Jr.	1977-1979
James A. Mullins	1979-1981
Hilmar G. Moore	1981-1983
J. Richard Pringle	1983-1984
Donald D. Jackson	1984-1986
Patricia Adrian	1986-1988
Robert Rebholtz	1989-1990
Francis Gregerson	1991-1992
Raymond L. Larson	1992-1993
Ralph (Buck) Bell	1993-1994
L.R. (Ron) Curtis	1994-1996

The National Beef Council

Promotions Were Basic in 1959 *compared to the slick multi-million-dollar advertising campaigns of the 1990s. But it was an important start for these NBC members.*

While traveling in Montana, Jay Taylor made note of the new Montana Beef Council, which had a five-cents-per-head checkoff and whose secretary was C.T. (Tad) Sanders. *This program is so good, we need to take it national*, Taylor told Sanders. *If you will come run it, I'll raise the money and we'll form a National Beef Council (NBC).*

So in 1955, while still President of ANCA, Taylor initiated the setup of the National Beef Council and became its first president.

Sanders agreed to become Secretary-Treasurer and proposed that the headquarters be in Kansas City, the geographic center of the United States. Retorted Taylor,

> *No, you go to Chicago and rent office space at 407 South Dearborn Street (the address of the Meat Board). And make damn sure that you're a couple floors above the Meat Board.*

Sanders said later with a chuckle, *Jay somehow figured there was added prestige to being above the Meat Board.*

The NBC did headquarter above the Meat Board for a few months. Forest Noel of Lewistown, Montana, was the first executive director, followed by V.H. (Bud) Brandenburg of Boulder, Colorado. But after moving their headquarters to Kansas City in 1956, Sanders was the virtual head.

Then ANCA led the effort for a national legislated checkoff. Seven checkoff bills were introduced in Congress, but they were opposed (and killed) by the Meat Board and the American Farm Bureau Federation Federation, both of which favored promotion for all red meat as a group.

Hence the NBC attempted to make it on voluntary contributions of eight cents per head marketed, at the same time the Meat Board continued to collect two cents per head from producers through market agencies. By 1956, 17 state beef councils had been formed in support of the NBC. But the financial drain was too great for the leaders and the members. An industry split resulted and the NBC filed suit against the Meat Board and others.

The Beefeaters. *Mimicking the yeoman of the guard of a British monarch, these "beefeaters" are having fun during festivities at the annual meeting of the National Beef Council in Kansas City. Beneath his outsize authentic Beefeater's hat, Mayor H. Roe Bartle of Kansas City looks dubiously at the fit of the hat worn by Tad Sanders. (left to right) Forest Noel, Lewistown, MT, executive director of the National Beef Council; Ed Karlen, Columbia, SD, first vice president; the Mayor; Don L. Short, Medora, ND, president National Beef Council; and Sanders, Billings, MT, secretary-treasurer.*

Organizing A National Promotion Program. *John B. Armstrong, at the time an Alabama rancher and Chairman of the Alabama Beef Council, chaired the committee which led to the BIC in 1963. He later became president of the King Ranch in Texas, and remained one of the more active and influential people in the Association.*

legislated checkoff programs and seven states had voluntary programs. By 1969 they had raised $1.9 million, including more than $800,000 of the Meat Board's $1.4 million revenues for the year.

With the onslaught on the industry that occurred in the 1970s, the BIC, with a 1973 grant of $200,000 from the Texas Cattle Feeders Association, rushed to step up public relations for the industry. The advertising in major city newspapers of the East was impressive—at least to cattlemen—and more funds came in.

But by 1975, cattle numbers had reached a record 132 million, which kept the market depressed. Further, consumer activists had learned how to get attention in the media and in Congress and seemed relentless in their attacks on beef.

The BIC and cattlemen concluded that it was "time to get serious about marketing our product." In 1976, the BIC estimated that it needed $35 million to bring beef back. So the industry turned to a national beef checkoff in hopes of securing "real funds."

However, two defeats, including the second one in 1980 in which John Huston took a leave of absence from the BIC to work exclusively on the Beeferendum campaign, left them without the resources needed and beef continued to lose market share. The BIC turned to the states to get more resources and the states responded.

Jay Wardell became vice president/secretary of the BIC in 1980 and remained in that position until 1996 when he moved to Denver with NCBA.

Finding the Market, Getting the Share

JOHN L. HUSTON

Vice President/Secretary
Beef Industry Council
1969-1980

President
National Live Stock and Meat Board
1980-1996

Executive Vice President
NCBA Center for
Consumer Marketing
1996 - present

With a longer tenure than any other staff member at NCBA, John Huston is a name that is synonymous with beef promotion. He joined the beef industry team in 1967 as assistant secretary of the BIC, and was named vice president in 1969. In 1980 he was appointed president of the Meat Board and continued in that position until 1996 with the creation of NCBA, where he continues as vice president.

NCBA, now a consumer-driven, product-directed organization, is exactly the kind of organization Huston has been

working towards throughout his career. His goals are for NCBA to increase United States and international beef markets by

1. Identifying market segments and opportunities;
2. Defining needs and trends for each market segment;
3. Identifying and developing products to meet the needs of each segment;
4. Developing differential advantages over the competition.

With a budget of some $40 million in 1997, Huston uses about half the NCBA dollars in his program. His work is the most visible and often the most controversial. Consequently, he is not only accountable to the Association, but to the 1.2 million producers around the country who have their own opinions about campaigns, advertising and the way checkoff dollars should be spent.

A native of Roseville, Illinois, Huston grew up on a livestock and grain farm. He has a B.S. degree in Agricultural Education from the University of Illinois. Houston was inducted into the International Stockmen's Hall of Fame and has received many awards and honors throughout the industry.

Executive Officers of the BIC

Donald E. Walker 1963-1968

John L. Huston 1969-1980

Jay H. Wardell 1980-1996

The BIC went to work on marketing studies and by 1982 had laid out a $7 million plan in advertising and promotion aimed at reaching the top markets in the United States. With 35 state beef councils in place, the BIC continued forward, introducing more plans and conducting more studies to educate themselves and thus their industry. One of the major conclusions from this work was that producer acceptance of a national checkoff had become stronger and by 1985 the Cattlemen's Beef Promotion and Research Act providing for a national checkoff was passed. Checkoff collections started in 1986 and by the time the referendum passed in May 1988, the BIC had already launched some major campaigns including "Beef. Real Food for Real People" and a declaration that "Beef is Back."

In the 1990s "Beef. . .It's What's For Dinner" was one of the most successful campaigns ever; the results of the checkoff dollars spent in promotion were beginning to be seen.

In the organizational consolidation of 1996, the pork and lamb segments of the Meat Board were spun off, leaving the Meat Board with only its beef functions. The Meat Board then merged with NCA to form the National Cattlemen's Beef Association (NCBA).

The NCBA took over the duties of the former BIC and set up the Center for Consumer Marketing, which assumed responsibility for promotion, marketing and advertising. John Huston, former vice president/secretary of the BIC and former president of the Meat Board, became the executive vice president for that NCBA center.

The Greatest Sales Tool Ever Developed. *At the end of the 1954 ANSLA convention, R.C. Pollock, manager of the Meat Board, brought in a television and told an awestruck audience, who had literally never seen one, that this device was the future of advertising.*

State Beef Councils

One of the major factors that has contributed to the success of the beef industry was the start of state beef councils, which were more successful in collecting from cattlemen than the Meat Board had been.

Enthusiasm for state beef councils was spawned in the 1950s when Jay Taylor, then president of ANCA, put beef promotion at the top of his list of priorities. States were quick to see the possibilities of having their own beef councils backed by legislation for a state checkoff. By 1956 there were 17 state councils and by 1982, there were 35, including 22 that were legislated.

Under BIC organization, which included assuming the headquarters for the federation of state beef councils, a new relationship developed. The state beef councils invested large shares of receipts in national programs through the BIC. Drawing upon one another for expertise as well as funding, the state beef councils and the BIC have developed a lasting synergy.

Alabama Cattlemen's Association
Montgomery, AL
Founded 1955

Arizona Beef Council
Phoenix, AZ
Founded 1971

Arkansas Beef Council
Little Rock, AR
Founded 1983

California Beef Council
Pleasanton, CA
Founded 1954

Colorado Beef Council
Englewood, CO
Founded 1965

Delaware Beef Advisory Board
Dover, DE
Founded 1989

Florida Beef Council
Kissimmee, FL
Founded 1955

Georgia Beef Board
Macon, GA
Founded 1976

Hawaii Beef Industry Council
Ewa Beach, HI
Founded 1988

Idaho Beef Council
Boise, ID
Founded 1967

Illinois Beef Association
Springfield, IL
Founded 1963

Indiana Beef Council
Indianapolis, IN
Founded 1976

Iowa Beef Industry Council
Ames, IA
Founded 1970

Kansas Beef Council
Topeka, KS
Founded 1973

Kentucky Beef Council
Lexington, KY
Founded 1978

Louisiana Beef Industry Council
Port Allen, LA
Founded 1978

Maine Beef Industry Council
Augusta, ME
Founded 1988

Maryland Beef Industry Council
College Park, MD
Founded 1986

Michigan Beef Industry Commission
Okemos, MI
Founded 1972

Fear of State Councils. *Farm Bureau and others were skeptical about the direction the new enthusiastic state councils, such as the state beef councils, were taking. They saw them as a threat to the national control of the Meat Board. From* Farm Bureau News*, April 8, 1957.*

Minnesota Beef Council
Minneapolis, MN
Founded 1972

Mississippi Cattle Industry Board
Jackson, MS
Founded 1968

Missouri Beef Industry Council
Jefferson City, MO
Founded 1986

Montana Beef Council
Helena, MT
Founded 1954

Nebraska Beef Council
Kearney, NE
Founded 1970

Nevada Beef Council
Elko, NV
Founded 1971

New Jersey Beef Industry Council
Newton, NJ
Founded 1996

New Mexico Beef Council
Albuquerque, NM
Founded 1979

New York Beef Industry Council
Westmoreland, NY
Founded 1986

North Carolina Beef Council
Fuquay Varina, NC
Founded 1986

North Dakota Beef Commission
Bismarck, ND
Founded 1973

Ohio Beef Council
Marysville, OH
Founded 1970

Oklahoma Beef Industry Council
Oklahoma City, OK
Founded 1975

Oregon Beef Council
Portland, OR
Founded 1959

Pennsylvania Beef Council
Middletown, PA
Founded 1976

South Carolina Beef Board
Columbia, SC
Founded 1986

South Dakota Beef Industry Council
Pierre, SD
Founded 1964

Tennessee Beef Industry Council
Franklin, TN
Founded 1986

Texas Beef Council
Austin, TX
Founded 1986

Utah Beef Council
Salt Lake City, UT
Founded 1969

Vermont Beef Industry Council
Colchester, VT
Founded 1986

Virginia Cattle Industry Board
Daleville, VA
Founded 1965

Washington State Beef Commission
Seattle, WA
Founded 1969

West Virginia Beef Industry Council
Buckhannon, WV
Founded 1986

Wisconsin Beef Council
Madison, WI
Founded 1986

Wyoming Beef Council
Cheyenne, WY
Founded 1971

For eons, cattlewomen have stood "side by side" with cattlemen, sharing ownership and work, keeping records and running the operation when necessary.

In the beginning of the cattlemen's Association, few women participated in the Association or in programs for the industry. But that changed in 1939 when Mrs. Ralph Cowan of Douglas, Arizona, entertained a group of ranch women at a luncheon in her home to discuss how women could become more involved in the beef industry. That day and event marked the beginning of "The CowBelles."

In 1940, Wyoming was the first to organize Cowbelles on a statewide basis. By 1952, 10 state organizations had been formed. At the 1952 American National Cattlemen's Convention in Fort Worth, the women formalized the American National CowBelles (ANCB) and elected Mrs. Mary Louise Lynam of Burdett, Kansas, as the first president. Mrs. Ralph Cowan became the second national president in 1953. The first ANCB constitution contained as their mission "to assist the American National Cattlemen's Association (ANCA) in its efforts to promote the welfare of the livestock industry." The stage was set for unprecedented beef consumer education, promotion and grassroots legislative activities by cattlewomen—the people who never say "can't"

One of the early success stories of the organization was the ANCB legislative calling tree, created to affect legislation and agency activities for the benefit of the beef industry. Through letters, phone calls, faxes and now internet communications, members have influenced hundreds of bills and policies.

Beginning in 1974, with humble surroundings and a $2,000 budget, the CowBelles began the National Beef Cook-Off. It has grown to be one of the nation's most prestigious cooking events and is one of the great success stories for the ANCW.

The National Beef Cookoff is just one of the many ways ANCW have promoted

(inset) **The First Cowbelle.** *On October 17, 1939, Mrs. Ralph Cowan of Douglas, Arizona, invited 15 women to lunch and they formed an organization. She admitted later that part of her motivation was social, not just an effort for the beef industry. In those days, ranch women were fairly isoleted on the ranches, and this gave them a good excuse to meet! She later became the second national president in 1953.*

(above) **An Early Delegation of CowBelles** *at the Colorado Springs Meeting, 1955. (center) Mrs. O.W. Lynam, Burdett, Kansas, and (to her right) Mrs. Ralph Cowan, the first two national presidents.*

Getting out the News. *Mrs. Dorothy McDonald of San Diego, California, was the one in-house voice of the CowBelles in the 1950s and 1960s. She kept information flowing through her page in* THE AMERICAN CATTLE PRODUCER, *"Through a Ranch House Window."*

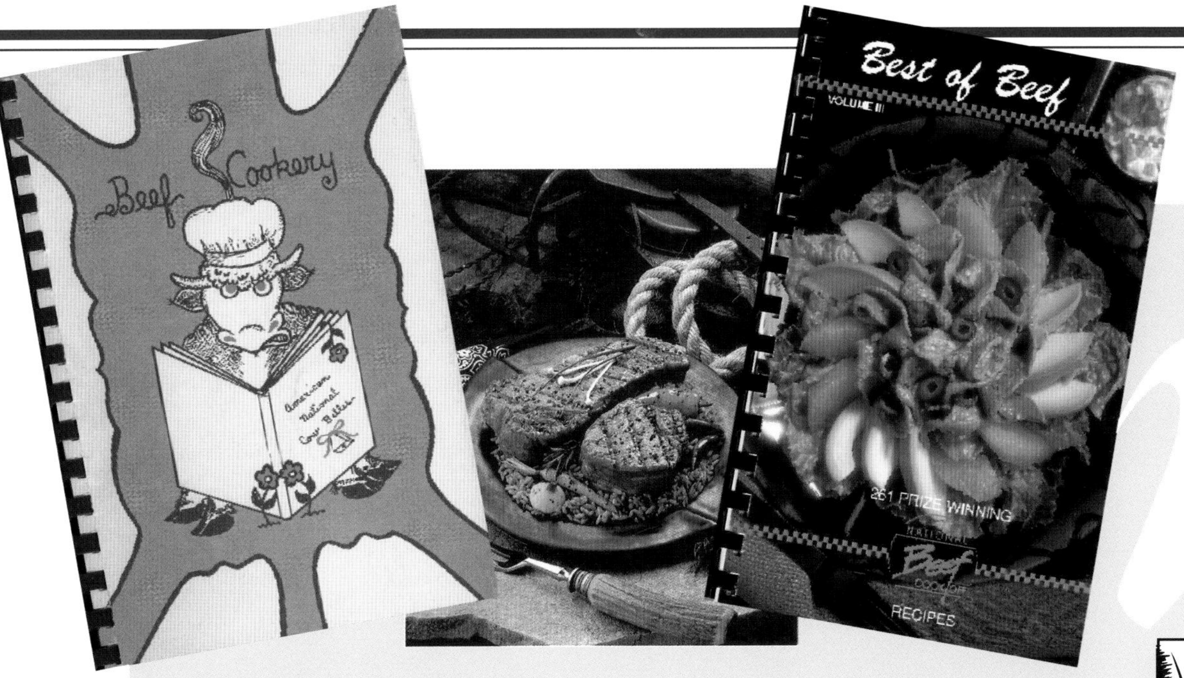

Beef Cookery *was the CowBelles first cookbook. At $2 a copy it sold more than 45,000 copies in its first year. Other ANCB cookbooks produced since that time were* Roundup of Beef Cookery, All Beef Cookbook *and Volumes I-III of* Best of Beef. *In 1993. Other cookbooks and recipes collections have been prepared over the years, such as the* 20th Anniversary of the National Beef Cook-Off *produced by the host state of Wyoming.*

Early CowBelle Promotions in the 1950s *positioned the ANCB very much as a woman's organization. As their work evolved, however, the ANCW became less gender specifc, but the work by women and directed to women remains at the core.*

beef. The CowBelles produced their first cookbook, Beef Cookery, in 1954, and more followed.

Additional promotion events developed and conducted by the organization's members have been Beef for Father's Day, launched in 1955; Beef Gift Certificates; Beef Shopping Guides, Ag in the Classroom, and Agriculture Day.

The National Beef Ambassador program began in 1988 as a vision of Codie Ray from Louisiana. Initially developed as a 4-H program, it has grown to provide opportunities for all young people to learn about the positive aspects of beef and beef production, and to share the beef industry's message with a variety of audiences. The 1994 winner, Monica Lyons of Louisiana, reached over five million people via personal appearances, radio, television and newspapers with the message that "Beef is versatile, convenient, nutritional and economical."

The American National CowBelles took a new direction in 1986, when its members voted to become the American National CattleWomen (ANCW) at their annual convention. In this way, CattleWomen addressed a new theme "Accept the Challenge of the Future." Since then, they have taken on a number of national programs such as Cattle Drive for Hunger, Project AgVenture, BEEF-ANCW, Collegiate CattleWomen and the Beef Dinner Solution Center. ANCW joined the new NCBA structure as an industry partner, and remains committed to fulfilling the mission of promoting and educating about beef.

Ambassadors of Beef. *Young people compete each year with their presentation on beef, including nutritional and economic values, cooking principles, versatile use of beef and to understand beef as an agricultural product. Grown from nine participants at its inception, today the program boasts over 30 participants each year.*

Beef for Father's Day, *begun in 1955, is still a popular program. State governors proclaim beef as the official Father's Day meal and advertising follows along. CowBelles also presented packages of beef to fathers of the first babies born each year. At a 1971 national promotion. (left to right) John Huston, BIC; Louise Wilson, ANCB; Clifford Hardin, secretary of agriculture; W.D. Farr, president of ANCA; and C.W. McMillan, ANCB executive vice president.*

Unprecedented Consumer Education. *With a force of thousands strong, ANCW has reached consumers at levels not otherwise approached: schools, country fairs, local clubs—just about anywhere. These women have truly been the grassroots promoters for the industry.*

Pamphlets, Brochures, Flyers and Booklets. *The ANCW has produced numerous colorful and educational materials to be distributed along with their presentations and wherever there is a need.*

PLATING IT SAFE
A Market-to-Mealtime Checklist to Help Keep Food Safe

20 Years of Success with The National Beef Cook-Off

The vision of the 1974 ANCB President, Irene Hoyt of Utah, was to conduct a national beef cooking contest. With the help of ANCA and Meat Board staffs, Hoyt and ANCB overcame extreme obstacles to stage the first Cook-Off, held in a Denver junior high school on October 5, 1974.

The National Beef Cook-Off (NBCO) has become one of the richest cook-offs in the nation, suppoted by the Beef Board, NCBA, and corporate contributors.

Recipes entered in the early cook-offs could use only the more economical cuts of beef from the chuck, round and brisket or ground beef. Entries were judged on appearance, practicality/ease of preparation, originality and taste.

Since, the NBCO has evolved greatly:

- Five honorable mention commendations, added in 1978, brought prize money up to $3,250.
- In 1979, funding from the BIC made it possible to include contestants from all 50 states and Washington, DC. The USMEF also sponsored a winner from Japan.
- First category change occurred in 1987, when NBCO was opened to all cuts of beef. The "Outdoor Barbecue" category was introduced and prize money escalated to $9,500.
- In 1988, total Cook-Off prize money more than tripled to $32,000, when the first "Best of Beef" overall winner was selected. The "Microwave" category was added and two special awards for "Best Beef Dish Under 300 calories" and "Most Convenient Beef Recipe" were given.
- Another special award was introduced in 1991— "Best Beef Recipe that Utilizes a Cut from the Chuck"—and prize winnings totaled $35,500. In 1992, the NBCO reached an all-time high with a $600,000 budget and sixty-four contestants from 50 states.
- In recent years, cash prizes have been enhanced by awards from TAPPAN® and KINGSFORD® with a top-of-the-line range and microwave oven, outdoor charcoal grills and a year's supply of charcoal.
- In 1993, the NBCO was streamlined to 15 contestants competing for more than $45,000 in prizes. Three new categories were added:
  - "Beef for Entertaining"
  - "Fast, Flavorful Beef"
  - "Budget-Wise Beef Entrees"

  The prize package totaled $39,000 including a $20,000 grand prize for the "Best of Beef" entry.

A selected state committee now hosts the competition every two years. The change from each year to every two years allows for a full year to market the winning recipes to consumers. The NBCO generates favorable publicity for beef worth millions of dollars. In 1995 alone, more than 29 milion impressions were made from local, state and national NBCO promotion activities.

Celebrity Status. *Beef spokesman James Garner was on hand at the 1987 National Beef Cook-Off in Sun Valley, Idaho, to congratulate winner Priscilla Yee of California. Garner, spokesperson for the "Beef. Real Food for Real People" campaign, also submitted his own favorite recipe to the Cook-Off!*

Ralston Crawford BUFFALO GRAIN ELEVATORS

A Land of Plenty

A new generation was born. They lived in a world of peace, abundance and prosperity. An inspired, confident generation, they looked upwards and contemplated space, and they set new standards for their own world. From this generation rose the all-powerful consumer. In a land of plentiful food, the consumer would demand new standards. Suddenly the cattle industry experienced a foe never anticipated. The consumer would tell producers what it would eat, at what price and when. This movement would decide the agenda of the Association for the remainder of the century.

CHAPTER EIGHT

The New Philosophy

The year 1960 signaled a turning point for ANCA. The country had a new president who represented a generation of Americans who saw the world in a completely different light from generations before. The country had grown more urban; it was at peace; and it was prospering. The Association, too, reflected a new era: it had a new executive and a new generation of leadership who would push the Association into uncharted waters.

Cattlemen had felt fairly secure during the Eisenhower presidency (1953-1960), when Ezra Taft Benson of Utah was Secretary of Agriculture. But they grew apprehensive when young John F. Kennedy was elected President and appointed Orville Freeman of Minnesota as Secretary of Agriculture. ANCA President Fred Dressler revealed cattlemen's reservations about JFK at the 1961 Convention in Salt Lake City:

> *He's going to need the help of the whole country to see that the whole country benefits. . .There is a period of confusion of ideals and objectives ahead, but this industry has proved that it can stand firm without compromising progress.*

C.W. (Bill) McMillan, the new executive secretary of ANCA (later to get the title of executive vice president), recognized the need for concerted effort in Washington and the opportunities that would bring. *One of the pressing needs,* he pronounced, *is to have someone in Washington to keep closer watch on legislative and administration developments.* He would repeat this need many times during the next 10 years, until the Association finally agreed to move him to Washington as its first full-time lobbyist. But, for the time being, the Association relied on another lobbyist. McMillan explained later:

TIMELINE

1959 Alaska becomes 49th state.

Hawaii becomes 50th state.

First National Finals Rodeo.

1960 Transportation shifts from rail to trucks; slaughter operations built near feedlots rather than stockyards.

1961 John F. Kennedy inaugurated as 35th President.

Peace Corps inaugurated.

1962 Rachel Carson's book, *Silent Spring*, warns of dangers of pesticides, begins environmental movement.

John Glenn becomes first American to orbit the Earth.

1963 Post office introduces ZIP code, first-class mail goes from three to five cents.

Lyndon B. Johnson becomes 36th President after Kennedy assassinated.

Supreme Court bans prayer and Bible reading in public schools.

1964 Chicago Mercantile Exchange (CME) offers first live cattle contract.

Food Stamp program started.

Beginning of Vietnam War.

1965 Medicare initiated, provides medical care for elderly.

1966 National Organization for Women (NOW) formed with objective of equal pay and representation.

Screwworms eradicated in the United States.

Beef boycotts begin in Denver.

1967 First football Super Bowl.

Boxed beef introduced.

1968 Beef Improvement Federation formed.

McDonalds introduces "Big Mac."

Cattle-Fax created by ANCA.

1969 First manned landing on the moon by United States astronauts Neil Armstrong and Edwin Aldrin.

Richard Nixon becomes 37th President.

ISSUES

Import Quotas
•
Beef Export Efforts
•
Pricing Beef
•
Consumer Demands
•
New Distribution Methods
•
Government Programs
•
Management Studies

For the past two decades, most of the lobbying for cattlemen had been done by Judge Joe G. Montague and he did it well. He was on the payroll of the Texas and Southwestern Cattle Raisers Association and represented ANCA gratis. The Judge soon decided that I had potential, so he showed me the ropes and retired in a couple years.

The affable McMillan came to ANCA from Swift & Co., where he worked in producer relations and had become well-known and well-liked by cattlemen. But hiring "a packer man" to head up a cattlemen's association was incredible to some cattlemen. Some snarled, *The packers will have a spy within our ranks.* In those Cold War days, "spy" was a scurrilous word. But McMillan's roots were really in cattle country. He was reared in Colorado, graduated from Colorado A&M College, and had worked as a county agent. He soon won over the detractors.

SUBSIDIES AGAIN REJECTED

Under the Kennedy Administration, one of the early proposals by Secretary of Agriculture Orville Freeman was "supply management" for cattle. Thus, production controls, marketing orders and subsidies would elevate prices to 90 percent of parity. Freeman was hand in glove with the National Farmers Union, which advocated subsidies and supply management for all commodities. This pitted ANCA in

Sleeping in the Lincoln Bedroom. *Not since Murdo Mackenzie and Teddy Roosevelt had there been such a close relationship between the Association and the United States President and such access to the White House as there was with Jay Taylor and President Lyndon Johnson. When Johnson became president in 1963, he admonished Taylor: "Jay, when you come to Washington, you have a bedroom waiting for you in the White House—regardless of the hour you arrive—and I don't want to hear of you renting a hotel room." Other ranchers were also welcome at the White House because Johnson considered himself one of them and loved to talk Hereford cattle.*

BEHIND THE SCENES

C.W. (BILL) McMILLAN

EXECUTIVE VICE PRESIDENT
1959-1970
EXECUTIVE VICE PRESIDENT - WASHINGTON AFFAIRS
1970-1981

During his 22 years with ANCA and NCA, Bill McMillan became known as "the most effective agricultural lobbyist in Washington."

A native of Colorado and a graduate of Colorado A&M, his career began as a County Extension Agent for six years. He then joined Swift & Co., where he spent five years in producer relations and became well known by ANCA leaders. With an outgoing personality and remarkable memory for names, he was a natural for ANCA, except for one thing: he was "a packer man" and many cattlemen just did not trust packers.

Nevertheless, he was hired in 1959 as the chief executive in Denver. But imports, water rights, taxes, grazing fees and other issues were becoming so urgent, McMillan spent half his time in Washington. Association officers soon recognized his talents for lobbying and in 1970 moved him there to become the first full-time industry lobbyist. His title in Washington initially was Executive Vice President-Washington Affairs, changed in 1978 to Vice President of Washington Affairs.

As a familiar figure around the capitol, he soon became an insider and knew most of the influential congressmen and senators on a first name basis. They liked his ready smile, his affable manner, and his reliability. His effectiveness amazed visiting cattlemen.

But McMillan is the first to admit that his effectiveness came from the use of affiliate associations and grassroots cattlemen. *They were the best lobbyists of all*, he declared.

After arranging trade teams to Europe, Japan and other Pacific nations, he became enthused about the potential for beef exports. So in 1975, he became co-founder of the United States Meat Export Federation and was elected its first chairman. *This probably was my greatest contribution,* he says upon watching the value of exported beef increase from $70 million in 1976 to $2.4 billion in 1996.

In 1981, McMillan left NCA to become Assistant Secretary of Agriculture for Marketing and Inspection Services. It was a position that elated cattlemen. After four years as Assistant Secretary—the first Association official to hold a high government post—he resigned and became a private consultant for agribusiness companies.

---

a running battle with the Farmers Union, and with Secretary Freeman. The Secretary once threatened ANCA, *If the farm bill fails, cattle prices will plunge 38 percent or $8 per cwt.*

Unfazed by such innuendoes, ANCA President Dressler and others asked the House Agriculture Committee to

> *delete from HR 6400 all provisions that would bring the beef cattle industry under any form of production or marketing controls, subsidies or compensatory payments. We do not believe that planned scarcity and artificial prices are in the best interest of our customers, the consuming public.*

SUBSIDIES VERSUS IMPORTS

While against a price subsidy, ANCA was not totally opposed to government help. So they pursued another route: legislated curbs on imported beef (uncooked beef: fresh, chilled or frozen). Some opponents labeled this a subsidy, which ANCA denied vigorously, maintaining the tariff was "protection against unfair competition."

The Association appeared before the United States Tariff Commission seeking relief. It was pointed out that from 1956 to 1959 imports increased 560 percent to 742 million pounds and depressed live cattle prices $1.50 to $2 per cwt. The proposed solution was to restore the

The Consumer Vigil

With their withholding of livestock from slaughter in an effort to boost prices, the National Farmers Organization (NFO) did capture national headlines. But their efforts provoked the watchdog consumer. NFO's claims of higher prices from withholding confirmed what the assertive consumer activists already believed—that farmers and cattlemen were intentionally jacking up food prices.

Always alert to consumers' emotions, some politicians fanned the fire. President Johnson named Betty Furness, a New York television personality, as the White House Consumer Affairs Specialist and appointed a National Commission on Food and Fiber to investigate and report the facts of the matter. Again, he called on his friend Jay Taylor, former ANCA president, to represent cattlemen on the Commission.

Congress then appointed a National Commission on Food Marketing. Former ANLSA President Albert K. Mitchell represented cattlemen on this commission.

The final report of the National Commission on Food Marketing (June 1966) showed, as cattlemen suspected, that consumers were faring better that year than any time in history. Purchasing power of income per person, after taxes, had increased nearly 50 percent in five years. The number of hours of work to feed a family for a year had dropped from 700 in 1947 to 400 in 1965. The percent of disposable income spent on food had dropped from 25 percent in 1947 to 18

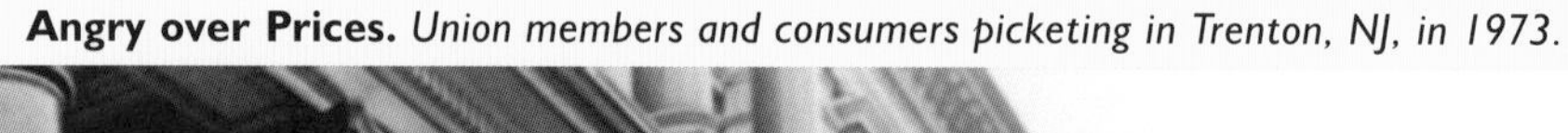

Angry over Prices. *Union members and consumers picketing in Trenton, NJ, in 1973.*

percent in 1965. This trend continued downward, to 11 percent in 1993.

Unimpressed, consumers were more concerned about inflation, which had increased five percent from the previous year and up 25 percent from 1948.

Consumer boycotts began to pop up like weeds in a corn field. They started in Denver, and they targeted food prices. Consumers lashed out at chain stores for boosting prices with *green stamps, games and gimmicks*. When the chains explained that their average net was only 1.5 percent of sales and farmers explained that they received only six percent of the food dollar, the boycott leaders switched their venom to the illusive "middle men."

Cattlemen also expressed a distaste for the gimmicks; some even objected to beef being used as a loss leader. Two cattle feeders, Paul Ganz of Arizona and Don Hamil of Colorado, attended the food chain convention in Florida and told them:

> *The pricing methods used in specials has created great confusion among consumers over the actual value of beef products.* [However, in later years, during times of low cattle prices, cattle industry leaders would call on chain stores to feature more beef in specials or otherwise.]

Amid such confusion and debates, consumer organizations were spreading across the country, many with the organizational help of the AFL-CIO. By 1967, there were 16 state organizations, most affiliated with a national organization, and scores of city associations.

Consumer Boycotts

The price freeze, intended to appease angry consumers, did little to check their boycotts. Thousands of women in scores of cities demonstrated, paraded, picketed, pamphleteered and badgered politicians. Cattlemen, who had so much difficulty organizing, were stunned that consumers could organize so well, so quickly, get so much publicity and be so effective.

In general, the protesters were liberal, anti-business and pro-government, meaning they favored more regulations. Often they were supported by unions and guided by experienced union organizers.

Inflation and escalating food prices were their concerns, but beef was their target. They considered beef the "King of Meats," and they thought they were being ripped off by *cattlemen who drive Cadillacs*.

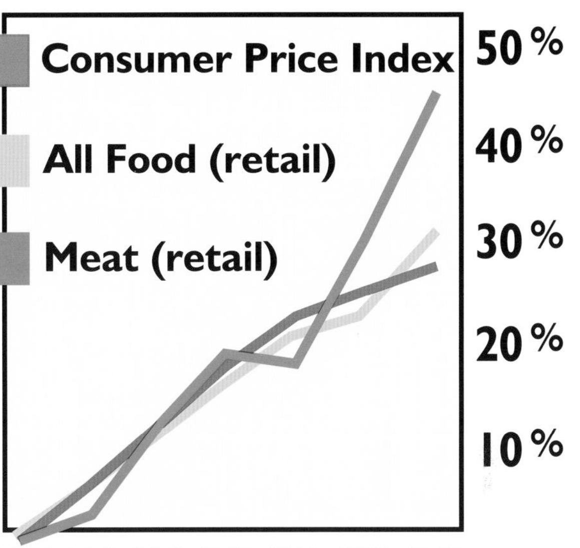

"If you have to ask 'how much', you can't afford one!"

Some of the anti-meat groups that sprung up were affiliated with a national or state organization, others were independent locals. Among the more creative names: FIT (Fight Inflation Together); STOP (Stop These Outrageous Prices); WASP (Women Against Soaring Prices); SCRIMP (Save Cash, Reduce Immediately Meat Prices); LAMP (Ladies Against Meat Prices); and UPD (Until Prices Drop).

From this era forward, the beef industry would be forever changed. The watchdog consumer had become all powerful. Whereas the industry had traditionally given consumers the kind of beef it felt was appropriate as well as when and at what price, the consumer would now dictate to the industry.

G.R. (JACK) MILBURN
President 1958-1959
Grassrange, Montana

In 1916, with a civil engineering degree from Montana State College, Milburn trained in the French Air Force and was a pilot with the American Expeditionary Forces during World War I. Back in Montana, he became a prominent Angus breeder. With 1,000 head of Angus—all purebred and 250 registered—he regularly topped the feeder calf market and enjoyed a strong demand for breeding animals. He also served on the boards of the Federal Reserve Bank and Montana Power Company, and was a veteran school board member.

tariff to its original six cents per pound, from three cents that had been established in 1948, and to establish import quotas in absolute terms or as a percent of domestic production.

This was the first proposal ever for import quotas—for any product—and it met much opposition in the years ahead. Thus, the Association would write a number of editorials and its leaders would make many speeches defending their idea of protectionism and denying that a quota was a veiled subsidy.

Imports continued to increase, reaching a record 11 percent of domestic production in 1963. So ANCA worked mightily to get legislated relief. In January 1964, ANCA President Radebaugh of Florida and Executive Vice President McMillan presented some convincing facts to the House Agriculture Committee:

1. The cattle industry in the United States had experienced tremendous growth, from 77 million head in 1948 to 107 million head in 1964.
2. The existing tariff (initially six cents per pound in 1930 but reduced to three cents in 1948) would have to be increased 550 percent to be as effective as the original six cents in 1930.
3. Imports had increased from 3.9 percent of domestic production in 1957 to 11 percent in 1963, depressing domestic prices $3 to $4 per cwt.
4. The value of beef imports in 1963 was 12 times the value of beef exports.

OMAHA WORLD-HERALD "Now what?"

THE STOCKMAN'S JOURNAL

At the 1964 Convention in Memphis, Radebaugh reinforced the case for quotas:

Stockmen recognize that other nations must trade with the United States in order that our export industry remains healthy. We also recognize that tariffs alone will not stem the tide of those who can raise cattle at a fraction of the cost here. In some countries, land costs only 11 cents per head per year, compared with $25 per head here in the U.S. for land, taxes and upkeep.

FRED H. DRESSLER
President 1960-1961
Gardnerville, Nevada

He became President of ANCA on the 100th Anniversary of the family ranch. He was the third Frederick to manage it, and two more Fredericks followed. From a cow herd of 1,300 head, including 300 registered Herefords, only 100 breeding bulls and slaughter animals were sold; the others were fed out and shipped directly to slaughter. Fred served 26 years on the local school board and also on the boards of the American Hereford Association and the Cowboy Hall of Fame. His wife, Anna, was the 1956 President of American National CowBelles.

HAMBURGERS IN HAMBURG

President Lyndon B. Johnson, who had become president the year before, opposed the idea of quotas. While he had empathy for cattlemen when prices dropped, being a cattleman himself, he believed the problem to be overproduction, rather than imports. [Like most presidents, before and since, Johnson felt that trade matters should be the prerogative of the president, not Congress.] So to divert the ANCA drive for quotas, he sent a Presidential Trade Mission to Europe on a White House plane to explore the potential for export markets.

To lead the mission, Johnson called on his old friend, Jay Taylor, the former president of ANCA. Others included Kenneth Anderson of Kansas; Aled B. Davies, vice president of the American Meat Institute; John Guthrie, first vice president of ANCA; Bill McMillan, executive vice president of ANCA; Don Magdanz, secretary of the National Livestock Feeders Association; and two USDA officials.

For two weeks, they toured England, Italy, France, the Netherlands and West Germany, calling on officials of the government and meat trade. Upon return, they reported back, with some trepidation, *a current interest in United States beef, due to a shortage of beef and high prices in Europe.* But they saw no long-term potential, because of high freight rates, a lack of refrigerated ships with rails to hang carcasses, competition from South America, and other complications. Also, there was nobody to develop the market

CONSERVATIVE CATTLEMEN

Always conservative, the Association passed scores of resolutions through the years in support of free enterprise and against big government. The following, passed by the Association in 1950 in Miami and reaffirmed in 1965 in Portland, is one example.

There impends today a threat to our country and the freedom of its citizens which so menacingly overshadows the future that we, American cattlemen of all shades of political belief, feel it our duty to speak out in unmistakable terms.

This threat lies in the fact that our country—without conscious choice on the part of its people—is rapidly and unmistakably drifting toward the consummation of a false concept—the socialized state. . . .

Government produces nothing and has no means by which to support these false and destructive theories except by exacting from its citizens the fruits of their labors. . . .

THEREFORE, BE IT RESOLVED, that we. . .reaffirm our solemn conviction that the future health, strength and prosperity of our country depend upon the re-establishment and maintenance of free and competitive enterprise and hereby pledge ourselves as individuals and as an association to work diligently and actively toward this objective and toward the defeat of the fallacious philosophies that are beguiling our country into socialism.

Dr. Irving P. Krick, *who became widely known after forecasting a break in the weather for the D-Day invasion of Europe, became a long-range weather forecaster for Cattle-Fax briefly in the mid-1960s. He was also an early advocate of cloud seeding to enhance rainfall.*

except government agricultural attaches. [It would be another 22 years before the United States Meat Export Federation was organized.]

So there were no apparent results from the Mission, which left President Johnson less than happy, so much so that he promised to veto a quota bill *if the Congress is dumb enough to pass it.* But compared to the Vietnam War, the problem of meat imports was a relatively minor one.

Whether or not there were big potential markets, Jay Taylor loved to tell about the Mission Team introducing hamburgers to Hamburg, Germany. *They never heard of hamburgers,* he chuckled, *but they loved 'em.*

So ANCA continued their lobbying efforts and, later in the year, Congress passed the Meat Import Act of 1964 and President Johnson grudgingly signed it. This new approach to dealing with imports (quotas) contained a formula limiting imports to 6.7 percent of domestic production. It was another major victory for the Association, perhaps the greatest since the Packers and Stockyards Act of 1921.

McMillan related 30 years later:

> *We discovered the "magic lobbying power" of the Association, magic that would be used again and again in the following years. The magic was in our ability to do grassroots lobbying, through the state affiliates. Our structure and our technique was unique, and it worked.*

No Price, No Production

For the country and the cattlemen, the 1960s were strenuous years. There were protests of various kinds; campus riots; the assassination of President Kennedy and his brother, Attorney General Robert Kennedy; the Vietnam War, longest war in our history; and civil rights marches. Even with plummeting cattle prices, consumers were protesting food prices, and farmers and ranchers were frustrated. There was the "confusion of ideals and objectives" that ANCA President Dressler had predicted in 1961.

The new National Farmers Organization (NFO) was started in Corning, Iowa. Although they claimed to have started in 1955, few people had heard of NFO until 1962. With organizational help, and suspected financial help, from the AFL-CIO, the NFO advocated higher prices through collective bargaining. With several thousand membership agreements, mostly in the Midwest, they sought master contracts with packers and other processors of cattle, hogs, grain and milk. These aligned processors were to check off at least one percent of the gross sale for the NFO and in some situations up to eight percent.

> ***We do not believe that planned scarcity and artificial prices are in the best interest of our customers, the consuming public.***
>
> —ANCA President Dressler
> *Addressing the House Agricultural Committee*

"No price, no production" was the NFO motto. At a time when choice steers were selling for $25 to $28, the NFO was demanding $32. NFO was determined to withhold livestock from the market until their price demands were met.

Spending Tax Dollars on Beef

While the Association traditionally opposed big social programs and deficit spending, they did support some government programs without reservation. Food stamps and school lunches were among the most beneficial to cattlemen.

Food Stamps

President Kennedy began the experiment in food stamps, initially in eight counties in 1962. In its early years, the Food Stamp Program operated along side the far larger surplus commodity program, which served seven million persons. It was considered a success, so in 1964 President Johnson pushed through Congress the Food Stamp Act leaving behind the experimental status of the program.

The Food Stamp Act had dual objectives: first, to improve the nutritional levels of low-income persons; and second, to expand the demand for farm products by utilizing abundant food supplies.

The Food Stamp Program proliferated and by 1975 became the subject of much controversy in Congress, in the media and with the public. One reason for the controversy was the $6 billion price tag, which accounted for over half of the United States Department of Agriculture (USDA) budget. Another reason, over 19 million people were drawing food stamps and 30 percent of these were on three or more additional assistance programs. On top of these reasons, there were reports of widespread fraud and abuse.

The program created a dilemma for cattlemen. While they abhorred the cost, food stamps did help move a lot of meat—nearly $1 billion of red meat in 1975. [By 1994, the number of food stamp recipients had surpassed 27 million and the total appropriation exceeded $27 billion. Of this total, USDA estimated that in 1994 approximately $3 billion was expended on beef.]

Free Lunches, Huge Markets

Through the years, when there was economic pressure from an over-supply of cattle, the Association was never bashful about asking the government to step up purchases of beef, especially for the military, school lunch programs and the like.

The school lunch program, which gained permanent status in 1946, grew in the number of children participating to 18.9 million in 1967-1968, or 37 percent of the national enrollment. Federal support in cash payments grew to over $160 million, plus nearly $276 million in donated commodities.

At a White House Conference on Food, Nutrition and Health in 1969, several panels recommended that every school child should have a lunch available to him or her, and in some cases a free lunch should be provided. Accordingly, by 1989, the Federal budget for lunch programs was $4.5 billion. But the program is bigger than that! Counting state matching funds and what some students pay themselves, the total school food service is a $10 billion program, representing 10 percent of all food purchased away from home.

Why do cattlemen go along with a program like that? For the 1984-1985 school year (the last year figures were available), the USDA estimated that 11 percent of the total was spent for beef.

U.S. DEPARTMENT OF AGRICULTURE
FOOD COUPON
A34786043N
DO NOT FOLD
OR SPINDLE
J
VALUE
1
DOLLAR
DECLARATION
OF INDEPENDENCE
SERIES
1994
B
NON-TRANSFERABLE
EXCEPT UNDER CONDITIONS PRESCRIBED BY THE SECRETARY OF AGRICULTURE
C9
333

CUSHMAN RADEBAUGH
President 1962-1963
Orlando, Florida

The first person east of the Mississippi to become Association president, Radebaugh was a native of Tennessee and got to Florida by way of Texas where he punched cattle for several years. "The big issue during my term," he once recalled, "was the all-out assault on our markets by New Zealand and Australian cattle producers." Imports in 1963 reached 11 percent of domestic production. "Tariffs will not stem the tide—only quotas will," he declared in support of the Meat Import Act of 1964.

The first major withholding started on Labor Day, 1962. Checkpoints were set up on highways to stop trucks hauling livestock. Many non-members were sympathetic with the objectives; but after reports of violence, some non-members were afraid to move livestock. So the number of cattle and hogs delivered to markets went down significantly, for a week or two, and prices did increase in the meat markets. In protest, supermarkets raised beef prices and featured other sources of protein.

While the NFO boasted their success in the short-term, the withholding was not feasible in the long-term for several reasons:

1. Not all farmers participated, and those who did not benefited at the expense of those who did.
2. Cattle and hogs diminished in value when held beyond their finished date.
3. Major packers refused to sign the master contract, saying it would be in violation of anti-trust laws.
4. Cattle held back one week would then glut the market the following week or whenever they went.
5. Retailers substituted other proteins for meat when meat prices escalated.

Throughout the NFO withholding actions, which ended in 1968, the ANCA blasted the approach and publicly denied any connection with it.

At the 1967 Convention in Colorado Springs, however, ANCA invited NFO President Oren Lee Staley to appear on the program. ANCA and NFO seemed like an odd couple, but Staley was a proven crowd drawer. In his opening statement to a roomful of curious cattlemen, Staley exclaimed:

> *There is one problem in American agriculture—prices! Farmers have lived in hope, planted in faith and sold on charity, while everyone else is economically organized. Our program involved not only economics but a principle, too. The principle was that farmers must put a price tag on their products. . . .The holding action is only used for the purpose of establishing bargaining power.*

POSITIVE SOLUTIONS

After several years on the defensive, ANCA decided in 1967 to pursue some boot-straps solutions and go on the offensive. ANCA President John Guthrie appointed a Market Development Committee, led by Co-Chairmen Joe Entz of Arizona and Girdner Crofoot of Kansas, who devised a two-pronged plan:

- A Guidelines Program for cattlemen to voluntarily get supply in line with demand.
- An Association-controlled market information service later known as Cattle-Fax.

The Guidelines Program, which was to involve all cattlemen and help all cattlemen, was promoted vigorously in speeches, newsletters, magazine articles and special publications. Its first call was for cattlemen to market all fed cattle at lower weights (thereby reducing tonnage), and slow down the increase in cow herds by culling stringently.

Cattle-Fax was set up to boost prices at the feedyard, with promises of trickle-down benefits to the cow-calf producer. It was operated by a separate corporation, Cattle Market Information Service (CMIS), under Staff Economist Bill Helming. Topper Thorpe, first market analyst, later became manager.

These two self-help programs were immensely successful, but they did not stop the beef boycotts or the grand-standing by politicians. ANCA made the headlines in 1969 when two congressmen called for a Justice Department investigation into possible violation of restraint of trade and an illegal conspiracy by ANCA, *which may be partially responsible for recent increases in retail beef prices.*

Shortly thereafter, Mayor John Lindsay of New York City wrote to New York congressmen urging repeal of the Meat Import Act, *which is keeping the price of meat artificially high and insures inflated profit for the nation's ranchers.* He blamed the "arrogant" ANCA.

BROOKS J. KEOGH
President 1964-1965
Keene, North Dakota

A tall Irish redhead, Keogh served in the marines during World War II. He returned to North Dakota to raise purebred Herefords and fine Quarter Horses. There he was president of the Stockmen's Association and the Grazing Association; he also served on the Livestock Sanitary Board and the Farm Bureau. He helped push through the Meat Import Act of 1964, which limited beef imports to 7.5 percent of domestic production.

Government Spending Spree

Ever since President Roosevelt's social programs of the 1930s, which has been presented to taxpayers as both experimental and also temporary, the Association had been concerned about irresponsible government spending. Now their "concern" had grown to "alarm." They noted that:

- Over the previous 50 years, the population had increased 100 percent, but state and local government budgets had increased 2,000 percent and the federal budget had zoomed 13,000 percent.
- From 1945 to 1961, tax income to the federal government had increased over 1,600 percent, from $4.9 billion to $84 billion.
- The first income tax in 1913 was one percent on income over $4,000; in 1932 it was four percent; and by 1965 it was 15 percent. (In 1953, the top bracket was 92 percent; in 1994, 39 percent.)

The Number One resolution at the 1962 Convention in Tampa was *to reaffirm our position of insisting upon economy in government and all its branches.*

Again, the main resolution at the 1963 Convention in Las Vegas said the Association

> *feels compelled to alert the public and our government officials to the fact that our government cannot safely continue its lavish spending of tax dollars. . .which can finally lead to chaos.*

JOHN H. GUTHRIE
President 1966-1967
Porterville, California

Rancher, farmer and cattle feeder, he was the only man to be President of both the California Cattlemen's Association and California Cattle Feeders Association. His wife, Marian, was 1954 President of American National CowBelles. While consumers were boycotting and NFO farmers were withholding, he appointed a Market Development Committee to develop self-help programs for cattlemen, one of which became Cattle-Fax.

The following year, 1964, President Johnson—not to be outdone by Presidents Kennedy and Roosevelt—announced his own social program, the "War on Poverty." During the 30 years to follow, the nation would spend over $5 trillion on impoverished Americans. Some folks still question whether poverty was reduced at all.

Ace Reid (ca. 1957)
"No, he didn't strike oil, he just put his whole place in the soil bank."

Beef Improvement Payoff

Legislative policy and marketing consistently dominated the Association agenda through the years, but the Association also was consistent in encouraging production efficiency in purebred bulls, better nutrition, animal health, and other issues important to continuing the development of the quality of beef.

In 1961, ANCA co-sponsored, with the American Society of Animal Science, a Coordinated Beef Improvement Conference at Colorado State University. It was heralded a great success and, thus, was repeated throughout the sixties at various land grant universities.

Such emphasis, along with the attention given to efficiency by experiment stations, Extension Services and the USDA, caused an impressive increase in beef production per cow: from 184 pounds in 1930 to 444 pounds in 1970. (This trend would continue, reaching 550 pounds of beef per cow in 1994.)

PLC, A New Organization

The sixties spelled uncertainty for public lands permittees, triggered by President Kennedy's appointment of Stewart Udall as Secretary of Interior (1961-1968). Udall made no bones about his feelings: grazing fees were too low and stockmen had too much influence in public lands policy.

So in 1968, they put together another private organization, the Public Lands Council (PLC). Harry Lee of New Mexico was the first president; Dave Rice, executive of the Colorado Cattlemen's Association, was the first secretary (for 22 years); Joe Tudor, a former attorney for Interior and an expert on the Taylor Grazing Act, was the first counsel. To finance the new organization, they asked all permittees to pay an assessment (not all did) of five cents per permitted animal unit month (AUM).

Buying Beef Gets Easier

The demands of consumers and new developments in the industry were changing the way beef was distributed and sold. But no two innovations were to have as long-lasting effect on the industry as were boxed beef and self-serve meat counters.

Beef In A Box

As the new independent beef packers began to build modern one-story plants near the developing cattle feeding areas and away from terminal markets, they introduced efficiencies that the old-line packers could not match. The concept of boxed beef had first been introduced as early as 1966 by Swift & Co. in Chicago, but they had boxed only primals, packaged the cuts in waxed paper and injected the packages with carbon dioxide.

Now the packers were breaking down the carcass into smaller portions, vacuum-packing the cuts in plastic and shipping them in boxes weighing approximately 60 pounds. Iowa Beef Processors (IBP) was first to cut up the whole carcass, inject ammonia and seal the cuts in Cryovac barrier bags. MBPXL and others followed quickly. Monfort of Colorado, keenly aware of the need of specific markets such as restaurants, was a leader in that marketplace. But all the packers generally agree they came forward with the boxed product at about the same moment.

The efficiencies and the savings were enormous. It sounds simple now, but prior to this time, the packer only slaughtered and dressed the animal, then shipped hanging half-carcasses (weighing 300-350 pounds, typically) to wholesalers or retailers, who broke them down into smaller portions. If a retailer had a greater need, say for sirloin, he still had to order the carcass and carry the other cuts.

Specific Cuts for Specific Markets. *Boxed Beef was one of the major innovations of the packing industry. Retailers, restaurateurs and others could get exactly what they needed without the waste of carrying the whole carcass.*

Boxed beef was also butcher friendly. It eliminated from each carcass 250 pounds or so of fat, bones and trimmings, which were of little value to the retail and food service customer.

At the same time, it eliminated many brokers, wholesalers and butchers, enough to attract the wrath of labor unions. Unions struck the main IBP plant at Dakota City, Iowa.

The unions also refused to let boxed beef into New York City, the largest meat market in the world, until IBP paid the union mafia—almost $1 million during 1970-1972—for which they were later indicted. A decade later, boxed beef became the standard of the trade and all major packers were boxing.

Self-Serve Meat Counters

A similar new efficiency, which was gaining popularity during the early sixties, was individual packages of meat wrapped in plastic trays and displayed in open, self-serve meat counters. The unions loathed this innovation, too, claiming it was necessary to have a union meat cutter on duty to service the fresh meat section.

Accordingly, seven unions, all local affiliates of the Amalgamated Meat Cutters and Butcher Workmen of North America, AFL-CIO, forced (under duress of a strike vote) 9,000 Chicago meat retailers into a contract which limited the hours beef could be sold, even if the stores were open longer. Jewel Tea Company, the third largest food retailer in the nation, signed the contract but sued the unions for restraint of trade. This became known as "The Chicago Meat Case." (*See page 169.*)

The Association treaded lightly on this issue, because other retailers in the Chicago area were involved, several on each side. But they did express concern with a resolution at the 1965 Convention in Portland, which said, *such union restrictions could be recognized as an interference to free trade and to the detriment of the consumer and the producer.*

BILL HOUSE
President 1968-1969
Cedar Vale, Kansas

A lawyer by training, a Hereford breeder by trade and an articulate spokesman for the industry, House was the first president on record to propose a merger with the National Livestock Feeders Association. Other firsts during his tenure: conventions in Honolulu and Washington, DC, neither of which have been repeated. But Cattle-Fax, which he helped initiate, has persisted. He was President of two ANCA affiliates: American Hereford Association and Kansas Livestock Association.

In addition, they solicited financial and staff help from ANCA, the National Wool Growers Association (now American Sheep Industry Association) and the National Grasslands Association. Each of the 13 public lands states has four voting delegates, including one on the Board of Directors. By 1994, the PLC had a staff of three and an annual budget of $220,000. While proclaiming autonomy, the Council shares offices with NCBA in Washington and is closely linked to the NCBA Federal Lands Committee.

Association Briefs

A few other developments about which the Association was concerned and in some cases involved:

- A system of dual grading, to reflect cutability, was recommended by ANCA leaders in 1960, and was offered by USDA in 1962.
- Cattle Futures Trading on the Chicago Mercantile Exchange (CME) began in 1964. Two decades later, they became so controversial that an NCA Futures Task Force was appointed in 1987 to study their impact on the industry.
- ProTen, a patented meat tenderizing process that injected enzymes from the tropical papaya fruit into the circulatory system of animals before slaughter, was offered in 1961 by Swift & Co. It offered great promise for a few years but did not prevail.
- Catt-L-Caps, often referred to by the press as "false teeth for cows," was introduced in 1963 by a Colorado firm. They offered to extend the useful life of a cow several years, but apparently the cows did not buy them.

Health of the Association

Two times in its history, the Association has had outside management studies, first in 1967 and again in 1983, each of which had lasting impact on the organization.

The 1967 study was a classic study by Strong, Wishart & Associates. It had as its primary objectives to evaluate the total organization structure and determine specific programs and services to gain greater support of present and future members. Among the *Findings and Conclusions* reported were:

- Payments to ANCA by the 28 state affiliate associations ranged from $100 to $4,000 and were determined to be an inequity that should be corrected.
- Approximately 57 percent of individual members paid the minimum dues of $12 per year, while the average, based on 10 cents per head, was $24.56.
- Total membership of ANCA at the end of 1966 was 4,950, only 4.5 percent of the total membership of affiliated state associations.

- Revenues during 1966 were $160,741—the highest in association history to that point.
- The size of staff—five executives and six clerical—was not large compared to other national associations; but a number of members believed the staff should never become very large.
- The myth of western domination should be destroyed and efforts made to ensure that no one section of the country is dominant.
- There is overwhelming support for ANCA activities at the national legislative level, with a strong feeling that ANCA should have a Washington office.

FINANCING THE ASSOCIATION

In 1969, the Association reported that it was in the best financial position in five years. That report, welcomed as it was and unusual as it seemed, possibly caused some over-expansion. A year later, after increasing the staff to 31 (including Cattle-Fax) and purchasing a new headquarters building in Denver, there were financial headaches.

To continue operations in 1970, the Association had to borrow money and float a note, secured by 50 key members who each signed for $5,000. The guarantors never were contacted for payment, however, and a year later the Association was back in the black.

It was time for that giant step to a permanent office in Washington with a full-time lobbyist, something the Association had desired since the beginning of the century.

> ***We discovered the 'magic lobbying power' of the Association. . . The magic was in our ability to do grassroots lobbying, through the state affiliates. Our structure and our technique were unique, and it worked.***
>
> —Bill McMillan
> *Executive Vice President of ANCA*

So finally in 1970, Bill McMillan was moved to the Nation's Capitol. He became executive vice president-Washington affairs, and George S. Spencer was hired as executive vice president-administration in the Denver office.

Knowledge and knowing what to do with it is the basis of good management. Charles Martin, the first secretary of the Association (1898-1904), recognized immediately that dissemination of information was a key to the success of an association and began a bulletin service dispersing any bit of information he could retrieve. Good information is still vital to cattlemen, as it was 100 years ago.

In the mid-1960s, the country was torn by the Vietnam War, inflation was soaring, the National Farmers Organization was withholding products from market, and consumers were boycotting beef. Cattlemen were on the defensive.

ANCA President John Guthrie of California challenged cattlemen to become offensive and develop some self-help programs. Accordingly, he appointed a Market Development Committee, led by Co-Chairmen Joe Entz of Arizona and Girdner Crofoot of Kansas. It proved to be one of the more significant committees in the Association's history.

One of their proposals was a market information program which would boost prices at the feedyard level, with the promise of trickle-down benefits to cow-calf producers. Cattlemen had little confidence in USDA figures, which were always late and often had to be adjusted. The idea was to collect and share confidential data among feedyards via two-way teletype machines. Thus, Cattle Marketing Information Service (CMIS), under the direction of Staff Economist Bill Helming, was initiated in 1968.

Although closely tied to ANCA, CMIS was set up as a separate, not-for-profit corporation. The officers of the two organizations were the same and ANCA financed CMIS initially.

Before CMIS was incorporated, however, ANCA obtained pre-clearance from the Justice Department and the Federal Trade Commission, authorizing members to exchange price information without the risk of collusion or anti-trust violation. This

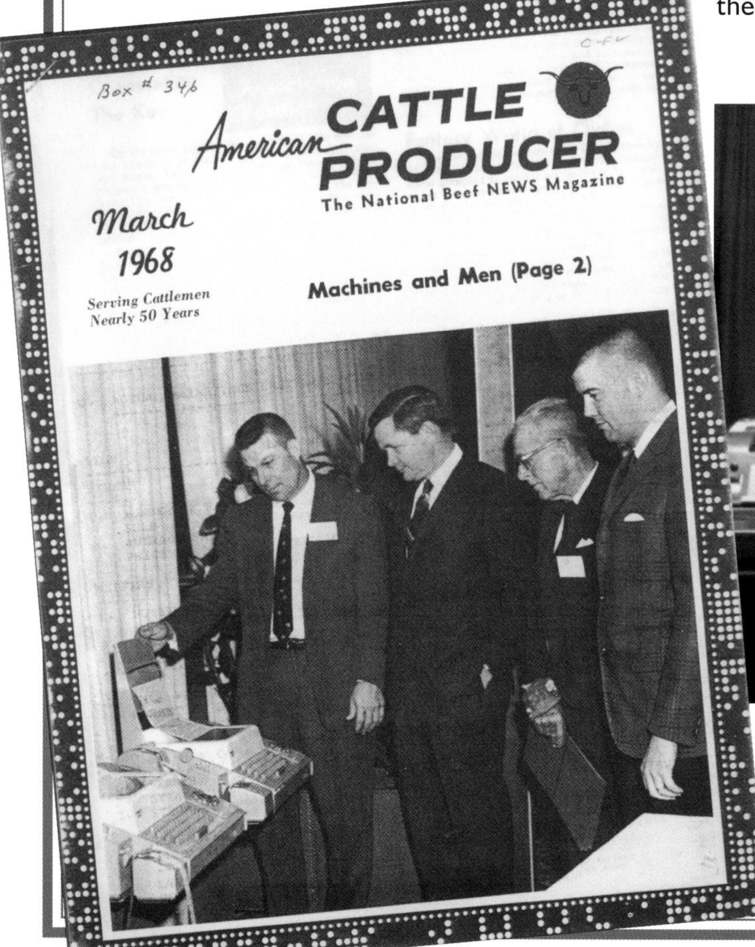

Teletyping Data Straight to the Producers. *(left to right) Girdner W. Crofoot, Bill House, Joe Entz and W.C. Helming review the teletype machines in 1968, after two years of intense effort to develop a market information program for cattlemen.*

Early Cattle-Fax Presentation. *Though primitive by standards just 20 or 30 years later, Cattle-Fax's first presentations were considered state-of-the-art. Cattle-Fax has remained on top since its inception and today maintains the largest independent database on beef cattle in existence.*

Catching the Market at Convention. *One of the most popular booths at each year's convention and trade show is the Cattle-Fax booth. Members get to see first-hand how information is disseminated as well as catch the day's latest figures.*

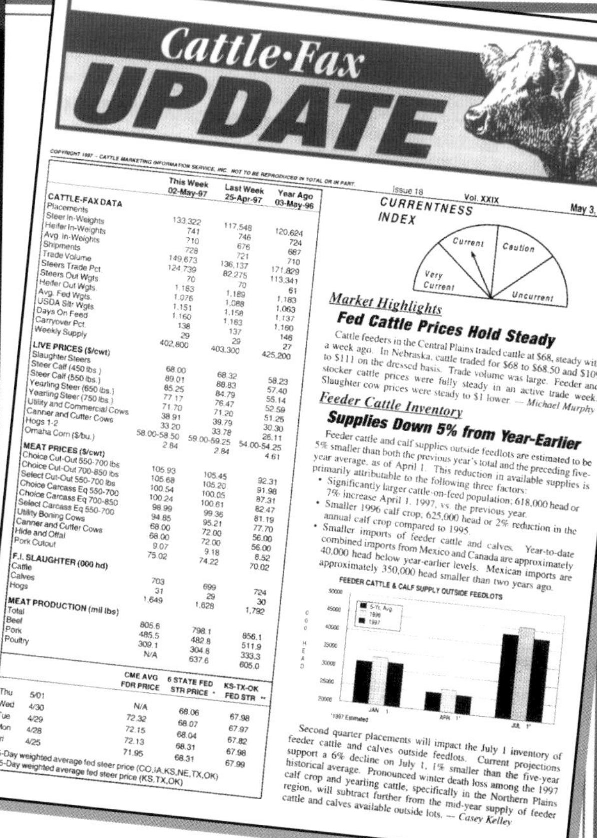

Cattle·Fax
UPDATE

	This Week 02-May-97	Last Week 25-Apr-97	Year Ago 03-May-96
CATTLE-FAX DATA			
Placements	133,322	117,548	120,624
Steer In-Weights	741	746	724
Heifer In-Weights	710	676	687
Avg. In-Weights	728	721	710
Shipments	149,673	136,137	171,829
Trade Volume	124,739	82,275	113,341
Steers Trade Pct.	70	70	61
Steers Out Wgts	1,183	1,189	1,183
Heifer Out Wgts.	1,076	1,088	1,063
Avg. Fed Wgts.	1,151	1,158	1,137
USDA Sltr Wgts	1,160	1,163	1,160
Days On Feed	138	137	146
Carryover Pct.	29	29	27
Weekly Supply	402,800	403,300	425,200
LIVE PRICES ($/cwt)			
Slaughter Steers	68.00	68.32	58.23
Steer Calf (450 lbs.)	89.01	88.83	57.40
Steer Calf (550 lbs.)	85.25	84.79	55.14
Yearling Steer (650 lbs.)	77.17	76.47	52.59
Yearling Steer (750 lbs.)	71.70	71.20	51.25
Utility and Commercial Cows	38.91	39.79	30.30
Canner and Cutter Cows	33.20	33.78	26.11
Hogs 1-2	58.00-58.50	59.00-59.25	54.00-54.25
Omaha Corn ($/bu.)	2.84	2.84	4.61
MEAT PRICES ($/cwt)			
Choice Cut-Out 550-700 lbs	105.93	105.45	92.31
Choice Cut-Out 700-850 lbs	105.68	105.20	91.98
Select Cut-Out 550-700 lbs	100.54	100.05	87.31
Choice Carcass Eq 550-700	100.24	100.61	82.47
Choice Carcass Eq 700-850	98.99	99.36	81.19
Select Carcass Eq 550-700	94.85	95.21	77.70
Utility Boning Cows	68.00	72.00	56.00
Canner and Cutter Cows	68.00	72.00	56.00
Hide and Offal	9.07	9.18	8.52
Pork Cutout	75.02	74.22	70.02
F.I. SLAUGHTER (000 hd)			
Cattle	703	699	724
Calves	31	29	30
Hogs	1,649	1,628	1,792
MEAT PRODUCTION (mil lbs)			
Total	805.6	798.1	856.1
Beef	485.5	482.8	511.9
Pork	309.1	304.8	333.3
Poultry	N/A	637.6	605.0

		CME AVG FDR PRICE	6 STATE FED STR PRICE *	KS-TX-OK FED STR **
Thu	5/01	N/A	68.06	67.98
Wed	4/30	72.32	68.07	67.97
Tue	4/29	72.15	68.04	67.82
Mon	4/28	72.13	68.31	67.98
Fri	4/25	71.95	68.31	67.99

*5-Day weighted average fed steer price (CO,IA,KS,NE,TX,OK)
**5-Day weighted average fed steer price (KS,TX,OK)

Issue 18 Vol. XXIX May 3, 1997

CURRENTNESS INDEX

Very Current
Current
Caution
Uncurrent

Market Highlights

Fed Cattle Prices Hold Steady

Cattle feeders in the Central Plains traded cattle at $68, steady with a week ago. In Nebraska, cattle traded for $68 to $68.50 and $109 to $111 on the dressed basis. Trade volume was large. Feeder and stocker cattle prices were fully steady in an active trade week. Slaughter cow prices were steady to $1 lower. — *Michael Murphy*

Feeder Cattle Inventory

Supplies Down 5% from Year-Earlier

Feeder cattle and calf supplies outside feedlots are estimated to be 5% smaller than both the previous year's total and the preceding five-year average, as of April 1. This reduction in available supplies is primarily attributable to the following three factors:

- Significantly larger cattle-on-feed population; 618,000 head or 7% increase April 1, 1997, vs. the previous year.
- Smaller 1996 calf crop; 625,000 head or 2% reduction in the annual calf crop compared to 1995.
- Smaller imports of feeder cattle and calves. Year-to-date combined imports from Mexico and Canada are approximately 40,000 head below year-earlier levels. Mexican imports are approximately 350,000 head smaller than two years ago.

FEEDER CATTLE & CALF SUPPLY OUTSIDE FEEDLOTS
5-Yr. Avg.
1996
1997
000 HEAD
JAN 1
APR 1*
JUL 1*
*1997 Estimated

Second quarter placements will impact the July 1 inventory of feeder cattle and calves outside feedlots. Current projections support a 6% decline on July 1, 1% smaller than the five-year historical average. Pronounced winter death loss among the 1997 calf crop and yearling cattle, specifically in the Northern Plains region, will subtract further from the mid-year supply of feeder cattle and calves available outside lots. — *Casey Kelley*

clearance, which made CMIS a unique organization, was granted under provisions of the Capper-Volstead Act of 1922.

Almost from the beginning, the service became known as Cattle-Fax. The name stuck and was later trademarked. Topper Thorpe, the first market analyst, became general manager in 1972, and now is one of the best known names in the business.

In an industry where confidentiality is sacrosanct, Cattle-Fax has helped producers realize both the value of good information and also the benefits of sharing information. This real-

Sorting Out the Facts and Figures

Raised on a livestock and crop farm in southern New Mexico, Topper Thorpe has revolutionized the output of information about the beef business while serving as executive vice president of Cattle-Fax. Under his management, Cattle-Fax has grown to a state-of-the-art information output program providing data used for developing information and analyses that members now depend upon for making marketing and management decisions.

Thorpe joined Cattle-Fax as a market analyst in 1968 and became General Manager in 1972. During his career he has established transmission of Cattle-Fax data through the Commodity News Service and today information easily reaches members over the Internet, WATTS lines, written reports and video screens.

Cattle-Fax continues to maintain an unequaled data service on cattle and beef. Beef magazine named Thorpe one of the 25 individuals who had made a major contribution to the beef cattle industry.

After serving in the military, Thorpe received a degree in agricultural economics from New Mexico State University in Las Cruces.

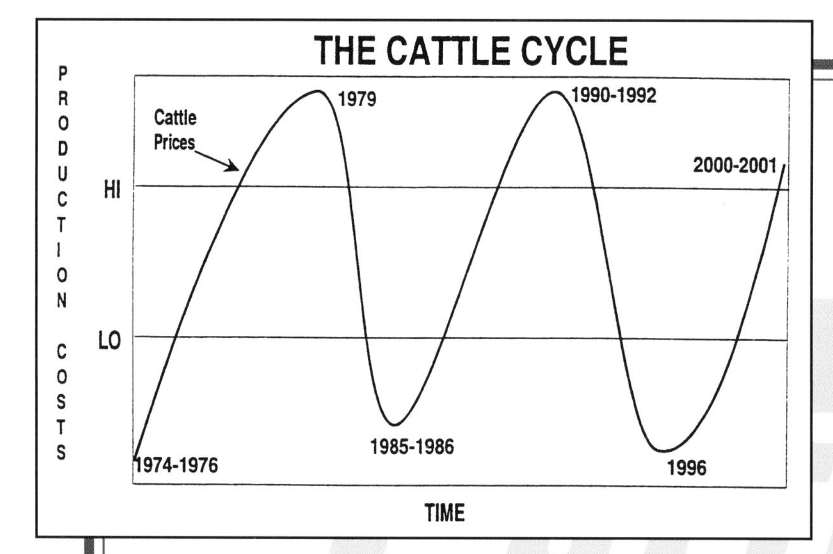

ization has helped the organization grow to 4,500 members (in 1997), about half feeders, the other half cow-calf and stocker operators. They represent about one-third of the total cattle on feed and about three percent of all beef cows.

With a bank of large computers and 30 years of collecting and analyzing data, Cattle-Fax has the largest independent data base on beef cattle in the country. To manage and analyze this database, Cattle-Fax has a staff of 27, including researchers and analysts who receive approximately 600 calls a day. With a "feel" for the trade and changes taking place, they are able to balance market psychology and statistics.

Originally, the data was collected and disseminated by two-way teletype machines. Now, it is collected via telephone and disseminated through the use of electronic video networks, FAX and the Internet.

The gamut of information disseminated is vast: cash prices for all classes of cattle; supply, demand and market psychology; what packers are doing; placements, including in and out weights; cattle contracting and formula pricing; feeder cattle availability and movement by region; feedyard conditions, performance of cattle and feedyard bargaining position; plus almost anything related to marketing that a member wants to know. Although Cattle-Fax never "officially" forecasts, it presents data and reasons which suggest what is most likely to happen.

In addition, Cattle-Fax supplies long-range weather forecasts and in-depth consultation for members as well as puts together seminars and conducts research studies. For non-members or commercial companies, they provide education and research through C-F Resources, Inc., a for-profit and wholly owned subsidiary of Cattle-Fax.

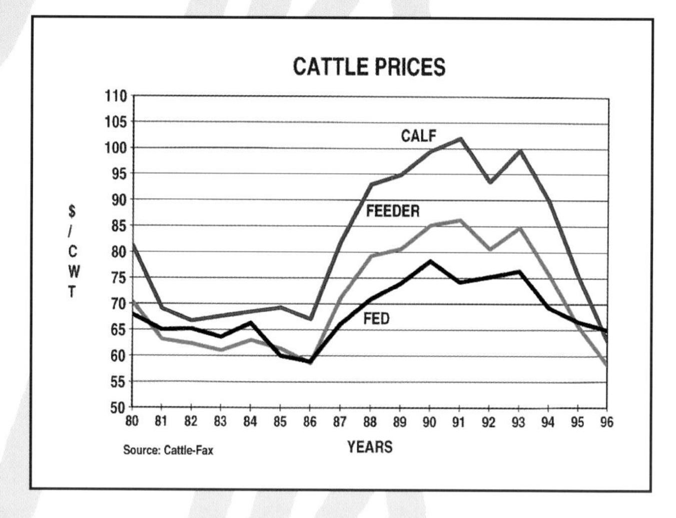

Analyzing Data. *(right) Topper Thorpe and Tommy Beall, Cattle-Fax research director, going through printouts in 1990. (above) Analyst reviewing data. Data collection and analysis is the backbone of Cattle-Fax.*

Explaining the Profitability Puzzle. *Charts and graphs given on these facing pages are taken from a popular Cattle-Fax seminar that is given at the Cattlemen's College during the NCBA Annual Convention. In this seminar, Cattle-Fax is helping cattlemen understand the influencing factors and find new ways to increase value and profitability in their operations.*

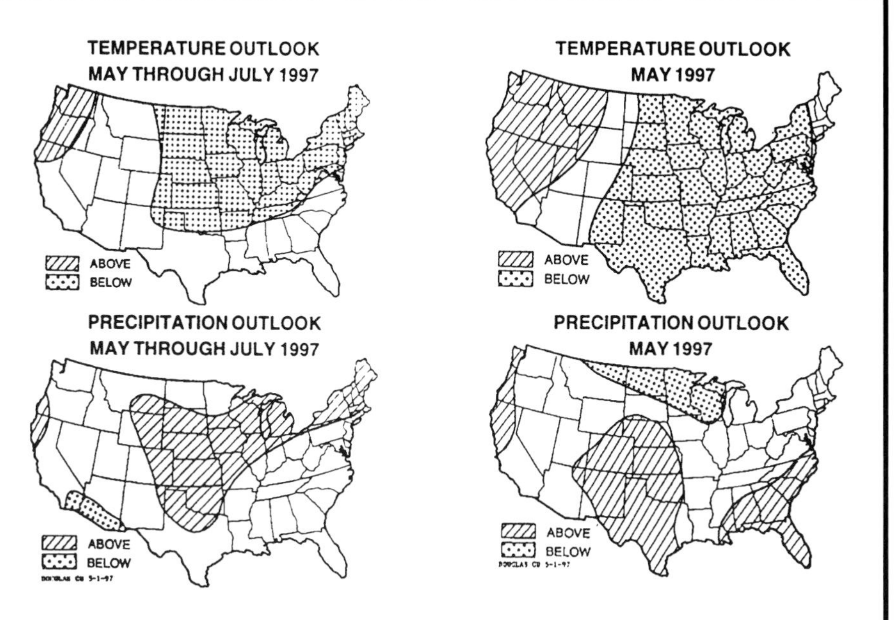

Art the Weatherman. *One of Cattle-Fax's most noted services to the industry is its weather forecasting. Dr. Art Douglas has year after year fascinated viewers and readers with his long-term weather forecasts and discussions of such things as El Niño and how that ties into this year's corn crop.*

Information is our business, says Topper Thorpe, *and we'll do almost anything that is information-based and that our members request.*

For these services, members pay dues of one cent per head per month—same dues as in 1968—plus a fee based on size of herd or feedyard. Depending on the services a member subscribes to, the actual dues-fees range from $10 to $365 per month.

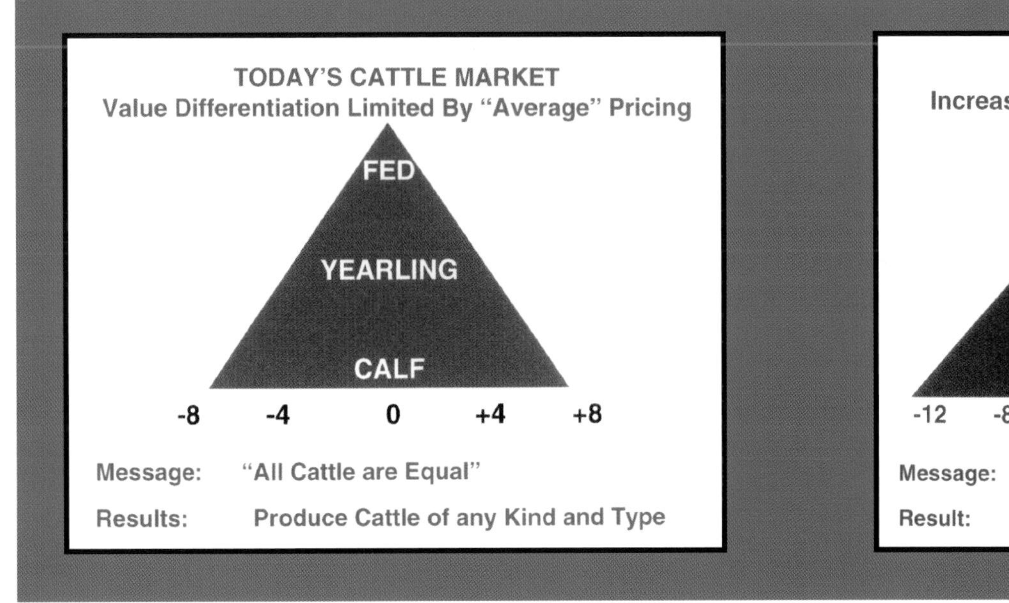

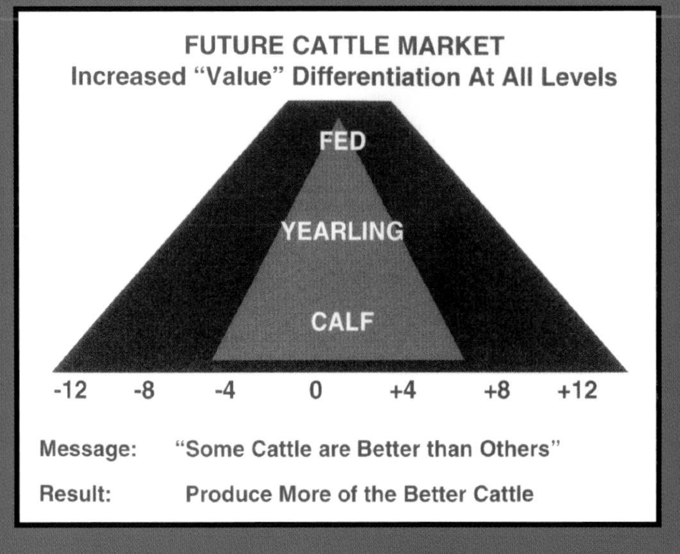

NLFA

The National Livestock Feeders Association

Prior to 1943 there was scarce need for a national livestock feeders association. Cattle feeding was not thought of as a business unto itself, but rather a way for corn farmers to get rid of excess corn. There was little poultry industry and little export market that needed corn. The major market for corn was as feed for hogs and cattle which could be converted to a salable commodity.

Cattle feeding, primarily in the Midwest, was highly dependent upon the corn crop. When there was ample corn, cattle were fed. When the corn was gone, cattle were sent to market.

During World War II, stockgrowers the country over became impatient with price controls on meat and livestock. About all the western rancher and the midwestern farmer-feeder had in common were their disdain of price controls and the fact that they both raised cattle. When it came to working together on mutual problems, they were miles apart.

ANLSA was still perceived as a western range organization largely interested in public lands, which did not appeal to farmer-feeders. The farmer-feeders were primarily corn producers. Many were interested in government programs of price supports and acreage controls on grain, which did not appeal to ranchers. There was no particular friction between the two groups, just no common interest. Western cattlemen produced yearlings they sold as feeder cattle; what happened to them after that point was of little or no concern.

Mark W. Pickell, *(center) was the first executive of the Corn Belt Livestock Feeders Association. "Our's is a single-purpose organization, to fight government controls of the industry," he said. He expanded the Association's services by starting a monthly magazine,* Corn Belt Livestock Feeder. *A public relations consultant in Chicago, Pickell was a part-time executive of CBLFA with a 1957 salary ot $2,100.*

Also, for years the ANLSA excluded cattle feeders, putting them in a black hat category with packers, commission firms and market operators. Midwestern feeders thought the ANLSA was controlled by "big, arrogant ranchers" not above taking advantage of "small, humble farmers" when trading calves.

All of which put an iron curtain between cattlemen in the West and cattlemen in the Midwest, except for their mutual stand against price controls.

A Corn Belt Association

In 1946, officers of the Nebraska Livestock Feeders Association (organized in 1943) and the Illinois Livestock Feeders Association (organized in 1945) ran into each other in Washington, where each was seeking an end to price controls. *The war is over,* they declared, *and controls are restricting beef production.* Frustrated by lack of attention in the Capitol, they speculated that they might be more effective if they combined forces and invited other midwestern feeders to join them.

So the two state associations held a joint meeting in December 1945, in Sioux City, Iowa, and another in January 1946, in Omaha, Nebraska. The latter meeting drew representatives from six states—Nebraska, Illinois, South Dakota, Colorado, Missouri and Iowa—who organized the Corn Belt Livestock Feeders Association (CBLFA). Lawrence Brock of Wakefield, Nebraska was the president and Mark W. Pickell of Chicago the secretary and treasurer. Chicago was selected as the headquarters, where it remained for almost 10 years. The three classes of membership for the new Association were:

1. Livestock Feeder, with dues of $5 per year: $1 for the county or local association, $2 for the state affiliate and $2 for the Corn Belt Association.

NLFA members were primarily farmers, *like Erwin E. Dubbert (left) and brother Ulrich, who owned 500 acres near Laurens, Iowa, and fed a few hundred Hereford cattle. Erwin was NLFA president, 1963-1964.*

2. Associate Member, with annual dues of $10, for commission firms, sale barns, banks, feed companies, etc.
3. Sustaining Member, with annual dues of $50, for stockyard companies, packers and "those whose future prosperity depends upon a prosperous livestock feeder industry."

Single Purpose Association

The new Association was essentially a single purpose organization, according to early membership brochures: "To fight government controls of the industry." They took credit for the demise of the Office of Price Administration (OPA), which was finally killed by President Harry Truman in October 1946. Also, they claimed the lead role in preventing a second price rollback during the Korean War and the ultimate end of the Office of Price Stabilization (OPS). The ANLSA also took credit for these actions but that was not uncommon for competing associations to take credit for similar successes.

Single purpose organizations often have difficulty surviving, as this one soon learned. In an attempt to expand services, Pickell started a monthly publication, *Corn Belt Livestock Feeder,* "to disseminate information as to livestock on feed, numbers raised, slaughter figures and other things pertinent to the successful operation of the livestock feeder." Pickell had an office in the Chicago Mercantile Exchange Building and had access to daily commodity trading. In an era of no television and little or no electricity, communication was a slow process, and thus his newsletter was popular.

To attract members, CBLFA countered unions in their brochures:

> *The labor unions have become a powerful factor. . .They are well organized and present a solid front to protect their interests. Their members are not only 'assessed' but are even fined if not in good standing.*

Despite this strategy, following the end of the Korean War and the death of the OPS, the CBLFA dwindled in membership and for a couple of years became almost destitute.

New Executive, New Life

Meanwhile, the Nebraska Livestock Feeders Association was growing under the direction of its new Executive Secretary-Treasurer, Don Magdanz. Then age 40, Magdanz was an experienced farmer-feeder from Pierce, Nebraska, and the son of A.F. Magdanz, the first president of the Nebraska Livestock Feeders Association (1943). The CBLFA asked Magdanz to take over as Executive Secretary-Treasurer of their nearly defunct organization, as well as continue on as executive of the Nebraska Association.

Magdanz agreed, provided the CBLFA would: (a) reorganize; (b) expand its mission; (c) move its headquarters to Omaha (from Chicago); and (d) consider a name change from "Corn Belt" to "National."

> ***The first 500 pounds put on a steer is no more important than the second 500 pounds. Likewise, the rancher is no more important in the food chain than the feeder.***
>
> —Don Magdanz
> *NLFA Executive Vice President*

He reasoned that "National" might attract feeders outside the Corn Belt and thereby give it more status in Washington, DC.

A 1957 financial statement indicated the plight of the CBLFA. Total receipts were $9,092, including $7,073 dues income. Salaries were $2,100, suggesting Pickell had been a part-time executive in Chicago. Total membership was 1,305, including 607 from Illinois, 379 from Ohio and an unknown number from Nebraska.

Under Magdanz's guidance, the Association grew immediately: to 10,000 in 1970 and 12,000 in 1976. The revenues grew, too, topping $206,000 in 1974.

The Number Two staff person for the NLFA (1962-1977) was B.H. (Bill) Jones.

Presidents of the NLFA

LAWRENCE BROCK
CBLFA 1946-1948
Wakefield, Nebraska

KNUTE JOHNSON
CBLFA 1956-1957
Elburn, Illinois

ERWIN E. DUBBERT
NLFA 1963-1964
Laurens, Iowa

CHAUNCEY WATSON
CBLFA 1949-1953
Dekalb, Illinois

JOHN H. LITZELMAN
CBLFA 1958-1960
Vermillion, South Dakota

ROBERT RAY
NLFA 1965-1966
Norfolk, Nebraska

ED HOLLENBECK
CBLFA 1954-1955
Dixon, Illinois

O.C. SWACKHAMER
NLFA 1961-1962
Fairfax, Missouri

CHARLES PHELPS
NLFA 1967-1968
Hastings, Iowa

GILBERT L. HADLEY
NLFA 1969-1970
CAMBRIDGE, ILLINOIS

DON HUNTER
NLFA 1975-1976
CENTERVILLE, SOUTH DAKOTA

TOM MONIER
NLFA 1977
PRINCETON, ILLINOIS

OSCAR BREDTHAUER
NLFA 1971-1972
GRAND ISLAND, NEBRASKA

MILTON J. BROWN
NLFA 1973-1974
MOUNT PLEASANT, MICHIGAN

Chicago Meat Case

In 1957, local unions of the Amalgamated Meat Cutters and Butcher Workmen, AFL-CIO, proclaimed that fresh meat should be sold only between 9:00 am and 6:00 pm, Monday through Saturday, when union butchers were on the job. That made no sense to cattlemen who work "from can 'til can't," nor to working housewives who shopped in the evenings.

The real issue was the handling of fresh meat for the consumer. The innovation of prepackaged fresh meat in self-serve counters pleased customers and improved the efficiency of handling the meat, but eliminated some butchers in meat markets who worked normal business hours. By restricting the time beef could be sold, butchers would have equal opportunity to reach their customers.

Under threat of strike, unions forced about 9,000 retailers into a contract. Jewel Tea Company, one of the larger chains in the area, signed the contract but sued the union for "unreasonable restraint of trade."

B.H. (Bill) Jones, NLFA associate secretary-treasurer at the time, tells what happened next: *The NLFA invited ANCA to join them in an amicus curiae (friend of the court) brief. But ANCA declined.*

The NLFA was later joined by the National Livestock Producers Association, the River Markets Group, American Stockyards Association and Certified Livestock Markets Association (as friends of the court) when in 1964 the case was argued before the United States Supreme Court. Jones, known for his skill in drafting regulations and laws, wrote most of the brief.

The NLFA argued that the contract not only inconvenienced consumers who shopped after 6:00 pm, but also adversely affected competition, placed fresh meat purveyors at a competitive disadvantage, and discriminated in favor of foreign livestock producers. They also maintained that the retail store operator was the "consumer contact" for the producer, whose financial well-being depended upon aggressive merchandising.

In the end, the original District Court ruled in favor of the union; the Appeals Court reversed and ruled in favor of Jewel Tea; and the Supreme Court, in a split decision, ruled that this was a matter to be handled in labor negotiations, and not in court.

It was a high profile, highly publicized case in which the NLFA gained the goodwill of many cattlemen, members and non-members, for their "courage to defend progress."

NLFA Directors *in Washington, DC, April, 1967, with Secretary of Agriculture Orville Freeman (front center).*

Later, Jones became Executive Vice President, the second Executive Vice President in the organization.

At the 1960 Convention in Kansas City, the name was changed to National Livestock Feeders Association. The name change did tend to increase membership, as hoped, although more than 90 percent of the members still came from the seven North Central states: Nebraska, Illinois, Indiana, Iowa, South Dakota, Minnesota and Michigan. At the same convention, dues were increased from the minimum of $5 per year to $10, of which $3 would go to the county or local association, $1 to the state affiliate and $6 to the NLFA. In addition, a graduated schedule, based on the number of animals fed, increased the maximum dues to $50 per year for 1,000 animal units. A unit consisted of one head of cattle or four hogs or 10 lambs.

Non-Political and Democratic

The NLFA boasted that it was nonpolitical—but they did work on political issues—and that it was "democratic," in contrast with ANCA, which NLFA viewed as being "autocratic." Also, the NLFA emphasized grassroots policy development. Resolutions typically originated with the local or county associations, and the state affiliate was obliged to consider them. Likewise, when a resolution from a state reached the national, the national was obligated to consider it. Thus, resolutions and policy development took an immense amount of time, making NLFA conventions appear rather formal.

Further, to assure a pure producer association, committee meetings usually were limited to voting members and often went into executive sessions for final discussion and vote. They wanted to avoid the strong influence of auctions and packers, which some felt pervaded ANCA.

An Expanded Mission

The Association continued to expand its mission: "to address all matters of economic importance to cattle feeders." In a 1970 speech, Magdanz outlined the Association's accomplishments:

- A large role in passage of the Meat Import Act of 1964, a five-year effort.
- Adequate funds for the Packers and Stockyards Administration, the result of lobbying Congress.
- Approval by the IRS (reversing its earlier position) to deduct business meals and entertainment costs. The NLFA rationale was that red meat was the preferred entree for business meals and this would increase consumption.
- Communications with members through a magazine, *National Livestock Feeder*, 1956-1973, and a newsletter, *Feed-Lines*, 1968-1977.
- Agreement by USDA to release all livestock reports and estimates at 3:00 pm instead of 11:00 am, to give all time zones an even start.
- A major role in stopping a crippling strike and secondary boycotts against Iowa Beef Processors in 1969.

Later, when the Environmental Protection Agency (EPA) was created in 1972, farmer-feeders became quite nervous, because they were being threatened by EPA personnel who knew little to nothing about feedlots and had no guidelines to help them. So the NLFA wrote guidelines for feedlots, submitted them to EPA and they were fed back as official EPA policies for the North Central states. *The EPA seemed quite willing for us to do their work,* says a former staffer, *and we were willing, because we got what we wanted.*

Still later, the Association, following ANCA's lead, played a major role in helping pass the original Beef Research and Information Act in 1975.

In 1976, NLFA also worked with ANCA and state affiliates, over strong objections by packers and their associations, to add Prompt and Assured Payment amendments to the Packers and Stockyards Act. These amendments did two things: It required packers to pay for livestock by the close of the next business day following purchase, and In case of failure to pay, sellers of livestock were placed ahead of other secured creditors in claims on inventory and receivables.

Bankruptcy of American Beef Packers

The Prompt and Assured Payment legislation was precipitated by the 1975 bankruptcy of American Beef Packers, Inc. (ABP), one of the new, independent packers that sprung up with astonishing growth. A total of 1,270 feeders in 12 states, from Indiana to California, from Minnesota to Texas, were left short $22.5 million.

Frank West, ABP president, had been a successful hog buyer in western Iowa. He then set out to become the biggest beef packer in the business and soon was operating six plants in four states from his Omaha office, including a brand new one near Dumas, Texas. Scheduled to cost $14 million, this "largest and most modern plant in the country" ended up costing $20 million when finished in 1973.

At the same time, the cattle market was a wreck, possibly the worst in history. Prices dropped so rapidly following President Nixon's lifting of the price freeze in September 1973 that both packers and feeders lost big money. Rumors were rampant, including one that ABP's financier, General Electric Credit Corporation, was about to foreclose. ABP became very slow to pay, but were bidding 50 cents to $1.00 per hundred above the market. Of course this had some appeal to feeders who had been losing $100 to $200 per head.

Four days before West announced bankruptcy, he instructed his buyers to buy large numbers of cattle. When the announcement came on January 7, 1975, it appeared many cattlemen would go down with ABP.

NLFA led in helping to recover losses for feeders, whether or not they were members. Senior staffer Bill Jones was assigned the case. With skill and tenacity, he got a Creditors Committee appointed, helped find buyers for ABP plants, obtained assistance from United States senators with the Justice Department, had meetings with General Electric Credit Corporation, and negotiated with the bankruptcy judge.

To stop the 1973 price freeze, *Milton J. Brown, 1973-1974 NLFA President, sent this photo to every senator and congressman in Washington.*

Just when it appeared feeders might get nothing because they had no priority as creditors, they were awarded 51cents on each dollar due. The feeders were pleased. It was another victory for NLFA.

Not Always Hand in Hand

NLFA and ANCA did not always work together, however, and were even opponents in court on one occasion. In 1974, the USDA proposed a grading change that lowered the marbling requirements for Prime and Choice, also coupling yield grading with quality grading. ANCA supported the change. But Omaha packers opposed it and, with NLFA backing, sued the USDA. To a farmer-feeder marketing corn through cattle, the change meant shorter feeding periods, less weight put on with corn, and a greater penalty for yield grade 4 or overly fat cattle. USDA and ANCA prevailed and the grading changes were implemented in February 1976.

Another occasion when NLFA and ANCA differed was the famous Chicago Meat Case (1957-1965). The NLFA invited ANCA to join them in a brief, but ANCA declined. (*See Box, page 169.*)

Denounced Packer Feeding

The NLFA was never bashful about controversial issues. In 1966, for example, they denounced packer feeding with a resolution calling it "extreme, unhealthy and detrimental to the preservation of competition for fed livestock." They further alleged that packer feeding "gives packers an advantage over farmer-feeders and also acts as a price depressant."

Representative Bert Bondstra (D-Iowa) introduced a bill in Congress that would make it unlawful for a packer with gross sales over $1 million the previous year to feed cattle. The bill would also prohibit packers from contracting with feeders if the packers exercised control over the time the livestock would come to slaughter. NLFA testified strongly for legislation. But again, the ANCA declined to take a position and the bill went nowhere.

Several times since then, as recently as 1995, some feeders have requested

Second-in-Command at NLFA was B.H. (Bill) Jones. *(right) Jones was an auctioneer by training, an agricultural economics graduate from the University of Illinois and an employee of the Chicago Stockyards Company before joining NLFA as associate secretary-treasurer. After the merger, Jones stayed on with NCA for several years then moved to Washington as administrator of the Packers and Stockyards Administration (1981-1989). Here he is shown receiving a commendation from Secretary of Agriculture John Block in 1986. As administrator, Jones reported to Bill McMillan, who had resigned from NCA to become Assistant Secretary of Agriculture. Both were natives of Colorado and their careers ran parallel for nearly 40 years.*

legislation or regulations to restrict presumed packer control of inventory or captive supplies. But the government has done no more than conduct investigations.

Preserve Central Markets

Another losing battle for the NLFA was their 1966 effort to preserve central markets or stockyards, which were prevalent in the Midwest. Among their contentions, in published guidelines, were:

- The concentration of supply and of buyers is a basic and sound economic principle in a market structure which depends upon free market prices.
- There is a definite need for third parties to furnish market facilities and professional selling services.
- Direct buying out of feedlots by buyers traveling the country is recognized as an expensive procurement system, in terms of cost per animal purchased.

In summary, the NLFA contended that direct buying would permit packers to divide and conquer feeders.

Cattle feeding was centered in the Corn Belt. In the late 1950s, terminal markets handled over 70 percent of the commercial slaughter and 98 percent of the federally inspected slaughter. In 1960, for example, Iowa fed the greatest number of cattle, followed in order by California, Nebraska, and Illinois. The 10 Corn Belt states marketed over seven million cattle a year or 58 percent of the nation's total. Most of their cattle were marketed through Chicago, Omaha, Kansas City or others of the 30 terminal markets.

Jones explained how the central market system worked in the farmers' favor:

> *Farmers would bring cattle to the central market by truck or rail and consign them to a commission firm, which represented only the seller. Here the farmer could witness the negotiations and the establishment of price. Most of the time, the base price was established at the Chicago Stockyards for the entire country. Some cooperatives would combine shipments for smaller farmers before offering them. Also, some cattle from country auctions would go to the central market for final sale. Major packers had located at the stockyards, so there was no transportation cost from seller to slaughter.*

But all that would change. Cattle feeding was moving west. Trucks made it possible to move cattle and grain in any direction. Commercial feedyards would begin to emerge on the High Plains and in the Southwest. Packers moved out of the cities and rebuilt plants near the cattle supplies. Farmer-feeders diminished in number and most of the terminal markets shut down.

It became difficult for the NLFA to hold its own. *A few people began to suggest the possibility of a merger with the ANCA,* said Charles Phelps of Hastings, Iowa, NLFA president (1967-1968), *but our people weren't yet ready to join hands with western ranchers.*

By 1970, ANCA had gained membership in the South and was striving to overcome the old perception that they were a western range association. They claimed to be the "spokesman for the industry;" and for that they needed the Corn Belt cattlemen and their political influence. So they continued to pursue the NLFA.

In 1972, W.D. Farr and George Spencer of ANCA made a trip to Nebraska to meet with NLFA President Oscar Bredthauer to suggest a merger, but the reception was cool. However, the pursuit continued and eventually, in 1977, a merger was consummated. Both Jones and Magdanz, plus Communications Director Frank Arney, continued as key players in the new National Cattlemen's Association. Magdanz became senior vice president and Jones became vice president for policy development

Don Magdanz: The Organizer

As an association executive, Don Magdanz was known to his superiors as the *best organized and most thorough person* they ever knew. Also, they described him as: *Totally dedicated to the Association. Thoroughly honest and frank—you always knew where he stood. . .A conservative economist. . .and an unwavering Republican.*

At the University of Nebraska, Magdanz was active in debate, the University Band (played cornet), editor of *Cornhusker Countryman* and president of Farm House Fraternity. After graduating in agricultural economics in 1938, he worked three years for the Federal Land Bank of Omaha.

He then returned to the family farm in Pierce, Nebraska, where he became a sizable livestock feeder: cattle, sheep and hogs. His father, A.F. Magdanz, was the first president of the Nebraska Livestock Feeders Association in 1943 and Don became the Secretary-Treasurer in 1953.

When the Corn Belt Livestock Feeders Association was almost defunct, they asked Don to take over as Executive Secretary-Treasurer in 1956. He did and the Association began growing immediately.

With unending energy, Magdanz ran both the Nebraska Livestock Feeders Association and the NLFA initially while he continued to farm 640 acres and feed on a large scale. In a typical year, he would market 600 to 800 cattle, 4,000 to 6000 lambs and 500 to 1,000 hogs.

Running the NLFA required thrift and forbearance. Total revenues during his first year on the job were only $49,092. Some months, Don did not get paid. To pay their own bills, Mrs. Magdanz went back to school and got a job as a teacher.

After his death in 1995, his widow told how Don had learned frugality.

> *During the war, we had no electricity, hence no refrigeration. And we always had five—sometimes up to 10—hired men living with us, in a dormitory on the second floor of our house. Of course, fresh meat of all kinds was readily available. We had huge gardens and canned. . . .We also had bees and produced our own honey for cooking. So about all we had to buy was flour and coffee.*

DON F. MAGDANZ

Executive Vice President
CBLFA-NLFA 1956-1976

Senior Vice President
NCA 1977-1980

But Magdanz's missionary spirit never waned. He was a visionary who knew cattle feeding needed to mature as a business. He also had good political instincts, and with Corn Belt states having several congressional votes, he used his clout successfully in lobbying efforts. His ability to communicate with his members resulted in strong membership growth.

In the early years, he managed the NLFA on weekdays and edited the monthly magazine, *National Livestock Feeder*, on weekends.

For several years, he resisted the consolidation pursuits of ANCA, but when it finally occurred, he became Senior Vice President of the new NCA and an advocate for the entire cattle industry.

Even when the staffs from the two organizations disagreed, professionalism prevailed in a consensus effort towards the broader issues in the industry.

Magdanz worked diligently to elevate the image of farmer-feeders. The glamour and romance attached to the western rancher did not seem justified to him. Neither did the lesser image of the smaller farmer-feeder seem quite fair. He frequently made the point:

> *The first 500 pounds put on a steer is no more important than the second 500 pounds. Likewise, the rancher is no more important in the food chain than the feeder.*

As one staff associate explained, *His goal was to keep the Association afloat and growing. The days never were too long or the miles too many.*

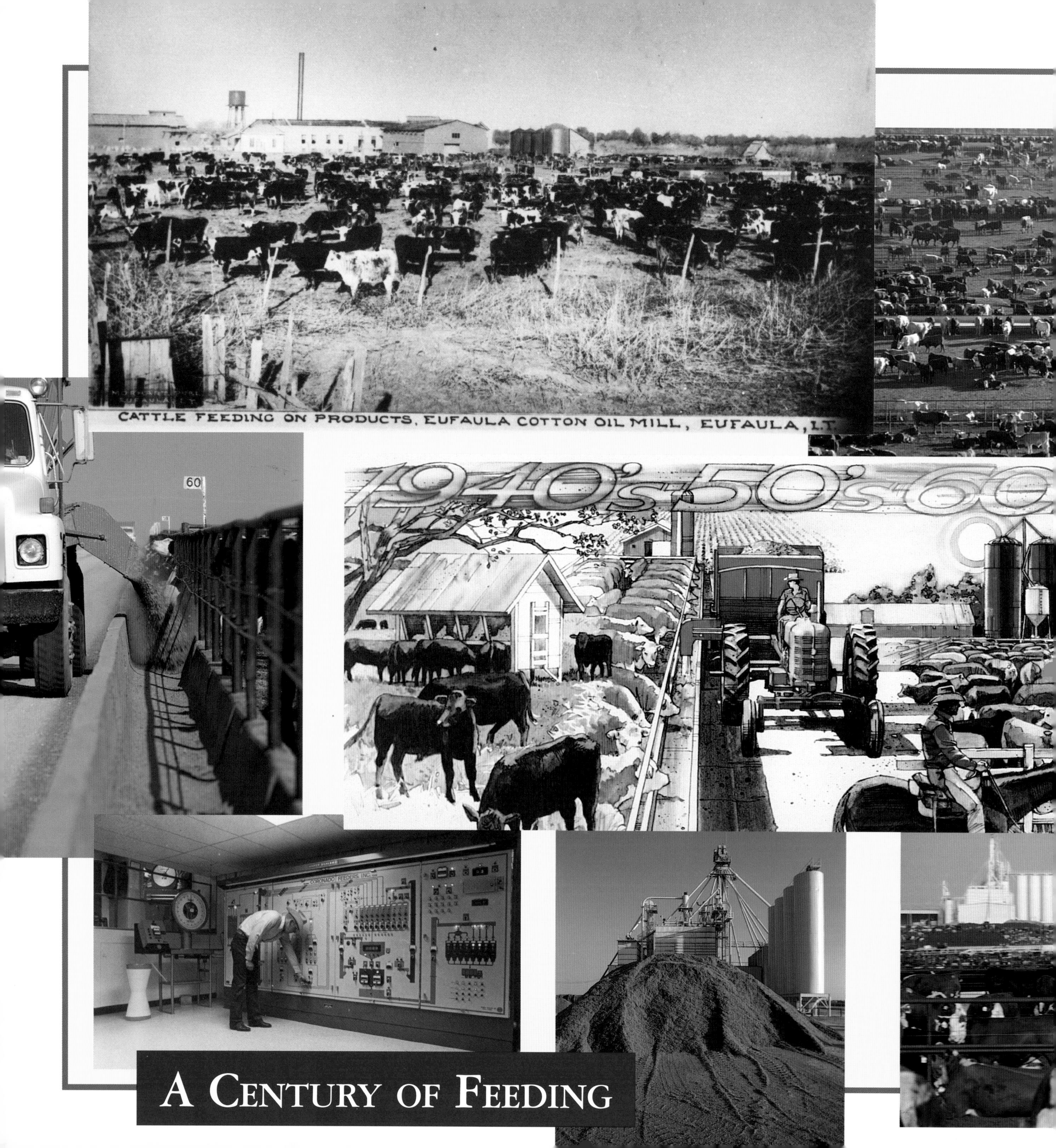

A Century of Feeding

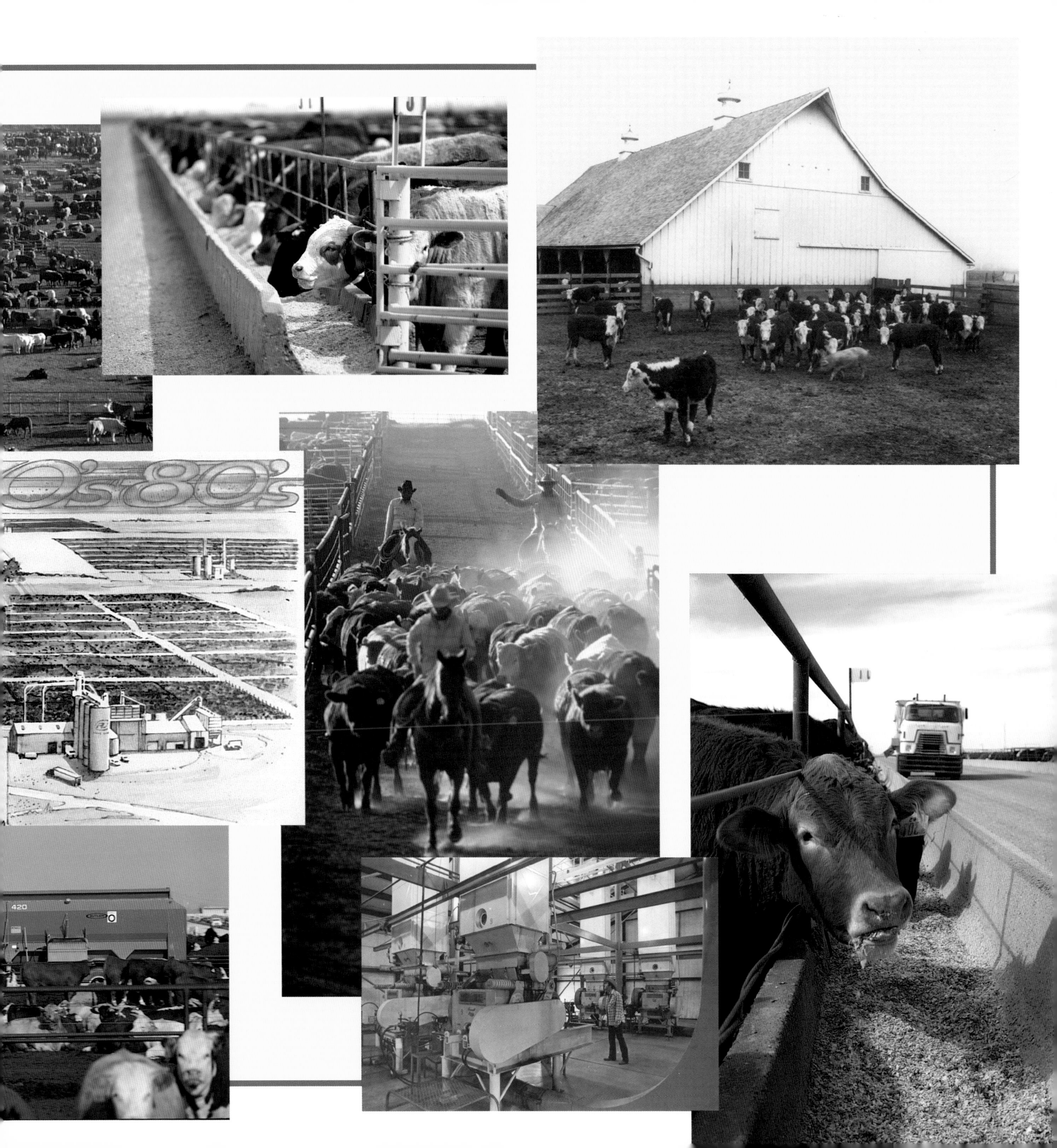

Grant Wood STONE CITY, IOWA

Fields of Grain

Corn.

The golden plains of the Midwest stretched out with a seemingly endless supply of grain. Feed to finish cattle in uniform weights and produce an excellent beef product. With diverse backgrounds and differing goals, the midwestern feeders and the cattle producers had little in common. But it would take their coming together before the Association could speak with a truly national voice.

CHAPTER NINE

Political Perception

Although there had been scattered consumer activities in the past, such as the 1902 consumer boycott in New York and the 1966 boycott in Denver, it was in the 1970s that consumer groups plunged into the socio-political arena and began to proliferate. They roared in blatantly, militantly and permanently to alter the direction of many industries, not the least of which was the cattle industry.

Few cattlemen welcomed the consumer movement, but it gained momentum, resulting in more than 400 new consumer activist organizations being recorded in 1976. They precipitated a host of developments and organizations that would impact cattlemen's business: the Environmental Protection Agency, animal rights groups, dietary guidelines, diet-health concerns, grading changes, closely trimmed carcasses, public relations campaigns, boot camps, beef checkoff and more. The Association was forced to take a strong stand just to maintain stability.

Mr. McMillan Goes To Washington

Prophetically, ANCA was prepared. The Executive Committee already had decided that C.W. (Bill) McMillan, the executive vice president in Denver, should move full time to Washington, where he already was spending nearly half his time. He was carving out an original objective of the Association, declared in 1898, "to protect cattlemen from the government at Washington." Several times since then, a full-time lobbyist in Washington had been proposed, but limited funds always prevented it. So in 1970, McMillan rented an office in the National Press Club Building, a prestigious address only two blocks from the White House.

Not everybody favored a Washington office. ANCA had been primarily a defensive organization, a protective group, which caused outsiders to label them an "agin" association. But younger

TIMELINE

1970 Environmental Protection Agency (EPA) created.

Occupational Safety and Health Administration (OSHA) established to develop and enforce workplace safety standards.

1971 Union Stockyards in Chicago closes after 106 years of operation.

1973 Texas Cattle Feeders Association proposes Beef Checkoff; NCA appoints taskforce to study proposal.

Vietnam peace agreements signed.

First peacetime price freeze imposed, leads to "the wreck" for cattlemen.

1974 Hank Aaron hits 715th home run.

Commodity Futures Trading Commission (CTFC) created to prevent price manipulation and unfair practices in commodity futures trading.

Richard Nixon resigns. Gerald Ford becomes 38th president.

1975 American Beef Packers (ABP) declares bankruptcy.

1976 Nation celebrates bicentennial.

First beef referendum for checkoff receives a 56.6 percent "yes" vote, but fails due to lack of two-thirds majority.

1977 ANCA and NLFA consolidate to form NCA.

Senate Select Committee publishes controversial "Dietary Goals for the United States."

Jimmy Carter inaugurated as 39th president.

American Agriculture Movement (AAM) protests low prices with "tractorcade."

1978 Second beef referendum fails with only 34.6 percent "yes" vote.

1979 DES banned as a growth promoter in cattle.

ISSUES

Washington Office
•
Peacetime Price Controls
•
The Wreck of 1973
•
Public Relations
•
Prompt & Assured Payment
•
Dietary Guidelines
•
Consumerism
•
NLFA/ANCA Consolidation
•
Meat Imports
•
Inflation
•
DES
•
Meat Pricing

members like B.K. Johnson of Texas, Wray Finney of Oklahoma and Peter Marble of Nevada got the move through along with help from more seasoned members such as W.D. Farr of Colorado, John Guthrie of California, Brooks Keogh of North Dakota, Albert Mitchell of New Mexico and Jay Taylor of Texas.

McMillan's move was announced at the 1970 Convention, the only time that the Association has had an annual convention in Washington. And with much fanfare and publicity, the cowboys let everyone know they were in town.

Bill House was the President of ANCA and Richard Nixon was President of the United States. The latter President invited the former, his Executive Committee and their new Washington representative to the White House to discuss imports, inflation, beef prices and the unlikelihood of price controls.

Cattlemen were reminded of a 1968 campaign statement by candidate Nixon, which ANCA gave national distribution. Under the title, "Fair Play for the Cattle Industry," the written statement pronounced in part:

> *The Nixon Administration will not turn its back on the needs of cattlemen. The Nixon Administration will be dedicated to seeing to it that cattlemen enjoy their full fair share of our increasing national prosperity and that federal policies encourage the health and growth of this vital industry.*

First Peace-Time Controls

By 1972, however, inflation had begun to disturb consumers and the pressure for price controls became intense. Against the wisdom and advice of economists across the country, President Nixon made the political decision to impose wage and price controls broken into four phases between late 1971 and early

The Cattlemen Have Come to Town. *One publicity stunt that ANCA held marking the opening of the Washington office gained much media attention. The media had been invited for "a special event" at the prestigious Shoreham Hotel, where 1,700 cattlemen were registering for the 1970 Convention. As the media and registrants gathered in the lobby, Big John clattered across the marble floor and was registered as the honored guest. Big John, a Hereford steer from the Eastern Livestock Show, was then ensconced in luxurious quarters outside under the hotel's front canopy.*

1973. These were the first peace-time controls in the history of the United States! It was a brazen move that apparently paid off politically; at least, it was credited as a significant factor in Nixon carrying every state in 1972, except Massachusetts and the District of Columbia.

But despite the controls, food prices continued to climb, up 23 percent in the first five months of 1973. By March the sentiment against high prices had reached a fever pitch. So on March 19, 1973, against the advice of the Food Advisory Committee of his own Cost of Living Council, President Nixon made another political decision, this time to impose a temporary freeze for seven months on the wholesale and retail prices of red meats.

President Nixon had miscalculated or had failed to consider several things:

First, cattle numbers had been increasing approximately three percent per year and were about ready to peak in a normal cycle, which would normally bring beef prices down anyway. If this occurred before the freeze ended on September 12, he calculated, it could be a political coup for his administration. Such a trick was desperately needed, because the Watergate scandal had already surfaced. Little did he understand how disruptive a temporary price freeze could be to a normal cattle cycle.

Second, a severe drought in the USSR, which usually exported grain, had caused a great shortage of grain there. Since the Cold War was beginning to thaw, the United States agreed to sell them $1.5 billion of grain. This triggered a series of ill-fated events for cattle feeders: grain prices jumped about 65 percent, cost of grain in feedyards escalated, and fed cattle lost up to $200 per head!

Third, President Nixon's policy of reduced grain acreage, implemented during the 1972 election year, was ill-timed, considering the sale to the USSR and the short crop that followed. In an attempt to offset over-reduction, Secretary of Agriculture Earl L. Butz in 1974 allegedly urged farmers to "plant fencerow to fencerow." He denied this statement but farmers blamed him for their subsequent over-production.

Do All Cattlemen Drive Cadillacs?

The consumer revolt and protests by politicians persisted. Slogans like "Let Meat Rot" and "Let's Eat Fish Until Meat Comes Down" began to wear thin with industry leaders. So they responded with the Industry Information Council (IIC), formed by the ANCA and American National CowBelles (ANCB), to carry out "a coordinated program of public information and public relations."

The IIC kickoff was in Pittsburgh, Pennsylvania, in July 1970, by industry spokesmen John Trotman, ANCA vice president from Alabama; Bill Webster, feeder from Colorado; and Mrs. Carl Stevenson, ANCB president from Arizona. They made speeches to assembled editorial writers, food editors and business editors. They also appeared before service clubs and on TV talk shows, where they were asked such questions as: *Why is beef so expensive?* and *Do all cattlemen drive Cadillacs?*

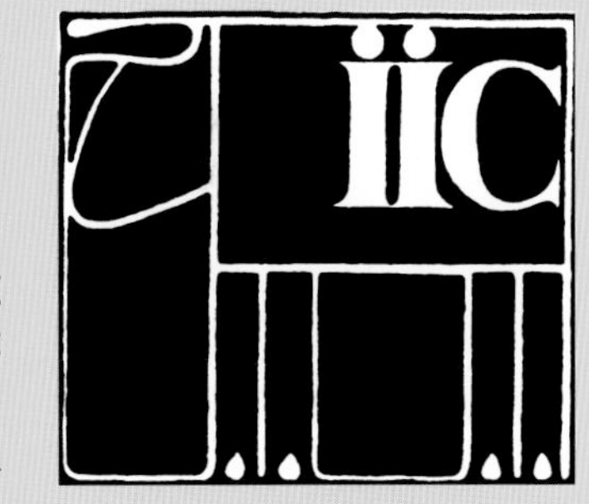

From a cattleman's viewpoint, cattle prices in 1970 were not high; they were merely back up to the 1952 average level of $179 per head, and that was a good year. But consumer activists were playing back different figures, which showed that cattle prices had increased over 50 percent in five years and a supermarket steak had jumped 25 percent.

Eat More Beef, was not an easy sell to budget-conscious housewives. But the profit-conscious cattlemen and CowBelles had to keep trying. So they proceeded to organize state and local Industry Information Councils, and generally felt they did some good. Their full-blown program included speakers bureaus, prepared speeches, publicity kits, suggested promotional events, facts on the industry, and other materials. It was the beginning of a public relations program that would gain momentum in the 1970s and eventually became a major focus of the Association.

Bill Webster of Colorado and Pat Stevenson of Arizona *tell the beef story to a food editor in Pittsburgh, 1970.*

BEHIND THE SCENES

GEORGE S. SPENCER
EXECUTIVE VICE PRESIDENT
1970-1980

The year George Spencer was born in Utah, 1932, the famous Swift Trips began in Chicago. Thirty years later, he was helping plan and run those trips. The tours were traveling marketing seminars for livestock leaders, who traveled by train and later by plane to visit packers and retailers in Chicago, New York, Washington and other distribution centers. In that position he became acquainted with leading cattlemen who, in turn, recognized him as a budding young leader. So in 1970, he was hired as executive vice president-administration of ANCA.

After attending Utah State University, he became a vo-ag teacher and coached winning judging teams in state and national competition. At Swift & Co., 1962-1970, he started in the Agricultural Research Division (mostly producer relations), then transferred to Clovis, New Mexico, then to Guymon, Oklahoma, where he headed the Beef Division and was responsible for buying live cattle and selling carcasses.

Spencer Works with Members of the 1972 Executive Committee. *(left to right) Curtis Avery, Fred Phillips, Bill McMillan, George Spencer, John Trotman, W.D. Farr, Wray Finney, Bob Child, and Charlie Wetzler.*

When he came to ANCA in 1970, the Association was in such poor financial condition they could not even borrow money to operate, he relates, *except to the extent we could secure with office furniture and typewriters.* So some members of the Executive Committee, plus other loyal standbys, signed a note with a San Antonio bank and basically considered it a donation. But with Spencer's frugal background, management training and corporate experience, he turned the finances around within a year and no one lost money.

Spencer initiated other programs and activities with lasting impact:

1. Communications with packers and retailers to substitute understanding and cooperation for suspicion and lawsuits.
2. Consolidation talks with NLFA, which materialized in the new NCA, in 1977.
3. A trade show during the annual convention, beginning in 1971, that was grown each year.
4. A public relations program that has expanded for 25 years.
5. The Young Cattlemen's Council with tours patterned after the old Swift Trips.

In the Mormon Church, he was a faithful and evangelical worker, filling a number of key leadership positions. His Christian approach and spiritual strength, combined with his articulate speech and mild manner, were assets in his Association work. He was a true behind-the-scenes leader, always coaching his volunteer leaders and pushing them to the fore.

In April 1980, disappointed over the defeat of the second Beeferendum, he resigned and returned to work for another packer, IBP. Fifteen years later, as elected secretary-treasurer of the Meat Board, he played a major role in yet another consolidation, that of NCA and the Meat Board into the National Cattlemen's Beef Association.

EMERGENCY FUND

Of course, those consumer concoctions angered the stressed cattlemen. The Texas Cattle Feeders Association, a state affiliate of ANCA, decided to set up an emergency fund. They asked members for $1 for each animal owned "to tell the cattlemen's story." A mimeographed letter went out April 7, 1973, and three weeks later they had $519,000 cash on hand—more money than they knew what to do with! So they opted to send $200,000 to the National Live Stock and Meat Board for beef promotion, and $100,000 to the ANCA for public relations.

Both national organizations were struggling financially. But this stimulus, and the support from other associations that followed, turned both organizations around; both have been growing ever since.

THE WRECK

When President Nixon imposed the price freeze on beef, beginning March 19, 1973, he also announced that it would end September 12. So cattle feeders, in anticipation of higher prices when the freeze was lifted, held many cattle off the market. Likewise, ranchers held their

The Nixon Administration Did Turn its Back on the Needs of the Cattlemen. *President Richard Nixon imposed the first peace-time price controls, followed by a price freeze, which provoked The Wreck of 1973 sending cattle prices plummeting. Here the ANCA Board of Directors meets with President Nixon (fourth from right) in 1970 to confront the issue.*

W.D. (BILL) FARR
President 1970-1971
Greeley, Colorado

The first full-time cattle feeder to be elected President. He remembers when cattle feeders were barred from business meetings, as competitors. He also did field testing of diethylstilbestrol (DES) in the 1950s; was first chairman of ANCA Grading Committee; instrumental in opening ANCA office in Washington; and active in the Association more than 50 years. He was selected "Feeder of the Year," in 1969 by FEEDLOT magazine, and one of "25 Who Made A Difference," by BEEF magazine in 1989. Most important development he has seen: *the hamburger*.

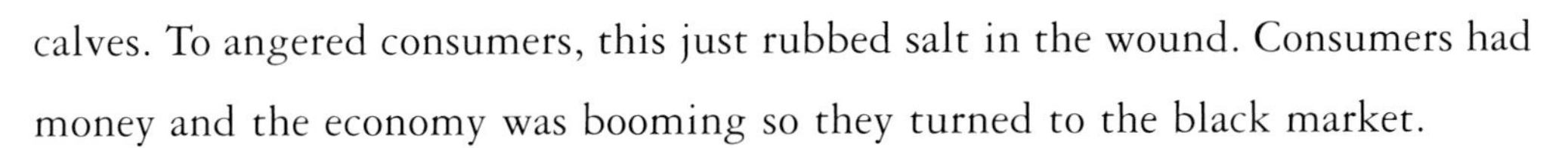

calves. To angered consumers, this just rubbed salt in the wound. Consumers had money and the economy was booming so they turned to the black market.

Some feeders held their cattle too long, up to weights of 1,300 pounds or more, when 1,050 pounds was considered the optimum weight for steers. Thus, when the freeze was lifted, as promised on September 12, the supply of fed cattle was too burdensome, and prices plummeted. In August 1973, for example, choice steers were selling for $58 per cwt.; by November, prices were down to $39—a 33 percent drop in three months. At the same time, grain prices jumped as much as 65 percent, triggered by the Russian grain deal.

For cattle feeders, the short-term result was losses of $100 to $200 per head, numerous bankruptcies and mergers of feedyards, all to become known as "The Wreck." The long-term result was an unprecedented reduction in cattle numbers, down from 132 million in 1975 to 95 million in 1990.

For consumers, the short-term result was lower prices for a few months; the long-term was a prolonged shortage and higher prices for several years.

W.D. Farr sorting cattle *on his favorite horse, Navajo, at the feedlot in Greeley, Colorado, in 1943.*

THE FABULOUS FARRS

Few families have furnished more leadership to the livestock industry than the Farrs of Colorado. So much so that you have to pay close attention to keep family members straight.

The Farrs got into the feeding business by accident in 1895 when over 500 yearling wethers got caught in a snowstorm near Greeley, Colorado. William H. (Billy) Farr had some hay and barley on hand, fed the lambs through the winter and made $1.25 per head profit.

His son, Harry W. Farr, and grandson, W.D. (Bill) Farr, followed in the sheep business and by the 1930s, were among the largest lamb feeders in the country.

H.W. Farr, *Chairman of the National Live Stock and Meat Board, 1942 to 1945. Primarily a sheep feeder, H.W. was a leader in the early attempts to advertise red meat, benefiting the cattle, hog and sheep industries alike.*

Between 1942-1945, Harry served as chairman of the National Live Stock and Meat Board. While selected as a lamb feeder, he believed in "red meat promotion," since many farmers raised all three species—cattle, sheep and hogs—and most packers were multi-species slaughterers.

W. D. Farr fed his first cattle in 1929 and went on to become one of the most prominent cattle feeders in the country.

> *When I first started attending Association conventions which were controlled by the ranchers, I was known as a half-breed. They had guards at the doors to keep out enemy cattle feeders. I was able to get in only because my father owned a ranch.*

But when ANCA accepted "Cattle feeders as a reality" at the 1955 convention in Reno, W.D. Farr stepped forward as the chairman of the first Cattle Feeders Committee. After that he served the industry in many roles, including president of ANCA (1970-1971), chairman of the first ANCA Grading Committee, National Livestock Tax Committee, chairman of the National Cattlemen's Foundation (1972-1983), several state and local organizations, and as a member of the National Live Stock and Meat Board, the USDA National Cattle Industry Advisory Committee and others.

Rarely has their been a need in the Association when W.D. Farr did not step forward to alleviate. And, in his late eighties, he is still leading, currently as a member of the NCBA Centennial Task Force and the Editorial Board of this book.

W.D.'s sons, W.R. (Bill) and H. Richard (Dick) Farr, are keeping the family's leadership tradition intact. Bill served as chairman of the NCA Building Committee, which raised over $2 million for the current NCBA headquarters in Denver, the NCA Foreign Trade Committee and, in 1990, chairman of the United States Meat Export Federation.

Dick, who now manages Farr Feeders, the old family feedyard in Greeley, has served on several NCA committees, including the Grading Committee, Animal Health Committee, Market Committee, for 10 years as chairman of the Futures Sub-Committee and currently is President-elect of Cattle-Fax.

W.D. Farr shocked members *of a cattle feeders meeting in the early 1970s when he predicted that per capita consumption of poultry would pass beef consumption by the end of the decade.It happened in 1977. A man of uncommon wisdom and foresight, W.D. Farr is considered one of the true dignitaries in the history of the Association.*

Noted for their innovations and keen business sense, the Farrs have always been a family of vision. Prophetically in the words of W.D. Farr, *just because your father or grandfather did it that way, is no guarantee that it will be done that way in the future.* It is with this philosophy that the Farr Family has helped the Association move from one era to the next.

Family partnerships *have long been a tradition with the Farrs. Originally W.H. (Billy) Farr formed a partnership with H.W. (Harry) Farr, who then formed a partnership with his son, W.D. Farr, who likewise formed a partnership with his sons Bill and Dick.*

Working Out the Problems of The Wreck of 1973. *Don Magdanz (right), while executive vice president of NLFA, meets with President Nixon and Secretary of Agriculture Clifford M. Hardin.*

President Gordon Van Vleck testified before the Senate Agriculture Committee in 1975: *The entire beef industry has sustained operating losses of $5 billion, plus a reduction in inventory value of $20 billion.*

Later, he explained how that frustrated cattlemen and the Association:

> *Because of the decline in inventory value, some banks would not loan to cattlemen, and that put many out of business. Members were calling on their Association for help, so we worked for and got an Emergency Loan Program from the FmHA and the Small Business Administration. And this irritated some conservative members who objected to government help, even to emergency loans.*

The Yellow Sheet

During "The Wreck" of the 1970s, many cattlemen were looking for someone to blame. Most overlooked the fact that cattle numbers had increased 18 percent in the last 10 years, 33 percent in the last 20 years. So they blamed—some even sued—packers, retailers and *The Yellow Sheet*.

The Yellow Sheet is a daily price report, printed on yellow paper, which was started in 1923 at the request of packers. It was published by the *National Provisioner* in Chicago for 69 years, now by Urner Barry Publishing Company in New Jersey. Packers and others in the meat trade once relied on it as the only means of keeping up with wholesale prices, since anti-trust laws prevented them from exchanging price information.

Although the USDA reported a range of prices for the previous day, with a dozen reporters calling meat traders, *The Yellow Sheet* could report the closing price at the end of each day, which the wholesale meat trade liked. These prices were mailed out and sent over the wire.

Many cattlemen were convinced that *The Yellow Sheet* was manipulated by the packers, a charge they never were able to prove, in court or elsewhere.

Lester I. Norton, *fiery publisher of the Yellow Sheet added fuel to the debate over meat pricing. With a sharp tongue and pen, he remained controversial until his retirement in 1988.*

In 1978, the Meat Pricing Task Force, comprised of 10 cattlemen and consumers appointed by the Secretary of Agriculture, concluded that *The Yellow Sheet* was not manipulated. But they recommended an increase in the price base for price reporting. They also recommended that formula trading should not be banned, mandatory price reporting should be avoided and electronic meat marketing should be explored. In short, they concluded that the existing system was working quite well.

While *The Yellow Sheet* reported wholesale carcass prices, two things occurred during the 1980s that contributed to its diminishing influence: (1) the growing popularity of boxed beef, meaning that carcass prices were less meaningful; and (2) the decision of major packers to rely more on USDA's cut-out values, a weighted average of all cuts in the carcass.

Lester I. Norton, publisher, and his sheet were key parts of meat pricing until the late 1980s when boxed beef essentially replaced carcass beef trading and the USDA developed Boxed Beef Cut-Out Values.

The Yellow Sheet continued to be published but no longer was the pinnacle of blame for cattlemen's ills. That eminence was to be taken over by cattle futures.

JOHN M. TROTMAN
President 1972-1973
Montgomery, Alabama

"Southerners still were not considered cattlemen," says this affable Southern Gentleman, the second president from the South. He worked hard to change that image, because "cattle numbers in the South increased 200 percent in 25 years following the war." Price controls in 1973, the only peace time price controls ever, was "the biggest issue during my tenure." When controls were lifted, it triggered "The Wreck," and fed cattle prices dropped 33 percent in three months. He instigated an industry Public Relations program that has prevailed and grown for 20 years.

WHO WAS TO BLAME

Cattle producers turned several directions in their search for a reason behind the Wreck and their inability to recover quickly.

The Nixon Administration will not turn its back on the needs of cattlemen. The Nixon Administration will be dedicated to seeing to it that cattlemen enjoy their full fair share of our increasing national prosperity and that federal policies encourage the health and growth of this vital industry.

—1968 Nixon Campaign Statement

A lightning rod for criticism in those days, by producers and consumers alike, was the *YELLOW SHEET,* a market news report. The criticism usually ran like this: Approximately 70 percent of all carlot carcass sales are based on *THE YELLOW SHEET* quotes. . .*THE YELLOW SHEET* reports only about two percent of the sales. . .Packers often convert these carcass prices into live cattle bids. . .Packers can and do manipulate reports to *THE YELLOW SHEET.* None of these complaints were ever proven.

Likewise, producers turned towards the retailers and packers as adversaries. Claiming price fixing and market manipulation, producers filed suits against retailers and packers totaling over $1 billion. ANCA, however, took the official position that the only way out of The Wreck was to sell more beef and put its attention to that end.

A CHECKOFF FOR BEEF

Following the 1973 consumer boycotts and the market wreck, it became clear that more—big—money was needed to tell the beef story. Further, the success of the TCFA Emergency Fund indicated that cattlemen were willing to fund expanded programs. Thinking that the time was now right and borrowing the idea from the successful $1-per-bale checkoff in the cotton industry, Charlie Ball, TCFA executive vice president, proposed a national uniform checkoff for cattle to the TCFA on March 23, 1974. (Ball had written about the cotton checkoff many times and helped promote it while an editor of *FARM JOURNAL.*)

TCFA liked the idea and recommended it to the ANCA Executive Committee, who in turn got enthusiastic approval of the ANCA Board of Directors. So on September 5, 1974, ANCA President Van Vleck appointed a Beef Development Taskforce (BDT) of 15 people, representing eight national organizations, to develop a plan. O. J. Barron of Spur, Texas, was the national chairman and Charlie Ball was national coordinator. However, despite this enthusiastic beginning, it would take three attempts at a checkoff before one would finally pass in 1986.

Opening Markets. *Bill McMillan with a group of Japanese. Japan was the first market that the USMEF successfully entered with beef exports from the United States.*

GORDON VAN VLECK
PRESIDENT 1974-1975
PLYMOUTH, CALIFORNIA

"Volatility" best described his times: inflation, consumer boycotts, record cattle numbers, dismal prices, record losses, many bankruptcies. And he was "the man for the times:" solid, respected, a "rock" of a leader who inspired confidence. He appointed a Beef Development Taskforce to pursue a national uniform checkoff; he led the effort for dual grading; and later he co-chaired the ANCA-NLFA Consolidation Committee. Still later, he served on the Long Range Plan Committee that led to the consolidation of NCA and Meat Board into NCBA. *(below)* With McMillan in Washington.

PUBLIC RELATIONS FOR CATTLEMEN

In 1974, when consumers were conducting anti-beef campaigns and producers were struggling to stay in business, cattlemen demanded that ANCA do something to improve their image and their standing with the public. So Van Vleck and Spencer hired Roger Berglund, an experienced agricultural journalist who headed an agressive public relations program for the next 20 years.

UNITED STATES MEAT EXPORT FEDERATION

Throughout the history of the Association, it has recognized the importance of exports but felt almost helpless to increase them. But by 1974, the Association felt the time had come to pursue overseas markets aggressively, and the Executive Committee traveled to Japan, Australia and New Zealand. These travels led to the formation, in 1975, of the United States Meat Export Federation (USMEF); McMillan was the first interim chairman; Peter Marble, chairman of the ANCA Foreign Trade Committee, was elected its first chairman.

PROMPT AND ASSURED PAYMENT

The domino effect of the consumer wake—from boycotts to price freeze, to producers withholding cattle, to a flooded market, to huge losses, to packer bankruptcies—seemed to have no end. When American Beef Packers, Inc. (ABP) went bankrupt in 1975, owing producers $22.5 million, ANCA and NLFA went to Congress for future protection.

The result was a Prompt and Assured Payment amendment to the Packers and Stockyards Act, obtained over fierce opposition by packers. The objective was to eliminate unreasonable "packer float" defined as follows:

The packer would buy cattle at the feedyard, but would delay in paying. And then the check might be mailed, taking two or three more days for delivery, or perhaps written on a remote bank, maybe 1,000 miles away. So the delay in the feedyard getting paid, after the cattle were picked up, was often substantial.

Interest on a 1,050-pound steer could cost the owner about 16 cents per day, or $1.60 per head for 10 days, or $160 for a pen of 100 head for 10 days. Conversely, for a packer slaughtering 3,000 head per day, a 10-day float was worth $48,000.

The "Prompt Payment" part of the Amendment required the packer to *deliver* the check to the feedyard, not mail it, by the close of the next business day following purchase.

The "Assured Payment" part of the Amendment, which some people considered even more important, dealt with packers who went bankrupt or otherwise failed to pay. It placed sellers of livestock ahead of other secured creditors in claims on inventory and receivables.

Dietary Goals for the United States

The initial concerns of protesting consumers related to food prices, particularly to beef prices. But the consumer activists seized this moment of unrest and took it further to concerns about diet-health and the morality of feeding grain to livestock. Some politicians saw a parade forming and got in front of it.

Senator George McGovern (D-SD), chairman of the Senate Select Committee on Nutrition and Human Needs, conducted hearings in 1976 and on January 14, 1977, released the controversial publication, "Dietary Goals for the United States." Among seven suggestions in the report was this inflammatory one: "Decrease consumption of meat and increase consumption of poultry and fish."

Cattlemen's tempers flared! NCA called the recommendations "arbitrary and with no valid scientific basis." A group of 14 scientists chosen by the Council for Agricultural Science and Technology (CAST) concluded that "the goals are not appropriate if applied to the general public." Further, the scientists contended that the goals did not address the two most important aspects of applied nutrition: reduced caloric intake to control obesity and eating a variety of foods to achieve a balanced diet.

Suits Against Retailers & Packers

The Wreck left producers broke and looking for somebody to blame and retailers and packers were easy targets.

By August 1976, producers had filed nine suits against 23 retail food stores and a dozen meat packers for damages in excess of $1 billion. They all alleged collusion and price fixing.

ANCA officers, knowing that the best way out of The Wreck was for retailers to feature more beef, worked hard to develop rapport with chain stores and their National Association of Food Chains. But after a rash of law suits, chains became unwilling or afraid to even talk to ANCA leaders.

These suits were based on the well-publicized Bray case filed in 1969. Lawyers Joseph L. Alioto, the colorful mayor of San Francisco, and his son, on behalf of Irwin Bray of California and six other cattlemen, charged A&P, Safeway and Kroger with conspiring to fix prices at both wholesale and retail levels.

Safeway and Kroger settled out of court for $90,000 between them. But A&P opted to fight it. In 1974, a six-person jury in San Francisco ruled against A&P and awarded $10,904,027 in damages, which automatically were tripled under antitrust law to $32,712,000. A&P later settled for $9,000,000. This gave false hope to some discouraged cattlemen and their opportunistic attorneys.

Later cases were ultimately dropped, based on a 1977 ruling by the Supreme Court (the Illinois Brick case) that sellers were generally precluded from recovering damages if they did not sell directly to the defendant. Thus, cattlemen could not collect from retailers.

Most feeders did not want to sue packers, to whom they sold directly and must continue selling. The Meat Price Investigators (MPI) of Iowa did sue packers, however. They charged in 1976 that IBP, MBPXL (now Excel), Spencer Foods and Flavorland Industries violated anti-trust laws by manipulating *The Yellow Sheet*. Spencer and Flavorland settled, depositing money into an interest-bearing fund, which grew to over $2 million. But IBP and MBPXL went to court.

The case was finally settled in 1991, with no findings against IBP and MBPXL, although MPI lost the final court case. But by this time, the Dallas judge could not find proper recipients for damages in the class action suit. So he searched for an organization that represented all cattlemen and awarded $750,000 to the BIC of the Meat Board. The remainder—over $1 million—went to the trial lawyers involved.

Mending Fences. *In an effort to get retailers to sell more beef, and thus work their way out of the The Wreck of 1973, ANCA members called on retailers. Bill Canning, (left); George Feaster and Jack Owens paid a call on Safeway.*

New Nutrition Guidelines. *Cattlemen took great interest in the the hearings held by Senator George McGovern (D-SD) (left), chairman of the Senate Select Committee on Nutrition and Human Needs in 1976 and were inflammed when he published his findings, recommending people decrease their consumption of meat and increase their consumption of poultry and fish. Cattlemen declared such statements as unfounded and unscientific, but the public picked up on the idea.*

TRACTORCADES

Cattlemen were not the only ones who felt mistreated by government during the 1970s. After the "boom and bust" of the USSR grain deal, grain farmers were pinched. The 1977 price of corn, for example, was 47 percent of parity, compared with 61 percent for beef cattle. Some said they were betrayed by Secretary of Agriculture Earl Butz who, they claimed, had encouraged their overproduction.

A new organization, American Agriculture Movement (AAM), surfaced in 1976. They demanded 100 percent parity and threatened to strike if they did not get it. Most AAM membership was believed to be in the Midwest, but it extended as far south as Florida and Texas. Following is an excerpt from an AAM message in late 1977:

> *American agriculture is planning a large strike. We, the American farmers, are demanding 100 percent parity for all agricultural products produced in the United States. We are also willing to produce for any foreign country or any organization that will guarantee 100 percent parity. This proposal is being presented to all existing agricultural organizations in the U.S. If these organizations do not endorse and support these proposals, we will cancel all memberships and insurance held in these organizations by the American farmers and stockmen. This ultimatum is also being presented to the Congress of the U.S. by the deadline of Dec. 14, 1977, for action. If this proposal is not enacted by law by our deadline, we will strike. We, the farmers of this nation, will halt all agricultural production and distribution immediately. This action will continue until our demands are met.*

The entire beef industry has sustained operating losses of $5 billion, plus a reduction in inventory value of $20 billion.

—ANCA President Van Vleck

Testifying before the Senate Agriculture Committee in 1975

For three centuries, exports have been considered essential by United States cattle producers. As early as 1680, Carolina producers were shipping salt beef and pork to the West Indies. Between 1868 and 1885, according to a government report, the export value of cattle and cattle products was six percent of the total value of United States production, more than it was in 1985. In 1898, when the National Live Stock Association was organized, exports of animals and animal products were valued at $238 million.

But there was no organized effort to expand exports until the 1970s.

In 1974, part of the ANCA Executive Committee traveled to Japan to explore expanded markets there. The importance of this effort was underlined by the fact that each member paid his own expenses. They also visited Australia and New Zealand to see what the opposition was doing. Members of this trade team included: Gordon Van Vleck, ANCA president from California; Dick McDougal from Nevada; Peter Marble, chairman of the Foreign Trade Committee from Nevada; W.D. Farr, former president from Colorado; Jim Hughes of Arizona; Bob Johnston of Colorado; Girdner Crofoot of Kansas; Fred Phillips of Oregon; and Bill McMillan, ANCA executive vice president-Washington affairs.

Upon return, McMillan reported *an exciting potential* to the administrator of Foreign Agricultural Service (FAS), USDA, who in turn committed to support a cooperator organization with the USDA putting in $2 for each $1 the industry put in, *if the industry could form a cooperator organization to represent all red meat.*

Thus, the United States Meat Export Federation (USMEF) was organized in 1975, to represent beef, pork and sheep producer organizations along with packers and exporters. At the first meeting on February 20, 1976, there were 20 charter members (including 12 beef producer groups), who put up $100,000 to be matched with $200,000 from the FAS.

Peter E. Marble, *first elected chairman of the USMEF. From Deeth, Nevada, Marble served as the Chairman of the ANCA Foreign Trade Committee during the early 1970s.*

Bill McMillan was the interim chairman. A few months later, Peter Marble became the first elected chairman of USMEF.

Alan R. (Bud) Middaugh, with a packer background, was hired as the first President-CEO. Middaugh was succeeded in 1990 by Philip M. Seng, who had served as USMEF Asian Director at its regional headquarters in Tokyo.

Since then, the USMEF has been the shining star among beef organizations and the increase in beef exports has been spectacular. With headquarters in Denver, USMEF now has foreign offices in Japan, Germany, Hong Kong, Taiwan, Korea, Mexico and Singapore. Also, they have representatives covering Russia, China, the Caribbean, Central and South America, Israel and the Middle East.

By 1995, USMEF had 177 organizational and corporate members, a budget of $25.6 million, including $14.8 million from the government and $8.1 million in checkoff funds.

More important, beef exports increased to $3.3 billion in 1995, a 30-fold increase in 20 years. That amounted to seven percent of the total tonnage and 11 percent of the total value of production in the United States.

After 20 years of glowing reports, cattlemen had grown to appreciate the impact of exports on prices. A 1995 study by CF Resources, for example, showed that exports increased the value of fed cattle by $7.29 per cwt. and increased the value of calves by $15.31 per cwt.

When the new organization, National Cattlemen's Beef Association (NCBA), was organized in 1996, with the early objective of including all beef organizations, the USMEF was initially included.

Alan R. (Bud) Middaugh, *was the first president-CEO of the USMEF.*

USMEF officers helped draw up the plan and recommended it to their members. However, because USMEF is a multi-species organization, some members feared losing a significant portion of the USDA funding for the red meat export programs. Consequently, they voted not to merge. Thus, USMEF remains a primary contractor for beef checkoff funds but outside the NCBA umbrella.

Philip M. Seng. *After serving as Asian Director, Seng returned to Denver in 1990 as president-CEO of USMEF.*

TOTAL UNITED STATES BEEF EXPORTS

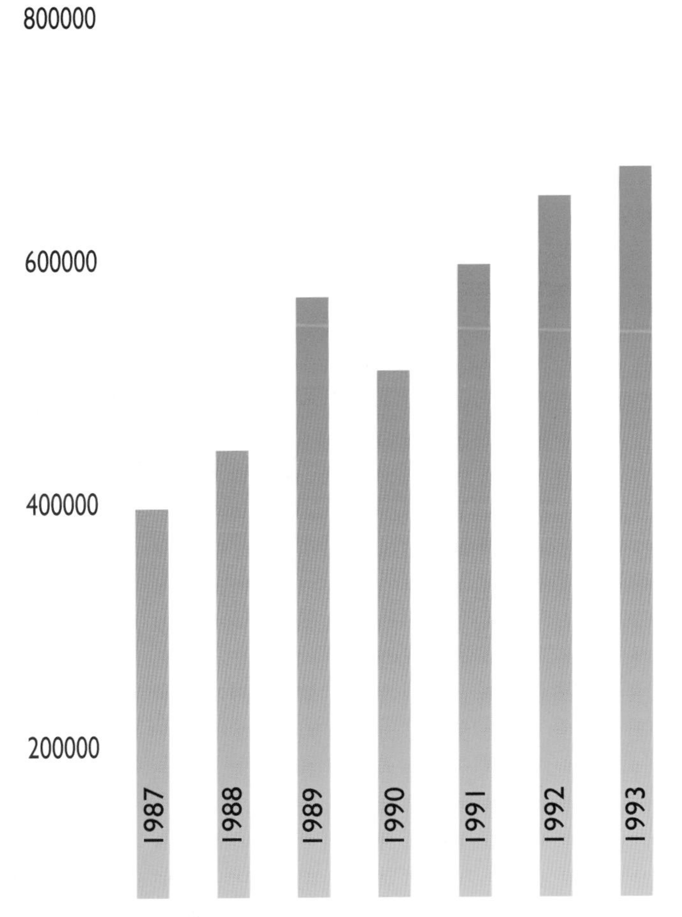

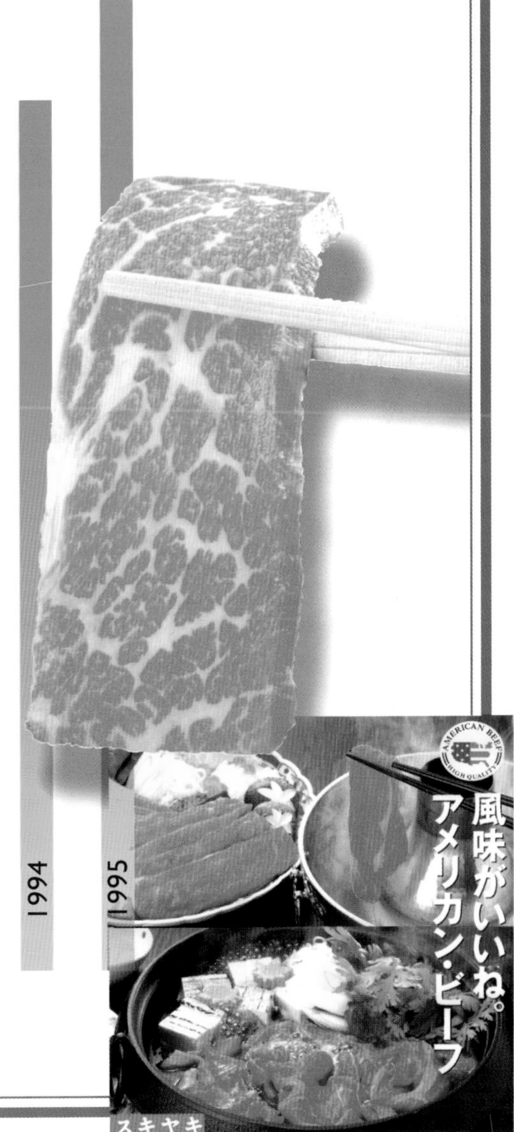

WRAY FINNEY
President 1976-1977
Fort Cobb, Oklahoma

A large, jovial man who worked tirelessly to prevent cattlemen from being run over by the steam-rolling consumer movement. He rented an apartment in Denver and made a near full-time job of the presidency. "Dietary Goals for the U.S." was his worry, while the Association accomplishments included passage of the Beef Research and Information Act, Prompt Payment legislation and the ANCA-NLFA consolidation. His wife, Dolores, was President of ANCB in 1967, and Wray was the last ANCA president.

"Tractorcades" took Over Washington. *Hundreds of sign-carrying tractors gathered in processions. The largest one occurred in December 1977, when more than 5,000 tractors drove through Georgia. Several days later, hundreds of tractors arrived in Washington and created "mass chaos" as they encircled the Capital, White House and Washington Monument. A rowdy mob of farmers cornered Secretary of Agriculture Robert Bergland in the USDA Administration Building, until he managed to escape through a ground floor window. All 4,100 officers of the District of Columbia Police Department were called out and worked around the clock in 12-hour shifts, while the farmers camped on the grassy Mall. When they finally left, the government estimated damages to the grass and streets and police overtime at $3.6 million.*

When their demands were not met, AAM members began a series of demonstrations known as "Tractorcades." Hardly the way to "win friends and influence people," but NCA treaded lightly. NCA President Richard A. McDougal issued a written statement explaining why the Association was not taking an official position on the strike.

> *Participation or non-participation by any member is strictly an individual decision. Some cattlemen are participating. It appears, however, that most beef cattle producers and feeders are not. In any event, the strike is calling the public's attention to the extreme cost-price squeeze in which most farmers and ranchers now find themselves.*

Actually, after the strike date had come and gone, no effects were noted. The AAM lived on for a number of years.

NCF AND CALF

Adversities of the stressful seventies did not seem to deter ANCA. Instead, the Association grew and expanded, partially a response to the consumer stand.

ANCA membership grew from 6,436 in 1970 to 16,450 in 1976 (before the merger with NLFA), while membership revenues increased from $356,472 to $1,150,837. By 1994, NCA membership had reached 42,183 and membership revenues a record $3,226,014.

STAMPEDE By Jerry Palen

"Senator, that farm lobby is here."

Part of the expansion was the formation of American Cattlemen's Foundation in 1972, later to be named the National Cattlemen's Foundation (NCF), for the purpose of "charitable, scientific and educational activities to benefit the cattle industry."

The year after ANCA opened an office in Washington, Congress passed the Federal Election Campaign Act, which authorized the formation a Political Action Committee (PAC) by trade associations and certain businesses. That prompted the formation of Cattlemen's Action Legislative Fund (CALF), another expansion while W.D. Farr was President. Bob Johnston, Jr. of Fowler, Colorado, was the first chairman and, in the first year of operation in 1972, receipts topped $11,000.

Although Johnston worked hard at soliciting funds, it was difficult times in the industry to raise money. CALF then became relatively dormant until it was reorganized in 1978 and the name changed to NCA-PAC. That year, receipts were more than $106,000; and the momentum has continued ever since.

MEAT IMPORTS CHALLENGED

One of the first challenges for the new Association was to amend the meat import law. And this turned out to be another of its major legislative accomplishments.

Cattle numbers increased dramatically during the early 1970s to a record 132 million head in 1975. Then liquidation started, reducing numbers to 122 million head in 1977, a seven percent drop in two years. Under the Meat Import Act of 1964, which allowed imports up to 7.5 percent of domestic production, such liquidation caused imports to increase, and further depress prices.

NCA President McDougal testified in Washington that the national cattle inventory dropped from $41 billion on January 1, 1944 to $21 billion in 1975 and was at $25 billion in 1977.

Further aggravating the problem, importers had learned how to circumvent the law. The law covered fresh, frozen and chilled meat, not processed or cooked meat. So by doing superficial processing at Foreign Trade Zones, they produced processed beef, exempt from the law.

Decrease consumption of meat and increase consumption of poultry and fish.

—Recommendations from "Dietary Goals for the United States," 1977

The NCA goals, according to Tom Cook, at the time staff secretary to the Foreign Trade Committee, were to get: (1) all beef covered; (2) a counter-cyclical formula, so that imports would decrease as domestic production increased and vice versa; and (3) quotas on a quarterly basis, rather than an annual basis, to avoid bunching.

Inflation was raging like a prairie fire and reached 8.8 percent in 1979 (before going to 12.5 percent in 1980), which caused new rumblings of consumer boycotts. President Jimmy Carter, feeling the heat from consumers, had opened the gates to imports in 1978, triggering a $10-per-cwt. drop in cattle prices. This whetted the resolve of the Association to get a counter-cyclical bill, which they did get through Congress in November 1978, only to have it vetoed by President Carter.

Cattlemen were hopping mad, as reflected in McDougal's scathing letter to President Carter:

> *It is unbelievable to me that. . .your concern for giving up some of your authority over beef imports took precedence over the bill's*

THE HANDSHAKE

Sealing the Deal. *Milton J. Brown, NLFA immediate past president, and Gordon Van Vleck, ANCA immediate past president reach an agreement on the merger.*

In 1970 when W.D. Farr became president of ANCA, he and George Spencer, the new executive vice president-administration, traveled to Nebraska to visit with NLFA President Oscar Bredthauer. *We had an enjoyable dinner visit,* Farr later said, *But when I mentioned consolidation, he suggested it was time to go home.*

Consolidation of beef industry organizations was a goal that Spencer brought with him from his earlier employment with Swift & Co.:

> *I had observed in the livestock industry a tendency to form a new organization for each new problem or issue. We had several organizations: ANCA for legislative matters, NLFA for feeders, Meat Board for promotion, National Livestock Tax Committee, Public Lands Coun-*

For the American National Cattlemen's Association (ANCA) and the National Livestock Feeders Association (NLFA), the consolidation into the new National Cattlemen's Association (NCA) was a giant step for the industry. NCA became official in 1977. This was the Association's second major consolidation. The first occurred in 1906, when the National Live Stock Association and the American Stock Growers Association combined into the American National Live Stock Association. (Name changed to ANCA in 1951).

Talk of an ANCA-NLFA consolidation began in 1968, when ANCA President Bill House suggested it to NLFA President Charles Phelps. *I told Mr. House*, Phelps said 25 years later, *that I thought it had merit but our members weren't ready.*

Signing the Agreement. *Dick McDougall, president of ANCA, signing, and Tom Monier, president of NLFA looking on, as they officially created the new National Cattlemen's Association.*

cil, American National Cow-Belles, Cattle-Fax, Cattlemen's Action Legislative Fund, United States Meat Export Federation and more—all financed separately but all financed by cattlemen.

In 1971, the Iowa Beef Producers Association, with Baxter Freese as President, made a strong appeal to both national associations for consolidation, but were turned down. Past presidents of both associations said the primary resistance came from key staff executives, Bill McMillan at ANCA and Don Magdanz at NLFA, who had opposed each other on legislative and grading issues.

ANCA issued an invitation to consolidate through a press release, according to Spencer, *hoping some members would see the need and press for it. But to no avail.*

By 1976 Gordon Van Vleck, ANCA immediate past president, and Milton J. Brown, NLFA immediate past president, agreed the timing was right. They liked each other and had the same goal of "one strong association for cattlemen." They co-chaired the Consolidation Study Committee: five men from each organization.

The original ANCA-NLFA combined logo was explained in this way.

NCA Mark—What It Symbolizes

The mark is comprised of three elements:

1. Stylized steer head represents what's basic—cattle production.
2. White figure between the steer heads represents NCA cattlemen joined together, with arms outstretched, in a circle of industry unity.
3. Letters "NCA" represent the National Cattlemen's Association.

The mark, in one image, symbolizes what NCA is all about: the unification of cattlemen for the benefit of members and the entire cattle industry.

But the logo created a big problem. A few members recall with humor that the first logo for the new NCA was seen in many ways. Some people could see 10 men holding hands in a circle, some saw a cross-section of 10 steer heads, and some saw a corn cob! The logo was so controversial that it was dropped in 1981 and a stylized version of the earlier ANCA logo, a steer's head extended across a map of the United States, was adopted for the remaining years of NCA.

During the next nine months, the Consolidation Committee met nine times, usually in Kansas City, and hammered out an agreement. *Initially, they sat on one side of the table and we sat on the other,* said Charles Phelps, *but later we intermingled, grew to trust each other and it became apparent we could work in one organization.*

The consolidation was not that of two equal entities. At the time, NLFA had 12,308 members and total annual income in 1976 of $180,412. ANCA had 16,450 members (up from 6,436 in 1970) and total annual income of $1,584,695. Dues were a problem and it took two typewritten pages to define them. The Plan A and Plan B, the minimum and the maximum, and the other intricacies were so complex that neither the officers nor the staff could quote them from memory.

The consolidation presented a stronger national look to the Association, while allowing greater grassroots involvement. Under the new structure, the United States was divided into seven regions, each served by a vice president. The strength of the organization was placed in its 13 committees, made up of individuals from across the regions, who established policy for the Association. This structure was well received and changed little during the following 19 years of the NCA.

The NLFA-ANCA Consolidation Committee in 1977. *(left to right) Don Magdanz (NLFA), George Spencer (ANCA), Jo Ann MacDonal (secretary), William G. Amstein (ANCA), Curtis B. Avery, Jr., (NLFA), Tom Monier (NLFA), Lauren E. Carlson (ANCA), John C. Klosterman (NLFA), P.H. White, Jr., (NLFA), Charles E. Phelps (NLFA), Milton J. Brown (NLFA), W.H. (Bill) Webster (ANCA), and Gordon Van Vleck (ANCA).*

RICHARD A. (DICK) McDOUGAL
PRESIDENT 1977-1978
LOVELOCK, NEVADA

As the first President of the new NCA, he set out to *make every member feel welcome, especially new members from NLFA*. With a winning personality and intense effort (away from home 250 nights in 1978) he was successful in his goal, and NCA became a truly national organization. His other challenges were a counter-cyclical meat import bill, vetoed by the President; curbing inflation and 20 percent interest rates; dealing with the consumer activists appointed to government posts by President Carter. He was a feeder and farmer, originally from California.

Consumer Activists in USDA. *When Jimmy Carter was elected President in 1976, he appointed consumer activists to many government posts, including Carol Tucker Foreman as Assistant Secretary of Agriculture. She had been President of the Consumer Federation of America and knew little about agriculture, but was suddenly put in charge of meat grading, meat inspection, livestock reporting and several other government programs that affected cattlemen. Some cattlemen considered her a fox in the hen house. But NCA's Bill McMillan got along well with her. (Coincidentally, when Ronald Reagan replaced Jimmy Carter as President, McMillan replaced Foreman as Assistant Secretary.) Twenty years later, few cattlemen could remember who was Secretary of Agriculture in the late 1970s; but many could remember Carol Tucker Foreman as Assistant Secretary.*

> *positive attributes. . .You have singled out the cattle industry as a major cause of inflation. This is nothing short of an insult.*

Then McDougal gave President Carter a bit of advice:

> *I would suggest that now that this damage has been done, you address the real cause of inflation—and the best place to start is right at home with the federal budget. We could support that.*

According to Tom Cook, *It was high drama for cattlemen, especially for the 150 Association members who had been called to Washington to lobby congress. We had gone all out and were not about to quit.*

The Right Man at the Right Time. *Again the Association was lucky to have strong leadership when it needed it. Mc Dougal (here checking grain) worked diligently to bring together the staffs and members of NLFA and ANCA into one cohesive organization.*

But cattlemen had picked up an unusual ally: Alfred E. Kahn, chairman of the Council on Wage and Price Stability. With food prices up more than 12 percent in 1978, President Carter appointed the Council to fight inflation. Testifying in April 1979 that beef prices were rising at an annual rate of 72 percent, Kahn said he would not propose *any concerted effort to break the price chain as long as cattlemen were rebuilding herd numbers.*

An economics professor on leave from Cornell University, Kahn explained with candor and humor that beef prices were rising because cattle were in relatively short supply. He blamed that situation on the price freeze action in 1973. *The President gave me a tremendous range of authority and jurisdiction,* he cracked, *but it does not extend to the mating habits of the cow.*

So NCA relentlessly continued its push for a counter-cyclical formula and got it through Congress again, with slight changes, the following year. And on December 31, President Carter signed into law the Meat Import Act of 1979.

INFLATION, NO. ONE PROBLEM

Throughout its history, the Association has expressed concern about the federal budget and passed numerous resolutions calling for less government spending. By the late 1970s and early 1980s, this concern had grown to alarm and mild panic.

Several times during this period, NCA presidents declared, *Inflation is our Number One problem.* By 1978, the value of the dollar (in purchasing power) was almost half what it was in 1968 and one-fifth its value in 1939. And inflation was continuing at a horrendous rate: 8.8 percent in 1979 and 12.5 percent in 1980. Interest was running 10 cents per pound of gain in the feedyard and represented 14 percent of the cost to produce a calf. Then, in 1981, prime interest rates exploded to 21.5 percent! Agriculture credit began to dry up.

A resolution at the 1978 Convention in New Orleans put NCA in "full support of a constitutional amendment for a balanced federal budget." Then the Association commissioned a study by Michael R. McLeod of Washington entitled, "The Case for an Absolute Requirement to Balance the Federal Budget and to Reduce the Expenditures of the Government of the United States." Another study in 1981, led by Don F. Magdanz, NCA Senior Vice President, showed similar alarm. It traced the increase in federal outlays from $521 million in 1900 to an "appalling" $615 billion in 1981, most of which had occurred in the last 15 years. [This trend continued, increasing the national debt from $994 billion in 1981 to $5.4 trillion in 1996.]

> ***I would suggest that now that this damage has been done, you address the real cause of inflation—and the best place to start is right at home with the federal budget. We could support that.***
>
> —ANCA President McDougal's Advice to President Jimmy Carter

Meat Imports and Inflation. *NCA Executive Vice Presidents George Spencer and Bill McMillan meet with President Jimmy Carter. President Carter was not especially sympathetic to the cattlemen's pleas on the subjects of meat import restrictions and inflation. However, after much lobbying on the part of NCA, the President finally signed the Meat Import Act of 1979.*

The proliferation of government regulations in the late 1970s was considered a major cause of inflation by NCA. Outlays of 41 regulatory agencies were $4.8 million in 1979, according to a study for the Joint Economic Committee of Congress. But the big cost was for compliance of new regulations by industry, over 20 times larger than the federal expenditures on the agencies, bringing the total cost to nearly $98 billion. The typical feedyard was confronted by eight to 10 or more federal regulatory agencies, plus a half-dozen state agencies.

One agency that drew a lot of criticism and laughs from cattlemen was the Occupational Safety and Health Administration (OSHA). In 1976, OSHA published a booklet, *SAFETY WITH BEEF CATTLE,* which amused cattlemen with its simplicity. Some sample quotes: "When floors are wet and slippery with manure, you could have a bad fall. . . .bare feet or sneakers are not safe around cattle. Wear heavy shoes. . .watch your step. Many people trip over animals and fall."

NCA officers and staff appealed to the Federal Reserve Board for economic relief. NCA President J.W. (Bill) Swan of Idaho told Federal Reserve Chairman Paul Volcker in October 1981:

In the Camera's Eye

When Roger Berglund was hired as Public Relations Director in 1974, the Association made a commitment to its members to improve the image of beef in the public eye. It was a formidable task. The industry was beginning to be attacked by groups other than consumers who had merely wanted a better product for less money. Soon, issues such as beef safety, environmental conservancy and nutrition became major concerns for the industry; they had never been so before.

This was not the first Association PR effort. In 1948, for example, ANLSA declared that "the year of public relations." In 1953, ANCA hired Lyle Liggett, who for 15 years operated a classic one-man PR program on a shoestring budget. He was followed by Jim House. And in 1968, the Industry Information Council was established. All these programs relied primarily on volunteer help from members and the CowBelles. The people involved were good, but the programs lacked continuity and the specific professionalism necessary to take on the issues.

From 1974 on, public relations became a major activity for the Association. Following his retirement in 1993 as vice president of communications, Berglund reflected on some of the more successful public relations efforts:

Roger Berglund, *the Association's third public relations director. Beglund had a masterful career for 20 years heading the PR program against many odds.*

News Bureaus

During the middle and late 1970s, when beef prices were still an issue, news bureaus, operated by established PR agencies, were established in Washington, New York, Chicago, San Francisco and Denver. They had long-standing contacts with the media and were excellent at arranging interviews for ANCA officers and at getting answers to questions.

Retail price surveys

Nobody had a handle on true beef prices. So in 1974, ANCA started monthly surveys of three supermarkets in each of 19 cities and put out a release to the media. This added to our credibility and has continued to this day.

Filming a TV newsclip *at the John Benton Ranch in Burns, Colorado. Spokesperson training became one of the more effective ways to tell the beef story. Members from all over the country received training on how to handle the media and cast a positive light on the production of beef and the good aspects of the product.*

Roger Berglund helps ANCA President Van Vleck *produce a message for the Cattlemen's Newscall—a service whereby radio stations could call in and receive a recorded message.*

President Wray Finney *prepares for a News Conference in 1977. The media generally put the Association on the defensive. One of the main thrusts of the Association's PR efforts was to take the offensive, but it took time and training both of officers and members to assume the role of aggressor.*

(below) **Bill Webster of Colorado** *(right)* **responds to Journalist Peter Jennings** *during an ANCA Industry Information Council Tour (IIC) in 1970.*

Food editor tours

Six tours of ranches and feedyards, beginning in 1982, did wonders in establishing credibility with food editors. The romance of our industry and the rugged, strong cattlemen captivated the food editors as no professional staff person could ever do.

Other successful PR programs, according to Berglund, included: studies on what consumers wanted in beef; the War on Fat; changing the "Good" grade to "Select;" Safety Assurance Programs; voluntary withdrawal of low-level antibiotics in feed; and spokesperson training.

National Beef Cookoff

This annual event by the CowBelles (now the American National CattleWomen), with initial staff support from ANCA and BIC, has grown every year since its beginning in 1974 and been a very effective media event.

ANCA President John Trotman *in New York, 1973. One of most comfortable presidents in front of the camera, President Trotman was always eager to tell the story of beef.*

Inflation Led to Agricultural Ruin for Many. *Inflated land prices and the push to plant fencerow to fencerow encouraged farmers to become overextended. Soon deflated grain and cattle prices, and the almost immediate withdrawal of agricultural credit led many families to lose their farms and ranches. The shakeup in the agricultural sector in the late 1970s approached that of the depression years of the 1930s.*

> *NCA consistently has said that inflation is our biggest problem, and we have strongly supported reduced government spending, reduced tax rates and reduced regulatory burdens, all of which will contribute to reduced inflation.*

DES Debacle

One of the regulatory agencies with which cattlemen had to deal was the Food and Drug Administration (FDA). And one of the early drugs that FDA approved for use in cattle, in 1954, was diethylstilbestrol (DES). A few dollars for DES in the feed or a few cents for a DES implant would increase the rate of gain 15 to 20 percent and reduce the amount of feed required 10 to 15 percent. So it quickly became a popular animal drug. That is, until DES was declared a carcinogen (when fed in huge quantities to rats) and the FDA started questioning the possible effect that beef from DES-treated animals might have on humans. Cattlemen argued that DES was never found in the muscle tissue, only in the livers of animals. Further, they argued that a person would have to eat 15,000 pounds of liver to get the amount of DES that a woman gets in one birth control pill. But that was a no-win argument.

On his final day in office, June 29, 1979, FDA Commissioner Donald Kennedy banned DES as a growth promoter in cattle and sheep. That was a loss, but not a crisis, because other growth promotents were available. The crisis came a few months later when the government learned that cattlemen were using up the DES implants they had on hand, plus some implants that were in warehouses.

Although most cattlemen complied with the regulations and ceased use of DES, 240 operators were cited for illegally implanting 412,000 head of cattle. In addition, they were ordered to *explant* all 412,000 head, which was an expensive procedure for animals that were fat and almost ready for market.

The Wild Horse Dilemma

When Wild Horse Annie got a federal law passed in 1959, and another in 1971, she assured a safe home on the range for at least 30,000 wild horses and burros.

The 1959 law prevented mustangers from capturing wild horses with aircraft or motorized vehicles, a controversial practice which reduced numbers to about 9,000 head. They would sell the better ones for riding horses and slaughter the poorer ones for dog food.

The 1971 law called for management, maintenance and control of wild horses and burros on public lands by the Bureau of Land Management (BLM) and Forest Service. Control meant destroying the over-population, but public sentiment prevented that, even by humane means.

The numbers began to increase at about 18 percent a year, moving up to more than 67,696 by 1980.

Bill McMillan, ANCA lobbyist at the time, recounted:

> *The Wild and Free-Roaming Horse and Burro Act of 1971 was the stickiest lobbying effort in memory. Annie got an article on mustangs published in* WEEKLY READER, *which circulated to grade schools. Teachers seized on the idea for a lesson in civics, and congress was flooded with letters from kids. Thus, the bill passed the house and senate without a single dissenting vote!*

Annie—Velma B. Johnston of Reno—also formed a successful non-profit group called Wild Horse Organized Assistance (WHOA). She died in 1977.

The problem for ranchers and also government agencies, after the 1971 Act, was that growing numbers far exceeded numbers needed for "natural ecological balance," as prescribed in the Act. So the agencies started an adoption program, which found private homes for the younger, trainable animals, totaling 123,000 from 1972 to 1993. Adoption fees were $125 for horses and $75 for burros, with the latter being in surprising demand.

But this left a few thousand older horses, which were placed in sanctuaries and moved around by the government. Sanctuaries were found in Nevada, Bloomfield, Nebraska and Muleshoe, Texas. The government paid board of about $1.30 per horse per day.

The same horses were then moved to South Dakota to another feedyard sanctuary, then in 1989 to Bartlesville, Oklahoma, for "final retirement" on bluestem pastures. For board and care of some 1,500 horses, NCA member John Hughes received $1.10 per head per day.

In recent years, the national wild horse program has cost $13 million to $17 million a year.

Ranchers paying grazing fees *were not happy with the free-roaming horses. About two-thirds of the wild horse population roamed on the rocky ranges of Nevada, hardly a haven for horses that thrive on grass but a real problem for ranchers who were paying grazing fees for cattle.Most were not native wilds, but feral descendants of domestic horses that had been loosed through the years.*

Santuary for Horses. *Dick McDougal, NCA President 1977-1978, provided one such sanctuary for horses at his feedyard in Lovelock, Nevada.*

"Charitable, scientific and educational activities to benefit the cattle industry." That was the stated purpose of the American Cattlemen's Foundation, organized in 1972, and later to be named the National Cattlemen's Foundation (NCF).

NCF has had three presidents: W.D. Farr of Colorado, 1972-1983; W.F. (Dub) Martin of New Mexico, 1984-1986; Don Williams of Oklahoma, 1987-1989: and one chairman, Don Butler of Arizona, 1990-present. The title was changed from president to chairman in 1990 and the board was expanded to include all living past presidents.

The first major project of NCF was the collection of funds for a new NCA headquarters building, started in 1980 and completed in 1982.

Other NCF projects through the years have included: awards such as Cattle Businessman of the Year and Special Breed Award (given by NCF but financed by national associates); grants for the Consumer Retail Beef Study, software for Integrated Range Management (IRM), Cattlemen's Newscall (operated by NCA); Cattlemen's Leadership Institute (for officers of all beef organizations); College Beef Bowl (contest for scholarships); and CME scholarships.

In the early days of the checkoff (1987-1990), checkoff funds for Industry Information Programs conducted by NCA, were routed through NCF and appeared to inflate the Foundation budget up to $3 million, but these were pass-through funds. During the early 1990s, the NCF budget otherwise has varied from $75,000 to $100,000. It operates as a non-profit organization and accepts charitable gifts of money and property.

One of the major recent projects has been to plan the NCBA Centennial Celebration (1998) and to publish this history.

The NCF Board *is made up of all past presidents of the Association, who oversee the fundraising and projects of the Foundation. Here fifteen past presidents, one of the larger gatherings, attend a Foundation Meeting. (front row, left to right) Dressler, House, Farr, Trotman, Monier, Lauren Carlson. (back row, left to right) Merlyn Carlson, Washbrun, Waldrip, Smith, Butler, Dahl, Josserand, Lacey, Smith.*

The Building Fund. *Dub Berry, ANCA executive vice president, receives check from the Colorado Cattlemen. NCF raised over $2 million from nearly 1,100 contributors to build the headquarters building in Denver.*

The NCF Mission

The National Cattlemen's Foundation serves the beef cattle industry as a charitable institution whose mission is to preserve the rich heritage and promote the future of the industry through research and education.

- *Sponsors educational programs that promote the nutritional benefits of beef to the general population.*
- *Creates awareness of the unique environmental stewardship and forage utilization character of beef cattle production.*
- *Equips young cattlemen to carry this industry into the 21st century.*

NCF Cattle Businessmen of the Year

1984	Jack Maddux Wauneta, NE
1985	John Armstrong Kingsville, TX
1986	Ron Baker Hermiston, OR
1987	Jim Roberts Lincoln, NE
1988	Martin Jorgenson Ideal, SD
1989	Ladd Hitch Guymon, OK
1990	John Harris Coalinga, CA
1991	Jack Knirk Quincy, MI
1992	Rogers Johnson Kit Carson, CO
1993	James Anderson Longmont, CO
1994	Ted Kendall III Boiton, MS
1995	Clayton Atkin St. George, UT
1996	Paul Engler Amarillo, TX

H.E. (Ladd) Hitch *(left) is presented "Cattle Businessman of the Year Award" by Zay Gilbreath. The award is currently Sponsored by Boeheinger-Ingelheim Animal Health, Inc.*

LAUREN E. CARLSON
President 1979
Morris, Minnesota

The first president to come from the NLFA, he had previously been President of the Minnesota Livestock Feeders Association. His major victory was the Meat Import Act of 1979. Wild horses in the West was *an* "intriguing issue, but not a victory." After a year in office, he concluded: "The people in Washington don't know as much as we do." An economist by training, he later was the NCA representative on the CME board.

MEAT PRICING DEBATE

Following The Wreck in the mid-1970s, triggered by the 1973 price freeze, there was rapid liquidation of cows: an unprecedented 15 percent reduction in three years. According to President McDougal, *Cattlemen lost $20 billion in three years: $15 billion in inventory loss and $5 billion in operating loss.*

So the law of supply and demand dictated an increase in beef prices, a rather rapid increase from 1977 to 1980. Which brought new protests from consumers and again scattered rumblings of beef boycotts. NCA and the Meat Board were busy trying to explain cattle cycles and why "the only solution to high meat prices is high prices."

Representative Neal Smith (D-IA), responding to some farmer-feeders who thought prices were being manipulated downward by packers, introduced legislation to regulate meat price reporting and trading. President Carter, responding to labor and consumer leaders who thought meat prices were going up too rapidly, ordered Secretary of Agriculture Robert Bergland to conduct an investigation. The Secretary, in turn, appointed a Meat Pricing Task Force of 10 industry and consumer representatives, who in 1978 conducted four public hearings around the United States. Jo Ann Smith of Florida was the NCA representative.

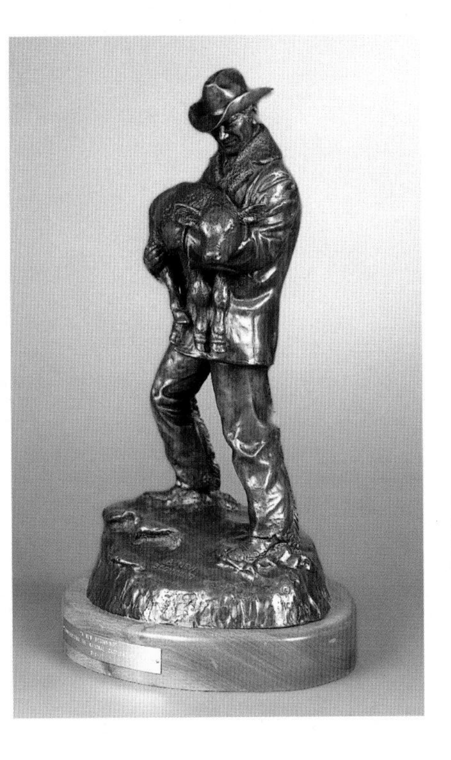

NEW BEGINNING

1978

ARTIST: JOHN D. FREE

LITTLE FELLA, YOU'RE THE HOPE

OF THE FUTURE.

COMMISSIONED TO

COMMEMORATE THE

FOUNDING OF THE

NATIONAL CATTLEMEN'S

ASSOCIATION.

SERIES: 30 BRONZES

Allied Industry Program

In 1972, the ANCA National Associate Program began imodestly as a means whereby commercial companies and ANCA could pool their resources for the good of the cattle industry. But the program grew quickly. ANCA President Wray Finney was the first president to see the advantage of using the commercial companies to support the Association and he pushed hard to establish the program.

It was John Cholis, who was in feed marketing and promotion with Ralston Purina who first proposed that ANCA have a trade show, and Ralston Purina has generally been credited as the first National Associate. Records indicate that Pfizer was the first to pay dues. They were the two leaders and by the end of 1972, 10 other companies had joined them as National Associates: American Cyanamid, Bank of America, Cutter Laboratories, Collier Carbon and Chemical, Elanco Animal Products, First National Bank of Chicago, Fort Dodge Laboratories and Merck & Co.

By the 1980s, the Allied Industry Program was providing much of the financial support and sponsorship for national conventions and many of the educational, information and award programs of the Association. The Annual Trade Show held in conjunction with the annual convention has become the showplace for Allied Industry members. The Trade Show has grown over the years to become the center gathering point of the convention with over 265 booths and exhibits in 1997 (although not all booths are bought by Allied Industry members).

The Associate Program Kicked Off *in 1972. W.D. Farr, ANCA president presents a cow skull to Max J. Harvey and staff of American Cyanamid Company. National Associates who contributed $2,500 in 1972 received a skull. This skull was a Braford from the J.O. Pierce Ranch in Florida.*

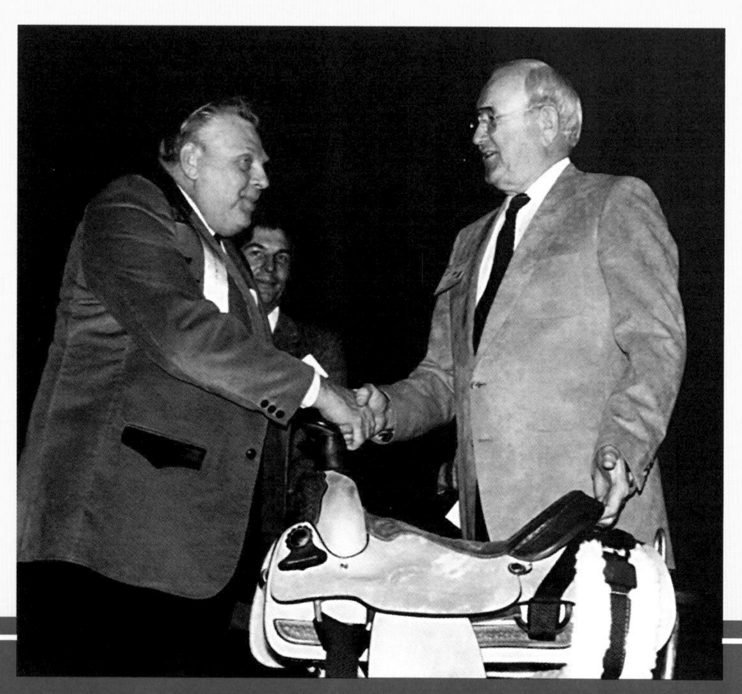

Jim Lewis of Cutter, Inc. presents Ron Lindeen the 1989 ***Top Hand Award.***

The program has expanded to three levels of membership, and in 1996 NCBA created a new membership level: Packer/Processor/Purveyor/Marketer. In 1997, participation and dues were as follows:

- **Allied Industry Council**: 28 members each paying $10,000 annual dues.
- **Allied Industry Associates**: 19 members each paying $2,500 annual dues.
- **Allied Industry Partners**: 19 members each paying $1,000 annual dues.

Together, the NCBA Allied Industry members paid over $346,000 in 1997 dues. In addition, the 1997 NCBA Trade Show grossed $450,000.

Allied Industry Centennial Partners

In recognition of the Centennial, the following companies increased their support of NCBA by becoming Allied Industry Council Centennial Partners.

Allflex USA, Inc.

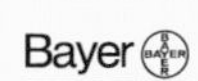

Bayer

Chicago Mercantile Exchange

DowElanco

Elanco Animal Health

Fort Dodge Animal Health

Grand Laboratories, Inc.

Merial Ltd.

Micro Chemical, Inc.

MoorMan's Inc.

Pioneer Hi-Bred International, Inc.

Purina Mills

UMB Bank

Zinpro Corporation

Allied Industry Council 1997

Allflex USA, Inc.
Bayer
Boehringer Ingelheim Animal Health, Inc.
Buick Motor Division
Chicago Mercantile Exchange
DowElanco
Elanco Animal Health
Farnam Companies, Inc.
Fort Dodge Animal Health
Grand Laboratories, Inc.
Hoechst-Roussel Vet
Leo Burnett USA
Merial Ltd.
Micro Chemical, Inc.
MoorMan's Inc.
Pfizer Animal Health
Pharmacia & Upjohn Animal Health
Pioneer Hi-Bred International, Inc.
PM Ag Products, Inc.
Protiva, A Business Unit of Monsanto
Purina Mills
Roche Animal Nutrition and Health
Schering-Plough Animal Health
UMB Bank
VetLife, Inc./Ivy Labs
Zinpro Corporation

Allied Industry Associates

Agri Laboratories, Ltd.
American Live Stock Insurance Company
Bank One, Arizona
Beef Magazine - Webb Publishing
Cargill-Nutrena Feed Division
Cenex Land O Lakes
Consolidated Nutrition L.C.
Deere & Co.
Hi-Pro Animal Health
Hubbard Milling Company
ITT Hartford Livestock Insurance
Kent Feeds Inc.
Lextron Inc.
Midwest PMS, Inc.
National Farm & Ranch Healthcare
NationsBank
Norwest Bank Colorado
Rhone Poulenc Inc.
Walco International, Inc.
Wells Fargo Bank

Allied Industry Partners

A.O. Smith Harvestore
Association of National Grasslands
Bio-Enhancement Systems Corp.
Cerestar USA Inc.
Excel of Wichita, KS Corp
FBS Ag Credit Inc.
GLA Agricultureal Electronics
Golden Sun Feeds, Inc.
Kunafin
Merrill Lynch
Mohrlang Manufacturing, Inc.
National Beef Packing Company
National Livestock Producers Association
North American Salt Company

Annual Convention and Trade Show.

Oberto Smokecraft Highland Stone Hall
Quali-tech Inc.
Rabobank Nederland
Urner Barry Publications
Western Farm Credit

Packer/Processor/Purveyor/Marketer

IBP

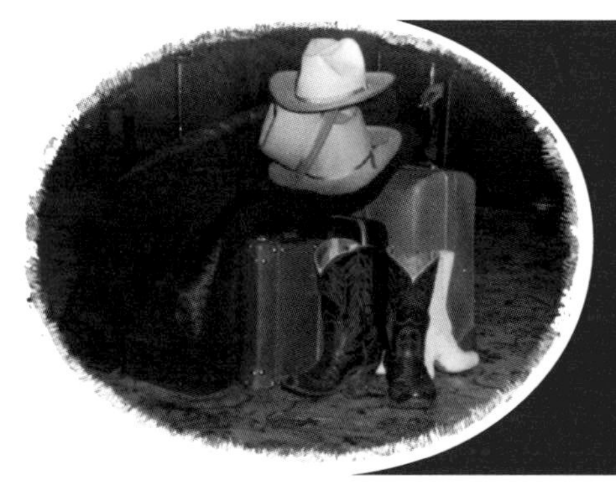

CONVENTIONS: THE GLUE OF THE ASSOCIATION

This page (clockwise from top left):
Convention-goers *participate in dance fun.*
The MGM in Las Vegas *displays a welcome to cattlemen.*
Delegates relax *at the blackjack table after a day of convention.*
Networking *during a break between sessions.*
Cattlemen's College. *Delegates attend educational seminars.*
Colorful delegates *Mr. and Mrs. Lyman Brewster from Montana.*

. . .and hear from important national figures.

This page (clockwise from top right):
United States President *Jimmy Carter addresses cattlemen.*
Ann Armstrong; *Ambassador to Great Britain, wife of Tobin Armstrong, Texas Rancher.*
President Ronald Reagan *addresses convention.*
John Trotman *introduces Secretary of Agriculture Earl Butz.*
Bill House *with United States Vice-President Spiro Agnew.*
Sam Irvin, *popular Senator from North Carolina.*
John Connally, *Governor of Texas.*

George Bellows FIVE COWS

On The Offensive

The Association blossomed with new sophistication. With a new enthusiastic young staff, Association leaders were dealing head on in Congress with more issues than ever, and working hard to open international doors to United States beef. Some say these were the years the Association "came of age." Courageously the Association stepped forward to be a major player in Washington, across the Nation and in international arenas. As its momentum grew, it gained confidence in defending and promoting what they knew was an excellent product, an excellent industry and an excellent way of life.

CHAPTER TEN

TAKING THE HIGH ROAD

Ronald Reagan, movie star and hobby cattleman from California, rode into the presidency in 1981, with a new agenda. He did bring inflation under control to a respectable annual rate of 3.9 to 4.6 percent during his eight years in the White House, but he lost control of the runaway national debt. It shot up threefold during his tenure as president, to $3.2 trillion.

A YEAR OF TURBULENCE

Merlyn Carlson of Nebraska was NCA president in 1980, which he described as *a year of turbulence*. On the negative side, he recalls that:

1. The second Beeferendum failed.
2. Three senior executives resigned.
3. Prime interest rates hit 21.5 percent.

But on the positive side, he cited:

1. NCA started the Young Cattlemen's Council (YCC).
2. Ground was broken for the new headquarters building in Denver.
3. W.T. (Dub) Berry, Jr. was hired as the eighth executive vice president, while J. Burton Eller became vice president-government affairs in the Washington Office.

The resignation of three senior executives in one year was a coincidence. George Spencer, Executive Vice President in Denver for the past year 10 years, resigned to go into private business; Bill McMillan, chief staff person in Denver and Washington for a total of 21 years, resigned to become Assistant Secretary of Agriculture under President Reagan; and Don F. Magdanz, Executive Vice President of the National Livestock Feeders Association for 20 years and Senior Vice President of NCA for three years, retired at age 65.

YOUNG CATTLEMEN'S COUNCIL

The Young Cattlemen's Council (YCC) was a long-time dream of George Spencer. Before he left NCA, he put together a program to bring in young cattlemen. The first trip in 1980 was

TIMELINE

1980 Prime interest rates peak at 21.5 percent, highest since Civil War.

Cable News Network (CNN) goes on air with speech by owner Ted Turner.

1981 Ronald Reagan Inaugurated 40th president.

Sandra Day O'Conner confirmed as first woman on Supreme Court.

1982 FAX machines introduced.

James Watt, friend of cattlemen, resigns as Secretary of Interior due to environmentalist pressure.

1983 AT&T, world's largest corporation, split up under court order.

Dairy PIC (Payment in Cash) bails out dairymen, leaves cattlemen holding the bag.

1984 Reagan elected to a second term.

1985 Beef Promotion and Research Act becomes law.

1986 NCA sues USDA over Dairy Termination Program.

$1-per-head checkoff becomes effective.

"War on fat" is launched.

All hands lost when space shuttle Challenger explodes.

1987 Stock market crash on October 19 precipitates a greater percentage of value lost than in the crash of 1929.

American Heart Association endorses beef as a healthy food.

Cattle first sold by satellite in "video auctions."

1988 Beef referendum passes on its third try with a 79 percent "yes" vote.

1989 George Bush inaugurated 41st president.

EEC imposes a hormone ban on United States beef.

Berlin Wall opened to the West after 28 years.

ISSUES

Foreign Trade
•
Food Safety
•
Management Studies
•
Dairy Buyout
•
Futures Trading
•
Packer Concentration

called the YCC Traveling Conference. Spencer described why he set up the YCC traveling program:

> *For several decades, young cattlemen felt they were not listened to, and the various things tried had not satisfied them. So I designed a program, copied after the old Swift Trips, which had been so popular and successful from 1932 to 1972. The idea was to identify and train potential young leaders for the industry. The Swift Trips typically took 30 or so industry leaders by train, and later by plane, to Chicago, Boston, New York and Washington to study the distribution and marketing of meat, and to visit with congressmen. Then, at the Association convention, they would have a reunion of all previous "Trippers," often attended by more than 200 leaders.*

Since 1980, more than 400 young cattlemen have made the YCC tour, most calling it "the best educational experience of my life." Two graduates of the original 1980 YCC trip (pictured below) have figured prominently in the Association. Dan Koons became NCA president in 1994, and Chuck Schroeder became CEO in 1996.

The First Young Cattlemen's Conference in 1980 sitting on the steps of the Capitol. *Actually started in the 1970s as an evolving project to differentiate younger from older members, the YCC first met together at conventions and other times. The tours started in 1980. Members were potential cattle industry leaders under the age of 40 nominated by their affiliate organizations. They typically spend a week on the study tour, starting with the NCA operation in Denver, then the Chicago Mercantile Exchange, a packing plant, a retail operation and winding up in Washington to meet their congressman. In recent years, the tours have been sponsored by IBP and Continental Grain. (left) A more recent YCC tour gathers at the White House.*

NEW HEADQUARTERS BUILDING

For several years there had been debate about where the permanent headquarters should be located: in Denver, the hub of cattle country, or in Washington, DC, the hub of the Association's activities. Denver won out and, in 1975, a six-year building campaign began. W.R. Farr of Greeley, Colorado, was chairman of the nine-man building committee, which raised over $2 million.

Occupants of the new building included NCA, Cattle-Fax, American National CowBelles, National Cattlemen's Foundation and, later, the Cattlemen's Beef Promotion and Research Board.

MERLYN CARLSON
President 1980
Lodgepole, Nebraska

"A year of turbulence," is how he describes his term of office: the second Beeferendum was defeated; three executives resigned; and interest rates reached over 20 percent. On the positive side: NCA started the Young Cattlemen's Council; groundbreaking for the new headquarters building; and Dub Berry was hired as EVP. Carlson later chaired several important task forces and was a leader in other beef organizations.

KANGAROO SKULLDUGGERY

Whenever cattlemen were feeling market pressures, they often blamed imports. Some would call for the labeling of beef in retail stores or restaurants as to the beef's origin. Such was the case in the early 1980s. Some retailers, as well as restaurants, obliged with signs in their windows and on menus: *We serve only American beef.* But it was difficult for stores to give real assurance, they admitted, because with blends of ground beef and processed meats they often did not know the origin.

This dilemma—to label or not to label—was exacerbated in 1981, when horse and kangaroo meat were discovered in some imports from Australia.

Cutting the Ribbon for a New Headquarters in 1981. *(left to right) Sam Washburn, Bill Swan, Merlyn Carlson and Lauren Carlson. The setting was Englewood, Colorado, a suburb of Denver, where 12 acres were purchased with a beautiful view of the snow-capped Rocky Mountains. The two-story building with redwood siding and cedar shake shingles not only fit the landscape, but it was also designed to resemble a ranch headquarters. Total cost of the project was $6,350,000. But following the sale of excess land and contributions by individuals, corporations and affiliate associations, including $2,145,000 by almost 1,100 contributors, the long-term debt was only $1.5 million.*

New Trade Relations

Trade has always been a frustrating and difficult issue for the Association. Obviously greater trade meant greater beef sales. But there was no consistency. Trade might be high, then slack off. Suddenly an unexpected abundance of beef on the market would drop prices quickly.

During both World Wars exports soared, but at the end of the wars, prices dropped sharply. In 1946, beef exports were at a high of 661 million pounds. By 1950, exports were down to 21 million pounds. But from that point, exports began a slow, steady climb.

There was an additional snag in 1989, when the European Community (EC) implemented an artificial trade barrier, stating that no beef could be imported which had received artificial hormones. Hormones which increased animal efficiency were used extensively in the United States. Scientific evidence showed they created no problems to humans, but the "hormone ban" essentially dried up exports to Europe, which was the intent of European cattlemen.

In the meantime, USMEF had been formed and cattlemen focused on new markets, especially Asian Rim countries.

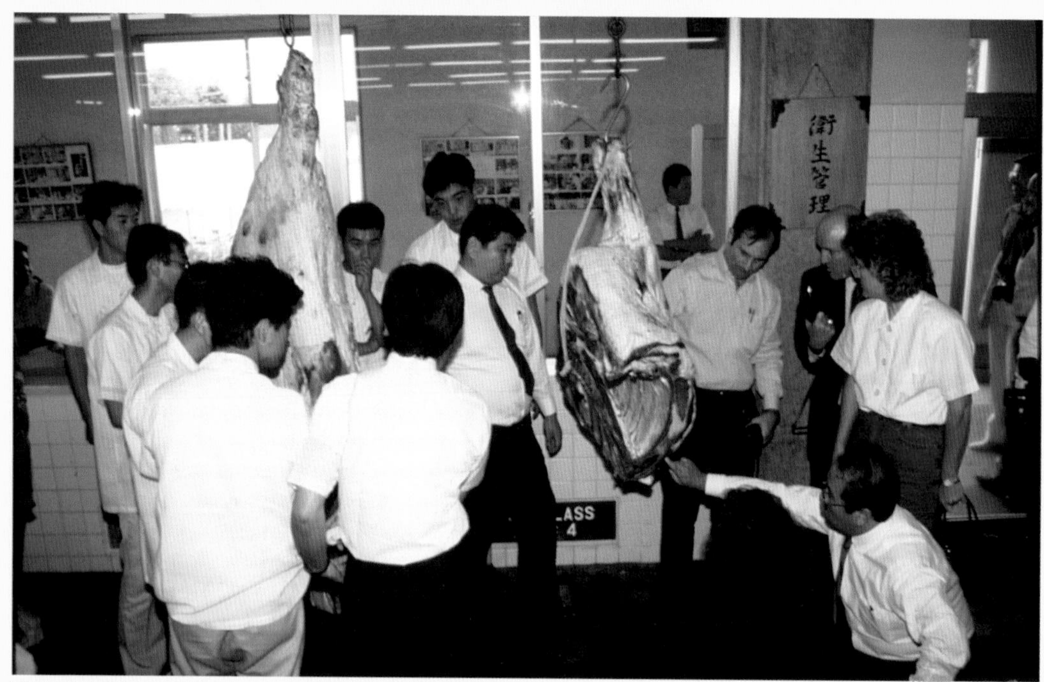

Showing United States Beef to the Japanese. *To open doors to beef exports, NCA officers made several trips to Japan. They found an enormously complex system of distribution and duties, but they persisted until liberalization was achieved in 1988.*

Sam Washburn, NCA Foreign Trade Committee Chairman, 1979 *(later NCA President), and Tom Cook, NCA Director of Industry Affairs, compare notes on trade legislation. Washburn and Cook were praised for their handling of the Australian meat scare. Their work led to meetings with Canada, Australia and New Zealand and the eventual establishment of the Four Country Meetings.*

1988 Japanese Trade Agreement

When the ANCA Executive Committee traveled to Japan in 1974 to study first-hand the market potential for United States beef, they found that the Japanese population was growing at one million a year, personal income was increasing four to seven percent a year, retail beef prices were four to five times higher than in the United States and beef consumption was under six pounds per capita, compared

Seasoned Professionals Take on the Japanese. *(left to right) Secretary of Agriculture Richard E. Lyng, Tom Cook, NCA vice president - industry affairs, and Special Trade Representative Clayton Yeutter worked incessantly to get the Japanese Trade Agreement of 1988.*

Learning New Markets. *Executive Vice President John Meetz (center) and others visiting Japanese Meat Counters in 1989.*

with 85 pounds consumption per capita in the United States.

The Japanese government presented the biggest obstacle. In attempting to protect small Japanese producers through a maze of quotas, tariffs and high prices set by the Livestock Industry Promotion Corporation (LIPC). The LIPC bought imported beef and resold it, providing handsome profits to subsidize local producers.

In 1975 USMEF immediately targeted the Japanese market. Exports increased gradually to 181,618 metric tons by 1987, but that increase satisfied neither United States producers nor Japanese consumers.

The problem remained largely between the Japanese and United States governments. But timing was right. President Reagan was concerned about the imbalance of trade with Japan; the United States Trade Representative was Clayton Yeutter, former cattle feeder from Nebraska; and Secretary of Agriculture was Dick Lyng, former president of the American Meat Institute (AMI).

Tom, Cook, NCA Vice President, Industry Affairs in Washington took the lead for cattlemen. With unrelenting pressure on the Administration by NCA, American Farm Bureau Federation and AMI, and with technical support from USMEF, Yeutter and Lyng put unprecedented pressure on the Japanese government. They rejected Japanese promises of increased quotas and decreased tariffs and demanded complete liberalization.

The result was a trade agreement, signed in 1988. It included a three-year phase out of quotas, removal of the LIPC from trade channels and a 70 percent tariff ad valorem to be reduced 10 percent a year for three years and negotiated thereafter. In 1997, the tariff was 44 percent.

By 1992, the first full year of liberalization, beef exports to Japan were 208,472 metric tons, valued at $1.1 billion. Exports have continued to grow since.

Four Country Trade Meetings

To support international beef trade, cattle industry representatives from NCA and cattlemen's groups in Australia, New Zealand and Canada meet each year to exchange views and offer recommendations for expanded trade opportunities. Some of the issues have included:

- Opposition to all unfair trade barriers, particularly that of the EC.
- Open beef trade in new markets.
- International inspection standards.
- Beef safety issues.
- Unfounded attacks on the industry.

Other participants were concerned with the United States Meat Import Law which imposes quota restrictions on beef imports. But the law has prevailed.

By 1995, total United States exports reached $3.3 billion. Japan, Canada, Mexico and North Korea (in that order) became the leading markets. But Japan still represented two-thirds of exports. It purchased 331,904 metric tons of beef (a 50-fold increase in 22 years) which was valued at $1.7 billion (a 90-fold increase).

Representatives of the cattle industries *of the four major beef-producing countries have met annually since 1982. (left to right) David Frith, New Zealand; Wally Peart, Australia; Morley Shepherdson, Canada; and Dale Humphrey, United States, at the 1988 meeting.*

BEHIND THE SCENES

W.T. (DUB) BERRY, JR.
EXECUTIVE VICE PRESIDENT
1980-1984

Few people in the cattle industry had the vast and varied experience that Dub Berry had when asked to head up the NCA staff.

Born in Texas in 1921, he was managing the family farm at age 14 and active in the 4-H Club. He worked at the cattle barns while attending Texas A&M and was on the livestock judging teams. He received a B.S. in Animal Science and orders to active military duty on the same day in 1942.

After serving in the Pacific Theater during World War II and being discharged as an army Lt. Colonel, he returned to Texas as a partner in an agribusiness that included registered and commercial cattle, custom harvesting and a farm machinery dealership, which he sold in 1953.

He returned to Texas A&M, where he earned a Ph.D. degree in animal nutrition and received the Outstanding Professor in Agriculture Award and Faculty Distinguished Teaching Award, all in 1960. He taught animal science and did research on animal nutrition as well as coached the livestock judging team.

At a show in Houston, in 1961, he met Governor Winthrop Rockefeller (D-AR.), who hired him as Operations Manager of Winrock Farms. During the six years there, he managed ranches in Arkansas and Oklahoma with 2,000 purebred Santa Gertrudis females, 4,000 crossbred Santa Gertrudis females and 1,200 registered Hereford females. After helping develop a Total Performance Records (TPR) program, which was adopted by the American Hereford Association (AHA), he was hired in 1967 as Executive Vice President of AHA in Kansas City for seven years.

From there, he moved to Phoenix in 1974 to become senior vice president of Victorio Corporation, which ran 1,000 registered Herefords and Brangus in two states, plus 25,000 to 50,000 steers in eight states. They also fed cattle in commercial feedyards in three states. At the same time, he was senior vice president of Western Farm Management, which had offices in seven states.

During these years, he was an active member of NCA, serving as chairman of the Animal Health Committee and a member of the National Livestock Tax Committee.

Soon after joining NCA, he made a memorable speech to the National Beef Forum in March 1981, a gathering of 72 organizations in Kansas City. It was memorable because he pointed out the *lack of unity, duplication of effort and lack of coordination*. Then he proposed a *coalition to unify the beef segments. . .and a superior total program.* This was the first public proposal for a unified beef organization, which finally materialized in 1995.

Dub Berry with his boss, Winthrop Rockefeller, *owner of Winrock Farms, who became Governor of Arkansas, 1967-1971. His son, Winthrop, later gave $50,000 to the Building Fund, the largest individual contribution ever to the Association.*

Our inclination was to blast 'em, related Sam Washburn, the 1982 NCA President.

> *But we decided this would arouse suspicion of all ground beef. So we downplayed it and met with the Australian Cattlemen's Association, who quickly corrected the skullduggery. {Only two small plants were in violation.} The Australian government was so appreciative of the way our Association handled it, their agricultural minister came to our next NCA convention and presented me with a plaque.*

Washburn, who had been chairman of the NCA Foreign Trade Committee, was also instrumental in setting up periodic meetings of the officers of national cattlemen's associations in the United States, Canada, New Zealand and the Counsel of Australia. As a result, he was made an Honorary Member of the Canadian Cattlemen's Association, which

Dollars & Sense

The purpose of NCA-PAC never has been to buy votes, said Burton Eller, NCA Executive Vice President (1990-1996). *Rather, the purpose is to (a) help elect candidates friendly to our industry and (b) gain access to them.*

Elections are crucial, says Chandler Keys, current NCBA vice president-public policy. *If we can help get pro-agriculture, pro-business people elected to Congress, we don't have to worry about how they'll vote.*

The year after ANCA opened an office in Washington, Congress passed the Federal Election Campaign Act, which authorized the formation of a Political Action Committee (PAC) by a trade association, corporation or ideological group. A result of the growing frustration with unlimited cash flow to campaigns and public mistrust, the introduction of PACs leveled the playing fields for all interests. Strict contribution limits were enacted and public disclosure of all donations mandated.

That prompted the formation of Cattlemen's Action Legislative Fund (CALF). Bob Johnston, Jr. of Fowler, Colorado, was the first chairman and, in the first year of operation in 1972, receipts topped $11,000.

CALF became relatively dormant until it was reorganized in 1978 and renamed NCA-PAC. That year, receipts were more than $106,000. After the Dairy Buy-Out of 1986, and members read the publicized size and influence of the Dairy PACs which were close to $3 million, as compared to approximately $100,000 in NCA-PAC, members began to recognize the need for a stronger PAC and the momentum has continued ever since.

Renamed again in 1996 after the association merger, NCBA-PAC is now one of the top five agribusiness PACs. In the 1995-1996 election cycle, NCBA-PAC disbursed $442,655 in support of 224 candidates. NCBA is prohibited by law from using membership dues or checkoff dollars to support candidates. All contributions to NCBA-PAC from cattlemen are voluntary.

In 1994, the Federal Election Commission reported that 3,954 PACs contributed $387 million to candidates for federal office. The affluence and perceived influence of PACs has drawn considerable criticism, especially from consumer groups. But as the 20th century closes, PACs seem to be a political way of life. The right of an individual to contribute to a campaign remains at the core of the debate over PACs. But for now, NCBA members seem content to exercise their voice through NCBA-PAC.

OH CALM DOWN! IF BURTON ELLER THINKS NCA-PAC SHOULD SEND THE SENATOR A CONTRIBUTION I'M SURE HE'S GOT A DARN GOOD REASON!
Jerry Palen
"NCA-PAC CONTINUES TO SEEK INPUT FROM NCA MEMBERS AND WELCOMES SUGGESTIONS REGARDING DISTRIBUTION OF NCA-PAC FUNDS."

NCA-PAC
Jerry Palen
"AS IN THE PAST NCA-PAC CONTINUES TO IMPARTIALLY SUPPORT BOTH POLITICAL PARTIES."

Jerry Palen

J.W. (BILL) SWAN
President 1981
Rogerson, Idaho

"It was a good year for NCA," recalls the tall attorney turned rancher: Ronald Reagan, a hobby cattleman and friend of the industry, was elected President; James Watt, an arch-conservative, was appointed Secretary of Interior and started the Sagebrush Rebellion; Bill McMillan, NCA vice president-Washington affairs, was appointed Assistant Secretary of Agriculture; and the Soviet grain embargo was lifted just as there was a record corn crop of 8.1 billion bushels. On the negative side: kangaroo meat was discovered in beef from Australia.

he said, *Some anti-trade members did not appreciate.* But the Four Country Meetings have become an annual affair and have greatly enhanced relations.

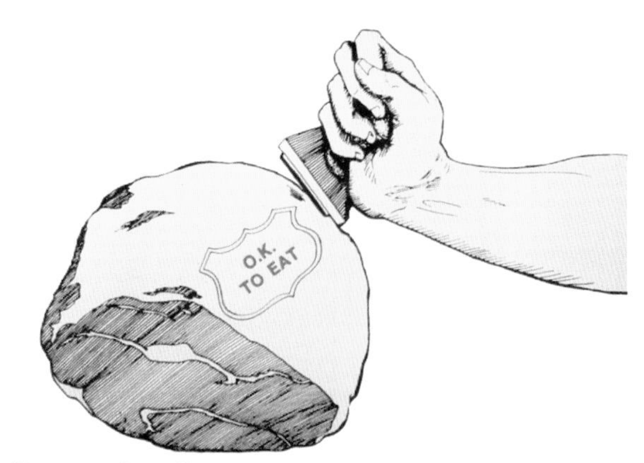

Reassuring Consumers. *Promotion campaigns in the 1980s showing the stamp of approval on beef.*

FOOD SAFETY MANIA

In the early 1980s, many cattlemen thought there was over-concern and possibly overkill in the nation's food safety laws. At least the subject was beginning to take a lot of time from the Association staff, and would continue to do so for the remainder of the century.

Of particular concern to cattlemen was the Delaney Clause (passed in 1958 and named after its author, Representative James J. Delaney of New York), which specified that no substance found to cause cancer in laboratory animals, even for huge doses, may be added to food.

When passed, science could only measure residues in parts per million. By 1980, parts per billion were not unusual. Scientists advocated, with NCA backing, the "risk-benefit" concept, that is, that a low risk might be justified if the benefit was great. At stake were animal health drugs and growth promoters that significantly increased production efficiency, benefiting both producers and consumers. NCA supported dozens of new laws introduced that were aimed at amending food safety laws in general and the Delaney Clause in particular. But the consumer activists protested and prevailed, charging that cattlemen and the drug companies favored "a little bit of cancer." As a result, clearance of new animal drugs has taken years and millions of dollars; fewer drugs are available; and costs have escalated several fold.

NCA PERFORMANCE REPORT

The benefits of belonging to NCA have always been difficult to sell. In 1981, the Association began an Annual Performance Report that listed the value of each accomplishments. That year, 28 areas of accomplishment were listed, including:

- Increase in estate tax exemption to $600,000, worth thousands of dollars to many ranchers;
- Counter-cyclical meat import law, worth $3 per head;
- "Beef Supply Awareness:" more than 100 ranchers visited major grocery chains, worth $2.50 per head;
- Challenges to unwarranted issuance of dietary advice, which hurts beef demand;
- Grazing fee formula based on price of beef and the cost of production, worth $8 per cow unit;
- Exemption of farmers and ranchers with 10 or less employees from OSHA inspections.

There were more, but all told, the value of the 28 accomplishments was estimated at $38 per slaughter animal or $100 for each $1 invested in NCA dues.

CALL FOR UNIFICATION

Following a stinging defeat in the 1980 Beeferendum, industry leaders were feeling considerable dejection and puzzlement about where the industry was headed or should be headed. So NCA called a National Beef Forum in Kansas City, March 28, 1981, which was attended by the leaders of 68 state and national beef organizations. Speaker after speaker noted the "multiplicity of cattlemen's organizations." Dub Berry, new executive of NCA, was acclaimed when he called for *a coalition or some lead entity to unify the beef segments and organizations.* And he added, *Let's think of a total effort that is more efficient and effective in the use of cattlemen's funds.*

As a result of this challenge, a 22-member Beef Industry Steering Committee was appointed by Bill Swan of Idaho, President of NCA, and James A. Mullins of Iowa, Chairman of the Beef Industry Council of the Meat Board. *The overall goal,* stated Swan and Mullins, *is increased unity and coordination, in order to overcome problems resulting from segmentation of the beef industry.*

> ***{Let's form} a coalition or some lead entity to unify the beef segments and organizations. Let's think of a total effort that is more efficient and effective in the use of cattlemen's funds.***
>
> —Dub Berry, one of the first calls for industry unification

While this committee was unsuccessful, the seeds were planted for a single industry organization and a vision that would be realized 13 years later with the formation of the National Cattlemen's Beef Association.

In the meantime, that committee was replaced, in 1982, with an NCA Special Advisory Committee of 11 members, chaired by Gordon Van Vleck, former NCA president. Their basic objective was *to provide a road map for the cattle industry through 1990.* During the following year, the Committee and staff heard from numerous sources: competitors in pork and chicken production; beef packers and processors; food retailers, restaurant and fast food operators; scientists and consultants. [Their approach was quite similar to that followed 12 years later by the Industry Long Range Planning Task Force.]

The Committee identified 36 trends for the 1980s, most of which proved to be on target. One perceptive observation was that

SAMUEL H. WASHBURN
President 1982
Lafayette, Indiana

A farmer-feeder and purebred Charolais breeder, he was an articulate spokesman for the industry, in the United States as well as in several foreign countries. Having been Chairman of the Foreign Trade Committee, he preached trade and liberalization every day. He worked on trade barriers in the Common Market and for greater access in Japan. He started talks with the Meat Board on greater cooperation and communications with NCA; eight years later, he became the first to call for unification. Earlier, he was named Cattle Feeder of the Year, by *FEEDLOT MANAGEMENT*, and was President of National Lamb Feeders Association.

W.J. (DUB) WALDRIP
President 1983
Lubbock, Texas

Waldrip initiated a management study of NCA, by Arthur Young & Co., which resulted in a number of changes. Gifted with wit and humor, he became the popular host for the Food Editors Tour. For a ranch manager and NCA president, his training was unique: he had a Ph.D. degree in range management from Texas A&M Univeristy.

the meat industry had reached "maturity," that the growth in average per capita consumption of meat appeared to be over. Total meat consumption in 1984 was 206 pounds per capita, in 1994, 208 pounds.

Also, the Committee put emphasis on the need for increased efficiency and cost reduction by beef producers. In 1950, they pointed out, the retail cost of a pound of chicken was 80 percent the cost of a pound of beef: 60 cents versus 75 cents. In 1980, it was 30 percent: 72 cents versus $2.38.

For both the individual cattleman and the industry, efficiency of production and marketing will have to improve.

—Findings of the NCA Special Advisory Committe, 1983

The point, probably as true today as when written, was driven home in their conclusion:

For both the individual cattleman and the industry, efficiency of production and marketing will have to improve. There is no real alternative. Product promotion can help, but improvement in beef's competitive position and profitability will depend largely on a narrowing of the price spread between beef and its competitors for the consumer's meat dollar.

With PAC Funds, *NCA was able to participate and win friends at political gatherings such as this 1985 Republican fund raiser in Washington. (seated left to right) Rick Hoyt, NCA-PAC chairman, Sharon Archer and Representative Bill Archer(R-TX), who later became chairman of the House Ways and Means Committee. (standing left to right) Representative Bob Smith (R-OR), who later became chairman of the House Agriculture Committee, NCA President Jo Ann Smith, D. Clyde Riley, chairman of the American Meat Institute and president, Hi-Grade Food Products Corporation; and Burton Eller, senior vice president-government affairs.*

ANOTHER MANAGEMENT STUDY

By 1983, when Waldrip was president, there was stress for cattlemen in the market place and rumblings about NCA among state affiliates. So the Executive Committee decided to have a Management Review of the Association. This one, costing $50,000 by Arthur Young & Co. of Houston, was similar to the 1967 study by Strong, Wishart & Associates. Among the many conclusions and recommendations:

- There is fragmentation and diversity within the membership of NCA. There are Easterners and Westerners, cattle raisers and feeders, farmers and ranchers, big operators and small operators, sophisticated businessmen and those who take a more traditional approach to cattle management. This diversity often causes differing perspectives on what is "right" for cattlemen.
- NCA's individual membership is only 12 percent of its affiliates' membership, and only one percent of all cattlemen in the country. This small level of membership places limitations on what NCA can do for the cattle industry.
- NCA should have a broader coordination and cooperation role with the Beef Industry Council, the United States Meat Export Federation, and the various state beef councils.

JOHN D. WEBER
President 1984
Alturas, California

A cow-calf and yearling operator who graduated from the University of California in animal science, Weber was the sixth president from California. Highlights of his term included: implementation of Arthur Young & Co. recommendations; hiring John Meetz as the new Executive Vice President; and initiating a new strategic plan, which continued (with updates) for 11 years. Earlier, he had been president of the California Cattlemen's Association and the Public Lands Council.

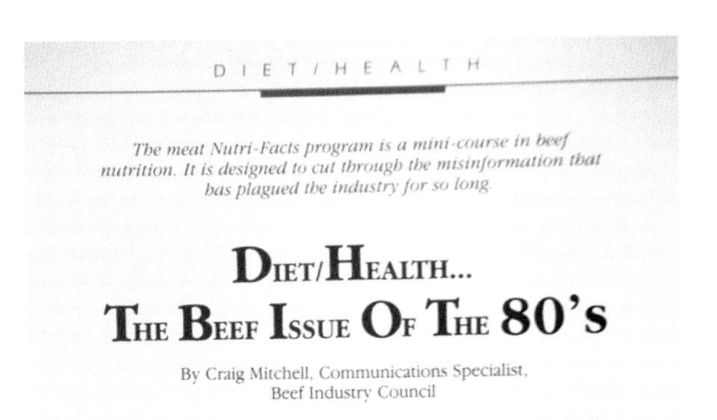

DIET/HEALTH

The meat Nutri-Facts program is a mini-course in beef nutrition. It is designed to cut through the misinformation that has plagued the industry for so long.

DIET/HEALTH... THE BEEF ISSUE OF THE 80's

By Craig Mitchell, Communications Specialist, Beef Industry Council

Consumer Activists, Animal Rightists and Environmentalists Kept Up Cattlemen's Defenses. *The media picked up on all the issues. To the cattlemen, it seemed that the media had gone far beyond a "watchdog" approach and was, in some cases, bent on doing away with the industry. However, by the end of the 1980s, cattlemen had checkoff funds and were fighting back with new programs designed to tell the true "Beef Story."*

JO ANN SMITH
PRESIDENT 1985
MICANOPY, FLORIDA

A tall, attractive, articulate, forceful person, Jo Ann not only was the first woman president, she was one of the most memorable leaders. Having worked for two previous Beeferendums and as Chairman of the Beef Promotion and Consumer Relations Committee, it was natural for her to push through Congress the Beef Promotion and Research Act. Then, with political savvy, she led the successful referendum campaign, and was the first chairman of the Cattlemen's Beef Promotion and Research Board. Later, she became Assistant Secretary of Agriculture.

- NCA does not anticipate and effectively plan its activities. Its communications processes have caused internal staff dissatisfaction and external resentment.

ANOTHER NEW EXECUTIVE

Following the Arthur Young study, John Meetz of Kansas was hired (in 1984) as the new Executive Vice President, and Dub Berry remained as Senior Vice President for Special Projects until retirement age in 1985.

Meetz and 1984 NCA President John D. Weber immediately implemented an NCA Strategic Plan, which endured for the life of NCA and became a model for other associations. "The mission of the National Cattlemen's Association," as stated in the plan, "is to advance the economic, political and social interests of the U.S. cattle industry." The plan contained general objectives, specific objectives, strategies and action plans, which kept the Association on course and helped it grow in all respects.

PIK and PIC. *PIK (Payment In Kind) was the USDA program to reduce grain production. PIC (Payment In Cash) meant that the USDA was paying dairymen $10 per cwt. to reduce milk production, which was the bigger problem for NCA. With the 1985 Farm Bill and the Dairy Termination Program, PIC would end; but the consequences of the bill and the Dairy Termination Program would be even more severe on cattle producers.*

Meetz also expanded the concept of non-dues income, which began in 1971 with the first NCA Trade Show. The trade show expanded each year and by 1995 attracted 485 exhibitors who added $388,000 to NCA revenues.

In 1976, dues of $1,150,000 accounted for 73 percent of the $1,584,000 income. By 1994, dues income had increased to $2,986,000 but accounted for only 23 percent of the total $13,269,000 income.

In 1990, even with the larger income, NCA suffered an operating loss of $650,000. *We simply had tried to respond to everyone's desire for new or expanded services*, says John Lacey of California, the 1990 president, *and became over extended.*

After six years as the Association's chief executive, John Meetz resigned in 1990. Earl B. Peterson, became the interim executive for six months. With a background in finance, management and administration, he quickly bolstered the financial position of the Association and put it back in the black.

Behind The Scenes

JOHN E. MEETZ
Executive Vice President
1984-1990

Born on a Kansas livestock farm in 1944, where he was active in the 4-H Club and showed steers and lambs, Meetz later attended Kansas State University. There he was President of AGR Fraternity and a member of four judging teams: wool, meats, dairy and livestock. His senior year, he was "high point" in the nation at the International Livestock Exposition in Chicago and second high at the Kansas City Royal.

After receiving a B.S. degree in animal husbandry in 1967 and a M.S. degree in animal nutrition in 1969, he went on the staff at Western Illinois University, then returned to Kansas to become Executive Vice President of the Kansas Livestock Association (KLA) from 1970 to 1984. At KLA, he developed a council structure that included feeders, cow-calf and purebred producers into one association; he then started the Kansas Beef Council and integrated it into one organizational structure. Also at KLA, he studied association management and became President of the Kansas Society of Association Executives.

John Meetz meets with Secretary of Agriculture Dick Lyng, *who was a good friend of the industry and former president of the American Meat Institute.*

Upon becoming Executive Vice President of NCA in 1984, his Number One priority was implementation of the new NCA Strategic Plan, the first one that would function and prevail. He skillfully integrated staff organization and budget with industry needs, which permitted the plan, with annual updates, to guide NCA throughout the remainder of its existence, through 1995.

Meetz was a strategist and principal in drafting the Beef Promotion and Research Act in 1985, which he considered the biggest industry development, with the most far-reaching impact, during his tenure.

His biggest contribution, he feels, was putting together an outstanding staff organization, with the right people in the right positions with the right responsibilities.

After resigning from NCA in 1990, Meetz became vice president of Koch Beef Company, and then in 1996, he became a management consultant.

J. Burton Eller, the vice president-government affairs and a 22-year employee of the Association, became the new executive vice president in 1991, and Earl Peterson stayed as vice president-finance and administration until retirement in 1996.

First Lady President

In its 87-years, the Association had a smattering of women as members, but never an officer. Jo Ann Smith of Florida would become the exception, and she was exceptional in many ways. It was during her term as president that the Agricultural Act of 1985 was being debated. Representative Tony Coelho (D-CA), a powerful member of the House Agriculture Committee whose family was in the dairy business in California, was the driving force for another dairy termination buyout program. NCA saw it coming and objected. When Jo Ann protested, Representative Coelho admonished: *We already have the votes in the House and Senate. The dairy buyout* is *going to happen. What would beef cattlemen like in return?*

To which Jo Ann answered, *A checkoff, and your support for it.*

A Public Relations Dream

She was the public relations dream!

So says Roger Burgland, NCA vice president of communications and public relations at the time. *She was unique, not only as a female, she was intelligent, attractive, articulate and tough. The national media loved her.*

One week alone in 1985, Jo Ann, as she became known throughout the country both within the industry and out, appeared on all three major television networks. But at a time when the industry was suffering difficult years both in low cattle prices and in attacks by consumers, Jo Ann gave a positive public relations boost that has not been equaled before or since. Psycologically speaking it was a turning point for the industry. The positive press that Jo Ann received was pivotal in turning the industry to the offensive in selling their product.

Chatting with Senate Majority Leader Bob Dole. *Her notoreity and political savvy led to her Washington career. After leaving the chairmanship of the Beef Board, She became Assistant Secretary of Agriculture, the second Association officer to move into that position. Bill McMillan filled that post after leaving NCA in 1981.*

Jo Ann addressing the National Press Club. *The media just could not get enough of this unusual lady who headed the National Cattlemen's Association, a group perceived to be largely male.*

Jo Ann first became involved in association activities through the CowBelles. Then she progressively moved up as a member of the Beef Development Taskforce, which developed the original Beef Research and Information Act and guided the first referendum, in 1976; as chairman of the NCA Beef Promotion and Consumer Relations Committee; and as chairman of the second Beeferendum effort, in 1979-1980.

After serving as NCA President, Jo Ann did not stop her fast pace. With great motivation from her work on previous referendums and the Agricultural Act of 1985, she led the referendum campaign to its successful conclusion in 1988 and became the first chairman of the Cattlemen's Beef Promotion and Research Board (the Beef Board). Jo Ann grew up in North Florida and still runs a family cattle operation with husband Cedric Smith near Micanopy, Florida. Son Marty Smith was the 1997 President of the Florida Cattlemen's Association.

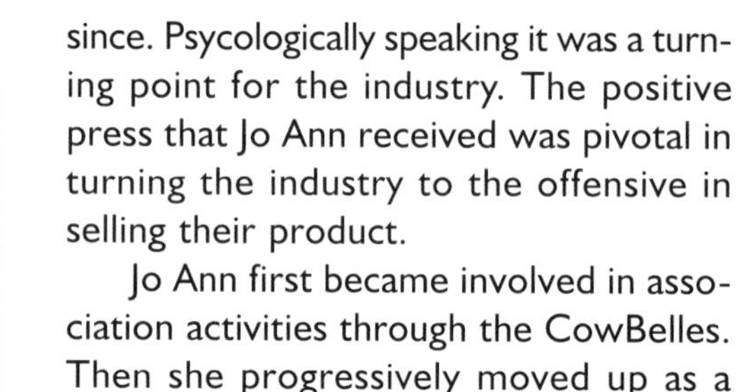

Articulate and tough, Jo Ann Smith *had a lot of practice testifying. Active in the debates over the Agricultural Act of 1985, she had to return to the tables over the Dairy Termination Program and passage of the Beef Promotion and Research Act, among a portfolio of other pressing issues.*

And Coelho responded, *Okay, you present it and I'll support it.*

So NCA did prepare the language for the checkoff and Coelho did support it, and the Beef Promotion and Research Act became law with bold provisions. The referendum on the checkoff was delayed 18 months after the checkoff started, and with no refund, but the delay gave producers time to see it working, provided funds for an extensive referendum campaign and helped it pass with a 79 percent "yes" vote.

Dairy Termination Program

Not all was roses for the Association or the industry, however. The Dairy Termination Buy-Out of 1986, a result of the Agricultural Act of 1985, threw the industry into turmoil. Not only was it a bump in the high road, it reopened old wounds between beef and dairy cattlemen. (*See Box, page 225.*)

> ***The dairy buyout is going to happen. What would beef cattlemen like in return?***
>
> ***A checkoff. And your support of it.***
>
> *—Dialogue between Representative Tony Coelho and NCA President Jo Ann Smith Debating the Agricultural Act of 1985*

A New Maturity for the Association

The Dairy Buy-Out awakened the Assocation to many of its own weaknesses. It realized that keeping its own agenda intact was not enough. In the Washington playing field, they were "playing with the big guys," and they had to assume a stronger demeanor.

Don Butler, who most folks know as a modest, mild-mannered man, could be tough when the occasion called for it. Burton Eller tells of such an occasion in 1986 when NCA was trying to get a grazing fee bill extended. Representative John Seiberling (D-OH),

Where's The Beef?

In 1984 the NCA awarded Clara Peller an honorary membership in the Association. Her brilliant pronouncement and feisty 82-year old attitude propelled Ms. Peller into an instant celebrity with one simple question, ***Where's the Beef?***

Featured in a hamburger ad sponsored by Wendy's Old Fashioned Hamburgers, Clara Peller went up to the counter of a fast-food restaurant and, disappointed over the size of the hamburger she was receiving, asked repeatedly, *Where's the Beef?* Not only did she become a star, but Wendy's accomplished one of the greatest advertising spots ever.

NCA issued a resolution thanking Ms. Peller for stimulating interest in beef and helping to make Americans more aware of the good values of beef. The Association also commended the entire Wendy's organization for its contribution to the success of the beef cattle industry.

Here's the Beef. *NCA President John Weber reads the resolution while Don Butler and Jo Ann Smith give Clara Peller "the Beef!" Pat Adrian, chairman of the promotion committee of the Beef Industry Council and Natalie McElroy, President of the American National CowBelles, look on.*

DON BUTLER
President 1986
Tucson, Arizona

Born to lead, Butler started early, as student body president in grammar school, high school and at the University of Arizona. Later, he worked to the top of Arizona Cattle Feeders Association, NCA, USMEF and National Cattlemen's Foundation. During his tenure as president, he helped resolve some tough issues: public lands grazing fee formula; suit against the USDA over dairy whole-herd buy-out; implementation of the $1 checkoff; the Consumer Retail Beef Study; and futures trading controversy. A cattle feeder, he has excelled in cattle management and international trade. Butler has served as the chairman of the National Cattlemen's Foundation from 1990 to present and has overseen the Centennial Task Force and the centennial history book project.

chairman of the sub-committee handling the bill, was a moving target and always had a new compromise to impose on cattlemen. After Butler had taken several compromises to the Public Lands Council and gotten their reluctant approval, he and staff went to Seiberling's office for a final agreement.

The chairman said, *My people tell me we need a further compromise, which we have included in this draft bill.*

Butler gritted his teeth, picked up the draft, tore in two and said, *Thank you, Mr. Chairman, we have nothing further to discuss.* And he led the shocked staff out. Impressed with such mettle, other congressmen and senators took the initiative and salvaged the grazing fee formula.

This set a new precedent for NCA, said Eller. *Since then, we have been a little tougher and a little more persistent in how we accomplish policy.*

FUTURES FRUSTRATION

Ever since the Chicago Mercantile Exchange (CME) introduced live cattle futures in 1964, they have been an enigma to some cattlemen and a target for blame when the market went sour.

In 1980, following numerous complaints, NCA surveyed its members and found that 59 percent thought the industry would be better off without futures. Most of the negative responses were from west of the Rocky Mountains, where there were no delivery points, or were from smaller cattlemen who had never used futures. At the same time, a slight majority of the members preferred to deal with futures in a positive way by recommending improvements and conducting educational meetings, rather than discontinue them. That is the line the Association took. But again in 1986, members became upset with futures and eventually in 1987, NCA President Jack Dahl appointed a task force to review the situation. In 1988, after much deliberation, the Task Force and the CME agreed on several significant changes in futures trading. (*See Box, page 229.*)

PACKER CONCENTRATION

For nearly 100 years, this Association, or some members of the Association, have felt a mixed distrust-dependent relationship with packers. It climaxed in 1921 with passage of the Packers and Stockyards Act but has resurfaced a number of times since, usually when cattlemen were losing money.

Such was the case in the late 1980s, which prompted President Dale Humphrey, the 1988 president, to appoint a 15-member NCA Beef Industry Concentration/Integration Task Force. Former President Sam Washburn was chairman. Their one-year study was expanded to include concentration/integration of cow-calf and feedyard operations, as well as packers, but it was the latter that really upset some cattlemen.

In the 1920s and 1930s, the four largest packers accounted for about 50 percent of the cattle slaughter. New entrants in the 1960s caused the concentration by the Big Four to reach a low of 19 percent in 1977. But by 1987, it had increased to 67 percent. Later, in 1994, the Big Four (IBP, Excel, Monfort and National) had 82 percent of the business.

The investigation shows that futures are not being manipulated. Rather, when properly used, futures can be a useful management tool.

—Kika de la Garza Chairman of the House Agriculture Committee
Speaking at the 1987 NCA Convention in Reno.

In his report, the Task Force emphatically concluded, *The free market system is alive and well. . . .Therefore, we are unwilling to recommend any major alternatives to the existing system.*

Chatting about 1988 Campaign Issues. *Burton Eller, NCA vice president - government affairs, joins Vice President George Bush in the Indian Treaty Room for discussion about the upcoming presidential election, in which George Bush was elected President.*

The Dairy Buy-Out

One of the political plays in the Agricultural Act of 1985 was the Dairy Termination Program. Association leaders had reluctantly agreed to the Program in return for getting a Beef Checkoff included. But it did not happened as planned.

Although dairymen accounted for only 18 percent of the country's cattle operations, they were the smarter lobbyists. They had PAC funds of some $2.9 million, 143 times greater than what beef cattlemen had been able to collect.

The milk price support system since 1949 worked well until 1977, when dairymen prevailed on Congress to support milk at 80 percent of parity. Milk production increased dramatically and the cost to taxpayers increased 10 fold in four years, up to $2.6 billion! Under the new buy-out program, designed to reduce this surplus, dairymen could sell their whole herd to the government, if they agreed to stay out of the business for three years.

In March 1986, the USDA bid up to $22.50 per cwt. for cows; 14,000 dairy farmers accepted. USDA agreed to slaughter 1.55 million dairy animals during the next 18 months at a cost of $1.83 billion to taxpayers. Within the first week in April, live cattle futures declined $5.67—the biggest one-week loss ever. Cash prices fell $3.50 to $4.50 per cwt. with losses to cattlemen of nearly $25 million.

Don Butler, the 1986 president of NCA, recalled,*The buy-out dominated everything. Our Executive Committee had two or three conference calls a day and finally decided to sue USDA for not following orderly marketing and for devastating our market.*

Within days, NCA was joined by 38 state cattlemen's associations as plaintiffs. The case was heard on April 22, in Lubbock, Texas. The Federal judge ruled in favor of cattlemen and gave USDA one month *to write and implement regulations in compliance with the law.*

So on May 9, Butler and Agriculture Secretary Dick Lyng reached an agreement on orderly marketing to offset the impact of meat purchases by USDA. *It was a handshake agreement,* says Butler with pride, *and Secretary Lyng lived up to every word of it.*

In the Thick of the Dairy Buy-Out. *President Don Butler presiding at the April, 1986 Board Meeting in Washington days after the first news of the buy-out hit. There was only one topic of discussion at this meeting.*

Where's the Value?

The industry has long worked on the commodity principle of providing beef in volume, with little attention to consistency and quality product. Cow-calf producers sell to feeders who have traditionally grouped cattle together from a number of sources, basing the groupings on weight and finishing dates rather than on the quality of meat a calf might, or might not, produce.

Dr. Russell Cross, meats researcher at Texas A&M, *did extensive research on value differences between yield grades which was presented at the 1988 NCA convention. He strongly advocated producers to set the standards. Since cow-calf producers are the ones being hurt the most by our current system, they need to be the ones to change it. Once the data and research has been established, it would be up to the producer to change the breeding over time and to demand payment for the true value of the meat being produced.*

But in the 1980s that approach began to change. Pressure from consumers and loss of market share led producers to look at new ways to produce better beef: leaner, tastier, more tender and above all, safe. Also, consumers were calling for a more consistent product.

The new emphasis was on consumer needs. Research flourished, as did the interest in new breeds and crossbreeds of cattle.

New ways to market beef also surfaced. The concept of "branded beef" came into play: one guaranteed product to the consumer. A number of producers began marketing an array of "designer beef" with various brands and guarantees to specific customers, such as "hormone-free," "fed only natural ingredients," and so on. Consumers were impressed with the trend, but still confused as to what was what.

There were, however, many inherent problems involved. First, the producer

The Trend is Branded. *Rod Bowling, vice president of Monfort of Colorado told cattle producers in 1986, branded beef is the future. "When you sell commodities, you leave money on the table. To go after additional margin, you have to do more for your customer, you have to produce a more refined product and assume more responsibility." He also said that the producer must assume some of the responsibility for producing that product if he expects to get paid more.*

Does the Consumer Really Know What It Wants? *The contradiction for the industry has been that the consumer says it wants a leaner product, but taste is more important. Taste comes from marbling, the fat mixture in the meat. Take out fat, lose taste. However, keeping close contact with consumers, through focus groups and other forms of consumer research, has been one of the great undertakings of the Association.*

The Packer Warning. *Bob Peterson, President of IBP, warned the industry in 1988, "Until the industry develops the technology to create real value, real value added to the customer, we will be frustrated in any effort to identify price value differences in cattle." He also indicated that it was the industry's responsibility to vertically integrate up to the packer and not expect the packer to spend money to vertically integrate backwards into feeding. "I'd rather take [that money] and go forward and make us more competitive in the marketplace."*

who was spending more money on records, tests and upgrading were getting no better value for their calves, because the feeders and the packers continued to sell on average. Second, the producer had no real idea whether his end product was above average or not.

As Dr. Darrell Wilkes, NCA vice president of research and industry information in the 1980s pointed out,

> *The more valuable cattle, bought at the average price, have been used to raise the value of the poorer ones, also bought at the average price.*

So, how could this change? The Association set forth a number of new approaches, such as retained ownership, vertical integration and strategic alliances.

A strategic alliance between a producer, feeder and packer, for example, would permit each to exchange information with the objective of learning which animals produced the more desirable product. Then the producer could adjust genetics and other factors—and get paid for the more valuable product.

"Value Based Marketing" is what it is called. But the changeover to that concept would still be in the developmental stages at the end of the 20th century.

Certified Angus Beef Program *(CAB) started in 1978 with the objective of providing consistently high quality beef to retailers and restaurants. "Marbling is the key, plus a solid business base," says Mick Colvin (shown here), CAB executive director for 20 years. "Marbling provides the juiciness, flavor and palatability that consumers want. We have no trouble selling it, only trouble in supplying the demand. In 1997, CAB was processed in 32 packing plants and sold through 2,600 retail stores and 25,000 restaurants in 33 countries.*

Successful Brand Marketing. *Taking on the new ideas in the 1980s put Roy Moore of Idaho and his Maverick Beef Association in the early forefront of branded products. He followed a vertically integrated program from the pasture to the retail counter, overseeing his product through each stage and establishing certain standards such as "fed without antibiotics or implants." His product, NaturaLite Beef, had immediate consumer appeal and he found he was gaining $100 to $200 per head premium for his efforts.*

JACK DAHL
President 1987
Gackle, North Dakota

With 600 head of Herefords and Salers, including 200 registered, he had a keen interest in animal health and served as Chairman of the ANCA and NCA Animal Health Committees. Also, observing the financial problems of farmers and ranchers, he made credit his top priority. He helped pass the Federal Agricultural Mortgage Act (Farmer Mac) and became its first chairman for six years. When members split over futures trading, he appointed an NCA Futures Trading Task Force, which brought major changes. Later, he represented NCA on the Meat Board.

IBP, One of the Big Four. *The IBP plant at Amarillo, Texas—the largest in the world when it opened in 1974—has a daily slaughter capacity of 5,000 head per day. IBP has 16 beef plants in eight states and Canada, with a combined capacity of over 35,000 head per day. The Big Four Packers—IBP, Excel, ConAgra and National—slaughtered 80 percent of all the fed cattle in 1994, a fact which renewed old concerns about packer concentration.*

Discussing Credit Problems. *Jack Dahl confers with Jimmy Powell of Texas, a long-time leader on tax and credit committees.*

In 1988, the Big Four procured 21 percent of their total supplies in other than the cash market: 16 percent by contract and 5 percent fed by packers. These were average figures; some packers might forward contract up to 40 percent of their needs.

In 1994, during another down market, captive supplies again became an issue and there were renewed calls for a government investigation. Captive supplies generally included cattle that were forward contracted, formula priced or owned and fed by the packer. That year, the USDA reported that captive supplies accounted for 21 percent of the Big Four's slaughter, an increase of 3.4 percent over 1993.

But as the 1988-1989 Task Force reported, *The Federal Trade Commission is not concerned that packers might have supplies tied up, and it is not concerned about a possible impact on prices for the remaining supplies.* This, plus the fact that many feeders and their bankers liked the security of forward contracting or formula pricing, suggested that nothing will likely be done about it, except possibly the appointment of another task force or another investigation.

How to Sell Cattle That Don't Exist

The Opening of the Live Cattle Futures Contract at the CME, *November 30, 1964. In welcoming the cattlemen, the traders donned cowboy hats and carried canes. A calf was brought onto the floor and auctioned off.*

Trading live cattle futures has long been a subject of confusion for cattlemen. Some use them regularly, while others do not use them at all and blame those who do for controlling trading. Those in between simply do not understand how it works or how it can be used effectively.

Live cattle futures are traded at the Chicago Mercantile Exchange (CME) founded in 1898 as the Chicago Butter and Egg Board.

In 1963, Everett B. Harris, president of the CME, met J.D. Sartwelle, president of Port City Stockyards in Houston, who was looking for a way to avoid cyclical losses. Harris had already been approached by a representative of Mellon Bank who was looking for a way to protect cattle loans. To solve all these concerns, the idea of trading live cattle was born. Then began the country-wide campaign to convince cattlemen that they could trade cattle before they were fed or even before they were purchased.

The new Live Cattle Contract was offered on November 30, 1964, the first time a live commodity had been traded.

Hedging is the major advantage of using futures. By hedging, a cattleman locks in on a price well in advance of the selling date. He can then manage the risk of price changes and be guaranteed a price, rather than taking what the market offers at the moment of sale. Hedging is also an added guarantee to banks, thus allowing cattlemen greater financing flexibility.

Likewise, feeders and packers joined in. In 1971 the Feeder Cattle Contract was offered. The Live Cattle contract expanded when options on futures began trading in 1984, and in 1987, Feeder Cattle options opened as well.

But the uniqueness and inherent problems of live cattle contracts, such as delivery, presented problems. In times of a down market, producers have claimed manipulation in the trading, or that futures were leading the live market downward. In 1986, the NCA Marketing Committee passed a resolution calling on the CME to "delist futures." When surveyed, 76 percent of NCA members opposed futures and advocated delisting them. This unrest prompted the Association to ask the House Agriculture Committee for an investigation by the Government Accounting Office. Chairman Kika de la Garza came to the 1987 Convention and reported the results. *The investigation shows that futures are not being manipulated,* he said. *Rather, when properly used, futures can be a useful management tool.*

Nevertheless, NCA President Jack Dahl appointed a Task Force on Cattle Futures, chaired by past President Merlyn Carlson. Sixteen months later, the Task Force and the CME agreed on what was considered "significant and far reaching changes" in futures trading. Most important, NCA was permitted to appoint a representative on the CME Live Cattle Feeder Committees and two representatives on each cattle advisory committee.

Opening of the Live Cattle Options Contract *at the Merc. (left) CME President Clayton Yeutter, (center) Illinois Governor Jim Thompson, and (right) NCA President Dub Waldrip, October 30, 1984.*

The CME and the Association, though not always in agreement, have had a longstanding and close relationship. One of the oldest associate council members of the Association, the CME has also contributed substantially to the National Cattlemen's Foundation in support of college scholarships for students pursuing a career in the beef cattle industry.

While futures trading may remain confusing to rank-and-file cattlemen, more and more cattlemen are using futures. In 1997, on a typical day, volume ranged from 15,000 to 20,000 contracts.

Trading by Hand Signals. *Though computers are appearing on the floor, handing trading is still practiced in a unique system. Arbitrage clerks (dressed in gold) relay information from phone clerks (dressed in their firm colors) outside the pit on the line with clients, to brokers (dressed in red) inside the pit. Money is made or lost through each hand gesture in a matter of seconds.*

DALE HUMPHREY
President 1988
Springville, Indiana

Three major victories, each with lasting impact, made his term memorable: (1) Passage of the Beef Referendum, with a 79 percent "yes" vote; (2) Signing of the Japanese Beef Agreement, which opened that market to United States beef; and (3) Repeal of the heifer tax, with aid of a meat industry coalition that got an overwhelming 222 House and 57 Senate co-sponsors. "Cattlemen are known the world over," he quipped at the end of his term, "for their integrity, their industriousness, their individualism. . .and their stubbornness."

THE HIGH ROAD

The beef checkoff of $1 for each animal sold, began October 1, 1986, and put the industry and the Association on a new "high road." NCA went into high gear. With contracts provided for through checkoff dollars and more money than they had ever imagined, NCA could launch more broadbased and larger programs, studies and services, and took on an expanded staff.

Under the new Beef Promotion and Research Act, the industry began collecting approximately $80 million a year, primarily for promotion and beef research (marketing and product research, not production research). Fifty percent of the checkoff funds stayed in the state(s) where collected, the other 50 percent went to the Beef Board for further distribution. Of $638 million in total collections during the first eight years of the program, $392 million or 61 percent ultimately went to the BIC of the Meat Board, a point of contention within other organizations.

NCA also received a portion of checkoff funds from the Beef Board, as a contractor for industry information and producer communications. In 1990, for example, NCA received $4.1 million in checkoff funds; and by 1994, more than $5.3 million. This contributed to a dramatic increase in total NCA revenues, from $3.9 million in 1985 to $13 million in 1994.

Thus began a new focus for the Association. Gradually over the next few years the Association would look toward industry-wide consolidation and concentration on selling the beef product.

A Dollar a Head

The first attempt to secure a Checkoff for Beef was introduced in 1973. This plan called for a "value added" checkoff of three-tenths of one percent of the value of each animal sold, projected to raise $40 million a year for the first three years. Ten percent of collections would be retained by the respective state beef councils.

Over opposition from consumer groups, American Farm Bureau Federation, National Farmers Union and others, the Beef Research and Information Act passed Congress and was signed by President Gerald Ford on May 28, 1976.

"Keep Beef King," a major national campaign, was supported by 11 national beef and dairy organizations, 10 national breed associations, 22 state beef councils and 40 state cattlemen's associations. O.J. Barron from Texas was national chairman and Charlie Ball from the Texas Cattle Feeders was national coordinator.

The referendum, held in July 1977, required registration and voting at the ASCS office. It was complicated, and confusing to producers. The Farm Bureau had insisted Congress add a two-thirds majority requirement to the referendum. Finally 56.6 percent of the producers voted for it, but not a two-thirds majority.

Second Beeferendum

With organization still intact, ANCA revised the Beef Research and Information Act slightly and tried another referendum in 1980. Revisions included reducing the assessment and lowering the affirmative vote requirements to a simple majority.

There were also new campaign strategies for the "Beeferendum" called "Take Charge." ANCA was responsible for the all-industry effort. Target audience was the 300,000 voters who belonged to state, regional and national cattle industry associations. Jo Ann Smith of Florida was national chairman; and John Huston, BIC, was national coordinator.

Support appeared even greater. 128 beef and dairy organizations, plus 30 state Farm Bureaus, endorsed the checkoff. Only five organizations openly opposed it.

The vote at the ASCS office, scheduled for February 19-22, 1980, coincided with signup for a government grain program. Thus, many showed up who had not been targeted for a "yes" vote; only 34.6 percent of the producers voted for it.

Third Beeferendum

Only a temporary defeat for the indomitable Jo Ann Smith, who by 1985 was President of NCA, she led the legislative effort to get the bill revised and renamed the Beef Promotion and Research Act. Among the revisions:

1. Fifty percent of the collections would remain with the state beef councils.
2. Ten of the 20 members on the Operating Committee of the Cattlemen's Beef Board (the committee that controlled expenditures) would come from the BIC of the Meat Board.

These decisions would later become controversial. Other key revisions called for: a checkoff on imported beef; a five percent cap on administrative costs; voting was at the county agent's office with a referendum to be held 18 months later. giving producers an opportunity "to see the checkoff at work before voting on it." It also provided funds for the Campaign, the most extensive and professional campaign ever staged by a commodity organization. Total cost exceeded $1 million.

Campaign co-chairmen were James A. Mullins of Iowa, immediate past chairman of the Meat Board, and Bobby D. Wilson of Texas, who gained the support of state Farm Bureaus. The vote on May 10, 1988, 12 years after the idea was first proposed, was an overwhelming 79 percent "yes!"

A 1991 study showed that the checkoff had accounted for a 2.24 percent increase in demand (or kept demand from slipping as much as it would have otherwise) and paid producers a return of $5.80 for each dollar invested.

Undoubtedly, the checkoff ranked as one of the boldest activities ever attempted by NCA or its predecessors.

Working through the Beeferendums. *Staff coordinators for the 1980 Beeferendum included (left to right) Jean Krause, NCA secretary; Keith Johnson, Iowa Beef Industry Council; Charlie Ball, Texas Cattle Feeders Association; Jim Fries, Livestock Marketing Association; and George Spencer, NCA. (standing) John Huston, national coordinator on loan from the Meat Board, and Jo Ann Smith, national chairman from Florida.*

The Cattlemen's Beef Promotion and Research Board (Beef Board) was created by Congress as the Beef Promotion and Research Act of 1985 to administer the new dollar-per-head checkoff passed by referendum in 1988.

With approximately $80 million a year in total collections, half of which stay with the beef councils in the states where they were collected, the Beef Board was considered well funded.

The Beef Board was initially set up with 113 members, who represented geographic areas in proportion to cattle numbers. Its first responsibilities were simple.

A. Write rules for collecting the checkoff funds.
B. Elect members to serve on the Operating Committee.
C. Approve or disapprove budgets submitted by the Operating Committee.

The Operating Committee, comprised of 20 members, 10 from the Beef Board and 10 from the BIC of the National Live Stock and Meat Board, had the responsibility to contract with other organizations for beef promotion and research.

However, dealing out $40 million or more a year was not simple.

The 113 members represented beef

producers, dairy producers (who claimed 20 percent of beef came from dairy cattle) and beef importers. This was the first time that beef cattlemen and dairymen had sat in one organization to work on industry problems. Cattlemen had insisted that the checkoff apply also to imported beef; thus importers, who wanted a voice if they had to pay, got five seats on the Board.

Top leaders from throughout the industry, many of them members of NCA, were nominated to the Beef Board by qualifying producer and importer organizations and *appointed* by the Secretary of Agriculture. The first Chairperson was Jo Ann Smith, the 1985 NCA President. Her strong and persistent work for the checkoff, covering three referendums, had led to the successful establishment of the Beef Board. Accordingly the Beef Board maintained a close relationship with NCA, with its offices located in the NCA headquarters in Denver.

Governing a new organization with such large funds was overwhelming for some board members. Smith appointed six committees, with each member assigned to a committee so they could better understand the large projects they were being asked to fund. This worked fine until some committees began to duplicate and sometimes encroach on the works of similar committees in the NCA, the Meat Board and the USMEF.

Another bone of contention was that half of the Operating Committee, which controlled the purse strings, was appointed by the BIC. As a contracting organization, the BIC was receiving over 70 percent of the funds, up to $37 million a year. Some leaders considered this a conflict of interest. The BIC explained that this structure was mandated by law in the Beef Promotion and Research Act of 1985. No one wanted to challenge the law and risk losing the program in a new referendum.

The Beef Board's program was big and effective. In 1994, for example, the expenditures were $25.3 million for promotion, $3.8 million for research, $4 million for consumer information, $5.1 million for industry information, $5.5 million for foreign market development, $454,000 for producer communications, $513,000 for program development and evaluation, and $1.6 million for administration. (These numbers did not include the other half of checkoff collections which stayed in the states.)

10 Checkoff Success Stories

1. Advertising on national television, radio and magazines which reaches millions of consumers each year, aimed at protecting our domestic market.
2. Export programs, through USMEF, helped market two million pounds of beef a year and, in 1995, increased value of fed cattle $7.29 per cwt. and calves by $15.31 per cwt.
3. Public relations efforts with leading magazine and newspaper editors result in more than one billion impressions a year favorable to beef.
4. Beef safety research ($5 million to date) has prepared the industry for Hazard Analysis Critical Control Points, quality assurance and other safety procedures.
5. Education materials that reach 6.5 million students each year.
6. Nutrition research and education has measurably increased beef's image among healthcare professionals.
7. Environmental Stewardship Awards portray a positive image of cattle in the environment to millions of consumers each year.
8. Beef Quality Audit and the Consumer Satisfaction Study, two landmark studies, have led to War on Fat, closer trimming, a national goal of quality and consistency, and refocused the Association on consumer needs.
9. Myth Stoppers program has trained thousands of men and women to be spokespersons for the industry.
10. In total, research shows that producers have received an average return of $5.70 for each $1 invested.

REPORT
TO THE
INDUSTRY
A comprehensive
in-home product test
among frequent
beef consumers
Beef
Customer
SATISFACTION
Developed and Managed by
the National Live Stock
and Meat Board

A 1996 report entitled "Economic Returns from the Beef Checkoff," prepared by Ronald W. Ward of the University of Florida, showed that $5.70 in returns were gained for every checkoff dollar collected since the program began. Over 80 percent of cattlemen surveyed give it an approval rating, year after year.

Nevertheless, dissatisfaction and discord grew throughout the industry on the duplication of money and efforts among the major industry organizations. A consolidation plan was put together that led four years later to the new National Cattlemen's Beef Association (NCBA). The Beef Board remained separate. It had been created by legislation and had the special requirements of collecting funds outside of the Association and other organizations. However, the members and the committees meet with the NCBA members and committees; but they vote separately on checkoff matters and do not vote on legislative issues.

Beef Board Executive Directors

Gary J. Enright
1986-1990

Monte N. Reese
1990-Present

Past Chairmen of the Beef Board

1986-88	Jo Ann Smith	1994	Jim Webb
1989	Fred H. Johnson	1995	Dave Wood
1990-91	Glen Klippenstein	1996	Jan Lyons
1992	Ronnie Holladay	1997	Bob Carter
1993	Mardie Hanson		

Annual Checkoff Collections
(Total Collections 1987-1996)

1987	$66,381,915	1992	$78,830,373
1988	$76,911,761	1993	$81,075,176
1989	$83,700,365	1994	$81,061,373
1990	$79,992,575	1995	$81,619,856
1991	$79,927,149	1996	$79,806,885

In Pursuit of Animal Health

The first dipping vat *was built in 1889 by Robert J. Kleberg of the King Ranch for control of Texas Fever.*

At the first known national gathering of cattlemen, contagious diseases of animals was the primary topic. Animal health, like Public Lands, has been on the agenda of all conventions of the Association.

In 1883, following a British embargo on American beef and cattle—allegedly because of Pleuropneumonia—George Loring, United States Commissioner of Agriculture, called a national gathering of cattlemen in Chicago to discuss federal legislation to deal with contagious diseases. From this gathering the National Cattle Growers Association was formed, one of predecessor attempts at national organization, as well as the Bureau of Animal Industry, USDA, which has survived to this day.

Contagious Pleuropneumonia was the most dreaded animal disease in the latter nineteenth century, costing $1 million a year because of the embargo of beef to Europe. The disease was eradicated in 1892 at a cost of $1.5 million to the government.

Cattle tick fever was one of the most illusive diseases of the last two centuries, because cattlemen did not know for 150 years that it was transmitted by a vector, the tick. While the malady, usually called distemper, was causing cattle deaths as early as 1744 in Georgia and South Carolina, it gained the most national attention during the big cattle drives of 1866 to 1895.

Because most of the cattle driven north originated in Texas, the disease became known as Texas Fever, much to the dismay of Texans. Missouri farmers established a "shotgun quarantine" against trail herds from Texas and 15 states closed their borders to Texas cattle. But not before it had spread as far east as Illinois and Massachusetts.

After it was discovered in 1892 that the fever was carried by ticks, quarantine lines were drawn, thousands of dipping vats were built and millions of cattle were dipped. By 1943, the cattle fever tick was eradicated from the continental United States.

Foot-and-Mouth Disease (*aftosa*) was probably the most dreaded during the first 50 years of the Association. (*See pages 236 to 237.*)

One of the more exotic animal health programs to be supported by the Association was eradication of the screwworm.

In recent decades, the Association's Animal Health Committee has been dedicated to the eradication of Tuberculosis and Brucellosis, both of which can affect humans as well as cattle.

Planning for Tuberculosis (TB) eradication began in 1916 with a $75,000 appropriation from Congress, and has gained support every year. Currently no breeding animals can cross state lines without being trested for TB. By 1997, 45 states were "TB free," meaning that no case of TB had been found in these states for five years.

Contagious abortion by cows became a serious problem in New England as early as 1843. Later it became known as Brucellosis or Bangs in cows, as Undulant Fever or Malta Fever in people. While it seldom caused death, the economic losses were greater than any disease, due to weight loss, loss of young, infertility and lameness.

A Cooperative Federal-State Brucellosis Eradication Program was launched in 1934, when the percent of reactors in all herds tested was 14 percent. The new program, which called for testing of herds, slaughter of the reactors and indemnity payments to the owners, continued through the years. Also, in recent years, officials have recommended the vaccination of heifers with an approved *Brucella* vaccine.

The fight against Brucellosis was not that popular among some southern cattlemen who felt the losses were less than the cost of vaccination. However, as Don Collins, Association president 1956-1957, expressed,

> *. . .Once in a while a fellow has to accept a government regulation despite his personal feelings. He accepts because he looks in the future and sees that it is going to be necessary to take the lesser of two evils. I think the Brucellosis shipping regulations which have just gone into effect fall right into that category.*

Although slow to get underway, the Brucellosis program has worked. The number of newly infected herds have been reduced from 124,000 in 1934 to 26 in 1997. The goal for eradication is 1998.

Other diseases such as Anaplasmosis, Blackleg, Infectious Bovine Rhinotracheitis and others are regularly treated by vaccination. Regional problems such as toxic plants and parasites cause special concerns. But the drive toward good animal health practices has generally been a unifying force in the Association.

Among the biggest supporters of the Association, and the greatest number of members on the Associate Council, have been the animal health companies who have formed a synergistic relationship with the Association and its members. Members view the presence of the animal health companies not merely as vendors, but as partners in an ongoing effort to build healthy herds and a safe beef product.

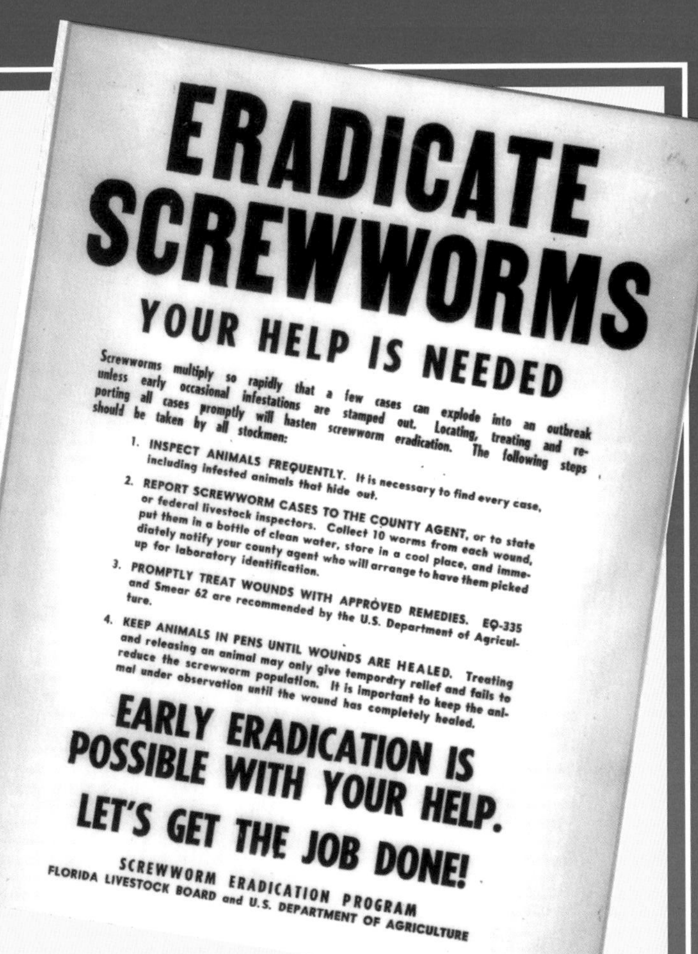

ERADICATE
SCREWWORMS
YOUR HELP IS NEEDED
Screwworms multiply so rapidly that a few cases can explode into an outbreak
unless early occasional infestations are stamped out. Locating, treating and reporting all cases promptly will hasten screwworm eradication. The following steps
should be taken by all stockmen:
1. INSPECT ANIMALS FREQUENTLY. It is necessary to find every case,
including infested animals that hide out.
2. REPORT SCREWWORM CASES TO THE COUNTY AGENT, or to state
or federal livestock inspectors. Collect 10 worms from each wound,
put them in a bottle of clean water, store in a cool place, and immediately notify your county agent who will arrange to have them picked
up for laboratory identification.
3. PROMPTLY TREAT WOUNDS WITH APPROVED REMEDIES. EQ-335
and Smear 62 are recommended by the U.S. Department of Agriculture.
4. KEEP ANIMALS IN PENS UNTIL WOUNDS ARE HEALED. Treating
and releasing an animal may only give tempordry relief and fails to
reduce the screwworm population. It is important to keep the animal under observation until the wound has completely healed.
EARLY ERADICATION IS
POSSIBLE WITH YOUR HELP.
LET'S GET THE JOB DONE!
SCREWWORM ERADICATION PROGRAM
FLORIDA LIVESTOCK BOARD and U.S. DEPARTMENT OF AGRICULTURE

A Costly Menace. *The screwworm caused cattle losses in the southern United States in excess of $15 million a year. As a result of USDA research, the release of sterile screwworm flies—irradiated and released from planes at the rate of 50 million per week —the United States was declared "screwworm free" in 1966. (right) Researchers performing studies on screwworm on a laboratory table. (below right) Screwworm-infected horn on a cow.*

Keeping Animals Healthy. *Animals being shipped, entering feedyards or at any point in which they are handled becomes a check point for health. With today's growing market of vaccines and more sophisticated medicines, animals receive top care. A healthy animal translates into better value as an end product and more profit for the producer.*

THE DREADED DISEASE

Throughout the first half of this century, nothing aroused the emotions of cattlemen or sparked unity as did Foot-and-Mouth Disease. Association leaders played it to the hilt, often implying that the disease "could wipe out our $10 billion cattle industry." No doubt it was serious, but cattlemen lived through eight outbreaks in this country.

The last foot-and-mouth outbreak in the United States was in Los Angeles, California, in 1929, when 3,591 animals (mostly cattle) were shot and buried. Earlier outbreaks had occurred in 1870, 1880, 1884, 1902, 1908, 1914 and 1924. With the exception of the 1914 outbreak, all were of short duration and limited to small areas.

Foot-and-mouth is unique, and illusive, since the animals do not suffer a high mortality rate. It affects only cloven-footed animals; animals get sores or blisters between the cloves and in the mouth and they become morbid and lose weight.

In 1935, the United States entered into the Argentine Sanitary Treaty (part of the free trade movement), which the Association contested from the beginning. It would have permitted meat from zones of Argentina, ostensibly free of foot-and-mouth, to be imported into the United States. But cattlemen's organizations, in one of their celebrated lobbying victories, kept the Treaty bottled up in the Senate Foreign Relations Committee for 12 years.

In 1947, President Harry Truman agreed to kill the Treaty, following alarm about a foot-and-mouth epidemic in Mexico. And that began a six-year, Herculean effort by a joint Mexico-United States Commission to eradicate the disease.

Before eradication was declared in 1952, nearly one million animals had been slaughtered, 60 million doses of vaccine administered and 365 million animals inspected. Over 8,000 people were employed (Mexicans and Americans) and the total cost to the United States government exceeded $35 million.

Also in 1952, at the urging of the Association, Congress appropriated $10

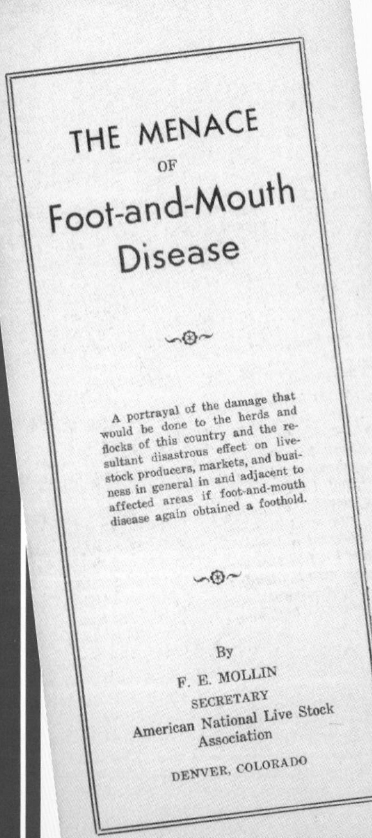
THE MENACE
OF
Foot-and-Mouth
Disease

A portrayal of the damage that would be done to the herds and flocks of this country and the resultant disastrous effect on livestock producers, markets, and business in general in and adjacent to affected areas if foot-and-mouth disease again obtained a foothold.

By
F. E. MOLLIN
SECRETARY
American National Live Stock
Association

DENVER, COLORADO

The Dreaded Disease. *Written by F.E. Mollin, ANLSA Secretary, in 1941, this pamphlet served as a defense for the Association's opposition to the Argentine Sanitary Treaty which they were keeping in the Senate Fereign Relations Committee. Cattlemen insisted it was an animal health issue while Argentina, importers and some consumer spokesmen labeled it an economic issue, a non-tariff barrier.*

Border Vigil. *Patrols on the Mexican-United States border kept close watch for violators bringing in animals with Foot-and-Mouth Disease. The patrols lived in remote locations and had their mail and other messages dropped daily from a plane.*

million to build the Plum Island Animal Disease Laboratory off Long Island, New York. Its primary purpose is to carry on foot-and-mouth research, but it also researches other diseases of foreign origin that threaten the livestock industry of this country. Imported breeding cattle from other countries are sent there for several weeks of quarantine before entering the United States.

Shooting Infected Cattle. *(top right) Hubbard Russell, ANLSA President 1938-1939, told about the 1924 outbreak when the government drove 3500 of his purebred Herefords into trenches and shot them. Cattle were shot in trenches so they could be easily buried to stop the spread of the disease. A million cattle were destroyed in this manner.*

After the shooting *(top), dead animals were usually covered with quicklime to control flies and odor.*

In the 1947-1952 outbreak in Mexico *(right), nearly one million cattle were slaughtered by the Mexico-United States Commisssion.*

PRESIDENTS & CATTLEMEN

This page
(top left) NCA president Merlyn Carlson with President Jimmy Carter.
(top right) President Bush with NCA President John Lacey.
(mid left) NCA President John Lacey presents President Bush with a copy of RANCHING TRADITIONS*. Looking on are Don Smith, NCA president-elect; Bob Josserand, past NCA president; and Jimme Wilson, vice president; John Meetz, executive vice president; and Burton Eller, vice president, government affairs.*
(mid right) NCA President Jimme Wilson greets President Bush.
(bottom right) NCA President Bill Swan meets President Bush.

Facing page
(top left) Posing with Vice President George Bush. (left to right) Burton Eller, vice president-government affairs; Tom Cook, director of industry affairs; NCA President John D. Weber; Bush; Jo Ann Smith, NCA president-elect; Don Butler, vice president; and John Meetz, executive vice president.
(top right) NCA President Sam Washburn chats with President Reagan
(middle left) NCA President W.J. (Dub) Waldrip "on the ranch" with President Reagan.
(middle right) ANCA Executive Vice President Bill McMillan greets President Lyndon Johnson with Orville Freeman, secretary of agriculture.
(bottom left) President Clinton greets NCA President Bob Drake.
(bottom right) President Reagan speaks with NCA President Jo Ann Smith and NCA Past President John Weber.

Kenneth Wyatt FEEDYARD

Raising The Bid on Beef

Quality, Consistency, Safety, Consumer Preference.
Creating the perfect product would be a new challenge and a new focus for the industry, and a new way of doing business for the producer. Many tools were in place for success: technological and scientific advances in genetics and nutrition; checkoff dollars to fund marketing and research activities; and an industry-wide movement toward consolidation. Could beef regain its previous market share? Or would it struggle with the status quo?

CHAPTER ELEVEN

CAN BEEF COMPETE?

Decline in market share, fluctuating market prices, attacks from all sides—from environmentalists to consumers—made being a cattleman a hard business. But there was more to the problem. Given the pressure on the industry, would beef be a viable product for the future? The Association turned all its energy toward making certain beef had a future. The issues the Association addressed in the late 1980s and early 1990s along with its movement toward industry-wide consolidation would put in motion the greatest overhaul the cattle industry has ever experienced.

Deciding the problems of competition led NCA to commission a study in 1989, which drove home the sobering conclusion of earlier studies: The cost of producing beef is too high.

Entitled *Competitive Issues in the Beef Sector: Can Beef Compete in the 1990s?*, this study was by six preeminent economists, not closely associated with the beef industry: Dr. D. Gale Johnson, University of Chicago; Dr. John M. Connor, Purdue University; Dr. Timothy Josling, Stanford University; Dr. Andrew Schmitz, University of California, Berkeley; and Dr. G. Edward Schuh, University of Minnesota. They reported:

One of the strongest messages that comes from the analysis is the need for producers to lower their costs of production. . .The principal reason beef is losing ground is cost in relation to other meats, not a change in consumer preference.

One reason for this seemingly unsolvable problem is that the beef industry is comprised of nearly a million operators who make independent decisions. A second reason, professional cattlemen are competing with part-timers and hobby cattlemen who are willing to operate for little or no return on their investment.

TIMELINE

1990 Spotted owl listed as endangered species.

1991 Operation Desert Storm defeated Iraqi forces in 100 hours.

United States population tops 250 million; world population reaches 5.5 billion.

Soviet Union breaks up after President Gorbachev's resignation.

1992 End of Cold War with Russia declared. by Presidents Bush and Yeltsin.

United States national debt tops $3 trillion, up from $735 billion in 1991.

1993 Bill Clinton became 42nd president.

Sears Roebuck ends 97-year-old catalogue business.

E. coli outbreak, stepping up food safety efforts.

U.S. beef exports exceed imports for first time.

Fed cattle prices hit a record $85.50 per cwt.

NAFTA went into effect.

GATT approved by Congress.

ISSUES

Environment
•
Food Safety
•
Animal Welfare
•
Quality Control
•
War on Fat
•
Industry Consolidation
•
Packer Concentration
•
EEC Hormone Ban
•
Loss of Market Share

Neither did some cattlemen like to hear talk about cutting costs, but Cattle-Fax said that from top producers to less efficient producers, there was a $100 difference in the cost to produce a calf. Also, NCA Economist Chuck Lambert in 1991 calculated the "lost opportunity" in the beef industry from rancher to retailer to be nearly $12 billion or $458 per fed animal. (*See Box, page 249.*)

Hence, NCA became relentless in its effort to help members increase efficiency through programs like the Cattlemen's College, Strategic Alliances, Carcass Data Service and Total Quality Management.

Big Three Issues

While some cattlemen were still concerned about the big packers, Robert D. Josserand, the 1989 President, was trying to refocus the Association and its membership on the "Big Three Issues," which he maintained *will dictate the direction and the activities of the Association for the remainder of this century.* The issues were:

1. Environment.
2. Food Safety.
3. Animal Welfare.

To dramatize his acceptance speech, Josserand, a large man with a forceful voice, carried to the podium a pair of post hole diggers to symbolize the work ahead in these areas and the help needed. He challenged all members to *become advocates of the Big Three, rather than defenders.* The Association has, in fact, become an advocate in all three areas.

It's All in How You Say It. *With so many attacks on the industry, Association leaders realized it was time for training and hired professional media trainer Susan Peterson. Concentrating on how to handle a hostile situation; understanding the media; and telling the beef story in its best light, she made professionals out of the volunteer leaders. Here she is working with 1989 NCA President Josserand.*

THE ORIGINAL ENVIRONMENTALISTS

Cattlemen have always considered themselves environmentalists, long before the environmental movement attracted activists and city folks who had no direct involvement in the land. After all, cattlemen—many third and fourth generation ranchers—have always depended on the soil, the water, the grass and the total environment for their livelihood. But in their preoccupation with business they told no one and got little credit. Their love of the land was inherent in their business and not a political subject.

> ***One of the strongest messages that comes from the analysis is the need for producers to lower their costs of production. . . The principal reason beef is losing ground is cost in relation to other meats, not a change in consumer preference.***
>
> —Findings from *COMPETITIVE ISSUES IN THE BEEF SECTOR: CAN BEEF COMPETE IN THE 1990S?*

ROBERT D. JOSSERAND
President 1989
Hereford, Texas

A large man with a forceful voice, who sometimes shocked people with his forthright drama, showed up for his inaugural speech with a pair of post hole diggers. *This symbolizes the work to be done,* he said, *and the help I'll need from you.* He identified "The Big Three" issues for NCA for the remainder of this century: environment, food safety and animal welfare. With feedyards in Texas, Arizona and Colorado, his AZTX Cattle Co. was ranked 7th largest in the United States. He later became President of International Livestock Congress and mayor of Hereford.

But in the 1980s, activist or advocacy groups such as the Nature Conservancy, National Wildlife Federation, Greenpeace, Environmental Defense Fund, Friends of the Earth, Wilderness Society, Earth First and many more, jumped on the environmental bandwagon and attempted to steer it their way. Cattlemen have been perplexed with the ability of these organizations to raise money, and raise it quickly, and with their hidden agenda which was apparently to get cattle off all public lands.

In 1993, the 12 largest environmental organizations (most headquartered in the Washington, DC area) had combined revenues of $633 million, or 51 times the total revenues of NCA. Even more galling to cattlemen was that some of these revenues came from the federal government. Federal grants totaling $2,554,578 were given to nine such organizations in 1993.

According to the Property Rights Foundation of America, the federal government spent $4.9 billion on environmental regulation in 1994. More important, the impact on business, individuals and other government levels was $136 billion, bringing the total cost of federal environmental regulations to a mind-boggling $141 billion per year!

FOOD SAFETY

Cattlemen have also been bewildered by the reckless charges about food safety and the emotional disregard by some consumer activists for scientific evidence. Since their industry has advanced with and is supported by science, cattlemen staked their fortunes on it.

Likewise, cattlemen knew that their future depended on producing a safe and healthful product. Accordingly, the Association worked with government agencies to improve regu-

BEHIND THE SCENES

J. BURTON ELLER

VICE PRESIDENT, GOVERNMENT AFFAIRS, 1981-1991
EXECUTIVE VICE PRESIDENT, 1991-1996

The last executive officer of NCA. By 1994, industry consolidation became "an idea whose time had come," and Eller worked faithfully to bring it about, even though it promised to eliminate his position.

He was the senior staff member in tenure, having joined ANCA in 1969 as membership director and association secretary, where he helped start the Association on a growth path that continued through 1995. Membership revenues reached $1 million in 1974, for the first time, and topped $3 million in 1995.

Born in Virginia, Eller grew up on a mountain farm and attended Virginia Polytechnic Institute, where he received a B.S. in animal husbandry in 1964 and an M.S. in animal physiology in 1969. Except for some years back on the farm in the stocker and cow-calf business, his career has largely been with ANCA/NCA. He returned to the Washington office in 1975 and became vice president, government affairs after Bill McMillan resigned in 1981.

Eller was unique in his 25-year career with the Association. When promoted in 1991 to executive vice president, he was the first career association employee elected to the senior position, and the first to come from the East. He had already made his mark in Washington as the industry's top lobbyist and was also recognized as one of the top 100 lobbyists there.

Previously, the chief executive had always been in Denver, but Eller maintained offices in both locations, to keep with cattlemen's desire for strong representation in Washington. After the formation of NCBA, Eller returned briefly to the top lobbyist post in Washington, but left in April 1996, to pursue private consulting at McLeod, Watkinson & Miller.

Despite the years in Washington where he fought his way through legislative and trade battles, grazing fees and farm-bill deliberations, and the long, complicated industry consolidation, Eller never lost his common sense approach to issues. Most members are reminded of his quick handshake, warm smile and endearing sense of humor.

Over his Association career, he recalled several "benchmark developments" in which he and the Association were involved: expansion of Cattle-Fax, first convention trade show, merger of ANCA and NLFA into NCA, Beef Promotion and Research Act, consumer movement, animal rights, environmental movement, the advocacy trend, development of the Public Lands Council and the building of NCA-PAC into a major force in the political process. His dedication to the Industry Long-Range Plan helped bring about the creation of NCBA.

lations and initiated voluntary programs to gain consumer confidence, among them the Beef Quality Assurance and the National Feedlot Quality Award.

One of the most blatant charges against the safety of United States beef was the European hormone ban, imposed in 1989. Under pressure from beef producers in the 12 countries of the European Community (now the European Union), the EC banned United States beef *unless guaranteed that it never has received any artificial hormone*, a demand that no exporter could guarantee.

NCA President Bob Josserand traveled to Brussels in October, 1989, to meet with EC officials, who he says, *agreed that it was not a safety issue but a restraint-of-trade issue.* Disregarding all the scientific evidence that United States beef was safe presented by Josserand and United States officials since, the EC ban has continued and significantly impacted our export market. For example, in 1988, the year before the ban, we exported 67,733 metric tons (metric ton=2,240 pounds) of beef to the EC, valued at $129,208,000. In 1989, this dropped 85 percent to 9,992 metric tons, valued at $10,045,000.

Other issues continued to plague the industry. When the FDA banned the use of diethylstilbesterol in 1979, some producers were reluctant to give up supplies and were caught using the drug illegally.

In 1985, in response to an adverse report on use of low-level antibiotics in feed, NCA called for a halt of low-level feeding of tetracyclines until scientific studies could resolve the issue. No clear link was

Quality in our product, quality in the way we manage our resources, quality in our associations. . .If we commit to excellence, we will satisfy our customers. We will improve the image of our industry. We will be more profitable.

—NCA President Don Smith, 1991

ever found between livestock antibiotic use and human disease, but it strengthened the EC's resistance to United States beef.

More recently in 1993 when there was an outbreak of illness from *E. coli* in beef, NCA immediately focused attention on microbiological safety issues and the public relations aspects of the issue.

"Now Mr. British Cattle Buyer, you should like these cattle here in the harmone free pasture!"

TOTAL QUALITY MANAGEMENT

When Don Smith became President, he pledged and preached Total Quality Management (TQM) until TQM almost became the industry motto. *I'm talking about excellence and quality in all we do,* emphasized Smith in his 1991 acceptance speech in Dallas. *Quality in our product, quality in the way we manage our resources, quality in our associations. . .If we commit to excellence, we will satisfy our customers. We will improve the image of our industry. We will be more profitable.*

The National Beef Quality Audit gave powerful impetus to Don Smith's TQM appeal and prompted the Associa-

JOHN LACEY
President 1990
Paso Robles, California

"One of the best years in the history of our industry," he declared, after fed cattle topped $80 per cwt. It was a turnaround year for NCA, which had borrowed money the year before. He knew the importance of the environment. "Constant vigilance is essential," he told members. And he boldly told President Bush, "Your wetlands initiative is unacceptable to millions of farmers and ranchers."

DON SMITH
President 1991
Tribune, Kansas

One of three brothers who operate Smith Cattle, Inc., 229,000 acres in Kansas, Colorado and Montana. Don is a graduate of Colorado State University and an army veteran. Total Quality Management was his thrust as president. "TQM in our product, in the management of our resources, in our Association." The 11 families of Smiths, who practice what they preach, won the 1993 National Environmental Stewardship Award.

Whose Land Is It Anyway?

Next to the right of liberty, the right of property is the most important liberty guaranteed by the Constitution and the one which, united with that of personal liberty, has contributed more to the growth of civilization than any other institution established by the human race.

—United States President William Howard Taft

The United States Constitution clearly states that private property shall not be "taken" for public use without just compensation to the landowner.

However, as the 1980s were winding down, the issue of what kinds of government action actually constituted a "taking" was under hot debate. New legislation designed to protect wetlands, endangered species, water quality and other natural resources added a new dimension to the debate. Under the new laws, some landowners found that they could no longer use some land as they had in the past. The environmental lobby had become so strong that suddenly these "takings" for the sake of protecting the environment were not considered areas for compensation. Cattlemen felt, as did other agricultural producers, that control over the use of agricultural property is critical to their economic viability.

After finding itself on the defensive and losing, NCA decided in 1991 that it would go on the environmental offensive.

To fight fire with fire, NCA leaders in 1994 established the CATL Fund (Cattlemen Advocating Through Litigation) as a separate non-profit organization. They observed that the brash environmental advocates, who seemed determined to penalize cattlemen if they did not get cattle off the disputed lands, were relying on the courts rather than legislation. This fund was set up to aid cattle producers who

National Cattlemen, November 1991.

MEAT IS MURDER
FREE the PIGS
BEEF STINKS
HUG A CHICKEN TODAY
I ♡ SPROUTS
DOWN WITH FACTORY FARMS
What do these people know about raising livestock?
Nothing! But they're going to tell you anyway.
Animal rights activists — whose sensationalistic charges get plenty of publicity — threaten the
We need your support to make this vital campaign a success. Please return the coupon below with your

Progressive Farmer, November 1991

were being challenged on "takings" and in court.

NCA also started a number of laudable programs, some in cooperation with other organizations, to encourage stewardship among members and to enhance cattlemen's image with the public. Programs like Environmental Stewardship Awards, National Feedlot Quality Award, Integrated Resource Management, Myth Busters, Water Quality Information Project and Grazing Lands Conservation Initiative have been very well received.

Respect for the Land is Inherent in the Cattle Industry. *Without land, there would be no cattle industry, and without land that had been nurtured and protected, there would be no ranches and farms passed from generation to generation.*

The Environmental Stewardship Award *was created by NCA in 1991 to honor farming and ranching families whose stewardship improves and protects the health of their land, and the health of their businesses.*

Winners are selected first by region. Then winners from each region compete for the national award, which is presented each year at the annual convention. Judges for the awards are environmental experts from various environmental groups and universities. The award has been provided by a grant from Pfizer Animal Health.

The program has allowed NCA to generate environmental success stories about the cattle industry that help promote the industry's positive story and counteract negative press, as well as position cattlemen as the "original environmentalists."

The War On Fat

NCA, along with BIC of the Meat Board and the Cattlemen's Beef Board, formed a 13-member Value Based Marketing Task Force, which issued a heralded report, "War on Fat."

It focused on the folly of producing excess fat during the last 20 to 30 days that cattle were on feed. Some 2.07 billion pounds of fat, which nobody wanted, was being produced at an estimated cost of 96 cents per pound for a shocking total of $1.99 billion.

Figures were based on 26.2 million head of cattle fed in 1989, with average excess fat of 88 pounds per head. Further, the cost to ship, trim and dispose of the excess fat adds another $2 billion!

A major cause of excess fat is that the current pricing system, based on grade, yield and dressing percentage, rewards feeders for adding fat. Also, because packers buy on pen averages, a lean steer in a pen will bring no more than an overly fat one.

Among the Task Force recommendations:

- Packers should supply retailers and food service businesses with more closely trimmed wholesale cuts.
- Packers should prepackage closely trimmed retail cuts for retailers and for consumers.
- Vigorously pursue the development of instrument grading as an objective measure of fat, lean and taste qualities.
- Price each animal on its value, rather than average pen value.

Importance of Factors In Food Selection

	"Very Important"
Taste	88%
Nutrition	75%
Product safety	71%
Price	66%
Storability	43%
Food preparation time	36%
Ease of preparation	33%

Source: TRENDS–Consumer Attitudes and the Supermarket (F.M.I., 1990)

The Contradiction for the Industry. *The consumer says it wants a leaner product, but taste is more important. Taste comes from the fat mixture in the meat. Take out fat, lose taste.*

While considerable progress has been made, such as changing the grade name from USDA Good to USDA Select, packer trimming to 1/8 inch of external fat, breeding bigger and leaner animals, and reduction of fat in ground beef, the War on Fat promises to be long.

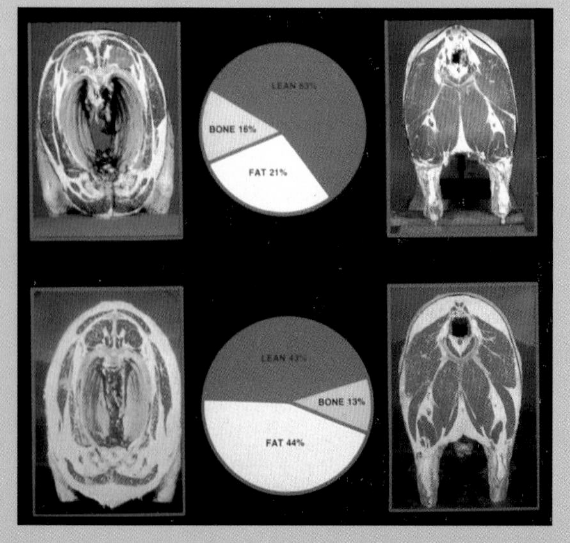

Where's the Fat? *The Association has encouraged research, especially on new ways to analyze carcasses (both before and after slaughter) to determine fat content.*

tion to adopt an endless series of supporting studies and programs: Beef Quality Assurance, Value Based Marketing, War on Fat, Carcass Data Collection Service, National Feedlot Quality Award, Integrated Resource Management, National Beef Tenderness Study, National Beef Market Basket Study and more.

Beef Quality Audit

In 1991, the National Beef Quality Audit revealed a number of pressing issues which were contributing to the poor record beef quality was receiving. The study, funded by checkoff dollars, involved 43 industry experts, interviews with more than 140 restaurants, retailers, purveyors and packers, plus inspections of carcasses in 28 major packing plants. The primary objective was *to establish baselines for present quality shortfalls and to identify targets for desired quality levels by the year 2001.*

The team of 11 researchers, with Dr. Gary C. Smith of Colorado State University and Dr. Jeff W. Savell of Texas A&M University as co-leaders, found that carcass "non-conformities," such as excess fat, overweight, bruises, injection site blemishes, and so forth, were costing an average of $280 for every fed steer or heifer slaughtered in the United States—a total of $7.2 billion!

The beef industry is its own worst enemy, the team alleged.

Beef Loses Market Share

Beef's market share was dropping. In 1970, beef sold for two times the price of broilers; and in 1990 for 3.2 times as much. In 1970, when total red meat consumption was 201 pounds per capita, beef had a 42-percent market share; in 1990, when total consumption was 220 pounds, beef's share had declined to 30 percent, translating into a decline for beef of 17 pounds per capita.

War on Fat

Continuing the industry effort to supply customers with the lean beef they wanted, a Value Based Marketing Task Force was as-

Telling the Beef Story. *Food Editor Tours have been one of the Association's more successful public relations efforts. Begun in the 1980s, the Asssociation takes food writers and editors from the national media and shows them beef at different stages of production explaining not only the process, but also the quality and safety controls.*

sembled in 1990, a 13-member group representing all segments of the industry: cow-calf, feeder, seedstock, packer and retailer. They proposed a Value Based Marketing System that would transmit consumer preferences for taste and leanness throughout the production and marketing chain—from retailers and restaurateur to purveyors and packers, then to cattle feeders, producers and seedstock operators.

Beef is losing market share, they reported, because (a) beef carries external fat that consumers do not want, and (b) the enormous cost of putting on that fat makes beef less competitive with other meats.

> ***The beef industry is its own worst enemy.***
>
> — Conclusions of the Beef Quality Audit

NEW FARM BILL

Still smarting from the dairy buy-out in the 1986 Farm Bill, Association leaders and staff took the attitude of "Never Again!" At NCA's insistence, the 1990 Farm Bill prohibited another buy-out and included market-oriented grain policies, while fighting against other commodity-program proposals that may wrongly affect the cattle industry.

LOST OPPORTUNITIES

When beef's market share dropped from 44 percent of total meat consumption in 1970 to 31 percent in 1990, it was a wake-up call for cattlemen. Waging the War on Fat brought great attention to waste in the industry.

Dr. Chuck Lambert, NCA economist, dug deeper into the "Lost Opportunities In Beef Production," and he listed the following inefficiencies and the economic opportunity of each (*in millions*):

Reproductive Performance	$2,600
Death Loss	$1,860
Hot Iron Branding	$180
Weaning Weight	$299
Multiple Processing	$110
Feed Efficiency	$325
Outlier [cull, unclassed] Cattle	$304
Excess Fat	$4,410
Management Losses	$143
Retail Shrink	$852
Out-of-Stock [retail]	$916
Total Lost Opportunities	**$11.999 billion**

Lambert concluded:

> *That amounts to 27 percent of the total beef sales in 1989, or a staggering $458 for each fed cattle. If only one-half of the lost opportunities could be corrected or reclaimed, it would increase gross returns by over $229 per fed steer and heifer.*

Such studies prompted NCA to strengthen its educational and information programs for producers to help them shave off inefficiencies and waste.

HOT IRON DEBATES

When the first cattle arrived in New Spain in 1519, they had been hot iron branded, as was the custom in Old Spain. Cortez branded his cattle with three crosses [+++], representing the holy trinity.

It was a procedure continued for several centuries. But not without controversy. At the 1887 Convention of the Consolidated Cattle Growers Association, in Kansas City, Dr. Azel Ames, a speaker representing the Montana Stockgrowers Association, discouraged the practice for economic reasons:

> *An average loss of $4 per head is not too high, he said, with an aggregate loss to the cattle industry of $1 million per annum.*

The main objections of tanners, he went on to say, were:

1. Size of the brand,
2. Location of brands (on the most valuable parts of the hide),
3. Branding on both sides, and
4. Needless multiplication of brands in change of ownership.

The National Beef Quality Audit, conducted 104 years later, showed that hot iron hide damage was averaging $7.41 per animal slaughtered or an aggregate of over $196 million per annum. And the reasons were essentially the same.

JIMME WILSON
President 1992
Trout Creek, Montana

This "Environmental Rancher" made quality environmental management his theme. "It's an issue that won't go away," he said in his acceptance speech. On his mountain ranch, he was fencing stream banks, developing alternative water sources and planting trees before such things became vogue. He addressed "the turf battle" between industry organizations and invited the chairmen of other national organizations to the peace table. This led to a task force that developed an Industry Long Range Plan and, ultimately, to consolidation of industry organizations into NCBA.

The Smith Family has Proven Success in the Cattle Business. *A.E. (Ab) Smith (second from right) shown here with his three sons, Robert, Don and Joe. All have been active Association members and leaders. Ab Smith was a permanent fixture at conventions, never missing an opportunity to draw a crowd around him discussing the issues of the moment. Son Don served as NCA President in 1991. Ab Smith left the depression years knowing that those who survived were diversified and turned his Kansas cattle operations into a multi-faceted business. Today the sons operate ranches in Kansas, Colorado and Montana, and two feedlots.*

ONE BEEF ORGANIZATION

During the campaigns for the first two Beeferendums (1977 and 1980), critics warned that *Money of this magnitude will result in new bureaucracies and competition between organizations for bigger staffs and still more money*. Even O.J. Barron, the Texan who led the first referendum, predicted in 1987, the year after the checkoff started: *When the money gets big enough, it will cause trouble and hard feelings.*

By 1990, the industry began to see evidence of those dire predictions. Because the checkoff was so popular and working so well, however, most leaders were reluctant to speak out. Sam Washburn of Indiana, the articulate and out-spoken former NCA president (1982), was an exception. In a 1990 article in *BEEF TODAY*, a national magazine, he questioned the rationale of four national organizations, four boards of directors, four staffs, four conventions and four sets of committees. Said he:

> *There is only so much expense that we can load on the back of one cow or one steer and still make a profit. We can't afford the duplicated efforts that now occur, let alone the divisiveness and competition for funds. It's time to consolidate and have one national beef organization in America.*

Running the Washington Office

When Bill McMillan opened an office in Washington in 1970, it was a big step for the Association and for the industry. The Association's permanent presence in Washington was long overdue and McMillan had the kind of personality that made up for lost time and quickly put the cattlemen in the forefront of agricultural politics and issues in Washington.

He was soon joined by Ron Michieli, a former congressional legislative assistant, who then held positions with the Association for 15 years as vice president for government affairs, executive director of the Public Lands Council and more.

Growing from McMillan alone in a rented office at the Washington Press Club, to a staff of more than 15 employees in a suite of offices located just blocks from the White House, the Washington Office has been both the weather-vane and the watchdog for the industry.

Two Easterners With Many Western Issues. *Eller and Keys exchange strategies.*

Senior Staffers, *Burton Eller and Tom Cook in the Washington Office atrium.*

When McMillan resigned in 1981 to become assistant secretary of agriculture, Burton Eller took over the senior lobbyist position as vice president-government affairs. Then in 1991, when Eller became executive vice president of NCA, Tom Cook assumed the top position in Washington.

In 1996, after the NCA and Meat Board merger into NCBA, both Eller and Cook resigned—Eller with 25 years seniority and Cook with 23 years. So Chandler Keys, already a NCA lobbyist for 12 years with the Association, became vice president-center for public policy.

In the last three decades, the Association has had four head lobbyists, helping shape legislation and regulations to cattlemen's advantage. It was a period when many felt the Association had come of age, due largely to the professionalism and expertise of the Washington office.

McMillan expressed that lobbying for this Association was so effective because it had so much grassroots support. Eller expressed the philosophy slightly differently, indicating that the power of the Washington lobbyist is derived, as it should be, from the grassroots leadership.

> *There are 300,000 guys and gals out there—counting state and affiliate members—who at any one time may have a different idea than I do.*
>
> *One good thing about having so many bosses is that accusations about lobbyists being off on their own don't hold water. We not only have clear policy, it's prioritized for us. That makes it easier. We don't have to assume what our members want, and a few members can't control us.*

Chandler Keys, *as vice president-center for public policy since 1996, also directs the NCBA Political Action Committee and the NCBA Political Education Fund. Keys was raised on a commercial Angus, grain and Thoroughbred horse farm in Maryland. He graduated from the University of Maryland with a B.A. in Political Science.*

Details and Experience. *Before becoming NCA vice president of government affairs in 1991, Tom Cook served as director of industry affairs in the Washington office and prior to that held offices in NCA and ANCA in Denver. Cook brought to his job as chief industry lobbyist a background in trade and government issues. He served on the Secretary of Agriculture's Technical Advisory Committee for Livestock and Livestock Products on trade issues and as coordinator for the Meat Industry Trade Policy Council, a coalition of meat groups that work to open foreign markets. Cook is a North Dakota native and received a B.S. in Animal Sciences from North Dakota State University.*

ROGER STUBER
President 1993
Bowman, North Dakota

In 1993 fed cattle set a record of $85 per cwt.! But, Stuber was cautious. "Cattlemen are facing uncertainty, caused by issues like animal rights, food safety, diet/health, endangered species, wetlands, clean water, clean air, federal land use, pesticide use, wildlife habitat, point and non-point pollution, foreign trade, meat inspection, futures contracts." Stuber was the third president who had also been president of the American Hereford Association.

DAN KOONS
President 1994
Shirley, Illinois

A charter member of NCA in 1977 from the NLFA and a member of the first Young Cattlemen's Council tour in 1980, Koons is known as an easy-going, level-headed, open-minded leader. After graduating from Southern Illinois University, he became a decorated Vietnam veteran, then followed his father as manager of Funk Farms Trust which was established in 1824.

NAFTA Results. *NCA President Roger Stuber greets President Bill Clinton with a package of beef being exported under the new conditions of NAFTA at a trade show promoting the exchange of products throughout North America.*

Toasting NAFTA. *North American beef industry leaders raise a glass to the promise of the North American Free Trade Agreement just one month after it went into effect, during the February 1994 International Livestock Congress (ILC) in Houston, Texas. From left to right, Bob Josserand, former NCA president and ILC president; Dan Koons, president NCA; Ken Cameron, president, Canadian Cattlemen's Association; and Cesar Gonzalez Quiroga, president, Confederacion Nacional Ganadera.*

With that apprehension in the open, scores of cynical industry leaders, perhaps hundreds, came out of the closet. Some of the criticism grew personal and venomous. While all four organizations, NCA, the Meat Board, USMEF and the Beef Board, had capable and dedicated leaders, some were accused of putting their organization ahead of industry welfare. Then "conflict of interest" was alleged, a reference to the BIC of the Meat Board having 10 of the 20 seats on the Operating Committee (the committee that determined where checkoff dollars were spent) and then receiving 70 percent of the dollars.

Recognizing that the decade of the 1990s would be a crucial one for the beef industry, elected officers of NCA, the Beef Board and USMEF saw the need for a unified effort to develop a plan to better position beef in the marketplace and improve organizational efficiency and effectiveness. Everyone agreed

Animal Rights versus Animal Welfare

Animal Rights Activists *demonstrate at 1991 NCA Convention in Dallas.*

Nothing during Association history has perplexed cattlemen more than the animal rights movement. It has been perplexing because cattlemen depend on animals for their livelihood and pride themselves on animal welfare. But animal *rights*? That implies God-given rights, which most cattlemen believe are reserved for humans.

Surprisingly, the issue is older than the Association. Henry Salt's book, *Animal Rights,* published in 1892, refers to other writings in the United States as early as 1725. But the current frenzy began in 1964 with the book *Animal Machines*, written by Ruth Harrison, an English vegetarian. In the following three decades, more books followed: *Animal Liberation, Animal Factories, Factory Farming, Modern Meat, Beyond Beef* and others. While rankling ranchers, these captured the fantasy of city activists, mostly women.

In 1992, there were about 7,000 animal protection groups in the United States, according to the Animal Industry Foundation. Of these, the 400 or so hardcore animal rights organizations controlled a combined budget of $50 to $75 million a year, more than all the cattlemen's membership organizations in United States.

Probably the most radical, and certainly the most successful, group is People for the Ethical Treatment of Animals (PETA). Founded in 1980, PETA raised more than $9 million from its 350,000 members in 1990. It employs about 90 people and has offices in the Washington, DC area. Their stated belief is: "Animals do not belong to us to eat, wear or experiment on."

Other well-known groups include the American Society for the Prevention of Cruelty to Animals, Humane Society of the United States, Humane Farming Association, Farm Animal Reform Movement (FARM), Farm Sanctuary, Earth First, Animal Liberation Front and Animal Welfare Institute.

At several NCA conventions, "animal rights" activists have demonstrated, using such slogans as "Go Vegetarian," "Meat Is Murder," "Meat Is Dead," "Respect Animals, Don't Eat Them," and "Beef Stinks."

The cattle industry has not stood idly by, but they have tried to avoid confrontation—recognizing that these groups thrive on the publicity which results from confrontation and misinformation.

The NCA approach has been to quietly work through such entities as an Animal Welfare Issues Management Team, an NCA Animal Care Subcommittee, the Farm Animal Welfare Coalition and the Animal Industry Foundation. Some strategies used have included legislation for the protection of animal research facilities; videotapes and brochures on "Cattlemen Care;" spokesperson training through a Myth Busters Program; finding and developing contacts with third-party experts who can disseminate facts about the beef industry, such as scientists, physicians and legislators; and an NCA Strategic Plan on Animal Welfare.

The stated mission of the Strategic Plan is:

> *To preserve and enhance the positive image of the cattle industry to the public by presenting producers as responsible caretakers of their animals and providing reliable information on care, production and handling practices.*

These strategies seem to be working. A 1995 survey by Associated Press revealed that 92 percent of Americans eat meat frequently or occasionally, while only two percent avoid meat altogether.

BOB DRAKE
President 1995
Davis, Oklahoma

"A pit bull with a personality" is the way he has been described. He came into office with two primary objectives: (1) consolidation of industry organizations; and (2) preservation of private property rights. The former was achieved during his term; the latter would take longer. A graduate from the University of Oklahoma, he and his brother, Tom, run 850 purebred and commercial Angus cows. (He is one of the few Angus breeders to become president.) Near the end of his term, he observed: "Right now we seem to have constant confrontation with the Department of Interior, USDA, EPA, FDA and Corps of Engineers. We're looking for cooperation with government, not confrontation."

that the duplication, discord and divisiveness was harming the industry and posed a potential threat to the checkoff program, although the Meat Board was reluctant to give up their autonomy.

Recognizing the growing concern, Jimme Wilson, the 1992 NCA President, called on the officers and CEOs of the four organizations *to sit down and work out our differences.* After a number of counter-productive meetings, which seemd to go nowhere, Wilson angrily left one meeting declaring he would not return until the organizations could begin some constructive exchanges. Finally, however, together with his NCA staff, Wilson concluded that in order for consolidation to come about, the industry must first decide which way it was going. So Wilson and Eller returned to the tables and put forth that idea. The officers of the different organizations then agreed to appoint an Industry-Wide Long Range Planning Task Force.

This Task Force would have a profound impact on the future of the industry and especially on the four national organizations.

LESSONS LEARNED

In the May/June 1995 NATIONAL CATTLEMEN, Roger Berglund, former vice president of public relations for NCA, wrote an article on the 18-year history of NCA from the ANCA-NLFA merger in 1977 to the new industry consolidation that would become NCBA. It had been a period of maturity for the Association, and in the industry. The Association had gone from defensive to offensive: it had looked at the needs of consumers and worked on a product to reflect those needs; it had helped producers become

School Lunches Still High Priority. *In 1995, consumer activist Ellen Haas, Undersecretary of Agriculture for Food, Nutrition and Consumer Services, 1993-1996 (former executive director of Public Voice) stressed the Clinton Administration's commitment to the school lunch program. Despite many cattlemen's aversion to government programs, the USDA purchases approximately 119 million pounds of beef annually.*

Frequent Critic of the Beef Industry, *Michael Jacobson, consumer activist, a vegetarian and director of the Center for Science in the Public Interest (CSPI), visited the NCA Washington Office in 1987 and challenged Clark Willingham (left), who became NCBA president-elect in 1997, and Bob Josserand (center), 1989 NCA president.*

more profitable; it had taken on anti-meat and environmental activists; it had written and carried through beneficial legislation in Washington; and it had told the very best side of the beef industry and the people behind it.

In reflecting over the past 18 years, Berglund enumerated the many lessons learned by the growing Association.

- A new organization, speaking with one voice and making more efficient use of available resources, will be more effective than multiple organizations.

> ***There is only so much expense that we can load on the back of one cow or one steer and still make a profit. We can't afford the duplicated efforts that now occur, let alone the divisiveness and competition for funds. It's time to consolidate and have one national beef organization in America.***
>
> —Former NCA president Washburn

- A pro-active, positive approach is more effective than a strictly defensive approach to issues. The best public relations is doing good and then telling about it. Producing and marketing lean, trimmed beef does more to build beef's image among health-conscious consumers than arguing against widely accepted diet-disease hypotheses. An industry-sponsored Beef Quality Assurance program does more to assure safety than simple denials of critics' charges. Cattle producers who win Environmental Stewardship Awards do more to build recognition of producers' resource stewardship than criticism of environmentalists.
- Unforeseen events and unexpected technical reports critical of beef or beef production can create crises for the industry. And those crises must be managed. But many potentially

Taxes and Credit

National Cattlemen, 1996

Tax issues have been a high priority for the Association beginning with the National Livestock Tax Committee in 1943 and continuing since 1978 with the NCA Committee on Taxes and Credit. Not only has the industry been affected by tax laws—dealing with subjects ranging from the methods of valuing inventory to capital gains to the death tax—but in recent decades it has been engulfed with a flood of government regulations dealing with air, water, environment, plants, animals and people—all the resources that cattlemen use to maintain a livelihood. Tax lobbying successes in recent years include:

"...and jist think, Son, some day all this will be yores."

- Preservation of cash basis of accounting, for all but the largest family operations.
- Recognition that livestock should be treated like assets of other businesses for capital gains purposes. A victory in 1997 reduced the capital gains from 28 to 20 percent and, in some cases, less.
- Special use valuation, in 1976, of $750,000 for valuing farm and ranch assets in a rancher's estate.
- Increasing the estate tax exemption, in 1981, from $250,000 to $600,000, and in 1997 to $1 million (for everyone), phased in to the year 2006.
- An additional estate tax deduction for farmers and family-owned businesses, beginning in 1998, which combined with the above exemptions totals $1.3 million.
- Income averaging which allows farmers and ranchers to average income for 1998-1999-2000.

The Long Range Plan

The Industry-Wide Long Range Planning Task Force was formed to develop a strategy for the beef industry focused on domestic and international marketing, issues management, public relations, effective use of resources and industry governance. In short, where the industry should be going for a successful future.

The 14-member Task Force included the chairman or president of each organization and 10 at-large members. Rob Adams chaired the Task Force, with NCA Chief Financial Officer Earl Petersen as Project Leader. After 18 meetings, 70 formal presentations, hundreds of interviews, numerous industry meetings and a year of studies, Adams presented the long awaited report.

> *The U.S. beef industry has, for too long, been focused inwardly. We have been production-driven, not consumer driven. We have demonstrated neither the ability nor the inclination to respond adequately to consumer signals in the marketplace. Beef has lost market share to poultry and pork for a number of years.*

The Task Force identified eight strategic leverage points:

1. Quality and Consistency
2. Domestic Marketing
3. International Marketing
4. Public Relations
5. Issues Management
6. Production Efficiency
7. Producer/Packer Alliances
8. Strategic Alliances

Almost everyone was pleased with the recommended goals, except for one.

> *The Task Force. . . found that, as an industry, the structural criteria of focus, coordination, control and cost effectiveness cannot be met. . .The Task Force. . . recommends a single consolidated national organization.*

The Meat Board and USMEF, both multi-species organizations, were reluctant to accept "a single, unified industry organization." Cattlemen, however, who paid the bills, were less than impressed with the big staffs and big budgets of the four organizations which had a combined staff of nearly 200 and annual budgets in excess of $92 million. All proclaimed that they had the mission to enhance the profit potential for cattlemen. By unifying the organizations, the Task Force calculated a savings of $3.6 million a year.

BEEF INDUSTRY STRUCTURE—1994

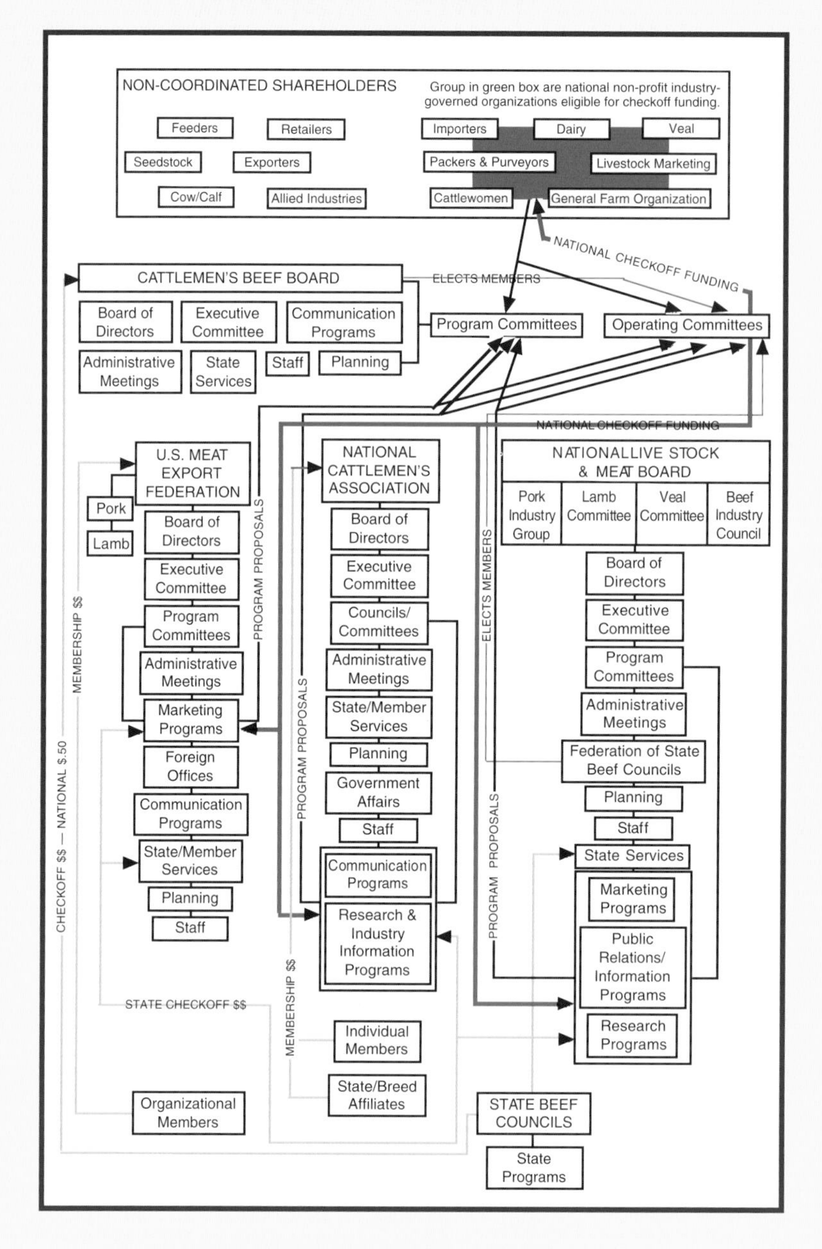

Members of the 1994 Industry-Wide Long Range Plan Task Force. *(left to right) Virgil Huseman of Kansas, Mardie Hanson of Colorado, Ralph (Buck) Bell of South Carolina, Burke Healey of Oklahoma, Linda Davis of New Mexico, Gordon Van Vleck of California, Robert Foster of Vermont, Jack Maddux of Nebraska, Rich Shuler of Iowa (facilitator), Rob Adams of Illinois (chairman) and Roger Stuber. Not shown: Tobin Armstrong of Texas, Bill Engelbrecht of Illinois, Joe Hampton of Illinois, James A. Mullins of Iowa, and Earl B. Peterson of NCA, Project Leader. Also, the executive officers of the four organizations served as liaison representatives: Jay Wardell of the BIC, Monte Reese of the Beef Board, Burton Eller of NCA and Phil Seng of USMEF.*

1995 Long Range Plan Oversight Committee. *(front row left to right) Jean Krause, Roger Stuber, John Huston, Bob Drake, Max Deets, Bob Carter, Dave Wood and Mardie Hanson. (back row left to right) Robert Foster, Philip Seng, Rick Allen, Jim Webb, Dan Koons, Jack Maddux, Clark Willingham, Monte Reese and Earl Peterson. (Committee members not pictured) Dadie Perlov, Ellard (Butch) Pfaelzer, James Mullins, Burton Eller, Ron Curtis and Ralph (Buck) Bell.*

Early on, USMEF, bowing to opposition from packer and Farm Bureau members, voted to stay out, even after their officers had helped devise the unified plan and their executive committee had approved it. This preempted ultimate consolidation. However, USMEF did remain "a contractor of choice" to carry out international marketing programs for the new organization.

The Meat Board was also slow to buy in. After all, they had a long history of success and were prospering financially. But intense pressure from all corners was put on them.

More pressure was applied when 22 past presidents of NCA pleaded in a December 1994 letter to the chairman of the Meat Board and the chairman of the BIC:

> *We believe it's time to do what is right for beef producers. We must unify the beef industry and move to a consolidated, efficient, producer-driven organization . . . . We urge you to join us in putting aside organizational interests for the greater good—a profitable and dynamic beef industry.*

A CONSOLIDATED STRUCTURE: OF, BY AND FOR BEEF

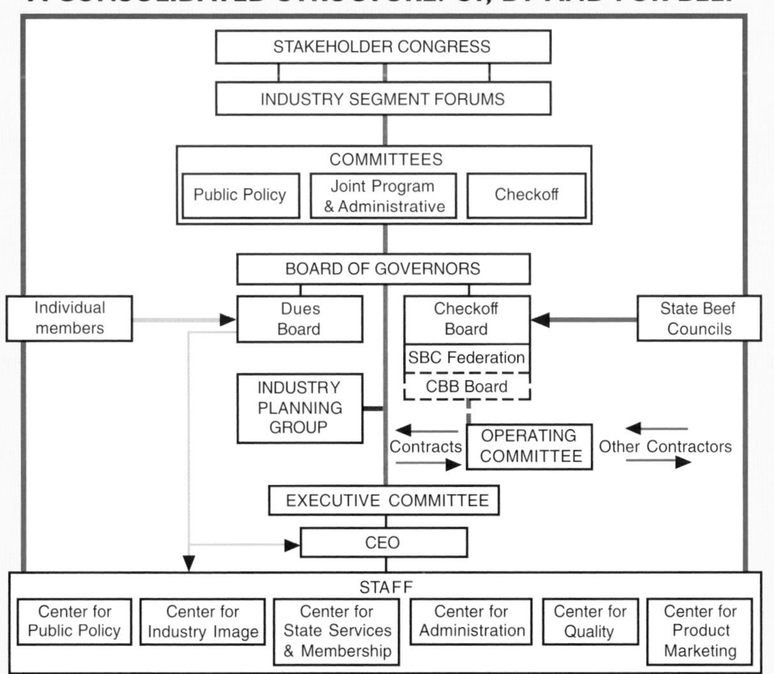

A Complex Structure

It became apparent that the structure of the new organization would be a tedious, herculean chore. So the Task Force was replaced with an Oversight Committee focused "to develop an acceptable structure for the new organization." This committee consisted primarily of officers of the four associations, plus some carryover members from the Long Range Task Force.

After two years of work and 24 meetings with committees, attorneys and consultants, the Committee came up with an organizational structure.

The unique structure created a stakeholder congress, which any cattleman could attend; a board of governors, on which various organizations could buy seats (divided into a dues division and a checkoff division); a 27-member executive committee with a dues and a checkoff section; and seven centers for programs.

Though complex, the structure had a number of positive features: one board, one executive committee, one set of coordinated committees, one long range planning group, one budget and one CEO.

While successful, the industry learned that restructuring does not come cheap. Expenses for the Task Force and the Oversight Committee came to approximately $1.5 million, half paid with checkoff funds and half by the four organizations.

Finally in August 1995 the Meat Board agreed to consolidate. Thus, the road was cleared for a new organization: The National Cattlemen's Beef Association (NCBA).

A Transition Executive Committee (TEC) began the work of joining the organizations fiscally. TEC also began searching for a new chief executive officer for NCBA. The nationwide search reviewed more than 200 candidates before they hired University of Nebraska Foundation Chief Chuck Schroeder.

The Golden Spur

The National Golden Spur Award, established in 1977, is presented each year at the Ranching Heritage Center in Lubbock, Texas. This unique award, the only national award of its kind, recognizes not only a lifetime of contributions and dedication, but also honors the reputation of the recipient. Current sponsors, in addition to NCBA, include American National CattleWomen, American Paint Horse Association, American Quarter Horse Association, American Sheep Industry Association, Ranching Heritage Association, Texas Cattle Feeders Association, Texas and Southwestern Cattle Raisers Association and Texas Sheep and Goat Raisers Association.

Albert K. Mitchell was the first recipient of the award. Since then five other former Association presidents have received the award.

Mitchell's daughter, Linda Mitchell Davis, was also given the award in 1992 marking the first time members of the same family have been so honored.

As families who have impacted the Association go, none have been busier than the Mitchells. Albert Mitchell served as Association President 1936-1937 and remained active in the Association throughout his life, while managing the renowned Bell Ranch (the largest in New Mexico), then to the Tequesquite Ranch, where he developed an outstanding herd of Herefords.

Linda Mitchell Davis manages the CS Ranch with her husband and family. A graduate of Cornell University, as was her father, Davis has been a part of the Association in all aspects, serving the Association, the American National CattleWomen, and the Cattlemen's Beef Board. A force in the New Mexico Cattle Grower's Association, she earned their 1990 Cattlemen of the Year award; she is also on the Board of the Cowboy Hall of Fame. At present, Linda Davis is Chairman of the NCBA Centennial Task Force.

National Golden Spur Award Recipients

1978	Albert K. Mitchell	1988	O.J. (Jim) Barron
1979	Jay Littleton Taylor	1989	Hilmar G. Moore
1980	Fred H. Dressler	1990	Jo Ann Smith
1981	Watt Reynolds Matthews	1991	Clarence Scharbauer, Jr.
1982	J. Ernest Browning	1992	Linda Mitchell Davis
1983	John B. Armstrong	1993	John S. Cargile
1984	Foy Proctor	1994	Kenneth Monfort
1985	Marie Tyler	1995	A.L. Black
1986	W.D. (Bill) Farr	1996	William J. (Dub) Waldrip
1987	Walter Pfluger	1997	Dolph Briscoe, Jr.

adverse public reactions can be headed off by smart issues management—anticipating issues, developing needed information and preventing adverse effects on the marketing climate for beef.

- Government and academic "experts" are becoming more suspect, research shows. Working cattle producers, using scientific facts and their own experience, will be increasingly credible spokespersons.
- Production-related issues, especially environment-related issues, are growing in importance. But product-related issues, including safety, quality and consistency, and healthfulness, remain important. The processing function will be more significant in future representation of the beef business.
- Organizations and their leaders must lead, but they cannot get too far in front of the parade. Grassroots involvement remains essential in policy development and implementation.
- Numbers of agricultural producers continue to decline. National and state cooperation and grassroots involvement will be more important than ever in government and public affairs work. Coalitions on specific issues will be essential.
- Competing industries—poultry and, to a growing extent, pork—are made up of businesses that develop, produce, process and market quality-controlled, differentiated, brand-identified products. The beef business, meanwhile, remains largely a segmented, commodity business. Until the industry changes, the industry's organization will have to carry out product-related initiatives—facilitating product improvements, promotion and research that help beef regain market share.
- An agricultural business is tough enough without throwing in rapid structural change, too. The organization will have to develop and disseminate information helping industry members cope with change.

The Industry Laughs

Natural disasters, market disasters, and government disasters—what this business has always needed is a disaster laugh.

For the Association, and the industry at large, three names mean humor: Ace Reid, Jerry Palen and Baxter Black. For the last forty years these humorists, more than any others, have poked fun at every facet of life on the farm, at the ranch and under the government's thumb.

Humor in the cattle industry is a long-standing tradition, dating back through the last century to such greats as Charlie Russell, Will Rogers, J.R. Williams, and many more who have given the cattlemen a sense of humor.

As the Association and its affiliate organizations have grown and become more sophisticated, so have their conventions, trade shows and publications. These humorists have adapted and filled roles as entertainers and representatives of associate organizations. Using their newspaper and magazine syndications, they have spread mirth throughout the industry helping just plain folks to see the humor in their lives and their situations.

When asked how many conventions Ace Reid had been a part of, Madge Reid, his wife, responded, *I don't know. It was so much a part of our lives, we must have gone to them all.*

"It's jist about this time every morning I wonder if there ain't some other way to make a living!"

Ace Reid, *creator of* Cowpokes *cartoon series. "I learned that I could starve to death chasin' an ole cow 'er starve to death drawin' pictures, so I picked the one I could do in the shade."*

Jerry Palen, *creator of* Stampede *cartoon series. Jerry's simple formula for success: "I like what I do."*

"All the smart money is getting rich in the bull market and I own steers!"

Baxter Black, *cowboy poet, ex-veterinarian and starvin' cattle feeder, and creator of* On the Edge of Common Sense

Cow Attack
by Baxter Black

What happened to your pickup seat? Is that buffalo track?
Well, I guess you had to be there. We had a cow attack.
It all began when me and Roy went out to check the cows.
We'd finished lunch and watched our "soap" and forced ourselves to rouse.

We's pokin' through the heavy bunch for calves to tag and check.
I spotted one, but his ol' mom was bowin' up her neck.
She pawed the ground and swung her head a slingin' froth and spit,
Then bellered like a wounded bull, "Say, Roy," I says, "let's quit!"

But Roy was bent on taggin' him, and thought to make a grab.
"Just drive up there beside the calf. I'll pull him in the cab."
Oh, great. Another stroke of genius, of cowboy derring do.
Shur'nuf, when Roy nabbed the calf, his mama came in too.

And I do mean climbed up in there! Got a foot behind the seat.
Punched a horn right through the windsheild and she wasn't very neat.
She was blowin' stuff out both ends, 'till the cab was slick and green.
It was on the floor and on the roof, and on the calf vaccine.

If you've been inside a dryer at the local laundromat,
With a bear and 50 horseshoes, the you know just where I's at.
At one point she was sittin' up, just goin' for a ride,
But then she tore the gun rack down. The calf went out my side.

I was fightin' with my door lock, which she'd smashed a passin' by,
When she peeked up through the steering wheel and looked me in the eye.
We escaped like paratroopers out the window, landed clear.
But the cow just kept on drivin' cause the truck was still in gear.

She topped a hump and disappeared. The blinker light came on,
But if she turned I never saw. By then the truck was gone.
I looked at Roy, "My truck is wrecked. My coveralls are soaked.
I'll probably never hear again. I think my elbow's broke.

"And look at you. Yer pitiful. All crumpled up and stiff.
Like you been eat by wild dogs and pooped over a cliff."
"But think about it," Roy said. "Since Granpa was alive,
I b'lieve that that's the firstest time I've seen a cattle drive."

-reprinted with permission of Baxter Black from On the Edge of Common Sense

Trends in Cattle Types

Throughout the century, the Association has concerned itself primarily with the business and political side of the industry, leaving the development and improvement of cattle breeds to the cattlemen. However, as the century closes, the emphasis on the final beef product has put the Association in a new, agressive position in research and development.

Cattle types have changed greatly over the years as cattlemen searched for the perfect animal and carcass. In the late 1800s, English breeds were imported to upgrade the beef animal. But not all cattlemen had the resources to support expensive herds and were still getting by with scrub cattle.

By the 1930s the government had taken an active interest in helping cattlemen and farmers upgrade their livestock (to become more competitive in the marketplace). From the 1950s into the 1990s, the English breeds faded somewhat as the trend towards a less fat carcass prompted a trend in cross-breeding and importing "exotic" breeds from around the world.

Today the Association has 24 recognized breed associations as affiliate members. Still, the search is on for the perfect beef animal, and now for the perfect carcass as well.

Grand Champion Steer *at the 1900 International Live Stock Exposition, Chicago, was "Advance," an Aberdeen Angus that weighed 1,430 pounds and sold for $2,145. He was shown by Woodlawn Farm, Creston, Illinois, owned by the Pierce family, who are still in business and the oldest continuous Angus operation in the United States.*

Longer, Taller and Larger. *Toward the end of the century, beef cattle types had become longer, taller and larger, which resulted in "exotic breeds" or crossbreeds winning most major shows. The Grand Champion Steer at the 1995 Houston Livestock Show and Rodeo was "Shoop," a 1,242-pound Chianina, owned by Morgan Moylan, an FFA member from Eastland, Texas. The champ sold for a record $500,000 to LeRoy and Lucile Melcher and Tom and Mary Steele.*

Compressed Beef. *By mid-century, beef types had become smaller and shorter, "compressed." The 1950 Grand Champion Steer at the 1950 International was "Big Spring Special," a 1,025-pound Hereford owned by Lloyd Robinson of Big Springs, Texas. Dr. A.D. (Dad) Weber, Vice Dean of Agriculture, Kansas State College, was the judge and one of the best-known judges in that era. Albert Pick, Jr., of the Pick Hotels Corporation, Chicago, paid $12 per pound for the champion.*

"I'll call you four Herefords and raise another two Angus."

With Purebred Bulls a Breeder Achieves More in Two Generations Than in Five with the Grade Bulls

Progress in Five Generations Using Grade Bulls and Native Cows
Replace Scrub and Grade Sires with Good Purebreds

See How Rapidly the Proportion of Native Blood (Black Portion) Diminishes When a Purebred Sire is Used.

For full information

WHICH WAY IS YOUR LIVE STOCK GOING ?
PUREBREDS
Let YOUR Animals March With The Purebreds
SCRUB ROUTE
JOIN THE "BETTER SIRES BETTER STOCK" CAMPAIGN
ENROLL AND GET AN OFFICIAL EMBLEM
CONSULT THE COUNTY AGENT, YOUR AGRICULTURAL COLLEGE OR THE UNITED STATES DEPARTMENT OF AGRICULTURE

Upgrade! *Posters from the USDA in the 1930s urged farmers and cattlemen to improve their livestock and become more competitive.*

Herd Improvement Day. *The speaker staged a mock trial of a scrub bull in the 1920s, convicting him of standing in the way of purebred bulls to upgrade the range herds (note the sheriff wearing a large star as a badge).*

Tim Cox   HELPIN' DAD

The Vision

Our Legacy

The Land, The Family, The Cattle

CHAPTER TWELVE

One Voice, One Industry

The consolidation of industry organizations was not official until the NCA board and membership voted on the proposition. And while there was widespread support for consolidation, it was far from unanimous. Some NCA members feared a takeover of their Association by the "Gucci loafer crowd" they believed to be in control of the Meat Board. And some Meat Board directors feared a raid on the checkoff funds by cowboys who wanted to control it all.

After several open forum sessions during which cattlemen asked questions about how the new organization would operate, a considerable floor debate ensued during the membership business meeting, January 1996, led in large part by the delegation from California. The delegation felt that due to the great importance of this step in the industry, all members, whether or not they attended the convention, should be allowed to vote. Finally, in a moving moment indicative of the spirit behind unification, Paul Hitch of Oklahoma stepped to the mike and declared, *The world is run by people who show up!*

Members then voted to end NCA and approved consolidation. The National Cattlemen's Beef Association (NCBA) became reality.

John Lacey of California, former NCA President (1990), was elected to head up the new organization. This was the second time in Association history that a president from a former organization became president of a new organization, the first being Murdo MacKenzie in 1906. Max Deets of Kansas was elected president-elect of the new NCBA, and Clark Willingham of Texas, vice president.

But the vote on consolidation was only a starting point. For NCBA, two issues remained unresolved at the end of its first business session. First was the question of direct participation in

TIMELINE

1995 Alfred P. Murrah Federal Building in Oklahoma City bombed, killing 168 occupants.

Republicans took control of both houses of Congress for the first time in 40 years.

1996 United States agricultural exports reach $60 billion, the second year in a row that agriculture was the nation's top exporting industry. Beef exports increased eight percent overall, but exports to Mexico nearly doubled.

NCA and BIC of the Meat Board merge into NCBA.

BSE becomes problem in England; no trace found in the United States.

Bill Clinton re-elected president.

ISSUES

Consolidation
•
Name of Association
•
"Mad Cow" Disease
•
Grassroots Control
•
Organizing Staff
•
Financing the Association

policy-making by NCBA members. The new bylaws provided member input through the committee process, but like many organizations left decisions about matters such as bylaws changes and establishing policy positions solely in the hands of the board of directors. Some contended that all dues payers—not just board members—should have the opportunity to ratify policy.

The second issue was the name itself. It was a compromise, with which not everyone was satisfied. It had come about because some felt the name, "National Cattlemen's Beef Association," relied too much on the tradition and image of the cowboy, and that this new organization, with its consumer focus and its stated purpose of rebuilding beef's market share, should focus on the word "beef" in its name. Others said the name should represent the people—the cattlemen who pay the bills and make the decisions—not the commodity they produced.

End of the National Cattlemen's Association and the Beginning of a New, Broader Association! *At the 1996 Convention in San Antonio, delegates debated for two hours, then voted to terminate NCA and become part of the expanded National Cattlemen's Beef Association. Members used pink cards to vote. In the new NCBA, members of the Board of Governors vote with three colors of cards: red for the Policy Division, white for the Checkoff Division, and blue for the Beef Board.*

FACING THE CHALLENGERS

The honeymoon was quickly over for NCBA. Its leadership faced immediate challenges from inside and outside the industry.

Inside were cattlemen who simply did not like the idea of consolidation. They believed their interests were better represented by several organizations which could maintain "checks and balances." There was talk of splinter organizations, and even a referendum on the checkoff.

But there was underlying cause of this unrest. After a decade of profits, cow-calf producers were losing money in 1996, the result of increased cattle numbers and calf prices dropping 25 to 35 percent.

New Leadership. NCBA officers for 1996. *(from left) President John Lacey, Paso Robles, California; President-Elect Max Deets, Beloit, Kansas, and First Vice President Clark Willingham, Dallas, Texas.*

> ***The world is run by people who show up!***
>
> —Paul Hitch, Oklahoma
>
> *Speaking on the floor at the debate over the vote on NCBA*

Feeders were also distressed due to a depressed market and corn prices increasing 50 to 75 percent. Under such pressure, some cattlemen were calling on their new Association to do *something*—about futures, about packer concentration, about packer feeding, about loss of market share—*just do something*!

So Lacey and newly hired Chief Executive Officer Chuck Schroeder opted to answer NCBA challengers face to face and they began attending several months of grassroots meetings. Lacey later told a reporter:

> *Failure was not an option. You do have to put a few things on the line for something like this to be successful. My goal was to stay focused, unify {members} and justify the merger.*

Then came the outside challenge: "Mad Cow Disease." Bovine Spongiform Encephalopathy (BSE), a rare, chronic degenerative disease affecting the central nervous system of cattle and known to exist in beef and dairy cattle in the United Kingdom (UK), was linked in scientific debate in the UK to Creutzfeldt-Jacob Disease (CJD).

Negative press coverage about "Mad Cow Disease," a popular misnomer used by the media, and the possibility that humans who eat beef from BSE-infected cattle could get CJD showed up in the British media. The first major story in the United States media about the possible link between BSE and CJD appeared in the December 25, 1995, issue of *BUSINESS WEEK*. By the time the industry consolidation into NCBA became official at the end of January, over 30 stories had appeared.

A related issue arose regarding the rendering of animal protein for feed. Predictably, animal rights and other activist groups began to use the BSE/V-CJD issue, "cow cannibalism" and protein derived from other animals, to damage consumer confidence in beef.

In concert with other groups including USDA's Animal Plant Health Inspection Service (APHIS), NCBA began to take "crisis management" steps:

- Provided advisories to affiliate organizations, a question and answer document and a list of people to whom media calls could be referred.
- Became a primary source of scientifically-sound information on BSE, and staff in all three NCBA offices handled more than 300 media interviews on BSE in the last 10 days of March alone.
- In cooperation with other livestock and veterinary groups, called for an immediate voluntary ban on the feeding of specified ruminant-derived proteins to ruminants (exempting blood products and

BEHIND THE SCENES

CHARLES P. (CHUCK) SCHROEDER
CHIEF EXECUTIVE OFFICER
1996-PRESENT

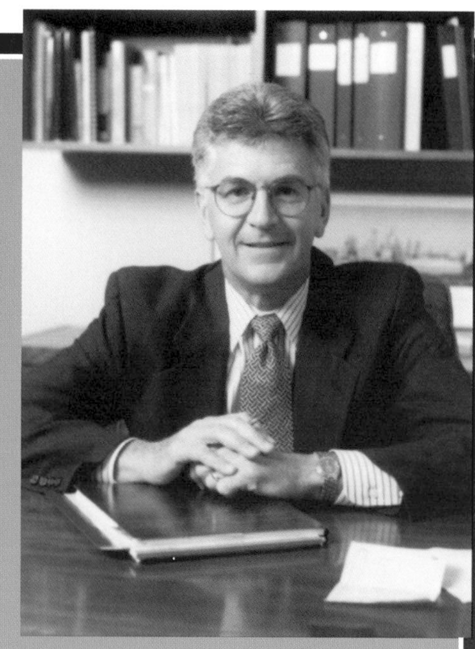

It did not take long for Chuck Schroeder to get his feet wet. He was given the enormous task of ironing out the internal details of the newly formed NCBA as well as selling the new organization to members who did not quite understand the new structure and focus. Then he faced his first industry crisis with the "Mad Cow" disease.

But Chuck Scroeder brought with him a new vision for the industry: the Association was going to move the industry forward into a new era of product development aimed at increasing market share for beef and profitability for producers. To accomplish this task, Schroeder has led a restructuring of staff and responsibilities to build a more efficient and effective organization under one common administration.

No newcomer to the industry, Schroeder is part-owner of Schroeder Cattle Company, a diversified ranching, feeding and farming business in southwest Nebraska. He served on the NCA board of directors 1981-1982 and was member and officer of the former Nebraska Stock Growers Association.

Schroeder came to the Assocation from the $350-million University of Nebraska Foundation where he served as executive vice president. A native of Nebraska, he has a B.S. degree in animal science and business from the University of Nebraska.

tallow), and stressed that this would provide an additional safety margin during the time interval required for the FDA to determine the need for a regulation.

In addition, the World Health Organization and the FDA proposed science-based and enforceable regulations to prevent the spread of BSE in the cattle population in the United States.

Even so, in April 1996, the widely-viewed talk show host, Oprah Winfrey, discussed BSE and gave anti-meat activists a platform to present biased and unsubstantiated claims against beef. Thanks to the work of NCBA and cattle producers across the country, Winfrey agreed to clear up unanswered questions and set the record straight on a follow-up show.

GRASSROOTS CONTROL CALLED FOR

At the first NCBA stand-alone board meeting, during the summer conference in Nashville, Tennessee, two changes were made to ensure that grassroots control was at the operational heart of the new organization.

The Bylaw and Policy Review Task Force recommended and obtained bylaw changes that would put ratification of policy and bylaw changes into the hands of members acting during the annual business meeting, not just board members. It was another victory for the grassroots.

At this same meeting, the Montana Stockgrowers Association presented a resolution of concern about allied industry participation in the

Association. (This was the same concern which in 1901 caused some members to bolt from the National Live Stock Association and form the American Cattle Growers Association. The only difference was the nature of the allied industries, which at that time were commission companies, stockyards, packers and railroads.)

> ***The problem is that the beef business has traditionally been commodity driven. And in a commodity-driven business, each segment views every other segment as an adversary.***
>
> —NCBA Chief Executive Officer Chuck Schroeder

The new Articles of Incorporation (1996) allowed allied industries to invest in NCBA and thereby earn a seat on the board.To limit the influence of allied industries, however, the Montana resolution was passed. Thus, (a) any allied industry investor is limited to one seat on the board, and (b) allied industries as a group are limited to 20 percent of board seats.

The second change was a plan to ensure grassroots input. The plan, developed by committee chairs and vice chairs in October 1996, was intended to assure that (1) committee members would receive relevant information in advance of meetings, (2) the meetings themselves would be run in such a way as to allow for a fair hearing of differing views and (3) that the decision-making process was informed and accountable. Also the plan called for staff and volunteer leadership training, meeting agendas which emphasized the business at hand and the use of expert teams of committee members to help sort out weighty issues for the full committees.

To the average outside cattleman, NCBA no doubt appears to have a complex structure. But NCBA represents a complex industry, compounded by several other factors. Some examples:

1. Dues-paying members have certain rights, while all cattlemen paying the checkoff (stakeholders) have some rights also.
2. The directors representing dues-paying members get deeply involved in policy; yet directors of the Beef Board are prohibited by law from involvement in government policy.
3. The two boards meet together—to enhance communications and coordination—yet they vote on different issues, using voting cards of different colors.

There are three types of committees:

- Committees with programs funded only by the checkoff.
- Committees with programs funded only with dues revenues.
- Committees with programs funded from multiple sources.

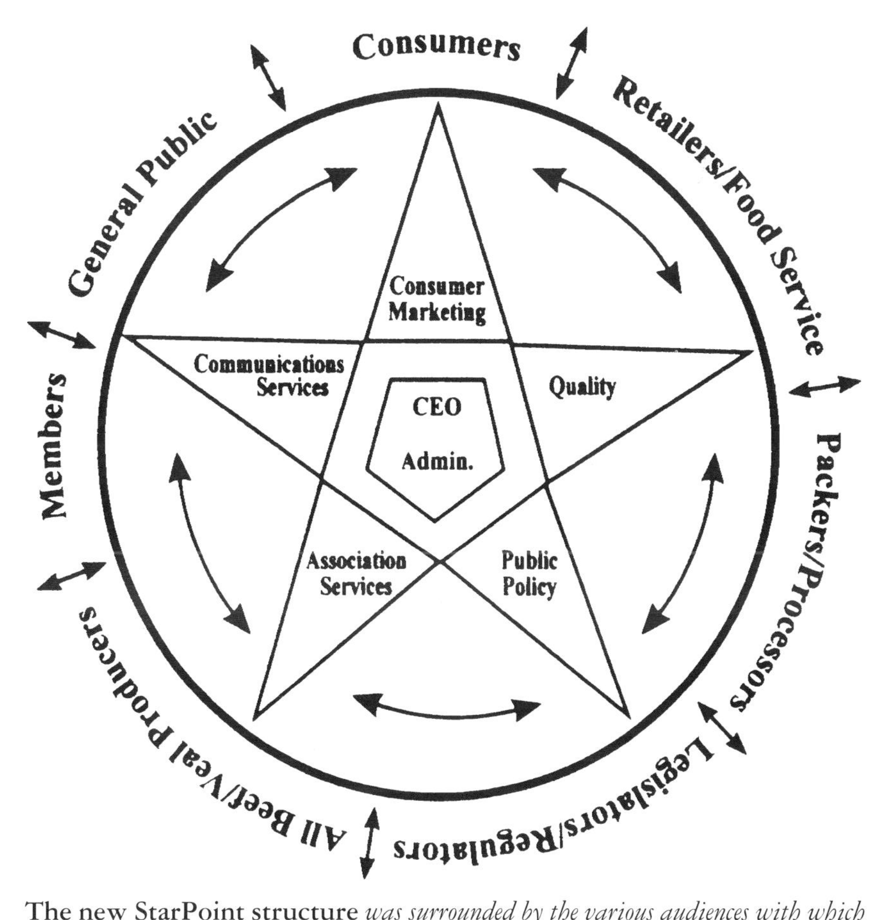

The new StarPoint structure *was surrounded by the various audiences with which NCBA staff would work.The new structure included five centers: (1) Policy, located in Washington to work with Congress and federal agencies; (2) Consumer Marketing, located in Chicago, to coordinate global marketing efforts; (3) Communications, with staff in all three NCBA offices, to work with media and those who influence others; (4) Quality, in Chicago and Denver, to carry out human and animal-based research aimed at producing better products; and (5) Association Services, in Chicago and Denver, to work with state affiliates and councils, and to interact directly with members.*

So a complex plan seems inevitable at this stage of organization. Association leaders hope, however, that it will be simplified as time passes.

ORGANIZING STAFF

Though most industry leaders already had realized that the Meat Board, Beef Board and NCA operated with different staffing priorities, planning processes, budgeting philosophies and fiscal years, it was not until after consolidation was official that the work of reforming these differences into a common foundation became the priority.

Schroeder, introduced a new staffing philosophy to replace the various corporate cultures. His structure included five operating centers, or StarPoints, operating around a single administrative center.

But the changes would be more than structural. In the first several months of operation, NCBA went through a major restaffing. Three senior staff members of NCA, (Burton Eller, Tom Cook and Earl Peterson) resigned or retired, and other staff were shifted from Chicago to Denver and Denver to Washington.

NCBA under Schroeder was a new organization.

GOALS FOR THE NEW ORGANIZATION

During the three years of discussion and negotiation which led up to the industry consolidation, there were heated disagreements over many issues. But all industry leaders agreed from the outset that their common goal was "to develop a dynamic and profitable beef industry." Dynamic denoting a forceful industry always in motion, continuously making progress. And profitable meaning it would provide livelihood to this and future generations. This goal was not limited to any single segment of the industry—not cow/calf to the exclusion of feeding; not feeding to the exclusion of processing; not processing to the exclusion of retailing.

For some the most important point, and for others the most radical point, was the complete change in philosophy. The new focus was on an industry that "consistently meets consumer needs."

FINANCING THE ASSOCIATION

The budget reorganization for NCBA was one of the most difficult challenges faced in the early days of the organization. In some areas, NCBA could save money over its predecessors by: (a) holding fewer meetings, (b) requiring less volunteer and staff time, travel and expense to oversee operations, and (c) a single accounting and administrative staff. By the end of 1996, NCBA was able to reduce the size of the staff and cut administrative expenses by more than $400,000.

Even so, it was a "red ink" year, because NCA and the Meat Board were both spending extra (from reserves) to stimulate beef demand during that period of low cattle prices, and eight months of their fiscal year fell to NCBA.

While more efficient, NCBA would, however, have to postpone until its second year its struggle to achieve even a balanced budget. The primary reason was that program costs—checkoff dollars spent for advertising, public relations, education and research, and dues dollars spent to influence public policy—continued.

The NCBA budget committee was charged with doing things differently for fiscal 1997. The result of their effort was a balanced budget for NCBA's first full year (fiscal 1997) of $79 million. Revenues included $45.5 million in Checkoff funds from the Beef Board; $14.5 million from state beef councils (also from Checkoff funds); $9.1 million from the USDA Foreign Agricultural Service, for export development by the USMEF; $3.2 million in dues; and $7.2 million from other sources.

Major expenditures included $50.6 million for advertising and promotion, domestic and foreign; $12.2 million for public relations and member communications; $7.6 million for product safety and quality; $1.8 million for legislative and regulatory; $3.5 million for Association services; and $3.4 million for other expenditures.

As the first year passed, a new concept developed at NCBA that would lead to a brand-like orientation at various stages in the production chain, as well as direct the NCBA staff.

Schroeder explained it during the 1997 Convention in Kansas City:

> *The problem is that the beef business has traditionally been commodity driven. And, in a commodity-driven business, each segment views every other segment as an adversary. The producer seeks solutions that work for him, as does the feeder, the packer and the retailer. The consumer simply stands at the end of the line and takes whatever the system delivers.*
>
> *This works as long as there is no competition, or when the competition is insignificant. What we have seen for the last*

20 years, however, was our competition increasing market share—at our expense—by being brand-driven and responsive to consumer needs.

To change that trend, NCBA came up with a new approach—the brand-like initiative. With the eye on the consumer, the Association was intent on getting the industry to create consistent and reliable beef products which exemplified the highest quality, safety and appeal that could be attained. Such products would also add value and subsequently profitability for the producer. In explaining the brand-like initiative, Lacey addressed cattlemen at the first NCBA Convention in Kansas City, at the end of his term as the first NCBA President:

There is little doubt in my mind that to compete, we first must satisfy the consumer by consistently producing beef of high quality. Second, there must be collaboration and communication within the industry, with those of us in various segments working as partners in the process of producing beef. . . . Third,

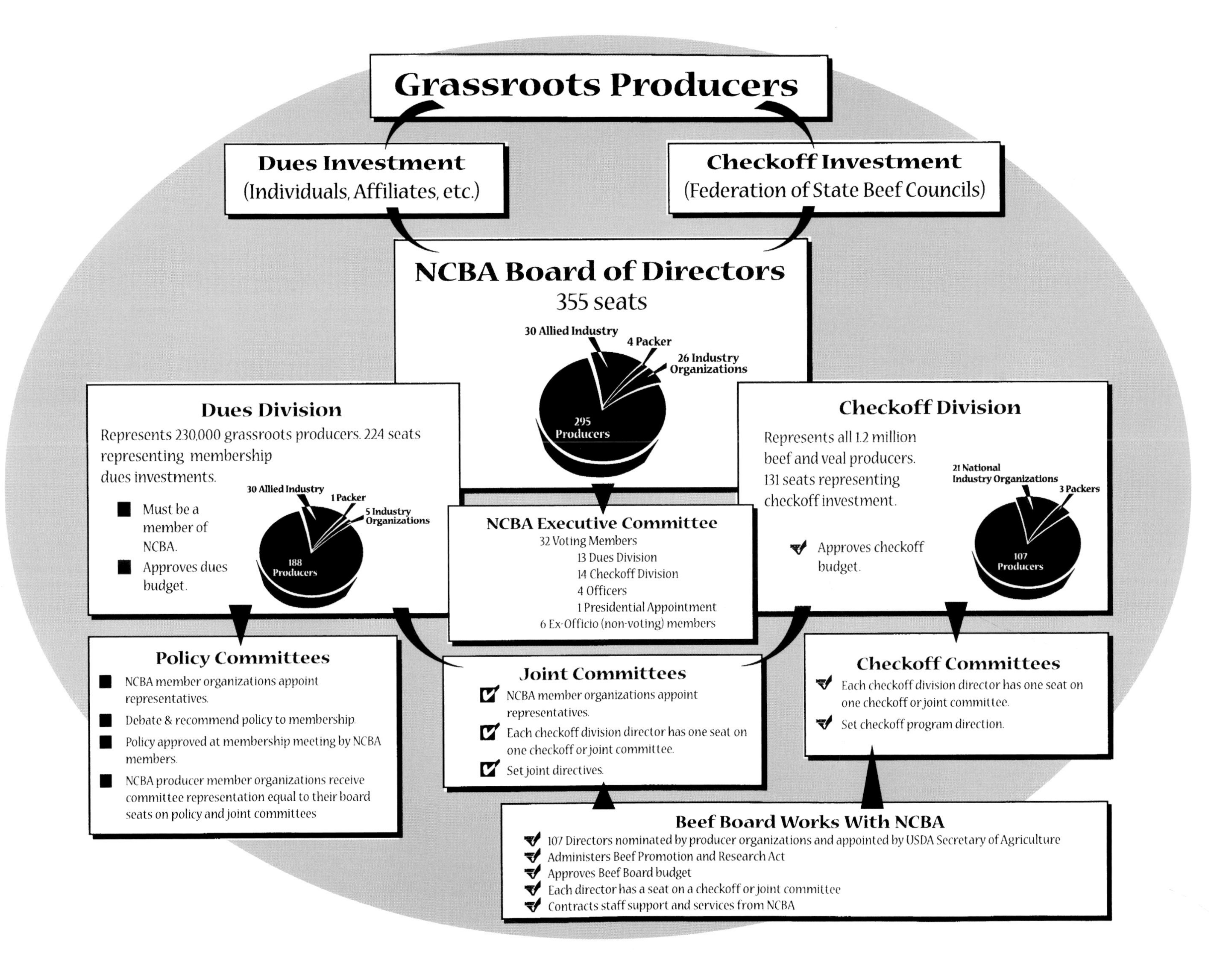

we must sharpen our global marketing strategies and skills to deliver the right products to the right markets at the right time. Fourth, we must insure beef safety and wholesomeness, based on science, because we cannot afford to have consumers doubting our products. Fifth, we have to brand our product.

As cattlemen left the 1997 Convention, they undoubtedly had more questions than when they came: If we adopt a brand, or mark, what will it stand for? Will there be different marks for different levels of quality? How will we enforce them? How will we get paid for higher quality? Who decides if premiums are fair? How will we know what products consumers want? How will we get this information? How does a brand manager think? Assuming I think like a brand manager, what will motivate others in the chain to think like brand managers? What happens to me if I don't adopt this mindset?

. . .we have to brand our product.

—NCBA President Lacey
Addressing the 1997 Convention

NCBA was a new organization, with a new staff and a new philosophy quite unlike the Association that helped built the beef industry during the last 100 years. Still, with all its product-driven, consumer focus, NCBA would remain under the control of producer members. It still is an association of cattlemen.

GOALS FOR THE DECADE

1. TO ESTABLISH UNITED STATES BEEF AS THE WORLD STANDARD FOR FOOD QUALITY AND SAFETY.
2. TO CREATE A SINGLE, UNIFIED INDUSTRY ORGANIZATION THAT IS LEAN, RESPONSIVE, EFFICIENT, AND EFFECTIVE.
3. TO INCREASE MARKET SHARE WHILE MAINTAINING INDUSTRY PROFITABILITY.
4. TO FOSTER STRATEGIC ALLIANCES WHICH ENABLE ALL SEGMENTS AND SIZES OF OPERATIONS TO ENJOY PROFITS AND CONSISTENTLY PRODUCE WHAT CONSUMERS WANT.
5. TO ENSURE THAT GRASSROOTS-DRIVEN POLICIES ARE EFFECTIVELY DEVELOPED AND MANAGED TO POSITION THE INDUSTRY WITH ONE VOICE, AS AN INFLUENTIAL FORCE IN PUBLIC AFFAIRS.
6. TO ADOPT EFFICIENCIES THROUGH THE BEEF INDUSTRY THAT ALLOW THE INDUSTRY TO PROVIDE ITS CUSTOMERS A QUALITY, YET COST-COMPETITIVE PRODUCT.
7. TO INSTILL CONFIDENCE AMONG CONSUMERS AND KEY INFLUENCERS THAT BEEF IS A SAFE, WHOLESOME, NUTRITIOUS FOOD PRODUCT THAT MEETS CONSUMER TASTE PREFERENCE AND IS PRODUCED UNDER ENVIRONMENTALLY-FRIENDLY CONDITIONS.
8. TO INCREASE ACCESS AND ACCEPTANCE OF UNITED STATES BEEF IN INTERNATIONAL MARKETS.
9. TO BASE PRODUCTION AND PROCESSING MANAGEMENT DECISION ON CONSUMER PREFERENCES FROM CONCEPTION TO CONSUMPTION.
10. TO PROVIDE A BUSINESS ENVIRONMENT THAT STIMULATES QUALITY BEEF PRODUCTION AT A PROFIT.

—from the BEEF INDUSTRY LONG RANGE PLAN*, 1993*

National Cattlemen's Beef Association

Alabama Cattlemen's Association
Montgomery, AL
Founded: 1944
Current membership: 16,500

American Angus Association
Saint Joseph, MO
Founded: 1883
Current Membership: 20,024 Adult, 8,399 Junior

American Gelbvieh Association
Broomfield, CO
Founded: 1971
Current Membership: 2,100

American Hereford Association
Kansas City, MO
Founded: 1881
Current Membership: 11,000

American International Charolais Association
Kansas City, MO
Founded: 1957
Current Membership: 4,500 Active, 1,200 Junior

AFFILIATE POWER

In 1898 the founders of the national Association recognized that its power and future success would come from the organizations and leadership of local and state groups; together they would form a mutually beneficial national presence. Thus, the National Live Stock Association was established as an association of these organizations, later known as "Affiliate Members."

Over the 100 years, the Association and its affiliates have grown and prospered as codependent partners. As the founders anticipated, affiliates have received national leadership and leverage from the national Association while they have kept it alive by providing leadership, financial aid, political assistance and strong grassroots support.

Without the influence of the earliest state associations—Colorado, Wyoming and Texas—the Association may never have succeeded. When the Association was unable to pay for or accomplish certain activities, the affiliate members have stepped forward to help. Texas and Southwestern Cattlemen's Association provided early industry lobbying in Washington. With the dominance of the public lands issue and western range demands, the western organizations dominated the Association until after World War II. When the southern associations joined, they brought with them the solid south Democrats who provided considerable political clout in Washington.

Today Affiliate Members include 56 state or regional cattlemen's and 11 national breed associations comprise Affiliate Members, reaching well over 200,000 grassroots producers. Annual dues are $3,000 for the first board seat and $25,000 for each additional seat. A seat on each committee is granted for each Board seat.

American Salers Association
Englewood, CO
Founded: 1974
Current Membership: 2200

AMERICAN
Simmental
ASSOCIATION®

American Simmental Association
Bozeman, MT
Founded: 1968
Current Membership: 13,000

American Veal Association
Harrisburg, PA
Founded: date unknown
Current Membership: unknown

Arizona Cattle Feeders Association
Phoenix, AZ
Founded: 1934
Current Membership: 108

Arizona Cattle Growers Association
Phoenix, AZ
Founded: date unknown
Current Membership: 1200

Arkansas Cattlemen's Association
Little Rock, AR
Founded: 1959
Current Membership: 16,393

BEEFMASTERS

Beefmaster Breeders United
San Antonio, TX
Founded: date unknown
Current Membership: 4,383

California Cattlemen's Association
Sacramento, CA
Founded: 1917
Current Membership: 2,266

Colorado Cattle Feeders Association
Denver, CO
Founded: 1955
Current Membership: 800

Colorado Cattlemen's Association
Arvada, CO
Founded: 1867
Current Membership: 2,700

Florida Cattlemen's Association
Kissimmee, FL
Founded: 1934
Current Membership: 5,000

Georgia Cattlemen's Association
Macon, GA
Founded: 1961
Current Membership: 6,600

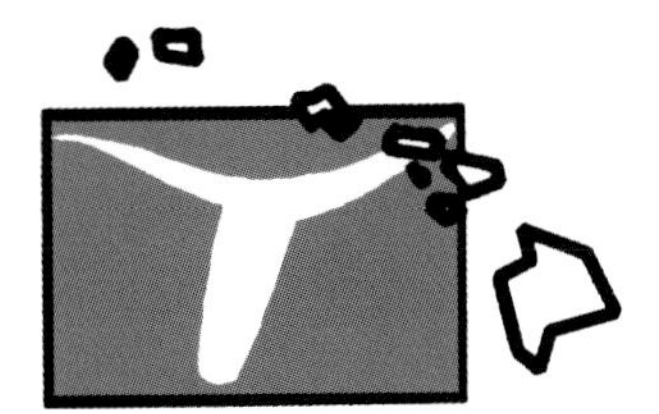

Hawaii Cattlemen's Council, Inc.
Ewa Beach, HI
Founded: 1959
Current Membership: 120

Idaho Cattle Association
Boise, ID
Founded:1914, merged with Idaho Cattle Feeders Associatioin in 1984
Current Membership: 1,175

Illinois Beef Association
Springfield, IL
Founded: date unknown
Current Membership: 1,600

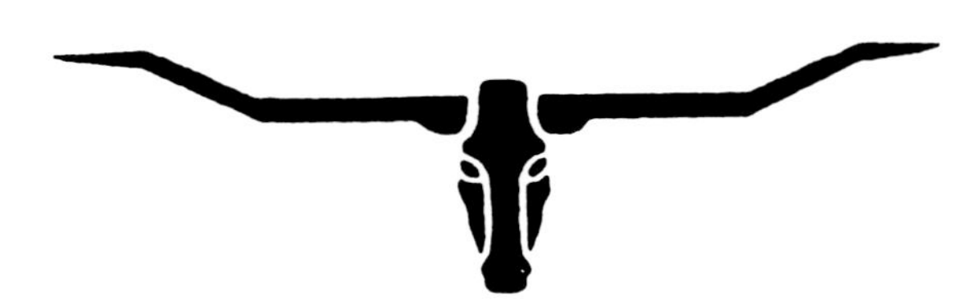

Independent Cattlemen's Association Texas
Austin, TX
Founded: 1974
Current Membership: 5,500

Indiana Beef Cattle Association
Indianapolis, IN
Founded: date unknown
Current Membership: 700

Iowa Cattlemen's Association
Ames, IA
Founded: 1972 {Iowa Beef Producers Association founded in 1912}
Current Membership: 12,000

Since 1894

Kansas Livestock Association
Topeka, KS
Founded: 1894
Current Membership: 7,150

Kentucky Cattlemen's Association
Lexington, KY
Founded: 1973 {Merger of Kentucky Cattlemen's Association and Kentucky Feeder Calf Association}
Current Membership: 5,000

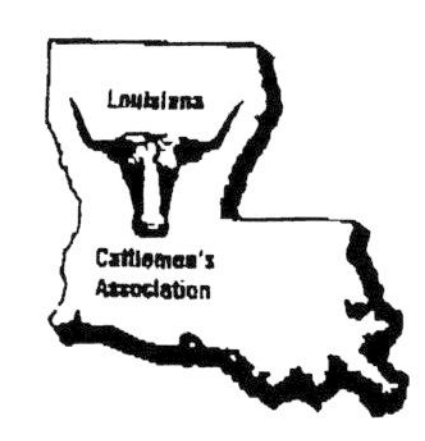

Louisiana Cattlemen's Association
Port Allen, LA
Founded: 1928
Current Membership: 4,100

Maryland Cattlemen's Association
College Park, MD
Founded: date unknown
Current Membership: 300

Michigan Cattlemen's Association
Dewitt, MI
Founded: 1960
Current Membership: 750

Minnesota State Cattlemen's Association
Comfrey, MN
Founded: 1962
Current Membership: 1,500

Mississippi Cattlemen's Association
Jackson, MS
Founded: 1946
Current Membership: 5,000

Missouri Cattlemen's Association
Columbia, MO
Founded: 1911 as Missouri Cattle Feeders Association
Current Membership: 4,532

Montana Stockgrowers Association
Helena, MT
Founded: 1884
Current Membership: 3,500

Nebraska Cattlemen
Lincoln, NE
Founded: 1889
Current Membership: 5,000

Nevada Cattlemen's Association
Elko, NV
Founded: 1935
Current Membership: 603

New Mexico Cattle Growers Association
Albuquerque, NM
Founded: 1914
Current Membership: 2,126

North American Limousin Foundation
Englewood, CO
Founded: 1968
Current Membership: 12,000

North Carolina Cattlemen's Association
Fuquay Varina, NC
Founded: 1955
Current Membership: 3,781

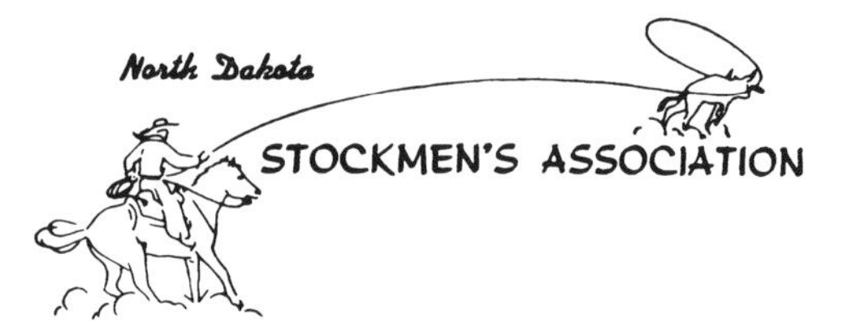

North Dakota Stockmen's Association
Bismarck, ND
Founded: 1929
Current Membership: 3,100

Ohio Cattlemen's Association
Marysville, OH
Founded: 1952
Current Membership: 2,000

Oklahoma Cattlemen's Association
Oklahoma City, OK
Founded: 1953
Current Membership: 4,500

Oregon Cattlemen's Association
Portland, OR
Founded:
Current Membership: 2,100

Pennsylvania Cattlemen's Association
Port Matilda, PA
Founded: 1969
Current Membership: 1,500

Senepol Cattle Breeders Association
Louisa, VA
Founded:
Current Membership: 145

South Carolina Cattlemen's Association
Iva, SC
Founded: 1951
Current Membership: 2,375

South Dakota Cattlemen's Association
Kennebec, SD
Founded: 1948 as South Dakota Livestock Feeders Association
Current Membership: 1,335

South Dakota Stock Growers Association
Rapid City, SD
Founded: 1891
Current Membership: 1,500

Tennessee Cattlemen's Association
Murfreesboro, TN
Founded: 1985
Current Membership: 3,650

Texas and Southwestern Cattle Raisers
Fort Worth, TX
Founded: 1877
Current Membership: 14,000

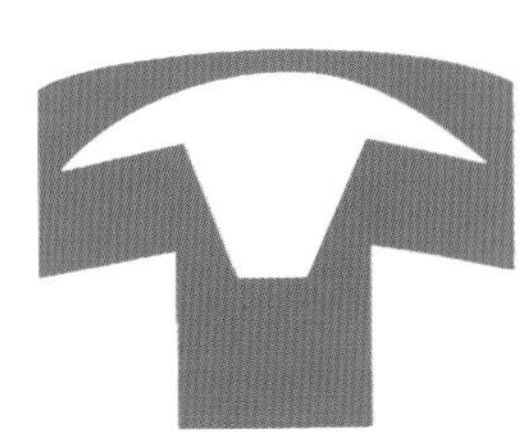

Texas Cattle Feeders Association
Amarillo, TX
Founded: 1967
Current Membership: 8,163

Utah Cattlemen's Association
Salt Lake City, UT
Founded: date unknown
Current Membership: 525

Virginia Cattlemen's Association
Daleville, VA
Founded: 1944
Current Membership: 7,876

Washington Cattle Feeders Association
Pasco, WA
Founded: 1925
Current Membership: 20

Washington Cattlemen's Association
Ellensburg, WA
Founded: date unknown
Current Membership: 1,800

West Virginia Cattlemen's Association
Buckhannon, WV
Founded: date unknown
Current Membership: 625

Wisconsin Cattlemen's Association
Richland Center, WI
Founded: 1945
Current Membership: 350

Wisconsin Veal Association
De Pere, WI
Founded: 1981
Current Membership: 350

Wyoming Stock Growers Association
Cheyenne, WY
Founded: 1872
Current Membership: 1,600

PACKERS, PROCESSORS, PURVEYORS, AND MARKETERS

IBP, Inc.
PO Box 515
Dakota City, NE 68731-0515
(402) 494-2061
Founded: date unknown

INDUSTRY SUPPORT

In addition to its long-standing core group of Affiliate Members, the Association has always depended upon the backing of all sectors of the industry for financial, advisory and other support. At the founding of the Association, it established that support. Each organization joining the national Association had one delegate at large, with an additional delegate for each 10,000 head of stock represented. Annual dues were $10 per organization, plus 25 cents for each 1,000 head it represented.

One hundred years later, dues from each sector of affiliate membership are still structured to reflect that sector's influence on the policies of the Association.

State and National Agricultural Organizations: farm organizations, livestock marketing groups, state and national commodity organizations. Annual dues are $5,000 for one board seat.

Beef Industry Associates: state or regional cattle/beef associations and national cattle/beef registry associations actively engaged in production of cattle. Annual dues are $500; no seat on the board or committees.

Industry Partner: state, regional or national cattlewomen organizations. Annual dues are $3,000 for the first board seat, $25,000 for each additional seat, with a seat on each committee for each board seat.

Packers, Processors, Purveyors and Marketers: groups involved in post-slaughter of beef. Annual dues for one board seat are based on sales: under $100 million, $3,000; $100 million to $1 billion, $6,000; Over $1 billion, $10,000, with up to (but not exceeding) a total of four individuals to serve on each committee.

STATE AND NATIONAL AGRICULTURAL ORGANIZATIONS

California Livestock Marketing Association
Cottonwood, CA
Founded: date unknown
Current Membership: 2266

DHIA Sevices,Inc.
Columbus, OH
Founded: date unknown

National Milk Producers Federation
Arlington, VA
Founded: date unknown
Current Membership: unknown

North American Meat Processors Association
Reston, VA
Founded: date unknown
Current Membership: unknown

BEEF INDUSTRY ASSOCIATES

American Blonde D'Aquitaine Association
Kansas City, MO
Founded: date unknown
Current Membership: 159

America Brahman Breeders Association
Houston, TX
Founded: date unknown
Current Membership: 1707

American Chianina Association
Platte City, MO
Founded: 1972
Current Membership: 1,500

American Highland Cattle Association
Denver, CO
Founded: date unknown
Current Membership: 1,541

American Maine Anjou Association
Kansas City, MO
Founded: date unknown
Current Membership: 1,978

American Murray Grey Association
Kansas City, MO
Founded: date unknown
Current Membership: 202

American Shorthorn Association
Omaha, NE
Founded: date unknown
Current Membership: unknown

Braunvieh Association of America
Lincoln, NE
Founded: 1984
Current Membership: 500

International Brangus Breeders
San Antonio, TX
Founded: date unknown
Current Membership: 1,663

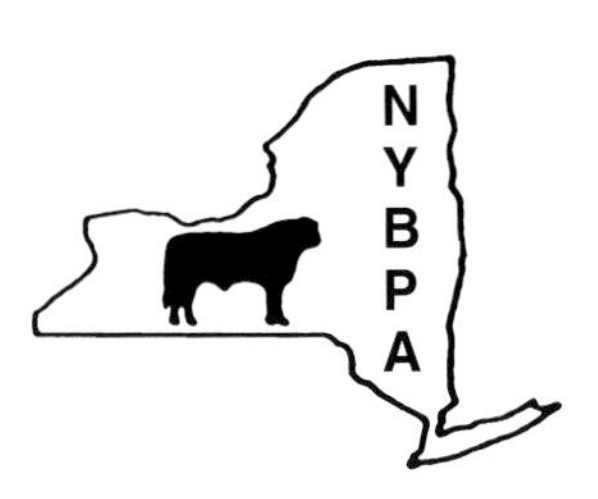

New York Beef Cattlemen's Association
Morrisville, NY
Founded: date unknown
Current Membership: unknown

Piedmontese Association of the USA
Denver, CO
Founded: date unknown
Current Membership: 251

Red Angus Association of America
Denton, TX
Founded: date unknown
Current Membership: 1,556

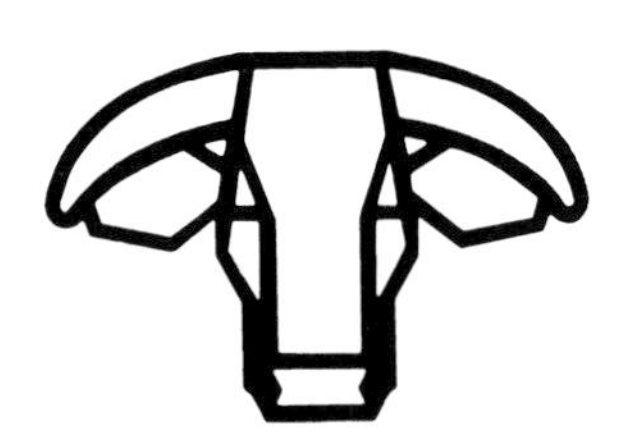

Santa Gertrudis Breeders International
Kingsville, TX
Founded: date unknown
Current Membership: 2,366

TX Longhorn Breeders
Association of America
Fort Worth, TX
Founded: date unknown
Current Membership: 3,750

UNITED BRAFORD BREEDERS

United Braford Breeders
Nacogdoches, TX
Founded: date unknown
Current Membership: unknown

INDUSTRY PARTNERS

American National CattleWomen
Englewood, CO
Founded: 1952
Current Membership: unknown

SE American National CattleWomen
Abbeville, LA
Founded: date unknown
Current Membership: unknown

Texas CattleWomen
Comfort, TX
Founded: date unknown
Current Membership: unknown

NEW GENERATION

1991

ARTIST: TOMMY BEALL

FIRST BRONZE COMMISSIONED TO BENEFIT NCA-PAC.

SERIES: 150 BRONZES

EPILOGUE

The history of the cattle industry over the past hundred years is well related in this book. The legacy of those rugged, determined men who developed ranches and herds of cattle in the 1800s on the frontier, has guided a blossoming industry through a tumultuous century torn by two world wars, burdened by communism, and pushed forward with dramatic advances in science and technology.

The United States agriculture and livestock industries took full advantage of the new knowledge and made quantum leaps forward in production. Our ability to produce food has fed and clothed our growing population as well as our troops and millions of people around the world, while at home, reducing the price of food (compared to income). Thus Americans have enjoyed the highest standard of living in the world. Now as the twentieth century closes, the United States is the most powerful and most developed nation on earth.

"Just because your father or grandfather did it that way is no guarantee that it will be done that way in the future."

W.D. Farr, Greeley, Colorado. *A member of the Association for more than half its hundred-year history, Farr has served the Association and the industry in numerous capacities (see pages 181-182) including Association president 1970-1971. Considered one of the visionaries of the industry, Farr shares here his thoughts for the future of the cattle industry as it enters the 21st century.*

Breakthroughs in communication and transportation, and scientific developments in cattle production gave a great boost to the beef industry. For most of the century, beef has been the most favored food. But, in recent years, beef has lost favor. It is now our mandate to give beef a new competitive status.

If the cattle industry hopes to survive another century, it must adapt to new consumer demands and adopt scientific knowledge—much of which is now available—to create a better product. If we wait too long to make these changes, we will not remain competitive.

There is much talk in the industry now about regaining market share. With the diversified diet most consumers follow today, beef will never regain the market share it had once had. We must recognize that beef is a food product that competes with all other foods in quality, taste, eye appeal and price.

The industry's real challenge today is to produce a consistent product of high quality. It has long struggled with this problem, and the structure of the industry itself has not encouraged consistency of quality. Today, with fewer than half of fed cattle grading Choice, we are not producing the kind of product that the consumer wants. Trends in today's restaurant business show that demand for Prime beef is on the rise, yet, the industry cannot fully meet that demand, thereby losing one outlet that should have been relatively easy to service.

Consumers want a quality product. If they get a mediocre cut, they will not buy again. There are too many alternative products available to them. For consumers to depend on what they are getting—and buy that product frequently—the beef product must have the same quality and consistency 12 months out of the year, year after year.

Built on a philosophy of independence, the industry has always been fragmented, and not currently to its benefit. Clearly for the industry to be successful, each segment will have to work toward a final uniform product. The Association has an unprecedented commitment to the industry to help it consolidate, form alliances, and become unified.

The infrastructure of the cattle industry will also have to undergo substantial changes at all levels. The producer must breed for his end product by realizing that he is not raising cattle but producing a food product, and must do that as efficiently as possible. He must also be given incentive, and be paid a premium for consistent and high quality cattle. The feeder must demand cattle proven to deliver a desirable product. The packer must be part of the alliance in order to move premium beef to the most advantageous market. And, at the end of the chain, retailers must be innovative in presentation of product for consumer appeal.

We are spending millions of dollars in advertising and product awareness, but we need to spend just as many dollars on research and development. We need information to define a perfect product, but we also need to help producers develop that product. For example, we do not need a hundred breeds of cattle. Instead, we need to identify and reproduce those few animals—even families within breeds—that are consistently producing the kind of product we hold as our goal.

Likewise, we need greater research in feeding. The cattle industry remains at the mercy of grain supplies. We cannot expect the large farm programs of the last half of this century that have given us cheap grain to be a part of our future. Grasslands are shrinking as urban areas expand, and public lands are far more desirable for recreational use.

Efficiency in production and feeding will be determining factors in producer profitability. The Association will be called upon to direct funds and create the programs to solve these needs.

Industry and Association leaders will need to focus on worldwide issues to move the industry forward. World population is growing at a rate of 217,000 people daily, providing us with new customers to be fed and clothed. Instant communications and rapid transportation have placed us in a global world. We have the ability to trade with few barriers and the best opportunity in the history of the industry to open new markets.

However, to reach these global markets, we must have very large companies that are well-financed and have the name recognition and reputations to deliver special products to many world markets. And sell worldwide we must, to have the channels of distribution needed to keep our industry prosperous.

In the last few years, a number of companies which impact our industry have already merged to take advantage of worldwide commerce. We must align ourselves with them.

It will be up to our leaders to maintain the political and economic environment conducive to the succes of our business. But cattlemen themselves must continue their faith in our economic system. Our free-enterprise system has served us well in the past and, as the industry moves forward, will do so in the future.

In 1900, John W. Springer, first president of the Association, inspired members to enter the twentieth century with these words:

> *The electric chariot of progress is sending its throbbing pulsations of activity up and down the commercial highways of the earth, and, my friend, if you cannot keep up with the procession, you will be rapidly relegated to that circle of "has beens. . ."*

His words ring true a hundred years later. A new century is here and the world is moving even more rapidly. During the next decade, those who are not willing to be optimistic and forward thinking will be lost in the dust of what promises to be the greatest century the world has ever seen.

Centennial

RANCHES

A Centennial Ranch has been in the same family and has been continuously producing cattle since 1898.

These ranches have an established legacy of survival in the cattle industry. They have lasted through 100 years of ongoing challenges and great changes. Many of the ranches have provided the leadership and stalwart commitment that has kept the Association strong and thriving throughout its history. Many Association presidents have come from these Centennial Ranches.

The theme of the Centennial Celebration — *Our Legacy: The Land, The Family, The Cattle* — is well reflected in the history of the Centennial Ranches.

Hitch Ranch
T & L Farms
Jim Ekker Ranch
Mann Family
McFaddin Enterprises
Top L Ranch
Butcher Block Cattle Company
Ellison Ranch
Kovar Family
Hagler Farms
Turner Ranch
Melroe Farm
Meyer Land & Cattle Company
Hartman Ranch
Rod & Brett Gierau
Golden West Cattle Compar
Tequesouite Ranch
Mitchell Ranch
Nielson's Shumway Ranch
Thomas Ranch
King Ranch
Long X Cattle Company
Lacey Livestock
Hess Ranch
Trail Ridg Farms
Heilmann Family
Davis Charolais
Flying R Ranch
Eagle Rest Plantation
Harder Hereford Ranch
Waco Cattle Co.
Claude Hardee Farms
Powers Ranches
Morgan Bros Farm
Robb Ranch
Funk Far Trust
Lofgreen Enterprises
Floyd McComas Ranch
Wilson Ranch
Jones Family Ranches
Neal Fan Ranch
D.T. Garlinger Ranch and Garlinger Cattle Company
Flying High Partners
Hart Ranch
Brock Live Stock Company
Stuart Ranch
Triple U Cattle Company
Rocking 4-K
Cheyenne Creek Ranch
Douglas C Stock F

Big Bend Ranch

Robie Ranch

Roney Ranch

Eaton Ranch

Bar-B-Ranch

Hugh Barton Ranch

Willard - Barton Ranch

Campbell Ranch

Floyd Cornia and Sons

Triple Hill Farms

Brite Ranch

Beard Land and Cattle

Grande Ronde Angus

Easy C Company

Rostad Ranch

Smith Brothers

The Bohl Ranch

Santa Fe River Ranch

Biaggini Ranch

Clegg Livestock Co.

Carlton Bar A Ranches and Groves

Reed Hamilton Ranch

Parker Ranch

S.O.S. Ranch

R. A. Brown Ranch

Lone Star Ranch

Price Ranch

Pendergrass Ranch

Palmer Ranch/ Flint Hills Beefingster

Dudley Ranch

Buggy Creek Livestock

Nelson C-C Ranches

Givens Inc.

C S Cattle Company

The Stuart Land & Cattle Co. of Virginia

Circle E Farm

Woodley Ranch

San Isabel Ranch

Runnells-Pierce Ranch

Kalsem Farm

The Ramsey Ranch

Eatinger Cattle Company

Woolley Ranch

Swanz Ranch

Rothleutner Family Partnership

Booksley's Clear Creek Farms

Cooney Hills Ranch

Renderbrook - Spade

Table Rock Ranch

John Riffle Angus Ranch

Rafter X Ranch

Clark Family

Lazy E4 Cattle Co.

Snepp Farms

Wiggins & Sons

Museum Ranch

Boot Bar Ranch

Convention Sites

1898-1998

Seattle
Spokane
Portland
Boise
Ogden
Salt Lake City
Rapid City
Cheyenne
Omaha
Chicago
Denver
North Platte
Reno
Washington DC
San Francisco
Colorado Springs
Kansas City
Las Vegas
Nashville
Memphis
Los Angeles
Albuquerque
Oklahoma City
Atlanta
Phoenix
San Diego
Dallas
Fort Worth
New Orleans
El Paso
Orlando
San Antonio
Tampa
Miami

NATIONAL LIVE STOCK GROWERS ASSOCIATION

1898 Denver, CO
1899 Denver, CO
1900 Fort Worth, TX
1901 Salt Lake City, UT
1902 Chicago, IL
1903 Kansas City, MO
1904 Portland, OR
1905 Denver, CO

AMERICAN NATIONAL LIVE STOCK ASSOCIATION

1906 Denver, CO
1907 Denver, CO
1908 Denver, CO
1909 Los Angeles, CA
1910 Denver, CO
1911 Fort Worth, TX
1912 Denver, CO
1913 Phoenix, AZ
1914 Denver, CO
1915 San Francisco, CA
1916 El Paso, TX
1917 Cheyenne, WY
1918 Salt Lake City, UT
1919 Denver, CO
1920 Spokane, WA
1921 El Paso, TX
1922 Colorado Springs,CO
1923 Los Angeles, CA
1924 Omaha, NE
1925 Albuquerque, NM
1926 Phoenix, AZ
1927 Salt Lake City, UT
1928 El Paso, TX
1929 San Francisco, CA
1930 Denver, CO
1931 Seattle, WA
1932 San Antonio, TX
1933 Ogden, UT
1934 Albuquerque, NM
1935 Rapid City, SD
1936 Phoenix, AZ
1937 El Paso, TX
1938 Cheyenne, WY
1939 San Francisco, CA
1940 Denver, CO
1941 Fort Worth, TX
1942 Salt Lake City, UT
1943 Denver, CO
1944 Denver, CO
1945 Denver, CO
1946 Denver, CO
1947 Phoenix, AZ
1948 Boise, ID
1949 North Platte, NE
1950 Miami, FL
1951 San Francisco, CA

AMERICAN NATIONAL CATTLEMEN'S ASSOCIATION

1952 Fort Worth, TX
1953 Kansas City, MO
1954 Colorado Springs,CO
1955 Reno, NV
1956 New Orleans, LA
1957 Phoenix, AZ
1958 Oklahoma City, OK
1959 Omaha, NE
1960 Dallas, TX
1961 Salt Lake City, UT
1962 Tampa, FL
1963 Las Vegas, NV
1964 Memphis, TN
1965 Portland, OR
1966 Kansas City, MO
1967 Colorado Springs,CO
1968 Oklahoma City, OK
1969 Honolulu, HI
1970 Washington, D.C.
1971 Las Vegas, NV
1972 Denver, CO
1973 San Antonio, TX
1974 San Diego, CA
1975 Las Vegas, NV
1976 Phoenix, AZ

NATIONAL CATTLEMEN'S ASSOCIATION

1977 Atlanta, GA
1978 New Orleans, LA
1979 Kansas City, MO
1980 San Diego, CA
1981 Phoenix, AZ
1982 San Antonio, TX
1983 Las Vegas, NV
1984 New Orleans, LA
1985 Phoenix, AZ
1986 San Antonio, TX
1987 Reno, NV
1988 Orlando, FL
1989 Phoenix, AZ
1990 Nashville, TN
1991 Dallas, TX
1992 San Diego, CA
1993 Phoenix, AZ
1994 Reno, NV
1995 Nashville, TN
1996 San Antonio, TX

NATIONAL CATTLEMEN'S BEEF ASSOCIATION

1997 Kansas City, MO
1998 Denver, CO

PRESIDENTS AND EXECUTIVE OFFICERS

PRESIDENTS

NATIONAL LIVESTOCK GROWERS ASSOCIATION

John W. Springer
Denver, CO — 1898-1903

Frank J. Hagenbarth
Salt Lake City, UT — 1904-1905

AMERICAN NATIONAL LIVE STOCK ASSOCIATION

Murdo Mackenzie
Denver, CO — 1906-1907

Henry A. Jastro
Bakersfield, CA — 1908-1910

Murdo Mackenzie
Denver, CO — 1911

H.A. Jastro
Bakersfield, CA — 1912-1914

Dwight B. Heard
Phoenix, AZ — 1915-1916

I.T. Pryor
San Antonio, TX — 1917-1918

J.B. Kendrick
Sheridan, WY — 1919-1921

Fred H. Bixby
Long Beach, CA — 1922-1925

Charles M. O'Donel
Bell Ranch, NM — 1926

L.C. Brite
Marfa, TX — 1927-1928

Victor Culberson
Silver City, NM — 1929-1930

Henry G. Boice
Tucson, AZ — 1931

Charles E. Collins
Kit Carson, CO — 1932-1935

Albert K. Mitchell
Albert, NM — 1936-1937

Hubbard Russell
Los Angeles, CA — 1938-1939

J. Elmer Brock
Kaycee, WY — 1940-1941

Frank S. Boice
Sonoita, AZ — 1942-1943

A.D. Brownfield
Deming, NM — 1944-1945

William B. Wright
Deeth, NV — 1946-1947

A.A. Smith
Sterling, CO — 1948-1949

Loren C. Bamert
Genoa, NV — 1950-1951

AMERICAN NATIONAL CATTLEMEN'S ASSOCIATION

Sam C. Hyatt
Hyattville, WY — 1952-1953

Jay Taylor
Amarillo, TX — 1954-1955

Don C. Collins
Kit Carson, CO — 1956-1957

G.R. (Jack) Milburn
Grassrange, MT — 1958-1959

Fred H. Dressler
Gardnerville, NV — 1960-1961

Cushman Radebaugh
Orlando, FL — 1962-1963

Brooks J. Keogh
Keene, ND — 1964-1965

John H. Guthrie
Porterville, CA — 1966-1967

Bill House
Cedar Vale, KA — 1968-1969

W.D. Farr
Greeley, CO — 1970-1971

John M. Trotman
Montgomery, AL — 1972-1973

Gordon Van Vleck
Plymouth, CA — 1974-1975

Wray Finney
Fort Cobb, OK — 1976-1977

NATIONAL CATTLEMEN'S ASSOCIATION

Dick McDougal
Lovelock, NV — 1977-1978

Lauren E. Carlson
Morris, MN — 1979

Merlyn Carlson
Lodgepole, NE — 1980

J. W. (Bill) Swan
Rogerson, ID — 1981

Samuel H. Washburn
Lafayette, IN — 1982

W. J. (Dub) Waldrip
Lubbock, TX — 1983

John D. Weber
Alturas, CA — 1984

Jo Ann Smith
Micanopy, FL — 1985

Don Butler
Tucson, AZ — 1986

Jack Dahl
Gackle, ND — 1987

Dale Humphrey
Springville, IN — 1988

Robert D. Josserand
Hereford, TX — 1989

John Lacey
Paso Robles, CA — 1990

Don Smith
Tribune, KS — 1991

Jimme Wilson
Trout Creek, MT — 1992

Roger Stuber
Bowman, ND — 1993

Dan Koons
Shirley, IL — 1994

Bob Drake
Davis, OK — 1995

NATIONAL CATTLEMEN'S BEEF ASSOCIATION

John Lacey
Paso Robles, CA — 1996

Max Deets
Beloit, KS — 1997

Clark S. Willingham
Dallas, TX — 1998

EXECUTIVE OFFICERS

NATIONAL LIVESTOCK GROWERS ASSOCIATION

Charles F. Martin
Executive Secretary — 1898-1904

AMERICAN NATIONAL LIVE STOCK ASSOCIATION

T.W. Tomlinson
Executive Secretary — 1906-1928

F.E. (Ferd) Mollin
Executive Secretary — 1929-1955

AMERICAN NATIONAL CATTLEMEN'S ASSOCIATION

Radford S. Hall
Executive Secretary — 1956-1958

David O. Appleton
Acting Executive Secretary — 1959

C.W. (Bill) McMillan
Executive Vice President — 1959-1970
Executive Vice President, Washington Affairs — 1970-1980

NATIONAL CATTLEMEN'S ASSOCIATION

George S. Spencer
Executive Vice President of Administration — 1970-1980

W.T. (Dub) Berry, Jr.
Exec. Vice President — 1980-1984

John E. Meetz
Executive Vice President — 1984-1990

J. Burton Eller
Executive Vice President — 1990-1995

NATIONAL CATTLEMEN'S BEEF ASSOCIATION

Charles P. (Chuck) Schroeder
Chief Executive Officer — 1996 to Present

SPREADING THE WORD

Charles F. Martin, first secretary of the Associa
made information one of his main priorities. In the
year of the Association he set forth his goal:

> *The National Live Stock Association. . .will eventually be utilized for the purpose of securing and publishing facts that will enable its members to conduct their business intelligently.*

Martin then set out to collect any available infor
tion — from railroads, stockyards, state boards of
culture, members, and elsewhere, and started
National Live Stock Bulletin. It became the only so
of information on markets, range conditions, c
movement, exports and other statistics for many ye

Supplying information to its membership was
important first step for the Association and
remained a cornerstone of the Association for its er
history. The bulletin service has continued — wi
number of name changes — sometimes monthly, so
times weekly.

In the first years, the Association had an arrangem
with the *Record Stockman* to publish Association in
mation in exchange for the Association recommen
the paper to its members. Similar arrangements
different trade journals have been made over the ye

In providing its membership with information
Association has also sought other channels to spr
information in addition to its publications. That effort
up to the sophisticated information retrieval
dissemination operation of Cattle-Fax. [See pa
162-165.] Today, the Association disseminates infor
tion through print, the Internet and ot
electronic media.

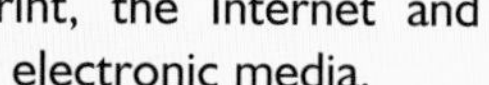

American CATTLE PRODUCER
THE CATTLEMAN'S BUSINESS MAGAZINE
Anaplasmosis, How It Spreads
Page 8
Research . . . Key to Future
Page 12
September 1963

1898-1903	Denver Daily Record-Stockman
1903-1919	National Live Stock Bulletin
1919-1934	The Producer
1934-1969	American Cattle Producer
1969-1972	American Beef Producer
1950-1961	Cow Business
1977-Present	Beef Business Bulletin
1985-Present	National Cattlemen

National CATTLEMEN
National CATTLEMEN
Genetics And Reproduction
National CATTLEMEN

Art Credits

COVER. *Centennial Bronze*, William G. Duncan. PAGE x. *The Longhorn Trail*, Amarillo Museum of Art, Amarillo, TX. PAGE xii. *The Cornell Farm*, Edward Hicks, National Gallery of Art, Washington, DC. PAGE xvi. Bronze. *The President's Bronze*, Jerry Palen, NCBA. CHAPTER 1. PAGE 2. *Unloading the First Cattle in North America, Vera Cruz, 1521*, Tom Lea, Dallas Museum of Art, Dallas, TX. PAGE 6. *Waiting for a Chinook*, Charles M. Russell, Montana Stockgrowers Association, Helen, MT. PAGE 17. Bronze. *The Maverick*, Tommy Beall, NCF. CHAPTER 2. PAGE 18. *White Man's Buffalo*, Charles M. Russell, Gilcrease Museum, Tulsa, OK. PAGE 22. *Moving to Slaughter: Union Stockyards, Chicago*, Tom Lea, Dallas Museum of Art, Dallas, TX. CHAPTER 3. PAGE 36. *Winchester Hospitality*, Joe Beeler, Cowboy Artists of America Museum, Kerrville, TX. PAGE 53. Bronze. *Unity*, Harold Holden, NCBA. CHAPTER 4. PAGE 54. *New Mexico*, Thomas Hart Benton, Denver Art Museum, Denver, CO. PAGE 69. Bronze. *Tight Gates Cold Fingers*, Harold Holden, NCBA. CHAPTER 5. PAGE 74. *Drought Stricken Area*, Alexandre Hogue, Dallas Museum of Art, Dallas TX. PAGE 79. *Transportation*, Keith McLendon, The Saratoga Publishing Group, Inc., Saratoga, WY. CHAPTER 6. PAGE 96. *Let's Give him Enough and On Time*, Norman Rockwell, The Norman Rockwell Museum at Stockbridge, MA. PAGE 113. *Uncle Sam*, Keith McLendon, The Saratoga Publishing Group, Inc., Saratoga, WY. CHAPTER 7. PAGE 114. *Evening, Lake Alto*, Martin Johnson Heade, The Vickers Collection, FL. PAGE 127. (TOP LEFT) *FLORIDA CRACKER COWS*, JOE AKERMAN, FLORIDA CATTLEMEN'S ASSOCIATION, KISSIMMEE. (TOP RIGHT) *STATE FAIR*, STEVAN DOHANOS, UNIVERSITY OF IOWA MUSEUM OF ART, IOWA CITY. PAGE 135. Bronze. *Executive Bust*, Jerry Palen, NCBA. CHAPTER 8. PAGE 146. *Buffalo Grain Elevators*, Ralston Crawford, National Museum of American Art, Washington, DC. PAGE 156. *Cushman Radebaugh*, Florida Cattlemen's Association, Kissimmee. Page 175. *Feedyard*, 1940-1960s. *SUCCESSFUL FARMING*. CHAPTER 9. PAGE 176. *Stone City, Iowa*, Grant Wood, Joslyn Art Museum, Omaha, NE. PAGE 203. *New Beginning*, John D Free, NCBA. **Chapter 10.** PAGE 208. *Five Cows*, George Bellows, The Metropolitan Museum of Art, New York. PAGE 215. PAC Panels by Jerry Palen, Burton Eller. CHAPTER 11. PAGE 240. *Feedyard*, Kenneth Wyatt, Texas Cattle Feeders Association, Amarillo, TX. **Chapter 12.** PAGE 262. *"Helpin' Dad"*, A.T. (Tim) Cox, Cheyenne Frontier Days, Old West Museum. Page 279. *New Generation*, Tommy Beall, NCBA-PAC.

Photo and Illustration Credits

Note. Unless otherwise credited, photographs and illustrations in this book are part of the National Cattlemen's Associaton Archives located at the American Heritage Center, University of Wyoming, Laramie, WY. Those credited to the National Cattlemen's Beef Association (NCBA) are at present available through their offices in Denver, CO, and Washington, DC. Photos in chapters 10, 11 and 12 not credited are in the files at NCBA. Photographs credited to the Meat Board (National Livestock and Meat Board) are available through the NCBA offices in Chicago.

FRONT. PAGES VI-VII. Monfort of Colorado, Greeley, CO. PAGE VII (right). Kenneth Monfort, *CALF* Magazine. PAGE XI. High Sidey. PAGE XII. Texas Cattle Feeders Association, Amarillo, TX. CHAPTER 1. PAGE 3. *AMERICAN CATTLE TRAILS 1540-1900*. PAGE 7. *Homesteaders*. Denver Public Library. *Free-Rangers*. Nebraska State Historical Society, Lincoln. PAGE 9. *Planters House*. Colorado Historical Society, Denver. *Cheyenne Club*. Wyoming State Archives, Cheyenne. PAGE 10. St. Louis Mercantile Library Association. Page 11. James Cox, *HISTORICAL AND BIOGRAPHICAL RECORD OF THE CATTLE INDUSTRY AND THE CATTLEMEN OF TEXAS AND ADJACENT TERRITORY*. CHAPTER 2. PAGE 20. *Springer*. *THE DENVER POST*. PAGE 21. Colorado Historical Society as reproduced in *THE DENVER POST*. PAGE 23. The Brown Palace Hotel, Denver. PAGE 30. Denver Public Library. PAGE 31. Denver Public Library. Page 32. Montana Historical Society. Helena. PAGE 33. *OKLAHOMA LIVE STOCK NEWS*, reproduced in *AMERICAN CATTLE PRODUCER*, 1935. Pages 34-35. (ERRATA: Photos has been credited wrongly; correct credits are given here). (top, 2-page spread) *Aerial View of Union Stockyards of Chicago. 1901*, Chicago Historical Society. (bottom left) *Kansas City Stockyard*, Kansas State Historical Society, Lincoln. (right center) *New York's Washington Market in 1859*, Museum of the City of New York. (right bottom) *Chicago Union Stockyards in 1865* (at its opening), R.L. Wilhelm, *LEGACY OF THE STOCKMAN*. CHAPTER 3. PAGE 41. Denver Public Library. PAGE 42. Texas and Southwester Cattle Raisers, Fort Worth, TX. PAGE 43. *Meat Inspector*, *MODERN BOOK OF KNOWLEDGE*, 1904. PAGE 45. Denver Public Library. PAGE 46. Kern County Museum, Bakersville, CA. PAGE 50. Denver Public Library. PAGE 51. Montana Historical Society, Helena. CHAPTER 4. PAGE 57 (BOTTOM). NCBA. PAGE 59. Hoover. National Archives, Washington, DC. PAGE 63. Courtesy of Manville Kendrick. PAGE 65. Swift Offices, Chicago Historical Society. PAGE 67. NCBA. PAGE 71. Meat Board. PAGE 72. *Cooking School*, *THE NATIONAL PROVISIONER*. other photos, Meat Board. PAGE 73. Meat Board. CHAPTER 5. PAGE 76. University of Texas at Austin. PAGE 80. Library of Congress, Washington DC. PAGE 81. Brite on horse, Courtesy of Mrs. James White. PAGE 83. Saddle and Sirloin Portrait Collection, Kentucky Fair and Exposition Center, Louisville, KY. PAGE 84. Montana Historical Society, Helena. PAGE 86. Wallace House Foundation, Des Moines, IA. PAGE 86. NCBA. PAGE 87 (bottom) National Archives, Washington, DC. PAGE 88. Texas Cattle Feeders Association, Amarillo, TX. PAGE 89. Illustration. *MIDWEST FARMING AS PORTRAYED BY A SELECTION FROM DING'S CARTOONS*. Pioneer Hi-Bred Corn Company, Drake Univesity Library, Des Moines, IA. Dust Bowl. Library of Congress, Washington, DC. PAGE 90. *THE CATTLEMAN*, Oct. 1934. Texas and Southwestern Cattle Raisers Association, Fort Worth, TX. PAGE 91. Mitchell with Plane. Courtesy of Linda M. Davis, Cimarron, NM. PAGES 92-93. Denver Public Library. PAGE 95. Russell on Horse and Russell in car. Courtesy of Hubbard S. Russell, Jr., Valencia, CA. CHAPTER 6. PAGE 100. Gooseneck trailer. Texas and Southwestern Cattle Raisers Asssociation, Fort Worth, TX. Auction. Library of Congress. PAGE 101. Meat Board. PAGE 102. Cartoon. *WASHINGTON STAR*, April 1941. Wickard. National Archives, Washington, DC. Page 104. *MIDWEST FARMING AS PORTRAYED BY A SELECTION FROM DING'S CARTOONS*. Pioneer Hi-Bred Corn Company. Drake University Library, Des Moines, IA. Page 106. Uncle Sam Mural. Collection of the Rensselaer County Historical Society, Troy, NY. Page 109. Will C. Barnes. Arizona Historical Society, Tucson. PAGE 110. National Agricultural Library, Beltsville, MD. PAGE 111. Going onto Public Lands. National Agricultural Library, Beltsville, MD. Cattle grazing on public lands. Public Lands Council, Washington, DC. CHAPTER 7. PAGE 116. J.R. Williams. United Media, New York, NY. PAGE 119. Cartoon. Fifth Plate. National Agricultural Library, Beltsville, MD. Cartoon (bottom right) Parrish. *CHICAGO TRIBUNE*, 1953. Brannan. National Archives, Washington, DC. PAGE 121. Texas Cattle Feeders Association, Amarillo, TX. PAGE 130. Winn-Dixie Stores, Inc., Jacksonville, FL. PAGE 131. Meat Board. PAGE 132. Courtesy of Polly Collins Johnson, Kit Carson, CO. Page 133. Texas and Southwestern Cattle Raisers Association, Fort Worth, TX. PAGE 137. NBC Exhibit. Meat Board. PAGE 138. Huston. Meat Board. PAGE 139. MEAT BOARD. PAGE 142. Mrs. Cowan. Courtesy of the Ralph Cowan family, Arizona. PAGE 143. Cookbooks and Ambassadors. American National CattleWomen, Denver, CO. PAGE 144. Brochures and Consumer Education. American National CattleWomen, Denver, CO. PAGE 145. American National CattleWomen, Denver, CO. CHAPTER 8. PAGE 148. Lyndon B. Johnson Library, Austin, TX. PAGE 150. AP/Worldwide Photos. PAGE 151. *LOS ANGELES TIMES*, 1972. Page 152. Cartoons. (bottom left) *OMAHA WORLD-HERALD*. (bottom right) *THE STOCKMEN'S JOURNAL*. *PAGE 156*. USDA. PAGE 158. Ace Reid. Ace Reid Enterprises, Kerrville, TX. PAGE 159. Boxed beef. Monfort of Colorado, Greeley, CO. PAGE 160. Jerry Palen. Stampede Cartoons, Inc., Saratoga, WY. PAGES 163-165. Cattle-Fax, Denver, CO. PAGES166-173. Nebraska State Historical Society, Lincoln. PAGE 172. Courtesy of Bill Jones. PAGES 174-175. Texas Cattle Feeders Association, Amarillo, TX. CHAPTER 9. PAGE 179. Courtesy of Bill Webster. PAGE 180. Courtesy of George Spencer. PAGE 181. Farr on horse. Courtesy of the Farr Family, Greeley, CO. PAGE 182. Henry Farr. Courtesy of the Farr Family, Greeley, CO. W.D. Farr. *CALF* Magazine. W.D. Farr with sons. Courtesy of the Farr Family, Greeley, CO. Page 185 (bottom). Courtesy of Gordon Van Vleck, Plymouth, CA. PAGE 189. Courtesy of Bud Middaugh. USMEF. PAGE 190. Texas Cattle Feeders Association, Amarillo, TX. PAGE 191. Jerry Palen. Stampede Cartoons, Inc., Saratoga, WY. PAGE 192. Handshake. Courtesy of Gordon Van Vleck, Plymouth, CA. PAGE 194. Courtesy of Dick McDougal, Lovelock, NV. Foreman. *BEEF* Magazine. PAGE 195. Courtesy of George Spencer. PAGE 196. Van Vleck with Berglund. Courtesy of Gordon Van Vleck, Plymouth, CA. PAGE 197. Webster and Jennings. Courtesy of Bill Webster. Page 199. Bureau of Land Management, Washington, DC. CHAPTER 10. PAGE 212. Washburn and Cook and Cook with Lyng and Yeutter. Courtesy of Tom Cook. PAGE 214. Winrock Farm, Courtesy of Dub Berry. PAGE 218. Fund Raising Dinner. Courtesy of Burton Eller. PAGE 220. Jerry Palen. Stampede Cartoons, Inc. PAGE 225. Eller and Bush. Courtesy of Burton Eller. PAGE 228. Packing plant. IBP, Dakota City, NE. PAGE 229. Chicago Mercantile Exchange, Chicago, IL. PAGES 232-233. The Cattlemen's Beef Promotion and Research Board, Denver, CO. PAGE 234. *HISTORICAL AND BIOGRAPHICAL RECORD OF THE CATTLE INDUSTRY OF TEXAS AND THE CATTLEMEN OF TEXAS AND ADJACENT TERRITORY*. PAGE 235. Squeeze Chute (2 photos). Texas Cattle Feeders Association, Amarillo, TX. Screwworm. Florida Cattlemen's Association, Kissimmee, FL. PAGE 236. Brochure, NCA Archives. Airplane. National Archives, Washington, DC. PAGE 237. NCA Archives. Page 239. McMillan with LBJ. Courtesy of Bill McMillan, Alexandria, VA. CHAPTER 11. PAGE 244. *TOP PRODUCER*. PAGE 245. Ace Reid. Ace Reid Enterprises, Kerrville, TX. Page 250. Smith Brothers. Courtesy of Mrs. Darlene Smith. PAGE 251. Eller/Keys and Keys. *TOP PRODUCER*. Cook and Eller/Cook. Courtesy of Tom Cook. PAGE 253. Texas Cattle Feeders Association, Amarillo, TX. PAGE 255. Cartoon. Ace Reid. Ace Reid Enterprises, Kerrville, TX. Page 259. Ace Reid Enterprises, Kerrville, TX. Baxter Black, Brighton, CO. Jerry Palen, Stampede Cartoons, Inc., Saratoga, WY. Palen with cow. The Saratoga Publishing Group, Inc., Saratoga, WY. PAGE 269. (top) American Angus Association, St. Joseph, MO. (center) American Hereford Association, Kansas City, MO. (bottom) Houston Livestock Show and Rodeo, Houston, TX. Page 261. Posters and photograph. National Archives, Washington, DC. CHAPTER 12. PAGE 264. *BEEF* magazine. **BACK.** PAGE 280. *CALF* Magazine. PAGES 290-293. State Breed Associations affiliated with NCBA.

BIBLIOGRAPHY

Abbott, E.C. (Teddy Blue) and Smith, Helena Huntington.
We Pointed Them North, Recollections of a Cowpuncher. Norman: University of Oklahoma Press, 1939.

Allen, Lewis F.
American Cattle: Their History, Breeding and Management. New York: Orange Judd Company, 1879.

American Meat Institute.
American Meat Institute 75th Commemorative Magazine. Arlington, VA: American Meat Institute, 1980.

Baker, Gladys L., Rasmussen, Wayne D., Wiser, Vivian, and Porter, Jane M.
Century of Service: The First 100 Years of The United State Department of Agriculture. Washington, DC: Centennial Committee, USDA, 1963.

Barnes, Will C.
Western Grazing Grounds and Forest Ranges. Chicago: The Breeders Gazette, 1913.

Bovard, James.
The Farm Fiasco. San Francisco: ICS Press, 1989.

Brayer, Garnet M. and Brayer, Herbert O.
American Cattle Trails 1540-1900. Bayside, NY: American Pioneer Trails Association, 1952.

Brisbin, General James S.
Beef Bonanza; Or How to Get Rich on the Plains. Philadelphia: J. B. Lippincott Co., 1881.

Caperton, Thomas J.
Rogue!...Stephen W. Dorsey. Santa Fe: The Museum of New Mexico Press, 1978.

Channing, Edward.
A History of the United States. New York: The Macmillan Company, 1948.

Chittenden, William Lawrence.
Ranch Verses. New York-London: G. P. Putnam's Sons, 1893.

Clay, John.
My Life on the Range. privately printed, 1924.

Cox, James.
Historical and Biographical Record of the Cattle Industry and the Cattlemen of Texas and Adjacent Territory. St. Louis: Woodward Tiernan Printing Co., 1895.

Dale, Edward Everett.
The Range Cattle Industry. Norman: University of Oklahoma Press, 1930.

Dary, David.
Cowboy Culture: A Saga of Five Centuries. Lawrence: University Press of Kansas, 1981.

DeGraff, Herrell.
Beef Production and Distribution. Norman: University of Oklahoma Press, 1960.

Dethloff, Henry C. and May, Irvin M. Jr.
Southwestern Agriculture: Pre-Columbian to Modern. College Station: Texas A&M University Press, 1982.

Dobie, J. Frank.
On the Open Range. Dallas: The Southwest Press, 1931.

Dobie, J. Frank.
The Longhorns. Boston: Little Brown & Co., 1941.

Douglas, C.L.
Cattle Kings of Texas. Fort Worth: Branch-Smith, Inc., 1968.

Forbis, William H. and the editors of Time-Life Books.
The Cowboys. Alexandria, VA: Time-Life Books, 1973.

Fowler, Stewart H.,
The Marketing of Livestock and Meat. Danville, IL: The Interstate Printers & Publishers, Inc., 1957 (2nd Edition, 1961).

Franklin, Ted E.
He Made the Ranges Safe: O. M. Franklin and the Blackleg Story. Manhattan, KS: Sunflower University Press, 1993.

Freeman, James W.
Prose and Poetry of the Livestock Industry of the United States, Vol. I. Denver and Kansas City: National Livestock Historical Association, 1904.

Friggens, Paul.
Gold & Grass: The Black Hills Story. Boulder, CO: Pruett Publishing Co., 1983.

Gray, Lewis Cecil.
History of Agriculture in the Southern United States to 1860. Vol. I. Washington, DC: Carnegie Institution of Washington, 1933.

Guither, Harold D.
The Food Lobbyists. Lexington, MA, and Toronto: Lexington Books, 1980.

Hage, Wayne.
Storm Over Rangelands: Private Right in Federal Lands. Bellevue, WA: Free Enterprise Press, 1989.

Hinman, Robert B. and Harris, Robert B.
The Story of Meat. Chicago: Swift and Co., 1939.

Hinton, Harwood P.(Introduction)
History of the Cattlemen of Texas. Austin: Texas State Historical Association, 1991.

Howard, David H.
People, Pride and Progress: 125 Years of the Grange in America. Washington, DC: National Grange, 1992.

Hunter, J. Marvin.
The Trail Drivers of Texas. San Antonio, TX: Jackson Printing Co., 1920. Reprinted 1985 by University of Texas Press.

Iowa State University.
Art About Livestock: An Art Exhibition That Celebrates Human Involvement With Livestock. Ames, IA: Brunnier Gallery and Museum, Iowa State University, 1990.

James, Will.
Cowboys North and South. New York-London: Charles Scribner's Sons, 1924.

Lambert, Roger.
"Drought Relief for Cattlemen; The Emergency Purchase Program of 1934-35." Canyon, TX: *Panhandle Plains Historical Review, 45.* (1972): 21-35.

Marrin, Albert.
Cowboys, Indians and Gunfighters. New York: Maxwell McMillan International, 1993.

Mason, Jim and Singer, Peter.
Animal Factories: The Mass Production of Animals for Food and How It Affects the Lives of Consumers, Farmers, and the Animals Themselves. New York: Crown Publishers, 1980.

May, Irvin, Jr. "Welfare and Ranchers: The Emergency Cattle Purchase Program and Emergency Work Relief Program in Texas, 1934-1935." *West Texas Historical Association Year Book, 47.* (1971): 3-19.

McCoy, Joseph G.
Historic Sketches of the Cattle Trade of the West and Southwest. Kansas City, MO: J.T. Reton & Co., 1874.

National Provisioner, The.
Meat for the Multitudes, Vol. 1. Chicago: The National Provisioner, 1981.

National Provisioner, The.
Meat for the Multitudes, Vol. 2. Chicago: The National Provisioner, 1981.

Nimmo, Joseph Jr.
"The Range and Ranch Cattle Business of the United States." *Report on the Internal Commerce of the United States, May 6, 1885.* Washington, DC: Government Printing Office, 1885.

Nourse, Edwin G., Davis, Joseph S., Black, John D.
Three Years of the Agricultural Adjustment Administration. New York: Da Capo Press, 1971. (Reprint Series of *Franklin D. Roosevelt and the Era of the New Deal.* General Editor: Frank Freidel, Harvard University.)

Osgood, Ernest S.
Day of the Cattleman. Minneapolis:University of Minnesota: 1929.

Pate, J'Nell L.
Livestock Legacy: The Fort Worth Stockyards, 1887-1987. College Station: Texas A&M University Press, 1988.

Pearce, W.M.
The Matador Land and Cattle Company. Norman: University of Oklahoma Press: 1964.

Porter, Glenn, *editor*.
Encyclopedia of American Economic History, Vol. I, II, III. New York: Charles Scribner's Sons, 1980.

Powell, Cuthbert.
Twenty Years of Kansas City's Livestock Trade and Traders. Kansas City: privately printed, 1893.

Press of Lawton and Burnap.
Brief. "Cherokee Strip Livestock Assn. Plaintiff Versus The McClellan Cattle Co., Cass Land and Cattle Co., Tom Green Cattle Co., Hall Bros., Winfield Cattle Co., The Kansas and New Mexico Land and Cattle Co., *et al.*," Kansas City: Press of Lawton and Burnap, 1890.

Remington, Frederic.
Crooked Trails. New York-London: Harper & Bros., 1898.

Roosevelt, Theodore.
By-Laws of the Little Missouri River Stockmen's Assn. New York: 1885.

Roosevelt, Theodore.
A Book Lover's Holidays in the Open. New York: Charles Scribner's Sons, 1916.

Rouse, John E.
Cattle of North America: World Cattle III. Norman: University of Oklahoma Press, 1973.

Rundell, Walter, Jr. and Butler, Anne M.
"Agriculture with Hoof and Horn: An Analysis of the Historical Literature (13 books) of the Cattle Industry." Washington, DC: Graduate School Press, USDA, 1977.

Russell, Charles Marion.
More Rawhides. Great Falls: Montana Newspaper Association, 1925.

Russell, Charles Marion.
Pen Sketches. Great Falls, MT: 1900.

Schell, Orville.
Modern Meat: Antibiotics, Hormones, and the Pharmaceutical Farm. New York: Random House, 1978.

Schlebecker, John T.
Cattle Raising on the Plains 1900-1961. Lincoln: University of Nebraska Press, 1963.

Skaggs, Jimmy M.
Cattle-Trailing Industry; Between Supply and Demand, 1866-1890. Lincoln: University Press of Kansas, 1973.

Skaggs, Jimmy M.
Prime Cut: Livestock Raising and Meatpacking in the United States, 1607-1983. College Station: Texas A&M University Press, 1986.

Stalbaum, Lynn.
National Milk Producers Federation, 75 Year History. Arlington, VA: National Milk Producers Federation, 1991.

Tanner, Ogden, and the editors of Time-Life Books.
The Ranchers. Alexandria, VA: Time-Life Books, 1977.

Taylor, Lonn and Maar, Ingrid
The American Cowboy. Washington, DC: American Folklife Center, Library of Congress, 1983.

Taylor, Thomas U.
The Chisholm Trail and Other Routes. San Antonio, TX: Naylor Co., 1936.

Thompson, James Westfall.
History of Livestock Raising in the United States, 1607-1860. Agricultural History Series, No. 5. Washington, DC: USDA, 1942.

Towne, Charles Wayland and Wentworth, Edward Norris.
Cattle & Men. Norman: University of Oklahoma Press, 1955.

US Department of Agriculture.
That We May Eat: The 1975 Yearbook of Agriculture. Washington, DC: US Government Printing Office, 1975.

Von Richthofen, Walter Baron.
Cattle Raising on the Plains of North America. New York: D. Appleton & Co., 1885.

Wheeler, David L.
"The Beef Cattle Indsutry in the United States: Colonial Origins." Canyon, TX: *Panhandle Plains Historical Review* 46, 1973.

Willham, R. L.
The Legacy of the Stockman. Ames: Iowa State University, Department of Animal Science, 1985.

Wilson, Mrs. Augustus.
Memorial Sketch and Official Report of the First National Convention of Cattlemen. St. Louis: Joseph G. McCoy, 1884.

Wilson, Mrs. Augustus.
"The Opening Session of the First National Cattle Growers's Convention, St. Louis, 1884." Parsons, KS: *Parsons Memorial and Historical Magazine,* 1885.

Woell, Melvin L.
Farm Bureau Architects Through Four Decades. Dubuque, IA: Kendall/Hunt Publishing Co., 1990.

HISTORIES OF STATE ASSOCIATIONS

(By Author)

Akerman, Joe A., Jr.
Florida Cowman. Kissimmee: Florida Cattlemen's Association, 1976.

Ball, Charles E.
Finishing Touch, The. A History of the Texas Cattle Feeders Association and Cattle Feeding in the Southwest. Amarillo: Texas Cattle Feeders Association, 1992.

Clarke, Mary Whatley.
A Century of Cow Business: A History of the Texas and Southwestern Cattle Raisers Association. Fort Worth: Texas and Southwestern Cattle Raisers Association, 1976.

Colorado Cattlemen's Centennial Commission.
Co-Operative Century, The: CCA 100th Anniversary. Denver: Colorado Cattlemen's Centennial Commission, 1967.

Fletcher, Robert H.
Free Grass to Fences: The Montana Cattle Range Story. New York: University Publisher Incorporated, 1960.

Goff, Richard and McCaffree, Robert H.
Century In The Saddle: History of the Colorado Cattlemen's Association. Denver: Colorado Cattlemen's Centennial Commission, 1967.

Hay, Jim.
Riding Point: A Centennial History of the Kansas Livestock Association. Topeka: Kansas Livestock Association, 1994.

Hollis, Dan W.
It's Great To Be Number One! The Dynamic Story of the Alabama Cattlemen's Association. Montgomery: Alabama Cattlemen's Association, 1985.

Matsushima, John K.
A Journey Back. History of Cattle Feeding in Colorado and the United States. Colorado Springs: Cattlemen's Communications, 1995.

Michels, Clair.
60 Years with the North Dakota Stockmen's Association. Bismark: North Dakota Stockmen's Association, 1989.

Montana Stockgrowers Association 1884-1984: A Century of Service to Montana's Cattle Industry. Helena: Montana Stockgrowers Association, 1984.

Mortensen, Robert K.
In the Cause of Progress: A History of the New Mexico Cattle Growers Association. Albuquerque: New Mexico Stockman, 1983.

Nordyke, Lewis.
Great Roundup: The Story of Texas and Southwestern Cowmen. New York: William Morrow & Co., 1955.

Schacht, Henry.
The Long & Winding Trail:The History of the California Cattlemen's Association. Sacramento: California Cattlemen's Association, 1991.

Stout, Joseph A. Jr.
Oklahoma Cattlemen: An Association History. Oklahoma City: Oklahoma Cattlemen's Foundation, Inc., 1981.

Texas and Southwestern Cattle Raisers Association.
The Cattleman. Fort Worth: Texas and Southwestern Cattle Raisers Association, 1895-1997.

I N D E X

Blonde D'Aquitaine ▶

◀ ***Brahman***

Brangus ▶

◀ ***Highland***

Saler ▶

◀ ***Angus***

INDEX

Beefmaster

Braford

Braunvieh

Charolais

Chiangus

Gelbvieh

INDEX

Hereford

Limousin

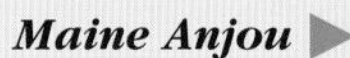

Maine Anjou

Murray Grey

Piedmontese

Senepol

INDEX

◀ **_Simmental_**

◀ **_Texas Longhorn_**

Santa Gertrudis ▶

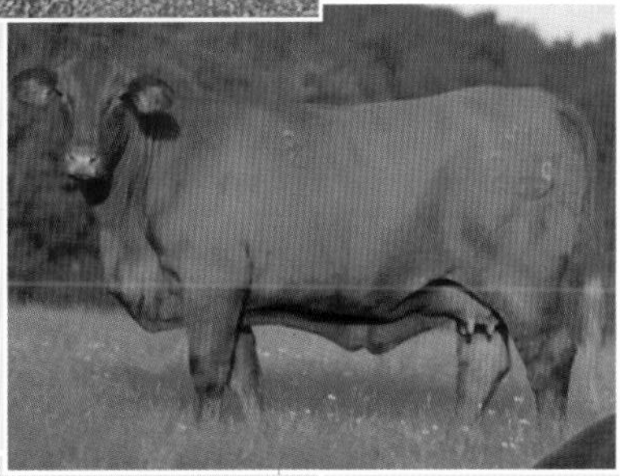

◀ **_Red Angus_**

Shorthorn ▶

Commissioned by The National Cattlemen's Foundation, Cowboy Hall of Fame award-winner William G. Duncan of Sedalia, CO, designed this bronze sculpture to honor the Association on its Centennial.

Embodying the indomitable spirit of the cattlemen who brought the industry successfully through the last hundred years, the senior character is in the place of honor at the top of the sculpture. Age shows in his demeanor as he stands at the gate and looks over the younger generation. While he understands the immediacy of their dreams; he is not yet quite ready to pass through the gate and yield. The younger couple looks forward to the future with dreams and ideas for a new dynamic beef industry. The children, lost in childhood pursuits, represent the ongoing legacy and strong values passed from generation to generation that has been the foundation of the industry.

A frieze around the base of the sculpture depicts a trail drive that moves to rail cars and packing plants, symbols of the industry in 1898.

The figures on the top of the bronze have been made into the smaller sculpture featured on the cover of this book.

THE CENTENNIAL BRONZE

William G. Duncan

BOOK DONORS

Donations $25,000 and Over

The Monfort Family Foundation

Chicago Mercantile Exchange

Winn-Dixie Stores, Inc.

Donations $5,000 and Over

The Hitch Family

Harris Ranch

IBP Foundation

True Foundation in memory of Jean Bina

Donations Under $5,000

Fred Stresen-Reuter
Arizona Cattle Growers Association
Colorado Cattle Feeders Association
Dale Humphrey
Dick McDougal
Loren C. Barnert

Fred H. Dressler
Iowa Cattlemen's Association
Jack & Phoebe Cooke
James Bell
Texas & Southwestern Cattle Raisers Association

Don B. Smith
John W. Lacey
John D. Weber
Tejon Ranch
Gordon Van Vleck
Linda M. Davis

California Cattlemen's Association
Don Butler
Montana Stockgrowers Association

Jo Ann Smith
Natalie McElroy
Jack Sparrowk
W.D. Farr

Robert D. Josserand
Agri Beef Company
Oklahoma Cattlemen's Association

Hawaii Beef Industry Council
E.H. Shoemaker, Jr.
Roger Stuber

John S. Runnells
Milton J. Brown
Scott S. Chandler

BUILDING THE BEEF INDUSTRY

Designed by Randy Taylor and Lynn Harster

Graphic Design by Keith McLendon

Composed by The Saratoga Publishing Group, Inc.

in Garamond 3 and Humanist

Printed by Paramount Miller Graphics, Inc.

on Vintage Velvet

Bound by Nicholstone

in Smythe Sewn Round Back Case Binding

Limited Edition of 100 Books

Hand Bound Calf Skin Tooled Cover

with Marbled End Sheets

by Distinctive Bookbinding and Stationery

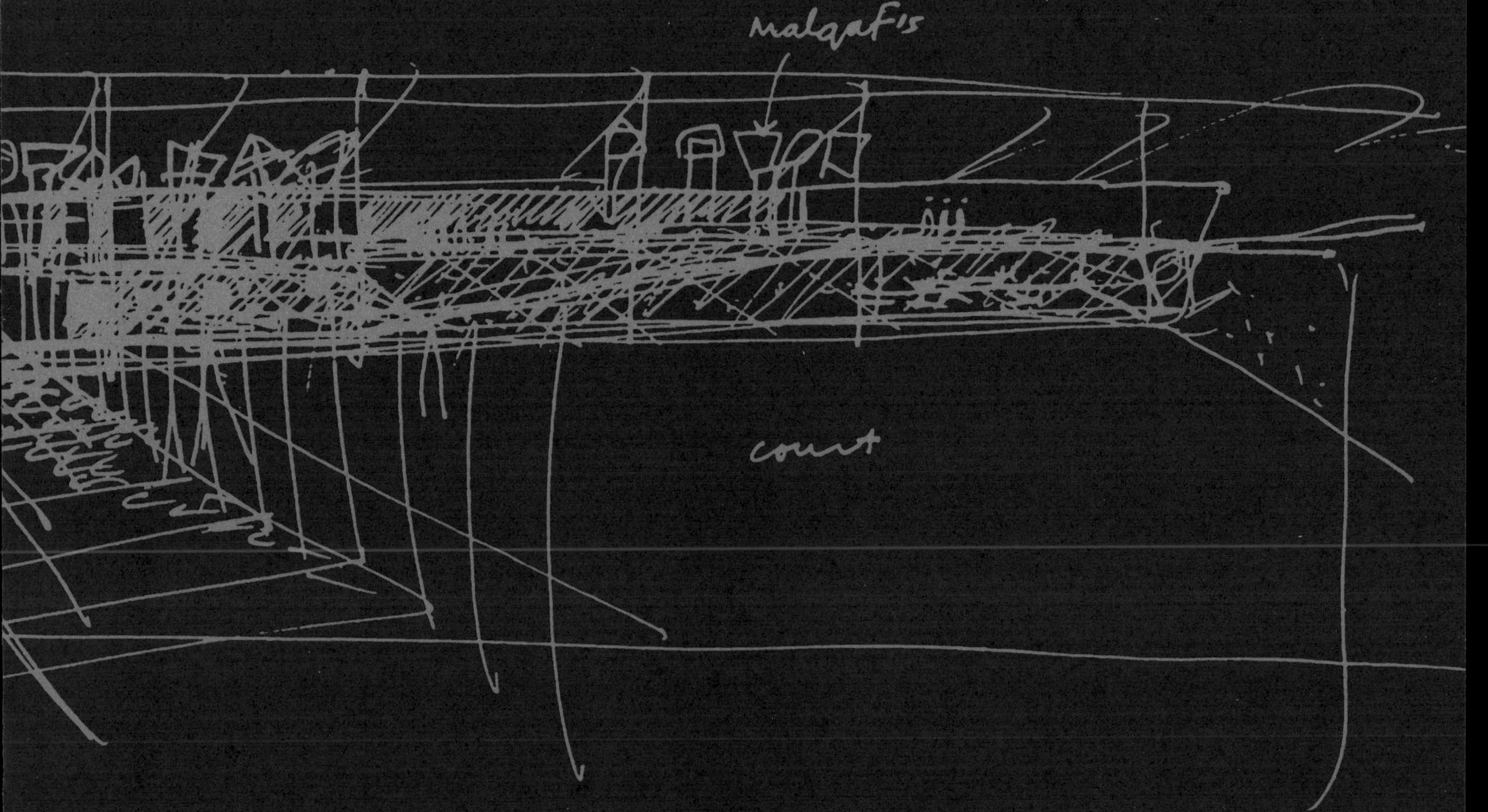
malqaf's
court

A singular architectural practice

Haig Beck and Jackie Cooper

Reprinted 2003
The Images Publishing Group Reference Number 515

First published in Australia in 2002 by
The Images Publishing Group Pty Ltd
ABN 89 059 734 431
6 Bastow Place, Mulgrave, Victoria, 3170, Australia
Telephone +61 3 9561 5544 Facsimile +61 3 9561 4860
Email books@images.com.au
Website www.imagespublishinggroup.com
The Images Publishing Group Reference Number 265

National Library of Australia
Cataloguing-in-Publication data

Glenn Murcutt: a singular architectural practice

ISBN: 1 876907 75 4

1. Murcutt, Glenn, 1936 – . 2. Architecture, Modern – 20th century – Australia. 3. Architectural design – Australia. 4. Architectural drawing – Australia. I. Murcutt, Glenn, 1936 – . II. Beck, Haig. III. Cooper, Jackie.

728.092

Concept design by Garry Emery Design
Final art by The Graphic Image Studio
Film by Pageset Pty Ltd
Printed by Everbest Printing Co. Ltd. in Hong Kong/China

IMAGES has included on its website a page for special notices in relation to this and our other publications.
Please visit this site: www.imagespublishinggroup.com

Contents

Glenn Murcutt's work attracts more international exposure than any other Australian architect's, despite his mostly solitary mode of practice. Murcutt is seen to produce an authentically Australian architecture that speaks of regional qualities while also participating in the international modernist discourse. (Alison Smithson once dubbed him 'the timber and tin Miesian'.) This blend of the exotic and the universal makes his work both intriguing and accessible. In Australia, Murcutt has been myopically portrayed as the mystic poet and spiritual guardian of 'Australian' architectural values, a contemporary national romantic who nonetheless transcends parochialism. He seems to occupy simultaneously two distinct positions: the pragmatic vernacular tradition of country buildings as well as the sophisticated international discourse of modernism. But Murcutt himself does not entertain such polarised design intentions. He operates as a rationalist. Inevitably, his use of steel and corrugated iron is understood as a vernacular reference to the tin buildings typical of the Australian outback, charged with sentimental connotations. Actually he prefers metal for reasons of economy and utility, and because few carpenters are sufficiently skilled to guarantee the precision he requires. The quest for national identity is a great mistake, in Murcutt's eyes. What matters is to design a building that responds to its particular place. Murcutt has been erroneously considered as an urban-shunning figure whose designs are for bush sites. In fact he has built extensively in crowded suburban contexts too, but this does not serve the bush myth of national identity so well. Here it is useful to adumbrate the major elements of the Australian architectural myth. Although architecture is not writ large on the national cultural psyche, if pressed to identify what makes Australian architecture 'Australian', most people would nominate the verandah. For an architectural element to impinge on the collective consciousness of a population otherwise so impervious to architecture, the verandah has to be more than just a commonly used architectural feature. As a transition space – between outside and inside, public and private, light and dark, hot and cool, prospect and refuge – the verandah is the architectural setting for experiences which are quintessentially 'Australian': experiences which encompass both the relaxed lifestyle and the warm climate. The significance of the verandah has another dimension for Australians: as the most (sub)urbanised people in the world, it is not surprising that they hold dearly the myth of the countryside (the 'bush'). The pioneer's isolated tin-roofed homestead with its perimeter verandah is a popular emblem of this myth. The verandah has become a cultural metaphor that acutely expresses the ambivalence that Australians sense at being 'between': between the reality of the city and the myth of the bush, and between diverse cultural memories as immigrants and a nation still forming its identity. The cultural imperative of the verandah is such that the work of Glenn Murcutt – whose buildings are notable for never having them – can only be fully explained by making reference to the verandah; his buildings have no need for verandahs because they function environmentally, socially, and (allowing for a certain amount of Miesian abstraction) semiotically as super-efficient verandahs. A Murcutt building *is* verandah. From this perspective it is clear why Murcutt is viewed both at home and internationally as the most 'Australian' of Australian architects. Yet his design concerns are considerably different from the non-urban, national romantic qualities widely ascribed to him. Murcutt is foremost an ideologue who works through architecture. His disposition is rationalist, not romantic. His design tactics are pragmatic, not poetic. His design method is governed by an ideological commitment to minimal exploitation of the site and maximum return on the use of natural and manufactured materials. This corresponds to his personal concern about dwindling natural resources. He is an environmentalist who draws inspiration from the land and is a perceptive observer of nature. Yet Murcutt as architect is defined by his interest in invention and manufacturing, and in shaping nature to serve human ends. Murcutt does not produce organic, Wrightian paradigms but an architecture of human intervention that is cerebral, rational, and conscious of its responsibility to ameliorate and minimise the inevitable disruption of human presence on the land. His buildings exist in an ethical partnership with the land, placed to preserve the integrity of the site rather than to consume its obvious features. The narrative route of the plan constitutes a journey of oblique revelation of both building and land, offering views and topography for contemplation, using breezes, sun angles – even the moonlight at times – to best advantage. There are other narratives presented too, disclosing how the building stands up and how it works. Typically, the sinews, structure, and skin are pulled apart and defined. Murcutt's aesthetic is posited in clarifying and expressing the practicalities and processes of architecture and enabling their order to be observed. When he obliquely slices an I-beam lengthwise, not only does he double the use of steel but he also produces a dynamic and attenuated triangular-shaped structural member precisely depicting the stresses resisted; moreover, there is no waste. Equally elegant and expressive are the corrugated iron roofs of several buildings. Their layered planes become steeper with each layer. This is highly practical because the increasing volume of rainwater is thrown off faster from the lower, steeper part of the roof; the architectural aesthetic emanates from the clear expression of the roof's fabrication and function. Murcutt uses stainless steel yacht rigging to peg down flighty roof profiles (he is more likely to have problems holding his efficient roof structures down than up). The rigging – frugal yet revelatory of the structural character of the member – again demonstrates how process is made legible; and this generates the aesthetic so typical of Murcutt's architecture. While he makes it look easy and inevitable, Murcutt's design resolutions are hard-won. Take a Murcutt hallmark, the long plan. It recurs so consistently throughout his work that we may assume it to be a tried and true design formula he can adapt to any given programme. But the linear plan does not come easily. With each new design Murcutt goes back over first principles, testing and discarding ideas before finally discovering the most simple, least wasteful design. He generally starts off by bunching together functions in a pudgy, ugly duckling plan form that yearns to be an Aaltoesque swan. In the course of his laborious, analytic design process, the linear plan only gradually emerges, and Mies takes over from Aalto. (See pages 25 to 29 for the typical design development processes of a Murcutt project.) The minimalism that is such a strong stylistic element of Murcutt's work is not so much an aesthetic device as an article of faith. It generates ideological as well as aesthetic satisfactions. Minimalism is both means and end. In accepting a moral responsibility to consume wisely and nurture resources wherever possible, Murcutt cannot avoid minimalism. He confronts its imperatives in the most practical terms. He works as a consummate artisan, creating the building as machine, refining until it performs optimally. He depends on rational observation of natural forces and phenomena to provide analogies for design – not poetic metaphors and organic suggestions, but explicit principles for problem-solving. He observes how, in order to conserve moisture, many eucalypts constantly twist their leaves in the course of a day to present their thinnest profile to the sun. He makes his buildings with that same delicacy of relationship to the sun; and the inhabitants remain in touch with the progress of the day and the weather – indeed, with the genius loci – as they manipulate the building's environmental control mechanisms. (Air-conditioning is unthinkable.) Roofs don't simply provide cover and protection from sun and rain. They are designed as active agents in ventilation and evaporative cooling techniques; and the shading is exactly calculated to give the best balance between summer and winter needs Murcutt looks beyond the vernacular solution for suitable models. He examines the aerofoil principles of bird wings and aircraft in order to increase the rate of airflow through his buildings, and also to bounce and balance light inside. He is fascinated by the lessons of bone structure and skin, how living organisms fine down at their extremities, how trees meet the ground, the edges of things and their points of contact. He is interested in expressing the underlying principles in his buildings, because he sees them not only as machines but also as organisms. And from this results Glenn Murcutt's powerful architectural poetic, most tellingly conveyed by the building lodged in the landscape; the building as line, holding the horizon and calibrating infinity; the building in submission – not subjugating the land; the building as expression of ideology and rationalism; the building as embodiment of an existential contract of human freedom and responsibility, confronting the unavoidable destruction that accompanies human occupation. ■

In the early 1960s I lived in the Greek islands for six months. It is easy to interpret this place as picturesque, and I was naturally moved by the wonderful effects of light and the romance and poetic force of Greek vernacular architecture. It's poetic and yet it's also tough as hell. I observed that there isn't much you could take away from this architecture.

There were many lessons, such as the sheer integration of a material like slaked lime: it reflects the heat and light, it is a waterproofing agent, a disinfectant in the joints between paving stones and house and street, it endows continuity to all forms, and it is a local product. It is painted on the tree trunks to prevent attacks by borers and microbes, and to deter the donkeys from eating the bark and ringbarking the trees. Seeing all this taught me that you can really understand and use a material comprehensively.

I learned from the Greek islands that material determines its own language. Understanding the nature of a material defines how to use it. Glass is a tensile material: hanging is ideal. Timber is good in compression but not in tension, and steel is good in tension, so elements in composite construction can be wonderful, such as timber teaming with steel. I'm really interested in these things.

Here I also learned something about the beauty of simple space, and about containment, security, prospect, refuge and materiality. I am interested in spaces with beautiful dimensions. I experienced beautiful dimensions in a courtyard on Mykonos in 1963, having lunch with an extended family. The courtyard was 20 metres long by 8 metres wide, and covered in grapevines. The canopy was a generous 3 metres high. The filtered green light from the vines made people look so well. Outside, the wind was blowing, but inside the courtyard it was perfectly serene. White walls, stone floor, a long table, a dozen chairs. The simplicity was remarkable.

I wondered why there were no handrails to many of the staircases on Mykonos. Then I noticed on the stairs the inevitable path of movement plotted by unpainted stones on the whitewashed treads and risers, indicating where to step. The route was worn over time by many feet. As the staircase rises, the unpainted stones in the treads shift in from the outer edge of the stair towards the protection of the wall. The front door is placed above ground, at the highest level, and suddenly I understood the psychology of security.

Outside on the street, the corners of buildings are cut away, forming seating. I worked out that the narrow streets were not made like this for people, but to accommodate donkey-laden traffic, and yet they encourage conversation and conviviality. It was a revelation to me: this is architecture.

Great poetic potential arises from the utilitarian. I cannot separate the rational from the poetic. The Greek islands taught me to look beyond the apparently rational. If you get the basics right, many other resolutions flow. This idea of things serving many purposes is crucial to me. If I can find a solution that answers more than one issue, that's the one I start working on. ■

It takes twenty years from deciding to be an architect to actually getting there. How do you hang on that long? How do you sustain the necessary confidence in your work to ultimately start to become a good architect in your forties? This issue needs to be understood in terms of the typical grounding that architectural students receive. Unfortunately today architectural education does not induce students to understand the nature of materials or the fundamental principles behind design. Our profession has lost whole chunks of empirical knowledge, all the rules of thumb, for instance, that made it impossible to design an awkward staircase, or a fireplace that smoked, or a roof drainage system that flooded. Once, the application of these rules of thumb made even a mediocre architect a reasonable designer. The problem is much more than whether an architect graduating now can detail downpipes or sunshading efficiently, or can properly insert an opening into a wall plane. The loss of basic knowledge and the contemporary disregard for design principles are symptomatic of an enormous general shift in attitudes about what is appropriate to teach architects. There aren't any baddies that we can single out for blame, because the schools, the profession and society at large over the past few decades have all been party to a sincere belief that moving from a prosaic, skills-based design education, where the architect was considered the design leader, to a technologically-led architectural education, where the architect was to be a social facilitator and team player, was a good thing. And they were wrong, for many reasons. We stopped teaching architects to go out and measure the real world and to observe natural phenomena, because we believed that sophisticated technology rendered this quaint sort of measurement obsolete. Instead of all those old-fashioned traditional craft-based materials and techniques, we put our faith in clever new materials. After World War II there was a touching confidence in the absolutely beneficial outcome of all science. There would be constant, technology-led economic growth leading to perpetual abundance. No one believed that resources were finite, that the air and waters could not absorb the pollutants we poured into them, that the land could not be bludgeoned into continuous fertility. Ideas like these had great impact on architecture and architectural education, and we are still, thirty and forty years later, directly or indirectly conditioned by them in the way that we allow ourselves to think about teaching. When I look back at my own architectural education, I can see why we are encountering some of the fundamental problems that we experience in architecture today. My first year set me up solidly for an architectural career, even though we had a class of 125 students and did no design as such in first year. Instead we spent the entire first term looking at the different ways that animate and inanimate objects sit, stand and lie. Many of my fellow students could not see much sense in studying spiders' webs, leaves, blades of grass, natural arched forms, or the cantilevers and root systems of Moreton Bay fig trees. My generation was very predisposed towards the benefits of untrammelled science and technology, and many went on as architects to inflict the worst damage on our cities, in all conviction and innocence. I am sorry that a few more didn't benefit from analysing continuity in nature. We progressed in second term to analysing continuity in constructed forms: bridges, vaults, cellular formations, foundations, reinforcing. We were learning how to design from nature. Things don't smash together, they transmute. There is a hierarchy of parts and a rational language in how the parts might fit together. I consider these the most important lessons in design, because they are the building blocks of architecture. And yet they are not taught any more. In our final term in first year we had to explore all the issues involved in designing a south-facing door in Sydney. If you consider that this was a rather poor design exercise, think about it. We had to know about the prevailing wind and rain, about air currents and how they affect access, the detailing of the jamb, where the weatherproofing goes, which way the door could open. It has to open outwards because otherwise you give yourself impossible detailing problems to solve. What are the aesthetic ramifications of each practical decision? It is all basic stuff, not complex. But it is about design principles that govern every line you draw and determine how you think as an architect. These principles are scarcely dwelled on in architectural schools any longer. Today there is not a driving attitude that governs a particular way of thinking. We have such choice that paradoxically we are impoverished. We depend on computers when we ourselves haven't mastered the principles behind what we are asking computers to design.

There is no doubt that design instruments determine the forms we make. In the twelfth and thirteenth centuries, tools chipped, cut and moulded building materials. People were rooted in the land and intimately understood the elements. When we look at their buildings we can appreciate how rationally – and therefore how beautifully – they are placed, and we can also appreciate the cultural integrity these structures possess. As tools and skills developed and as the level and straight line became commonplace in building operations, and as machinery was introduced, dimensions increased. Buildings became large and orthogonal. Topography was less relevant. Grids and economics took precedence. Built form was imposed on the land. And now we have buildings largely dictated by computers that are programmed to reflect parameters that have no basis in design principles. What does that tell us about cultural integrity? Where is the possibility for escaping from the meagre base systems of economic determinism that drive contemporary building? Perhaps we really deserve the cities that we get. The way we are taught to think as designers is significant. We operate within a dynamic political and economic system that almost invariably militates against truly fine human architecture and public spaces. Too many architects do not have the confidence and strength to influence the political and economic systems that shape cities. If the profession is to stand up to these forces, then it will only be through a deep understanding of the principles of ecology and design within our cultural context. The central design issues are humans – their history and culture; space; light; how things are put together; and responsibility to the land. What are the challenges and possibilities? Design is a chess game, and from rationalism and the aesthetic expression of building construction you can perhaps derive poetry. Design is not dependent on inspiration. We have to overcome this great twin myth of the architectural idea and the architectural ego. In fact anyone can design. Anyone can be taught to investigate and discover. It doesn't take great flair. Good design is more a matter of the ability to understand the issues – of pursuing the question until you make an appropriate discovery – and there are always many appropriate answers. If you understand how things are made and put together, you can at least produce good quality. ■

Mies, I believe, said that god is in the details. My view is that well-designed, integrated details can lift a work considerably. Well-designed taps, light switches, door handles, drawer pulls and such are small things but they give great finesse to any building. I don't use detailing as decoration. High-tech detailing is self-referential (and often highly expensive). Are buildings so boring that we have to resort to this? I deal with good but ordinary tradespeople. I generally can't get fully welded joints that look as though no human hand has been involved: the weld is visible. But a well-executed weld doesn't bother me if it doesn't interfere with the functioning of adjacent elements. I am not dealing with buildings with tight skins, where the joints have to be perfect. Many of my buildings have a loose-fit skin – like clothing, it's layered. Without air-conditioning and mechanical ventilation systems, the layers are removed or added according to climate, light levels, insects. Right from the outset of my practice, even before I had any work, I rang the manufacturers of standard componentry for buildings and yachting and requested their product literature. I was looking to apply standard systems in new ways. In 1969 I researched and modified a dry glazing system intended for commercial greenhouses, developing for it a sill with mohair set against the glass using standardised seals from other componentry. I have used the Lidco 1000 door system since about 1969. It is an interlocking structural edge system which is as good functionally and aesthetically as any I've seen. It is the only door and window system that withstood Darwin's Cyclone Tracy four storeys up. The stiles interlock, increasing the resistance to bending under high wind loads. The doors work structurally in concert. Many standard components have been beautifully thought out. For example, the Stylefinnish Lever 20 is a straight lever handle that is very comfortable to operate by hand or even by elbow. The end kicks inwards, so you avoid catching coat and shirt sleeves on it. I used flat satin stainless steel Clipsal light switch plates when the mechanisms were square with slightly rounded corners. The design changed so now I use HPM. If I had time I would like to design such components. Why not design a round plate to match a power outlet? And why not a double power point, a long plate for two points and two switches, rather than the large square plates? I generally use Louis Poulsen light fittings: PH4, PH5, AJ Royale for dining. The recessed light VL is a simple tin can for low wattage fluorescent or incandescent lights. (Poulsen Munkergaard have for years produced a semi-recessed light, a sheet of opal glass as a diffuser, designed for Europe where they have killed all their insects. In Australia the unit becomes an insect trap.) ____________ For the bathroom, wherever I can I use satin chrome or chrome Vola, a complete series of components designed by Jacobsen. I once used Seagram tapware, but it's been compromised by lookalike tapware. I specify Madinoz towel rails (or design my own). ______________________________ These are the tactile items encountered all the time. _My fireplaces have stainless steel inner flues and a steel or aluminium flue outside. The outer flue is perforated top and bottom so more heated air is discharged into a room. A standard Jetmaster firebox using their rotating stainless steel cowl generates a negative pressure at the outlet, ensuring the fire does not smoke.____ The Kempsey house fireplace has a double flue taken straight off the firebox; there is no gathering. This reduces the height of the fireplace by 200mm, and spatially that can be significant. ____________ The fireplace casing is painted with heat-resisting red oxide paint. I use a red oxide primer for the steelwork for the flue and the casing. The idea of heat is expressed through the colour. Fire engines are not red without reason. I've seen a pale blue fireplace, and it looked ridiculous.___________________ For wind suction, the 'Windworker' is the best system. The 'Western' rotary vent is good too, but can't turn fast enough under high wind conditions. ___________________ As I am making the working drawings, I am laying the bricks and thinking: is it a fat or thin joint? what is the position of the taps? And I know which tap system will be appropriate for the project. Everything is worked out. I am always thinking spatially as I draw. Adjustments sometimes occur on site. The structural framing systems I set up provide great freedom. But true freedom requires boundaries, and then to move sideways off the pattern becomes powerful. ____ Everything is designed and thought through before tender: it won't be modified. The fireplace steel jacket incorporating rock for thermal storage and heat transfer I have developed. Stairs and window systems are standardised. I might draw the handrails: 32 x 20mm solid steel section or I use tube, another standard. It depends on what's appropriate, whether or not it's a rail on its own or on a wall. Tube does not interfere with the spatial flow but a solid square section will accommodate a glazed balustrade. I can also see the handrail as a nice tactile thing. I'll use a tube on a long flight of sixteen treads or more, where security is important: it's more graspable. ______ Eliminate complexity. Minimise the number of joints. Keep it simple.____ ■

Any appraisal of the work of Glenn Murcutt demands an understanding of the modernist history of the linear house plan. The linear house is a modernist invention. It does not figure in traditional architecture, which employed the palace or villa as design model, always several rooms deep and usually also several floors high. ___In contrast, linear houses have evolved in the vernacular. Examples include the long houses of many traditional cultures as well as the nineteenth-century shotgun houses found in parts of the United States, notably New Orleans (fig 1). The shotgun is not the result of any architectural thinking. Generally they are humble, single-storey, timber-framed buildings resulting from laissez-faire planning requirements to maximise the number of frontages and thereby minimise infrastructure service runs: the shotgun plan type is the result of sanitary engineering planning, not architecture. ______________________Architecturally, the first evidence of the modernist provenance of the linear plan is in the late nineteenth century, with English proto-moderns such as Voysey. They are functionalists looking at ways to attenuate the plan form in order to gain solar access. Voysey's Turner house, The Homestead in Frinton-on-Sea, of 1905 does this (fig 2). This single-room-deep, L-shaped plan no doubt emerges from the butterfly plan of the period so favoured by the Art and Crafts. A good example is Happisburgh Manor, Norfolk, of 1900 (fig 3) by Detmar Jellings Blow. The deflection creates the maximum dimension of favourable orientation. This plan figure, in turn, is really a functionalist distortion of late-seventeenth-century English Palladian plans such as that of Groombridge Place, Kent, attributed to Wren (fig 4). The connection to Palladio is obvious (fig 5). ____________What is common to the butterfly plan types of the nineteenth century is their appropriation of the plan figure of the palazzo, which is disturbed to gain solar access and views. This combines proto-modern functionalist ideas and English romantic notions of the picturesque. ____In parallel with the English proto-moderns, Greene and Greene in California experiment with the linear plan for much the same reason: orientation. Their Earle C Anthony house of 1909 recalls Voysey's idea of the V oriented to the sun (fig 6). And at about the same time, Wright also attenuates the plan into the linear type, though he is probably less concerned here with solar access than he is about stretching out and colonising the site, as he does with the Avery Coonley house in 1906 (fig 7). _____It is really not until the 1920s that the Europeans start to experiment with the linear plan. Le Corbusier is one of the first. He sets about designing his mother's house on the lake in Geneva in 1925, making a rational analysis of the project (fig 8). Clearly functionalism drives the plan. 'The program: a house for two single persons, without domestics. Region: eastern end of Lake Geneva; situated on a dominant hill at the lake shore; front view to the south. Design procedure was contrary to normal practice: a plan was established – rigorous, functional, corresponding exactly to the program – a true machine for living. Then, plan in pocket, a suitable terrain was sought. There is actually more sense in this method than may seem at first glance. In this tiny house of 650 square feet there is a window 33 feet long and the reception area offers a perspective of 45 feet. Movable partitions and disappearing beds permit the improvisation of guest accommodations.' (*Le Corbusier 1910–65*, p38) Nevertheless, it is Wright who develops the linear plan as the plan type par excellence for the common man (as he would have seen it), in the Usonian house. The first house of this type is the Malcolm Willey house, Minneapolis, of 1934 (fig 9): 'The house wraps around the northwest corner of the lot sloping to the south – a fine vista in that direction. The plan protects the Willeys from the neighbors, sequesters a small garden, and realizes the view to the utmost under good substantial shelter.' (Frank Lloyd Wright, *The Natural House*, p59) Wright brings it all together here: functionalist ideas about solar access and opportunities for views, and colonisation of the site – stretching domestic architecture to achieve scale and dimension. The Usonian house reaches its apotheosis in the Goetsch-Winkler house, Okemos, Michigan, 1939 (fig 10). These little linear plan houses of Wright's are wholly modern. They do not indulge in traditional house iconography, and have abandoned totally the palazzo type of the Palladian villa. The linear house springs out of the servant-free, single family household, as Le Corbusier suggests, and expresses the values of social democracy and egalitarianism, as Wright perceived. After Wright, Mies van der Rohe takes the exploration of the linear house type to another level of experience and expression with the Farnsworth house of 1950 (fig 11). This house is not grounded like Wright's more organic Usonian houses, but is abstracted into two horizontal floating planes. Being transparent and suspended between earth and air, rather than embedded in the land, the house is dislocated from cultural tradition. The building elevates and isolates its inhabitants, and in the act of dwelling, they must occupy a stage. It is a position that requires reflection on one's place, and is both a physical experience and philosophical proposition. Glenn Murcutt inherits these various modernist architectural developments of the linear house type. Most notably, he combines Wrightian ideas about solar access (the functionalist tradition) as well as a Miesian formal abstraction and existentialist standpoint. For Murcutt, the linear plan arises initially out of a functionalist prescription he applies: maximise solar access and opportunities for cross-ventilation. Underpinning this functionalist prescription is his view that air-conditioning is unnecessary (attuned building fabric can modify climate); an existential idea about being in touch with place; as well as notions about using renewable resources and making buildings that are designed with sustainable principles in mind. ■

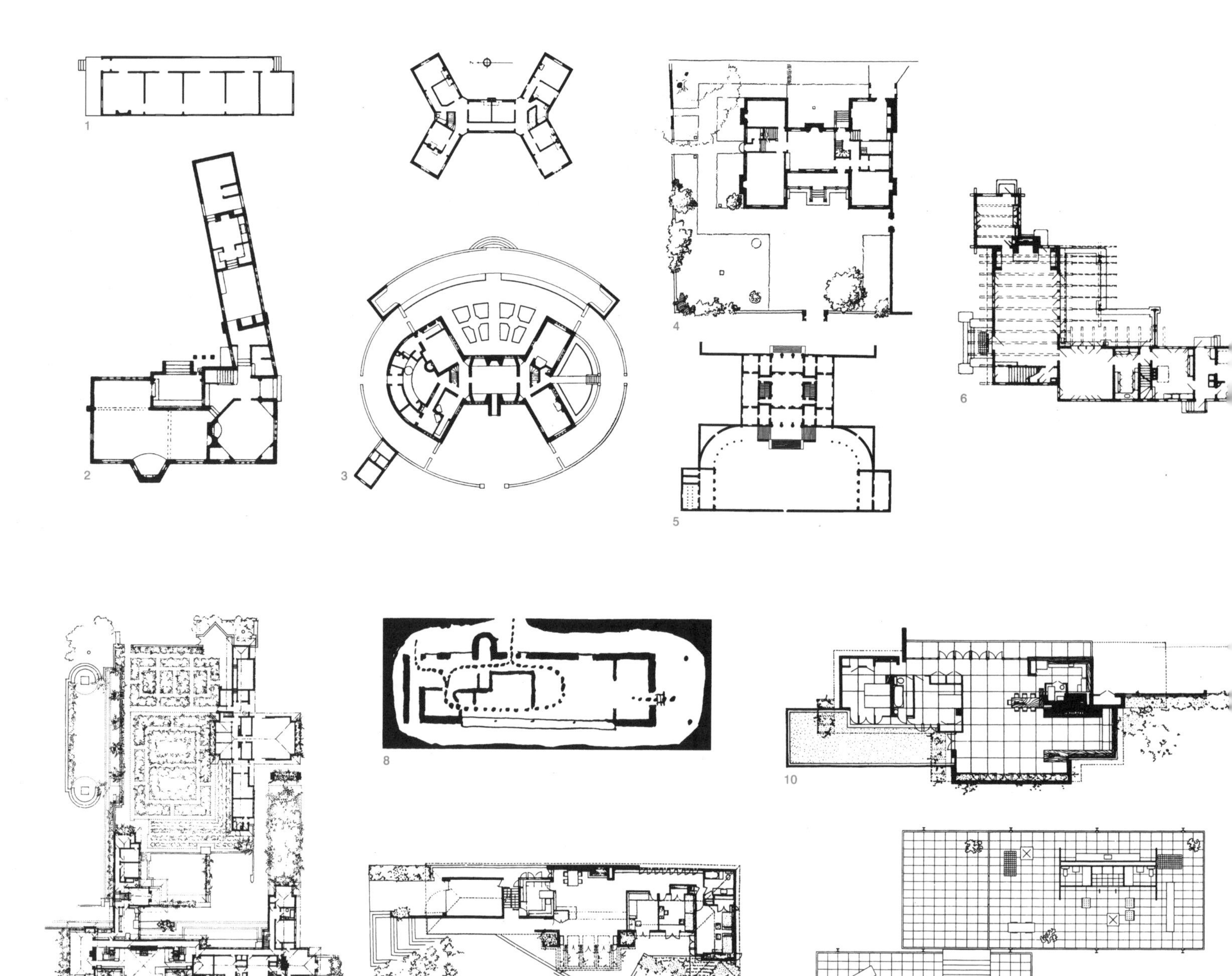

1 New Orleans vernacular shotgun plan type
2 CFA Voysey: Turner house (The Homestead), Frinton-on-Sea, 1905
3 Detmar Jellings Blow: Happisburgh Manor, Norfolk, 1900
4 Christopher Wren Attrib: Groombridge Place, Kent
5 A Palladio: Villa Thiene, Cicogna, 1554 to 1556
6 Greene and Greene: Earle C Anthony house, Los Angeles, 1909
7 Frank Lloyd Wright: Avery Coonley house, Riverside, Illinois, 1906
8 Le Corbusier: mother's house, Lake Geneva, 1925
9 Frank Lloyd Wright: Willey house, Minneapolis, 1934
10 Frank Lloyd Wright: Goetsch-Winkler house, Okemos, Michigan, 1939
11 Mies van der Rohe: Farnsworth house, Plano, Illinois, 1950

In compiling the significant drawings that depict the design development of Glenn Murcutt's Broken Hill Minerals and Mining Museum (for publication in UME 1, 1996), we undertook several lengthy interviews with the architect in his studio, and with him identified more than a hundred drawings and sketches of the project. The drawings were first organised chronologically and then forensically analysed in order to piece together Murcutt's design process. The design method disclosed through the development of this project is evident throughout Murcutt's work, even in the smallest projects, which can generate many dozens of drawings. This manifestation of the design process shows the operations of an eclectic: 'An eclectic is a philosopher who tramples underfoot prejudice, tradition, seniority, universal consent, authority, and everything which subjugates mass opinion; who dares to think for himself, go back to the clearest general principles, examine them, discuss them, and accept nothing except on the evidence of his own experience and reason; and who, from all the philosophies which he has analysed without respect to others, and without partiality, makes a philosophy of his own, peculiar to himself.' (Peter Collins, *Changing Ideals in Modern Architecture 1750–1950*, Faber and Faber) – Murcutt takes nothing for granted: even successful solutions of previous designs are subjected anew to critical analysis. The linear plan, which has become a hallmark of his work, is revealed to be not an a priori assumption but is rather the result of adjusting the programme to meet the parameters of site, orientation and cross ventilation. (In the southern hemisphere, the sun is in the northern part of the sky, so buildings are oriented north for solar access.) Murcutt generally draws in a ballpoint liquid pen on lunchwrap paper. The following annotations tell the story of his design process.

Drawing 1 reveals the rationalist at work: first Murcutt prepares an adjacency (bubble) diagram.[*] He assembles the elements of the brief at a scale of 1:200, indicating required areas, noting the critical relationships, distinguishing between public and staff access. As he develops the adjacency diagram he adds in courtyards (shown cross-hatched). While the diagram shows the functional relationships, these courtyards reveal Murcutt's search for an appropriate environmental strategy for building in Broken Hill's hot, arid climate. Further, they suggest that from the outset he is designing to a formal premise – the courtyard type. It will take him many months to reject this premise about the form of the museum.

Drawing 2 shows an attempt to use structure as the basis of the plan. A structural grid is set up which may be infilled or left open to form courtyards. Murcutt derives the size and proportions of individual rooms by tracing, more or less directly, from his adjacency diagram. From the outset he distinguishes between the cellular, repetitive elements of the brief, rigidly strung together, and the particular spaces of the galleries, with their much freer dispositions.

Drawing 3 shows Murcutt's response to the clients' requirement that he retain an informal shortcut across the site from the adjacent high school to the city centre. The result is an almost Aaltoesque reading of the split between servant and served spaces. The repetitive (servant) elements of the brief follow the street line. The public (served) spaces are skewed away from the orthogonal urban grid, with the galleries fronting the diagonal pedestrian desire line across the block. Courtyards and circulation occupy the interstices formed between these two geometries. Murcutt assembles this plan by tracing its various components from drawing 2. The question of structure recedes as consideration of the interior layout of individual rooms develops.

Drawing 4 questions whether the previous plan is getting a bit too fat for the long narrow site. Murcutt revises the free-form plan, pulling the galleries back onto the orthogonal geometry of the street grid. A covered open-air linear walkway now separates the servant and served spaces, and courtyards are located along the northern side of the public spaces.

Drawing 5 evaluates the effects of the diagonal shortcut across the site: its constraints suggest a long thin linear plan type, thickened at the western end of the site, with courtyards (cross-hatched) along the northern side of the building.

Drawing 6 (on the same sheet as drawing 5) tests the formal possibilities of the plan arrangement suggested by drawing 5: a double-loaded corridor type with the servant spaces to the south side and the served (public) spaces to the north; each is expressed with its own roof system. In the foreground Murcutt sketches in the existing mineshaft headframe to which his plan must be fitted.

Drawings 7 – in four small sketches – investigate the parasol roof form and show it separated from the building below. In one, the headframe structure suggests a means for suspending the roof. In another, getting rainwater off a skillion roof is aided by shifting its pitch. In a third, the effects of morning and afternoon sun are examined, and the idea is there for a pool for evaporative cooling. The eventual roof solution closely resembles the gabled trusses of vernacular farm sheds. But there is no suggestion in any of these drawings that this affinity to the vernacular occurs to Murcutt. He is not at all interested in iconic references: he is exploring only the functional requirements of the roof

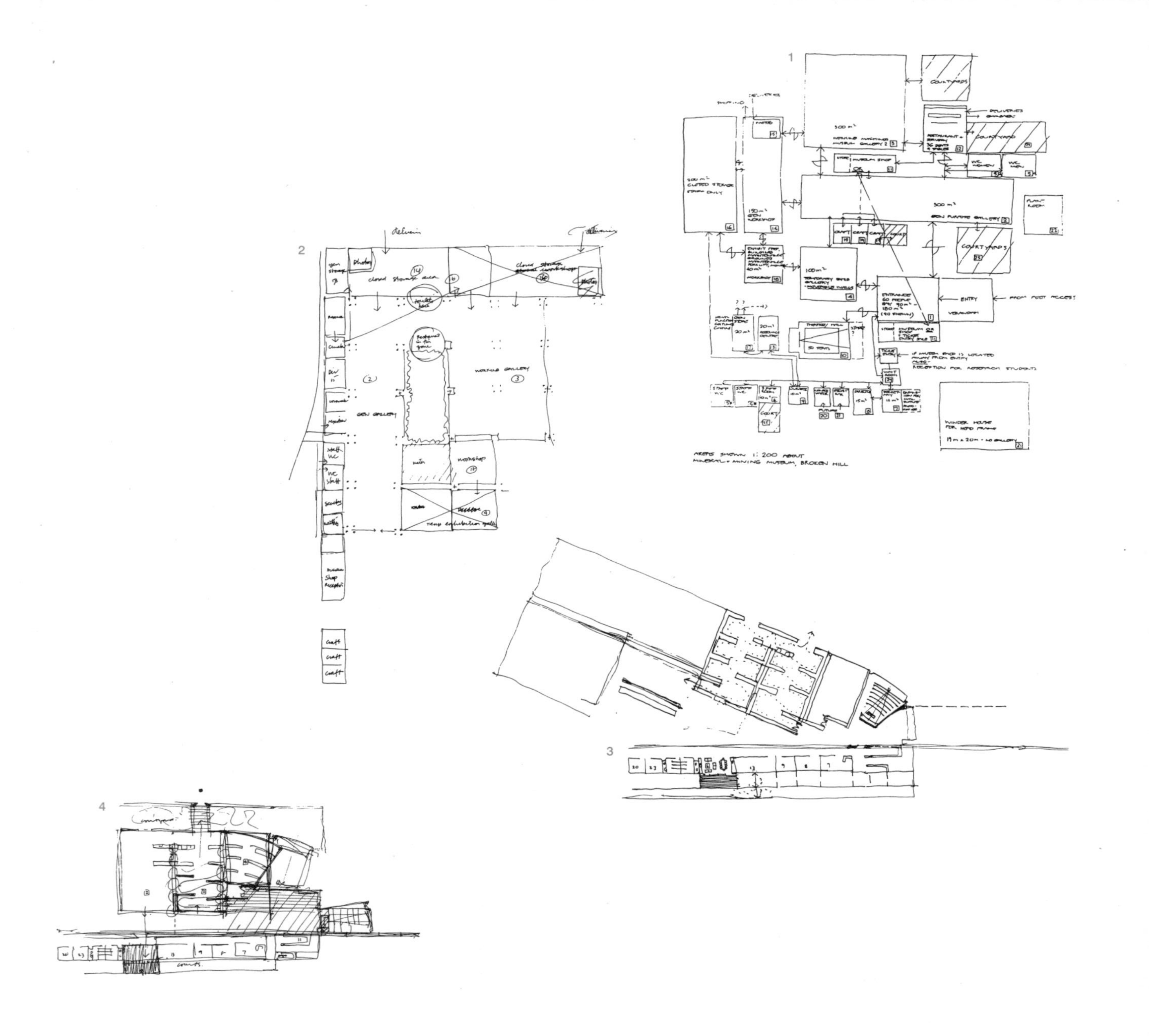

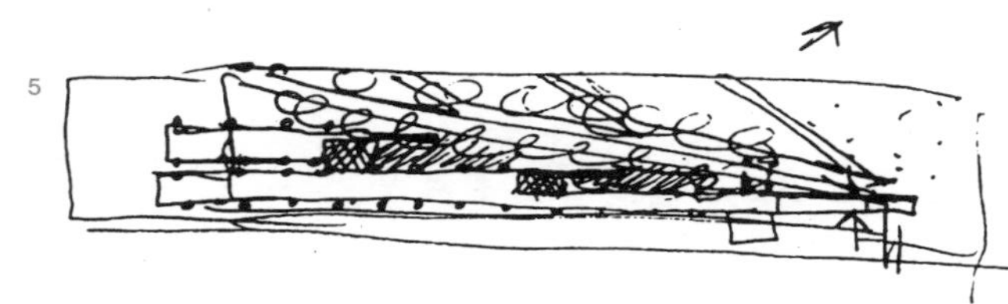

ideas noted in drawing 2, double-loaded corridor in drawing 5, skewed gallery spaces of drawing 3 (though at a much reduced angle to fit the site), the axe-like plan of the galleries (nascent in drawing 2 and evident, though flipped over, in drawing 3), and the internal courtyards of drawing 1. Murcutt begins here to think about rammed earth construction, showing a thick earth wall to the interior side of the long gallery. At the western end of the building he sketches in a ramp for access to an upper-level open-air covered display space. To the building's northern edge he proposes a stepped earth berm.

A small exploratory sectional sketch tests the feasibility of the parasol roof, concrete structure, earth berms, courtyards, and pools to aid evaporative cooling. To one side of the drawing he notes: 'Whole site makes an oasis...central to survival is water – for the operation of the mines + human survival'.

Drawing 9 is the first submission to the clients. It is a crude, tentative sketch, a work in progress, drawing as process – certainly not drawing as polished architectural product. The design at this stage shows the impact of the diagonal path and the existing placement of the headframe. The combined effect of these requirements is to make half the site effectively unusable. Both constraints are now reviewed and rejected.

Drawing 10 is done with the clients to show what the building might look like. Murcutt depicts the roof as a parasol, with the existing mine headframe as museum icon.

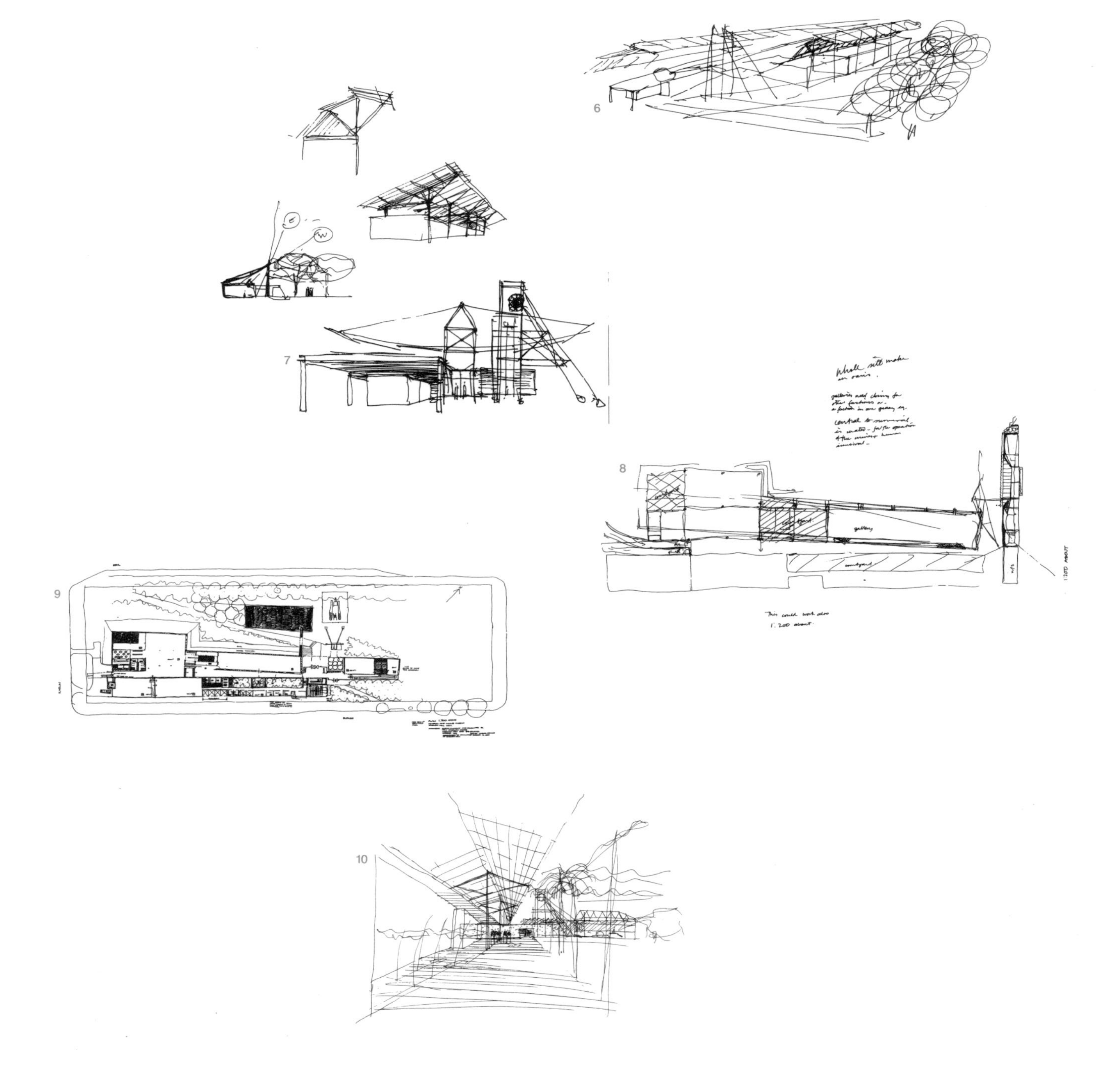

Drawing 11 persists with the idea of separating public and private elements of the programme around a courtyard. The headframe is now repositioned appropriately at the 'head' of the museum to announce entry. Earth berms have become rammed-earth walls. Murcutt is loath to abandon his first thoughts on an environmental strategy for the building based on the courtyard type. He does, however, start to question the resulting fat plan, realising that he can't draw enough air across the building for effective evaporative cooling. Will windscoops help? Almost as an afterthought, five chimney-like malqafs tentatively appear.

Drawing 12 begins to consider the single-loaded corridor plan to enhance natural ventilation techniques: to one side malqafs draw the prevailing breeze down into and across the building; to the leeward side, negative pressure created on the topside of the aerofoil profile increases exit velocity to aid cross-ventilation; the earth berm reappears as a buttress heat sink.

Drawing 13 develops this concept in plan: the fat courtyard plan is abandoned for the single-loaded linear corridor plan; an earth berm stretches the length of the southern wall; a pool is positioned to aid evaporative cooling; a rammed-earth wall forms the northern wall. Over the corridor running along this northern wall, Murcutt doodles with a triangular pattern for the malqafs (still envisaged as simple windscoops).

Drawings 14 – three small sketches – is the conceptual breakthrough. In the first drawing Murcutt explores circulation through the gallery, continuing to doodle with a smaller pitch for the triangular pattern for the malqafs. The second drawing continues these explorations, obsessively crisscrossing the triangular pattern of the malqafs into even smaller segments. The resultant diamond-form pattern suddenly suggests both a form for the malqaf throat and a zigzag form for the rammed-earth wall ('This is OK!' notes Murcutt). This configuration enables the malqafs to be made according to traditional vernacular design principles (of which Murcutt, as an admirer of Hassan Fathy, is well aware), ensuring evaporative cooling: air is drawn down over beds of water-laden woven fibre mesh and crushed desert herbs (for perfume). In addition, the malqafs are integrated into the wall structure – instead of being pushed up through the roof (the zigzagging form also strengthens the rammed-earth walls, avoiding the necessity of engaged piers). The third drawing, a small elevational sketch, confirms for Murcutt that he has the architectural solution: he has discovered the inevitable. Within a couple of hours he produces the final design. Murcutt recalls that all this happened on the evening before he was to fly to Broken Hill and present his revised design. This solution sprang to mind quite suddenly and unexpectedly in the early hours

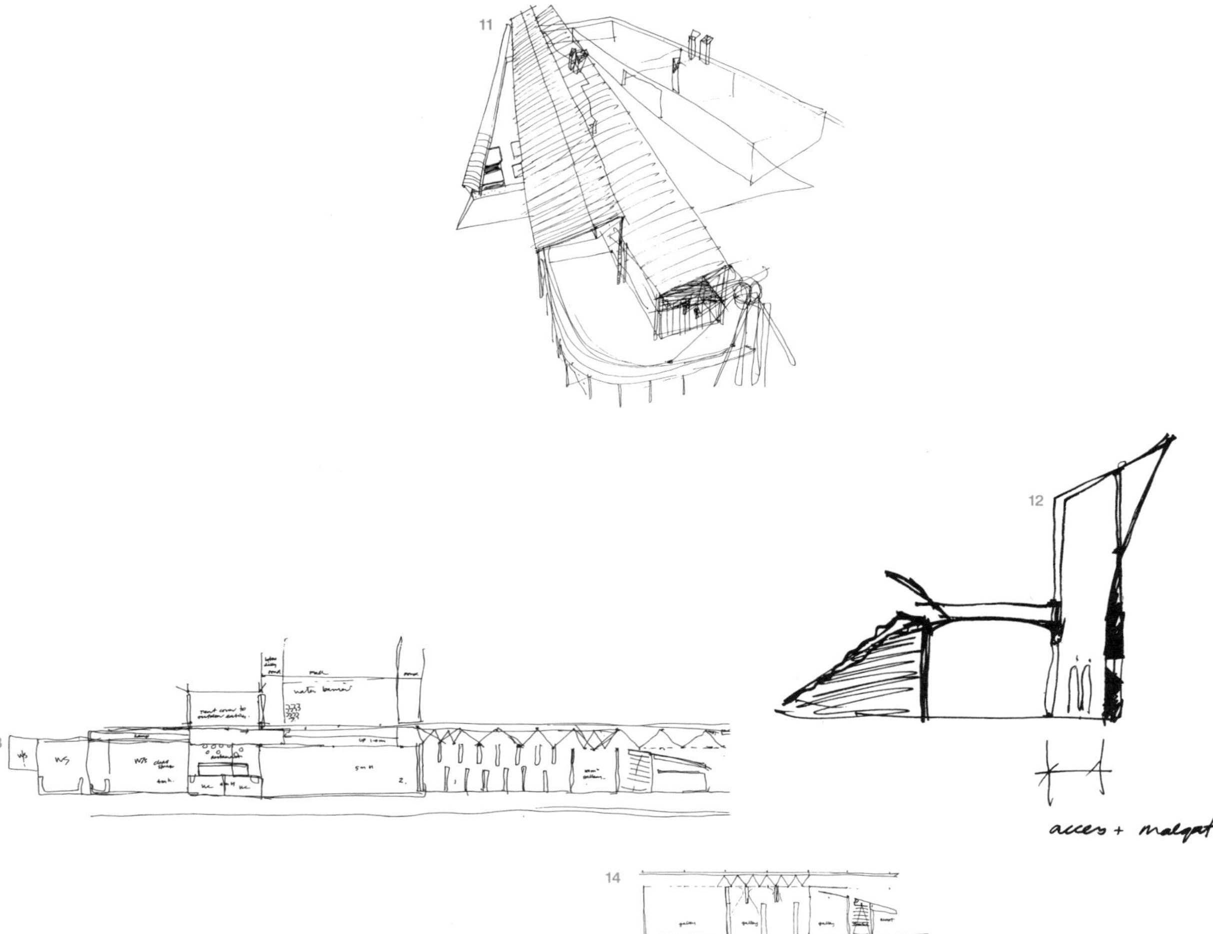

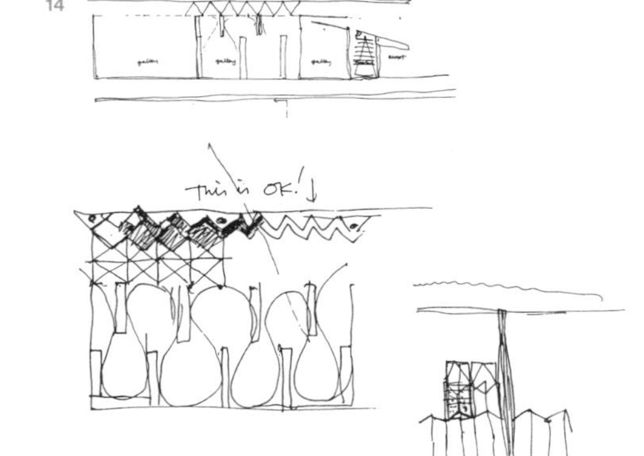

scraps of paper, stuck together with masking tape as each part of the building falls into place. All the ideas are here: the headframe is in its natural position at the main entrance, standing as both museum emblem and architectural metaphor presenting the linear route through the museum as journey down a mine shaft; the parasol roof is twisted on plan to provide porte-cochère entry points at either end of the building, to fine the museum down at its two extremities, and to present its ends as architectonic compositions rather than sectional truncations; the elongated plan with its single-loaded corridor facilitates a two-stage building programme – and enables the first built stage to look complete. The three different structural elements are expressed: the roof as parasol screening; the concrete container for the museum; and the pisé walls as thermal sink. Murcutt observes that this legibility is also powerfully present in the landscape.

Drawing 16 is drawing 15 redrawn to present to the clients. It is worth recalling that this is an urban building in the heart of the city, one of a sequence of civic institutions each placed as object buildings on an urban block: town hall, railway museum, civic centre. Murcutt's museum is contextually responsive in its longitudinal parti; and at some 300 metres long, its urban scale is undeniably monumental. At this stage Murcutt has done his calculations for the malqafs on the basis of Broken Hill's relatively constant north-west summer wind velocity, checking them against Hassan Fathy's figures. Later wind tunnel tests done on a model in a Melbourne laboratory will confirm these calculations.

Drawing 17 is done on the spot to explain the building to journalists after the delighted clients call an impromptu press conference and announce the design, using Murcutt's rough plan.

Drawing 18 is from the entrance looking across the oasis to the pool and courtyard beyond. Water in the desert is a potent, paradoxical image. Murcutt exploits more than its poetry and obvious amenity. The pool – which is feasible because the water table lies only 2 metres below the surface – augments the evaporative cooling capacity of the malqafs, which can draw in moist air. Sunlight reflected from the pool is bounced off the underside of the parasol roof onto the heavy mining machinery displayed on the open upper floor. In summer, the shaded red earth walls will glint as crystalline water patterns play on their surfaces.

Drawing 19 explores the compositional relationship of headframe, entrance, malqafs, and roof. By now Murcutt has decided on the roof form: a simple gabled truss with the two halves expressed as distinct layers. The truss is tipped up, forming a crippled skillion that brings sunlight into the building in winter and drains off rainwater along the lower edge. Tipping the roof creates negative pressure on the leeward side of the building, resulting in increased velocity of air drawn into the malqafs on the windward side.

Drawing 20 discovers the advantages of shifting in the columns supporting the roof along the north side: apart from the aesthetic benefits of fining the building down along its major extremity, the necessary summer shading is gained. Murcutt checks the sun angles. The design is complete, and from here it is a matter of refining details developed through the design process with the structural engineer.

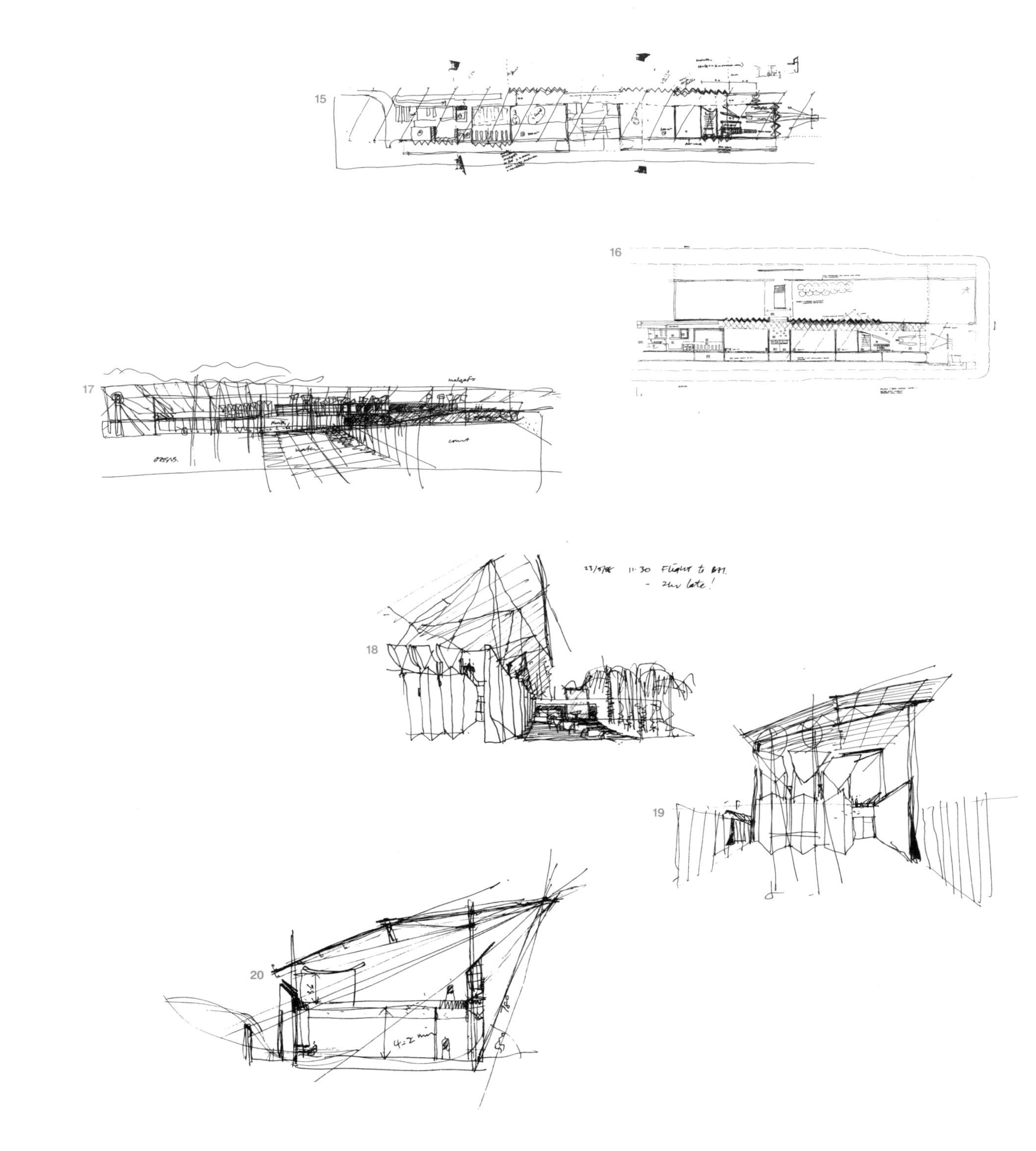

The desert and the great distances from anywhere make Broken Hill in far western New South Wales an unlikely urban proposition. The Australian outback is sprinkled with country towns with sprawling streets wide enough to turn around the bullock teams that once hauled the wool bales. But of these towns, only Broken Hill developed a sustained urban density and city bustle. This little city of 25,000 owes its existence entirely to mines that have been giving up the world's largest deposits of silver, zinc, and lead for over one hundred years. Broken Hill grew solid and prosperous despite the realisation that some day the mines would peter out. Now its population is in decline. It's a hard place to inhabit, several hundred kilometres from any major centre, surrounded by desert that sucks up what rain does fall, prone to baking summer heat and chilly desert winter nights. The flat, red landscape is relieved by the odd low range of hills. Blue saltbush is prolific and the only trees are the majestic river gums lining the few (mostly) dry watercourses. Broken Hill's longitudinal urban grid follows the line of lode that cuts the town in two. The town sits alongside mines and is pressed right up against a ridge of tailings that obliterates the horizon. The wall of mine tailings dominates the city physically, just as the mines have dominated it economically and politically. The project of 1988 for a minerals and mining museum (it was not built) came at a critical time, as the city was beginning to take stock of its future. After the mines finally do give out, Broken Hill has to survive by attracting tourism. Already people come to see this remote outback city – and the nearby country where *Mad Max* was filmed. But they must be enticed in greater numbers before Broken Hill can sustain itself from tourism. Yet the mining museum is more than a strategic tourist drawcard. Perhaps more important is its potential to show Broken Hill to itself, to pull together and codify the reasons for the city's existence and to celebrate the very mining operations that seem so ordinary in the minds of local people. The mining museum might forge a sense of identity and pride at the point where the city's single *raison d'être*, mining, has become tenuous. Glenn Murcutt addresses the proposition that architecture – built form – can act as cultural repository, triggering and enhancing awareness of local identity. This accords with the purpose of a museum to highlight and explain the seminal themes and artefacts of a culture. The mining museum building cannot expect to recreate a mine or the activities of mining, but it can evoke the experience of mining in this place. Murcutt's primary architectural objective is to express Broken Hill's genius loci, which is bound up with the mining operations, the desert terrain, and the extreme climate. He is struck by a hard beauty generated by these basic determinants. The looming ridge of mine tailings is a symbol of mining and of Broken Hill itself; the ridge is recalled in the longitudinal form of the building, which evokes the inescapable and endless horizon (the building also suggests the big tin sheds of the mines). Rich desert tones are recalled in the red earth walls. And the oppressive summer climate is acknowledged and harnessed by the hovering parasol roof, the windcatchers (malqafs), and a dense thermal blanket of rammed earth walls. Murcutt seeks out low-energy, environmentally efficient design solutions. Just as the negative climatic forces are parlayed into architecture, so are the constraints of a tight budget and difficulties with freighting in building materials across hundreds of kilometres of desert. Freight costs are kept low by specifying as little concrete as possible – for the two floor levels only. Instead of being concrete, the walls are rammed earth, using the red earth from the area. This answers economic as well as environmental and aesthetic needs, which satisfies Murcutt's sensibility for frugal design. Murcutt succinctly evokes Broken Hill in the building and makes understated references to the experiences and processes of mining: for instance, the linear corridor horizontally interprets the experience of going down a vertical mine shaft, with flashes of light registering each level of the descent via the malqaf light and vent shaft. Similarly, the effect of being underground is evoked in the exhibition areas, dark cavernous spaces with only the displays lit. And the pressure of the earth bearing down, which is characteristic of being deep underground, is sensed in the memory of the ponderous mining machinery located on the floor above, open to view from the streets around the museum site. So successfully have the building's functional, environmental, and iconographic objectives been woven together that the outcome has a sense of inevitability, as though the architect intended how these things would be resolved and envisaged them from the start. Yet examination of Murcutt's working method shows a slow, rational approach. Nothing is assumed. He searches to discover the inevitable, and he takes his clients on the journey with him.

(See pages 220 to 221 for the developed design drawings of this scheme.) ■

Daphne Murcutt house

Seaforth Sydney New South Wales
1968 to 1972 (several designs, unbuilt)

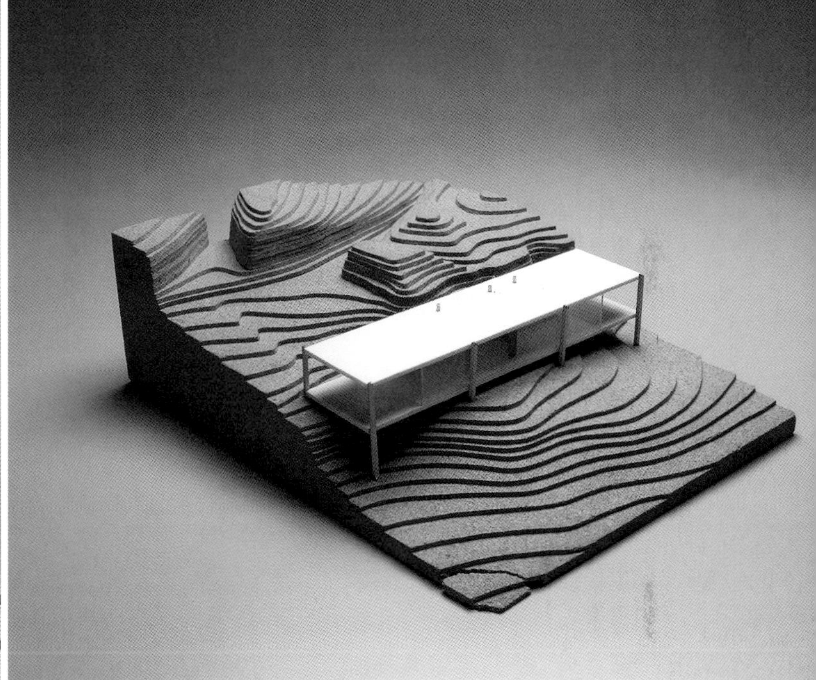

Murcutt's design for a house for his mother clearly owes a debt to Mies van der Rohe's Farnsworth house. Mies's work was imprinted on Murcutt as an adolescent as a result of his father's admiration for American architecture of the 1950s. It is not surprising that at the end of the 1960s, when Murcutt starts his own practice and the search for his own architectural voice (up to that time he had been working for other architects), he turns to these roots in order to establish himself in a phantom apprenticeship, as it were, to a master he especially respects.

The Miesian provenance of this design is explicit, but Murcutt also responds to the issues of solar access and view. In this respect the resultant plan is closer to Le Corbusier and his functionalist approach. Like Le Corbusier's plan for his mother's house – which identified solar access and views as its fundamental criteria for finding the site for the house – Murcutt's plan locates the entry at the rear of the house and sets up a route to the view by penetrating the centre of the building, moving across the plan.

There are here also ideas about the minimal house as prototype and laboratory. The single client permits a level of particularised scientific investigation that is usually not possible in a family house where design must shift across into more generic and therefore less critical solutions. But a house for just one person is an opportunity to go to extremes in both programmatic and constructional formal terms.

Murcutt designed numerous versions of this house variously exploring ideas of mass, single and multi levels, and Aaltoesque and Miesian planning. He also pored over yachting catalogues looking for alternative detailing solutions and components that might be used. He is starting afresh, not wanting to fall back on the nuts and berries, sub-Wrightian discourse operating in Sydney at that time, but actively looking for other sources for making architecture.

Glenn Murcutt

In the 1960s I worked for Ancher Mortlock Murray & Woolley. The office produced many very good domestic buildings. There was also fine work from other Sydney architects like Neville Gruzman, Bill Lucas, Bruce Rickard, Ian McKay, Philip Cox, and Allen and Jack.

Throughout the 1950s and early 60s, the influence of Frank Lloyd Wright was apparent in the way Sydney architects approached issues such as siting, material, colour. They were designing buildings that expressed structural legibility, order, and economy in the use of materials. But by the mid-1960s, the 'Sydney' school had become essentially romantic, at times even sentimental. And by then I was beginning to question the importance of avoiding the picturesque. I had been impressed by the strength and simplicity of the architecture of the Greek islands, but there was no way that I was able to apply any of the lessons in the architectural context of Sydney in the mid-1960s.

There were other influences on my design thinking. I had been raised on Mies van der Rohe through my father's great interest in his work. By 1969, even though Mies's work represented the antithesis of what was going on in Sydney, I felt a need to turn to the Miesian values I'd been introduced to in my early teens.

I remember also in the late 1960s Craig Ellwood was published in *Domus*. His work embodied clarity of structure, a simple plan, technological expression transparency and translucency, and space as shelter and refuge, with prospect in relation to the landscape. (The only great modification needed to the design of the Ellwood houses in my opinion would have been shading to avoid air-conditioning. I have always thought mechanical air-conditioning in Australia an unnecessary burden on resources and the atmosphere.)

At the beginning of 1968, I was designing the clinker brick buildings with deep recesses typical of the 'Sydney' school, but there is a clear shift in concerns in this house designed for my mother. I was obviously saying: this is not the right direction for me; I've got to cleanse myself of all this. This house represents a cultural turning point in my career, this and also an alteration to a house I was designing for myself in Mosman at the time I was first setting up my own practice.

The site was dominated by a large rock to the north, 2.5 metres high. The house was to be sited only 1.5 metres from the rock. Entry is from the north down to the roof; I was considering making the roof possibly concrete and turf. To the south is an extraordinary view on axis to Middle Harbour straight down to Balmoral beach.

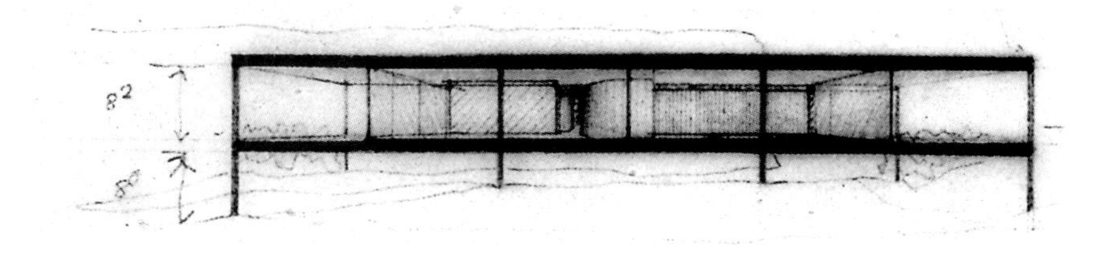

ntry is via a gully between two rocks, through
ne north facade and into the house, and the
ew of Middle Harbour beyond. The north facade
vas a blank wall of glass blocks with the sunlight
n it, giving not only privacy from houses uphill
ut also a diaphragm for light and winter warmth.
he kitchen looked to views to the west on the
arrow side, and a forest to the east, and to
ne north was the outline of the rock through the
lass blocks. The western verandah formed a
eep recess. You could sit on the verandahs with
omplete privacy and in winter enjoy the early
norning and late afternoon sun.

he house has just one bedroom, a living/dining
pace and a kitchen. Despite its size, there is
sense of spatial generosity. I designed the large
erandahs because I wanted dimensions that
ave a sense that you were not living in a rigidly
lanned, spatially internalised conventional house.
ven if spaces are small, you can connect them
vith courtyards and inflate the sense of space.
he ideal dimension in a house is one that lets
kid get up to full speed and stop before running
nto the end wall.

he materials are steel and glass block. I designed
version of the house in concrete at one stage,
nen I made it timber. I produced many solutions,
ut this version was always steel-framed.

he house didn't go ahead. But it was a good
latform for me to start cutting another edge
or myself.

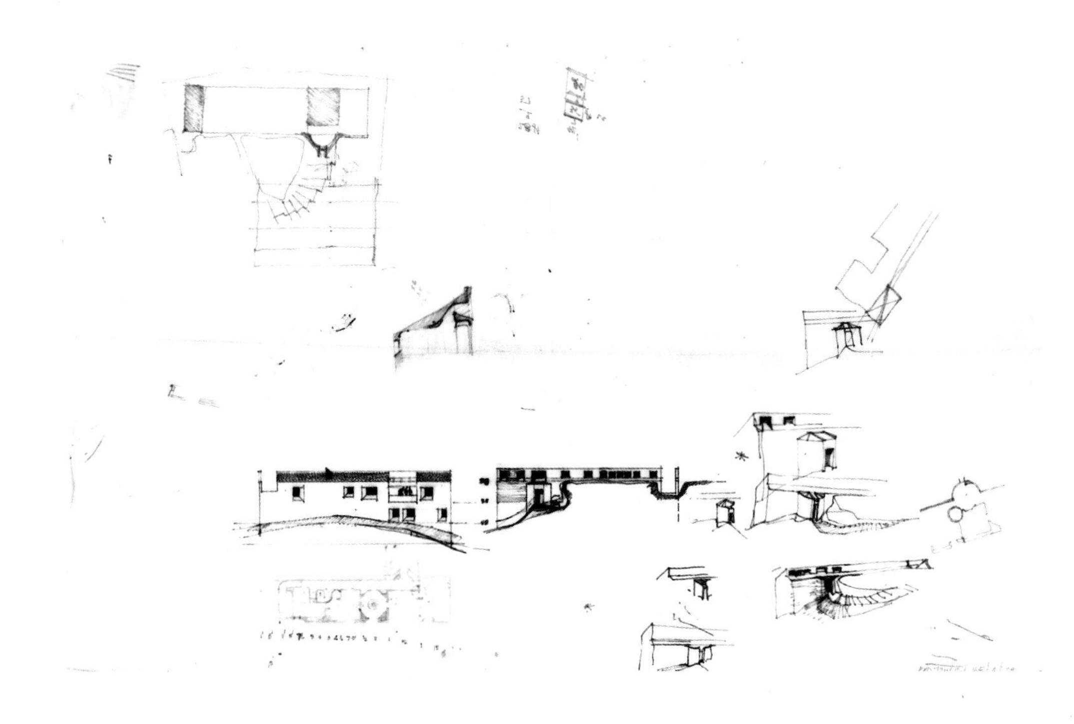

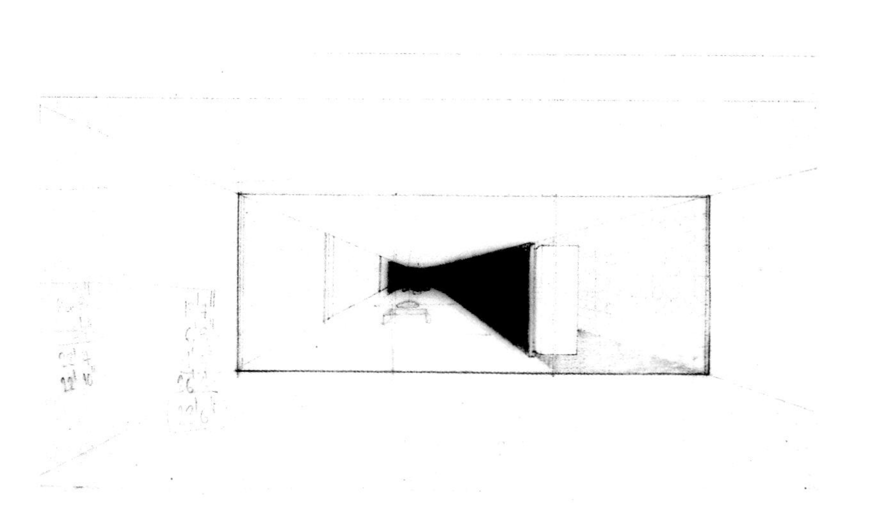

Murcutt's designs for both his mother's house and his brother's house form a pair: in effect, they are laboratory works. The first is based on the freestanding Farnsworth house, and the second on a Miesian investigation of the courtyard house.

Although Murcutt takes Mies as a starting point, even in these earliest independent works, he identifies climate – ie, aspect – as a prime planning imperative.

The bathroom is conceived of as an internalised service core, and used here in a Miesian way to separate the various zones of the house. This idea of the bathroom as a service core is evident right through Murcutt's work.

Glenn Murcutt

In late 1969 I decided it was time to go into private practice by myself. My brother and his wife asked me to design them a house in Sydney's northern suburbs. This was a chance to think about the courtyard. The issue was privacy and how to achieve it in the suburb. Australian suburbs typically consist of houses sitting at the 'fear line', 6 metres in from the street alignment boundary. The buildings form islands on their blocks, with big yards out the back. I observed the sun patterns on this site, and as a result I positioned the living areas in the space traditionally reserved for the backyard.

Both my brother and sister-in-law are musicians, teachers, and interested in sailing. They needed a large garage. They also needed a music teaching room and a foyer that would double as a waiting room for children learning piano. The spaces are layered: public, semi-public, semi-private, private. This layering also works from the north, in solar terms, with the daytime activities – sitting, dining, children – facing the sun, and the bedrooms to the south.

The courtyard is very important. It is a formalised backyard, and a powerful link between the day living spaces. It also provides dimension across both the length and width of the house.

This is the first of my works that has a sense of serenity, and it comes from dimension. It doesn't come from an architecture concerned with the tension between spaces and between inside and outside. I am really more interested in the work of Frank Lloyd Wright and Luis Barragan than in, say, Walter Gropius and Marcel Breuer, although I respect their work also. Later I would come to realise that any building designed without serenity in mind is a mistake.

The 1.5-metre overhang to the north allows the sun to penetrate deeply into the day living spaces during the winter but blocks it out in the summer. I failed sunshine and shade at NSW University of Technology and had to repeat the subject. That made me really learn it. Failure is an integral part of the learning experience.

I learnt a lot about ventilation from my father, who used ventilation principles and the sun to best advantage. At university they taught us to put up sunshades above windows to provide summer sun protection, but later I discovered there were other ways to provide sun screening based on the same principles, using predetermined, fixed angled slats.

This building runs east-west on the site because, within the constraints of the 6-metre setback, I wanted to make the most of the north light for all the daytime living spaces and have both a public and a private realm. It's a logical process. The light inside is beautiful, and the house is completely private.

The internal bathroom is quite private even when there are lots of people around. A natural connection exists between bathing and sunlight, and the bathroom has external light, with the sky framed by a roof light.

The idea of the courtyard house embodies my experiences in Greece, and also principles established by Mies – his legibility of structure, the connectedness between inside and outside, and division of space through the placement of structure.

It's a timber-framed house, which was a budget decision: it could equally have been built in steel. The house is not detailed according to the industry standard of a stud framing support system, but rather post and beam timber construction. By connecting the post to the face of the beam fascia rather than supporting the beam from underneath, I achieve continuity at the joint. Post and beam is traditional in Australian construction. My father did this many times and I was used to it. The T connection is very much more difficult, as a composite connection of timber and steel plates is required.

This house uses the Miesian core which defines the use of other spaces – spaces that are as much suggested as they are actual.

The roof is flat. I had only lived in flat-roofed houses built by my father, who was influenced by American architects such as Neutra, Mies and Gordon Drake. I was unaware of all my father's sources, I was simply taking on the baggage. I had never designed these sorts of buildings at university, but the simplicity of the flat roof released me from the architectural predilection prevailing at the time for pitched and skillion roofs constructed with unfinished or oiled sawn-finished timbers, and clinker-fired flush-cut jointed brickwork – hallmarks of the 'Sydney' school. However, flat roofs in Sydney are frustrating because of the extraordinary rainfall, and overflows at gutter points and leaks are not uncommon.

Engineer: Taylor Thomson Whitting

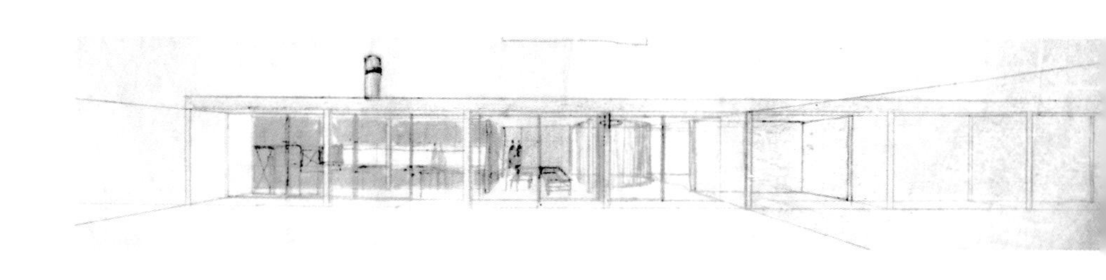

Laurie Short house
Terrey Hills Sydney New South Wales
1972 to 1973

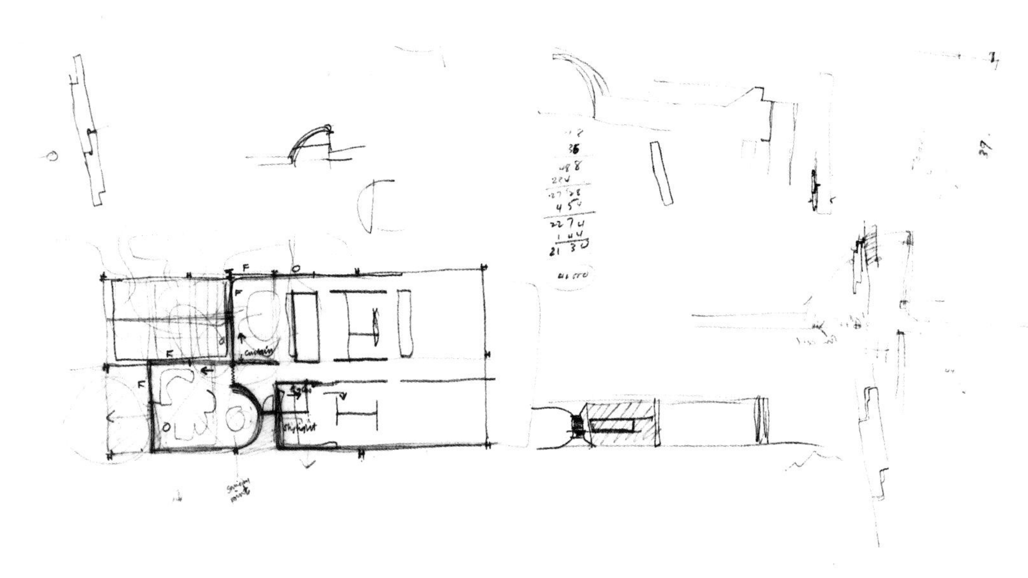

his house, like the earlier two, is also a Miesian exercise, but drawing from the lessons of late Mies, Chicago Mies: one is reminded of the public buildings and office buildings.

Murcutt builds a platform, a tabula rasa, somewhat like a temple space, to erect the house on. (It is almost the same temple space quality that he returns to more than twenty-five years later in locating the main hall of the Arthur and Yvonne Boyd Education Centre, 1996 to 1999.) The platform is a conceptual reading of the ground. In this design, Murcutt is beginning to abstract the landform into the house.

He achieves this through the abstraction of the horizontal surfaces: the floor plane is a continuation of the natural ground plane, and the roof is a floating plane. The effect is to reduce the conceptual organisation of shelter to just two horizontal planes.

The ceiling is seen to be structurally independent of the columns, which run up past the fascia – a Miesian device. This produces the effect of the floating ceiling plane, an idea Murcutt was beginning to grapple with in his brother's house.

In the design of this house, Murcutt remains constrained by the pleasures of the Miesian parti while he consolidates his interests in site, climate, technological innovation and abstraction as primary design parameters. He embarks on an eclectic analysis of the site/climate-induced design imperatives, focusing particularly on resistance to fire. He invests the building with a hoard of well-resolved experiments. The structural grid begins to assume a very powerful formal presence. And he takes on abstraction as an aesthetic.

This was a chance to explore steel frame. The house fronts onto the bushland of Kuringai Chase in the northern suburbs of Sydney. The site when I first saw it was burnt out, and it was obvious that there were frequent bush fires, so the design became the first for my fire analyses. This is not a place for a timber house. I thought about concrete, but it's too aggressive. Steel doesn't burn but it fails catastrophically under heat. I could make the house in steel with a concrete floor and roof, and good fire-rated materials. The issue was to keep the steel wet and cool: you reduce the potential of heat failure by inundating the vegetation around the house with water as fire approaches.

The roof is flat with water on it permanently as part of the fire protection system. It doesn't leak, and the extra thickness – 250mm rather than 200mm – reduced the potential for cracking. When we were pouring the slab, the engineer had said, put 50mm of extra concrete on top, block the outlets with tennis balls and flood the roof from the time the concrete goes off. It's produced the best-cured concrete, and we never sealed it. We just flooded the roof after six or seven hours with 200mm of water and left it there. As well as providing a barrier against fire, the water keeps the thermal variation of the roof even in summer and winter. There is also insulation immediately beneath the slab.

The 3-metre long light monitor captures the sunlit water reflections on the ceiling. The monitor is 600–700mm high with windows for ventilation, and drags the summer cooling north-easterly breezes in over the water and through the house. This was an early experiment in controlling air movement and quality of light, and also natural conditioning of the air. This is also my first use of angled sun screening louvres in the roof plane. Now it's familiar in my work.

There are pop-up sprinklers around the house and the parts of the site with eucalypts close by; and in a fire, the freshwater swimming pool acts as a water tank supplying the sprinkler system. During a fire, the sprinklers spray the windows.

The masonry walls are reinforced concrete, lightweight and fire-resistant. The external steel-framed and insulated walls are covered with Gail matt black ceramic tiles; they have a grip-on surface and don't fall off. These are fixed to a render on expanded mesh attached to a steel stud wall frame. There are expansion joints within and between the panels. They are on grid and half-grid. In terms of fireproofing, it's a rated wall.

Fire has been through several times. Wind-borne burning leaf litter and settling sparks are what usually cause the damage, but this house has a 1.5-metre cleared path all around it. It's a clay site with lots of mud in wet weather, so the path is brick-paved, which provides clear access for maintenance during and following a fire. To the north-east of the house, the direction of an advancing fire, the site is grass and planted with low-growing prostrate grevilleas on the banks.

Most of the trees retain the charcoal markings of previous wild fires, and the black tiles look burnt out. I could have used big flat steel panels bolted on, but the steel would have been 12–15mm thick, an inappropriate use of the material. I could have used a bronze roofing type panel, but it's difficult in the weatherproofing detailing at the head and sill in relation to material compatibility and the possibility of corrosion. I wanted an elegant building.

The forest is behind the house and to the west. The house is sited along the contours, which is a practical way to build. Big sliding screens to the east protect the glazing from the early morning summer sun and at times from wind. The glazing is standard aluminium-framed components.

From the outset I've always needed to plan for the northern sunlight to penetrate right into the day living spaces during winter. In this house the roof is opened up with 350mm-deep sun screening blades set so that sunlight penetrates from the equinox through winter and back to equinox, and is eliminated throughout summer.

There is a gas heating system located in a subterranean plant room, with cylinders behind the garage. I went to the Department of Mines for information: because natural gas is heavier than air, we had to dig a trench from the floor of the plant room into the landscape so the gas could drain if it leaked.

It's a very comfortable house to be in, with good cross ventilation despite the fattish plan and two corridors.

Engineer: Taylor Thomson Whitting

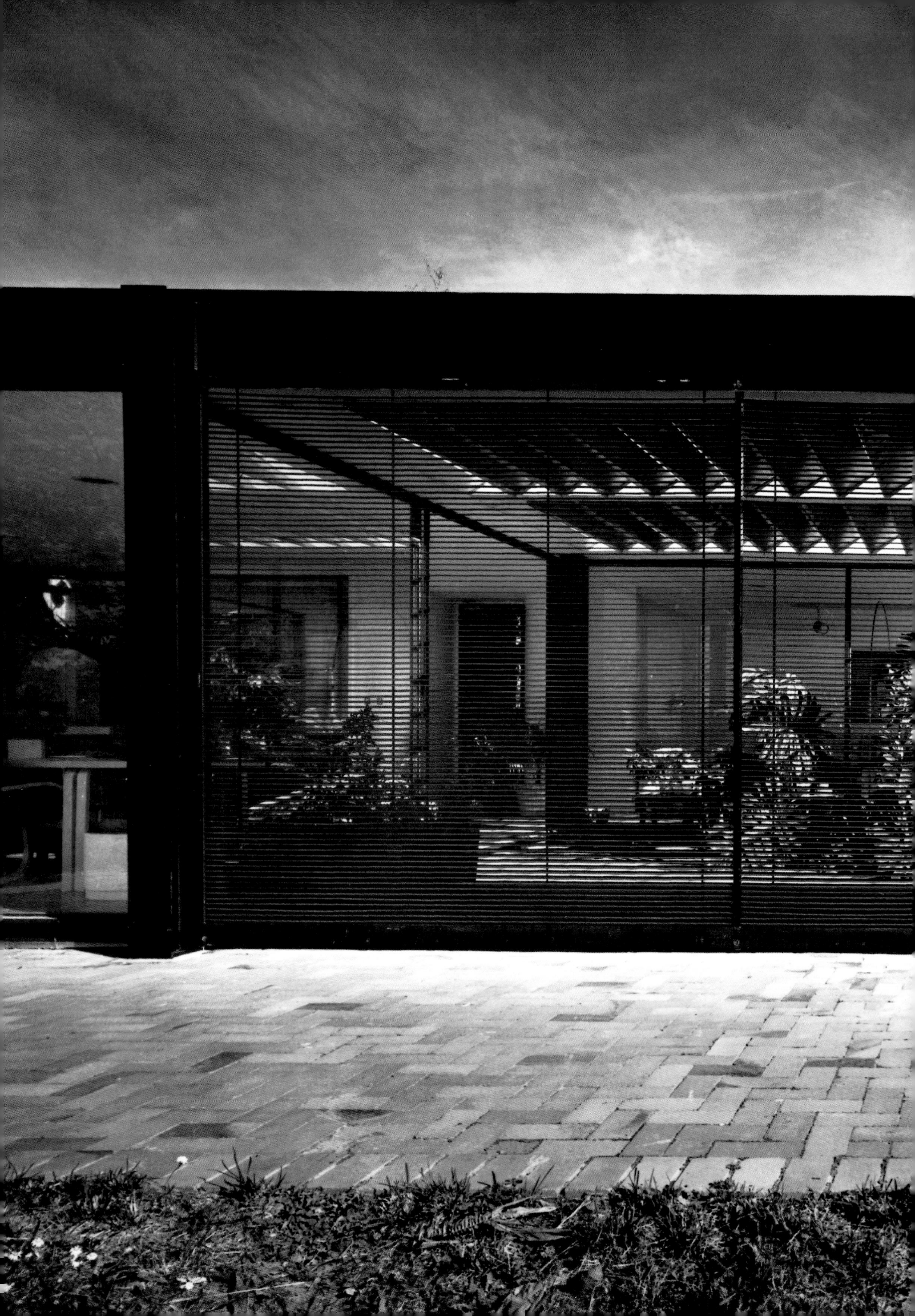

Marie Short house
Kempsey New South Wales
1974 to 1975; Murcutt extensions 1980

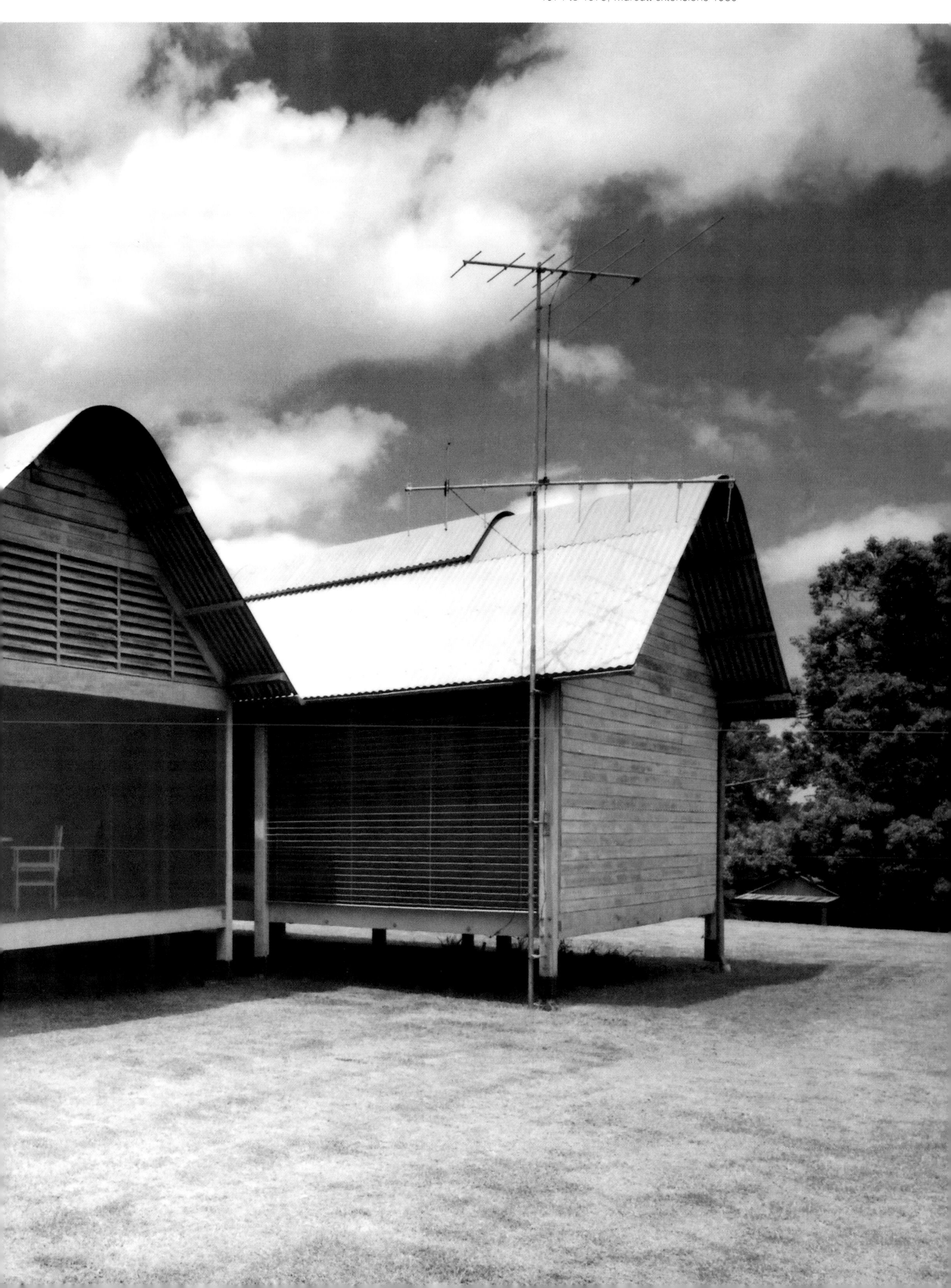

The design of this farmhouse marks the beginnings of the mature Murcutt. He is relinquishing Mies – and establishing his own aesthetic hallmarks – although still incorporating many references. The parti of the staggered plan is reminiscent of the Farnsworth house with its staggered deck, and Murcutt continues with the Miesian internalised services that feature in his previous houses, in which the services divide space and set up the layered zones of public and private. Also, the proportioning system of the timber frame recalls late Miesian monumental bay spacing, of course here on a completely domestic scale.

But Murcutt's interest in climate control dominates, and he seizes the opportunity to rethink how a roof can work not only as a static sheltering element but also to engage actively with climatic imperatives. His solution is a bold and innovative analysis of the roof as both aerofoil and sun screen.

This is certainly a laboratory building, and Murcutt's investigative analysis of climate issues and his lateral thinking regarding the application of building technology are becoming increasingly his way of working. He operates with an expectation that the inhabitants will engage directly in manipulating the building as an environmental machine. Yet he does not address design at a purely functionalist level but is equally interested in the experiential affects of space and shelter. The issue is not only about being comfortable but also about being connected to place through experience of the sun, breezes, light and shade, and materials. All this is approached with a high degree of formal abstraction, and the Murcutt parti emerges, consisting of the gridded plan and the clearly understood section.

Glenn Murcutt

This is the fat plan pulled apart and slid.

Marie is Laurie's mother. We looked at several properties together before she bought one with 7 kilometres of river frontage. It is a special place It has a freshwater tidal creek – there are very few in Australia – and is full of riverine rain forest flora as well as fish, reptile, animal and bird life. It is near the coast but 80 kilometres from the rive ocean outlet. The rainfall is high: it's gumboot territory. And it's humid in summer.

Marie asked me to alter the 1890s house and design some extensive new areas. Just before the builder started, I said to her: You could build a new house for the same cost. So she showed me where she'd like to build, which was a place between the river and a 3-hectare lagoon. She said: I want a house that is as cool in summe as standing under the mulberry tree, and as warr in winter (the tree being deciduous). That was on the Sunday.

I drove back to Sydney from Kempsey that Sunday night with my mind racing. I must have had this house in my head, because I went straig to it and designed it in two days. Over the next couple of days I completed the working drawings and on the Friday I returned to Kempsey with then Marie liked the design. I immediately contacted the builder. He was surprised by the new plans, which meant changes in labour, but he started the job within ten days of the new altered design

Kempsey is in the centre of the New South Wales coastal timber industry. There are timber species among the world's eight most durable timbers: tallowwood, ironbark, turpentine, spottec gum and stringybark. For years Marie had been collecting the ends of runs of timber: brushbox flooring, coachwood, tallowwood, oregon. Having measured them up, I designed the house around these materials. The objective was that they could be reused: Marie had indicated that at som stage she might like to move the house to a new site some two kilometres away, and she could simply unbolt it, pull it apart, transport the materia and reassemble the same components.

I already had an understanding of the technology of the region: farm fences, posts and rails. I knew that after rain the snakes head for a building, and you can find them in your gumboots. If you lift the house off the ground, the snakes go underneath it; that elevation also allows you to keep a watch out for termites below the suspended floor. It also enhances airflow and ventilation.

'he house is in two parts: one has its end facing vest to the river, and the other looks east to the agoon. A western verandah is wonderful in winter, ut if unprotected in summer it would be very hot. pulled the south wing westward to screen the 'erandah. Shutting down window areas on three ides of the northern wing forces the prevailing ummer breezes through the southern wing and reates ventilation through the rather thick plan.

Vhy two wings? There are several reasons. The eduction of scale is one. Also, the building could e more easily dismantled and relocated. And I vanted the quality of living to be close to the edge, nd to enjoy the landscape views.

raditionally, the kitchen, dining and living areas re separate from sleeping. It's a great experience ɔ get up from a cosy living room in winter and o out onto a cold verandah, and then off to bed. o the sleeping was designed to be in one wing nd daytime living in the other.

he main 'formal' entry for visitors is on the north-vestern corner. The informal work entry is on the outh-eastern corner. This gives direct access ıto the laundry and kitchen after working, like any armhouse, and provides the connection to the xisting farm buildings.

)uring construction, some of the delivery trucks id not deliver their loads because the drivers failed ɔ recognise a new house going up and thought was just a shed.)

Ve wanted natural timber finishes. I would have sed a bleach, but the product contains toxins. xternally I used Cabot's RH47 dark grey oil stain, aving compared swatches up against the trees ɔ see how well it matched. (It was excellent, but ıe colour is no longer available.)

ı northern New South Wales the humidity in ummer can be high, diurnal temperature variations an be 30°C, and rains are heavy. Flat roofs in these onditions leak. Here it is necessary to get water ff the roof quickly. And ventilation is necessary ɔ release the build-up of hot steamy air in ceilings nd roof spaces, and prevent mildew.

Ventilation is something I had rudimentary childhood knowledge of. My uncle Raymond Powys had given me a book around 1952, *The Principles of Flight*, by Camm, from which I learned about positive and negative airflow over forms. This building was the first opportunity to use these principles and experiment with suction for ventilation.

The overlapping curved ridge section junction with the pitched roof provides a roof ventilation slot, and also breaks down the scale of the roof area. This is the first time I had used a curved roof. It provides very good airflow, with good negative pressure on the leeward side of each roof. Cool air is sucked into the building. The roof is pulled apart two-thirds of the way up; the flutes of corrugation are offset, providing a cylinder of air flowing along every corrugation. When the wind turns to either hot or cold, from the east or west, slots in the gable ends of the weatherboards ventilate the roof space.

There are two diaphragms on the northern planes of roofing to each wing admitting winter sunlight. During winter and until the equinox, sunlight pours into the belly of the house.

The glazing system for the roof lighting above the breezeway is organised so that the sun screening is on the outside: it is important not the have sun control under glass. I devised a system of slats set at the angle of the midday mid-winter solstice, at about 32°. The overlap from the upper slat leading louvre edge to the lower louvre trailing edge is 55°. When the summer sun reaches 55°-78° it is blocked off by the overlap of 3mm slats; but during winter, full sun enters the room. Over the northern glazing, louvres are set on the vertical plane and can tilt to any angle or fully retract.

The roof overhang, blinds, insect screens and louvred windows are like layers of clothes that you can put on or remove: the blinds can be fully retracted; the louvred adjustable windows tilt and change the light levels and control ventilation.

For the human, it is important to break down the scale of the outside and filter it to the inside. In Australia I feel I am an ant in the landscape, but in the built environment by comparison I am a giant. This is the lesson of scale. In this house the verandah is the transition zone. The insect mesh-covered walls temper the sometimes harsh light levels and soften the outlook to the landscape. There is a progression here of light level changes and scale adjustments.

This is the first building in which I had the opportunity to look at country houses and the amount of time people spend in the first 3 to 4 metres of a house. What if I could make a whole building where it feels like one is living on the edge and can smell the rain and sense changes in the air and light?

Marie enjoyed living in the house. I showed her how to operate the building, like a yacht. It's dynamic: you open up the windows and doors and tune the house for different conditions. When winter came she said: it is beautiful, and the colour of the room in the moonlight is blue. It's extraordinary. Designing with the rational, it is possible to even achieve something poetic, something that was never planned for. I didn't design for the moonlight.

The house won the Royal Australian Institute of Architects New South Wales Wilkinson and Blacket awards and the National Timber in Architecture award in the 1980s.

I bought the house and farmland in 1980. I had been coming to the region for holidays nearby: I've been interested in farming ever since my father introduced me to the Geddes and Yeoman's keyline plan on his farm.

Because of the need for additional space, I extended the house beyond the kitchen end and added a main bedroom, and also a fireplace room with views to the lake in the other wing. To make way for the fireplace room I unbolted the tallowwood verandah and moved it to its new position, took the gable off and relocated it, and reused all the louvres, doors and stairs. The new elements were fitted in between the reused and existing ones. It was the first time I could make changes to a building without wastage.

Engineer: Taylor Thomson Whitting

Ockens house
Cromer Sydney New South Wales
1977 to 1978

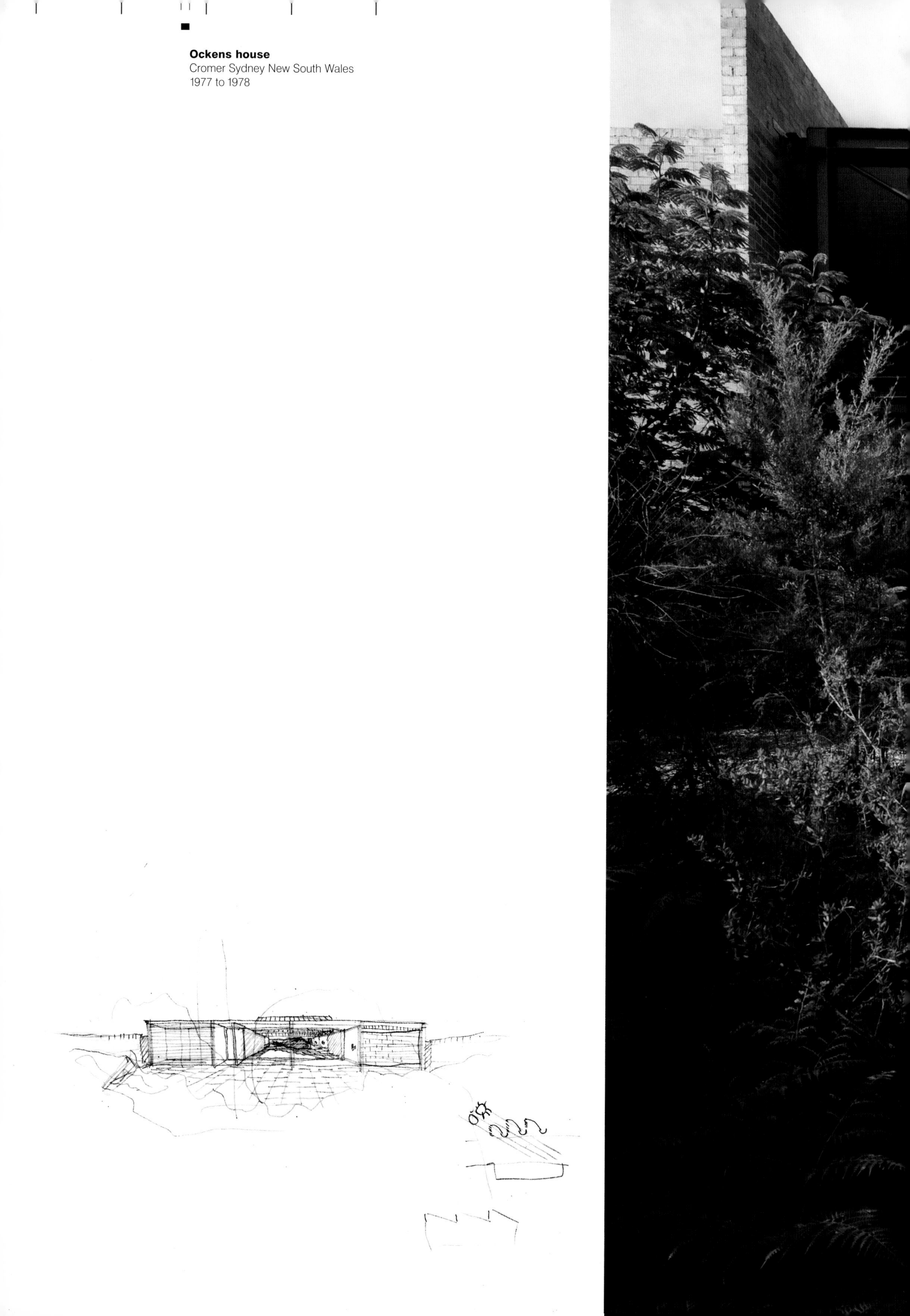

Murcutt is now treating every project as a laboratory work, an opportunity to investigate parameters for making his architecture: with this house, he reconsiders the suburban house type. Thinking laterally, he rejects the traditional suburban house (the site is a small suburban plot) and makes a courtyard house, though not one that extends to the boundaries in the way that his brother's house does; it is not the Miesian courtyard house that he explores here. The design combines two typologies: suburban house and courtyard house (giving privacy from the neighbours).

Once again, the bathroom is an internalised service core. A Murcutt bathroom is generally a utilitarian space, tightly planned and crisply detailed. Murcutt's ideal shower is naturally top-lit so the water feels like 'warm rain' and the bather feels as though she is under the sky. In all the earlier houses, the experience of bathing is primarily functional.

In this house, Murcutt remains strongly affected by Miesian proportioning systems. Lowering the ceiling achieves two significant effects: the spatial tension of compression and release (which is closer to Wright than Mies), and the late Miesian proportioning of the front elevation.

Murcutt has a sensibility for the order generated by the grid. He does not show any interest really in De Stijl-derived, Miesian spatial concepts, in which planes overlap to allow space to escape to infinity. He prefers the cave, an idea of the walls on three sides offering refuge and the opening on the fourth offering prospect. The space is static except in its connection to the land beyond.

Glenn Murcutt

The clients came to me having seen the Laurie Short house published: Karl Ockens loved its toughness and order. At the time, I was moving sideways from a steel, tough house.

The high sloping site looks down onto suburbia and north to Narrabeen Lakes. The clients wante the angle of view to take in the lakes, rather thar the houses for half a mile in front. And they did not want to see the neighbours.

The orientation is good. The north-east ocean breeze blows through the big glass doors of the first floor living spaces, through the courtyar and on through the kitchen. Each room has a vent in the roof and in the walls adjacent to the side boundaries. In the bedroom, air passes over the bed.

The walls are blank, but one looks out to the nor and the views. The sitting area has clear views to the lakes. The northern verandah plane provid a screen to the neighbours to the north, further down the hillside.

The courtyard – full of palm trees – has a raised, sun-controlled louvred glass roof. The lower roof of the court adjacent to the perimeter rooms allows ventilation between the two roof levels. By lowering the roof around the unglazed area of the courtyard and extending the level of the upper northern verandah, I achieved what reads as a low-scale first floor. Regulations require the average ceiling height to be a minimum of 2.4 metres, but I could drop it to 2.1 metres providin I maintained the average 2.4.metres across the internal courtyard space. This move considerabl reduced the height across the facade to the street. The front entrance verandah has a low head height: 2 metres. This spatial compression is released in the foyer, which rises to 4.4 metres

Light is admitted through skylights, clerestorey windows and the glass roof across the centre of the house and the bathroom. The sun control devices above the roof are adjustable elliptical industrial louvres used on factories for vertical sun control. The louvres over the study create beautiful striated sunlight and shadow patterns on the walls and floors.

Engineer: Taylor Thomson Whitting

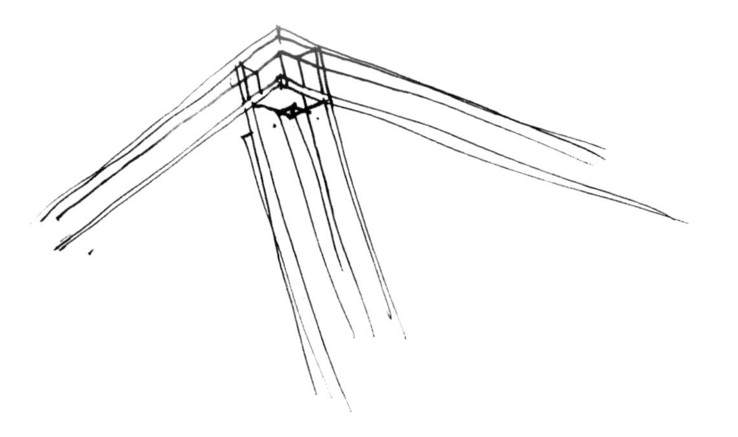

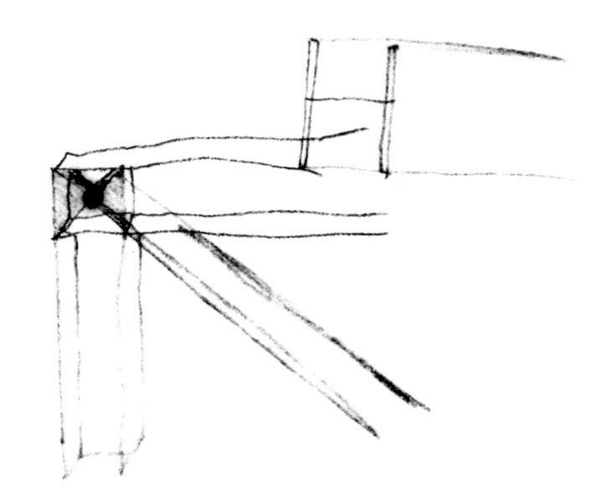

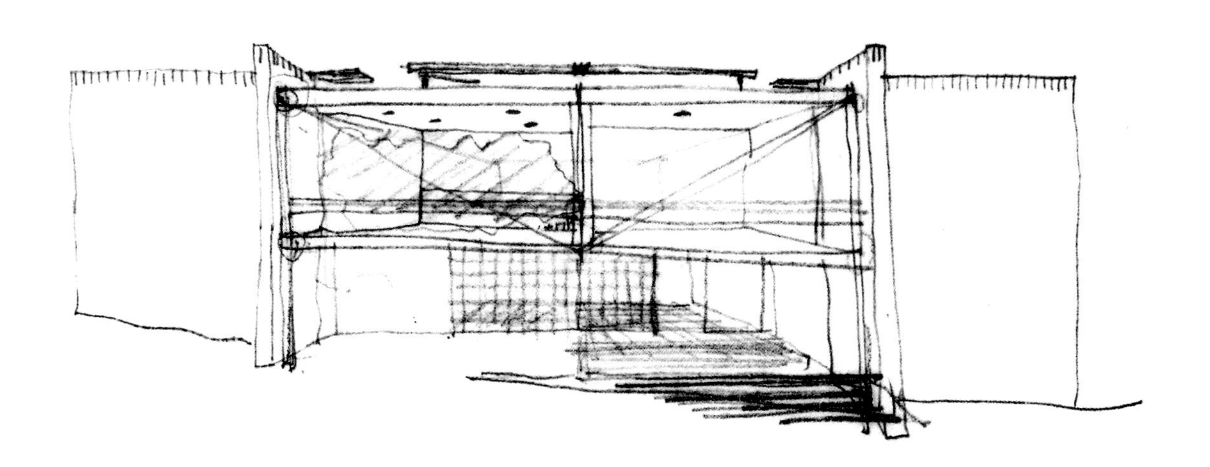

Ockens house

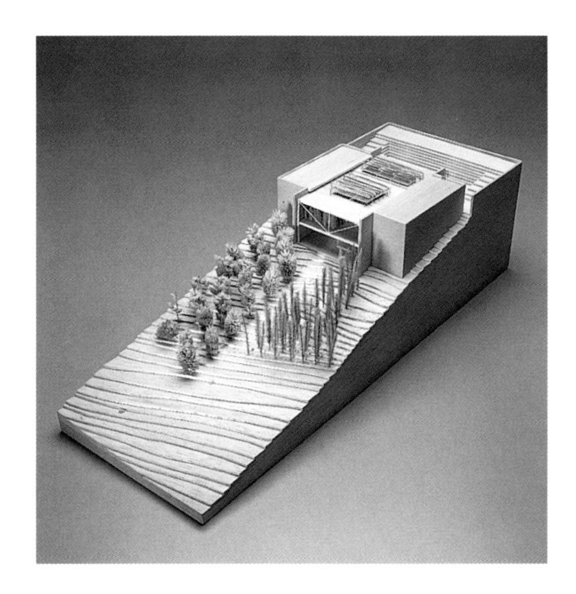

Museum of Local History and Tourism Office
Kempsey New South Wales
Stage 1: 1979 to 1982; Stage 2: 1986 to 1988

With this building, Murcutt relinquishes Mies. It is a significant design in other respects too: for so many of the issues that are importa to him, Murcutt now find solutions that are simultaneously formal and technical. For instance, the barrel vault is an even simpler roof expression than the gable: there are ideas here of minimalism and abstraction. In the big gutters and downpipes, he gives architectural expression to the way rainwater is dispatched. He also exploits every opportunity to turn the construction into a form of architectural expression based on reducing material to the minimum. Structurally, he strips the building down, using the least amount of steel, and turı that into an aesthetic of structural minimalism: fine columns, triangular mild steel gussets, mild steel bar tie rods.

There is also innovation. He reverses a vernacular method of building in Australia, brick veneer, in which the brick (which signifies 'value') is applied externally as a waterproof cladding. Murcutt puts corrugated iron on the outside, which signifies the opposite of brick ('industrial', 'low value') yet operates much more effectively in terms of waterproofing temperature control and maintenance. His aesthetics are driven not by preconceptions about the iconography of buildings but rather by making an aesthetic from rational building construction processes.

The references he makes to farm buildings are not to the way they look but to the way farmers have worked out that steel pipe is an easy way to build structural frames: the iconography of the farm shed is irrelevant. The iconography of Aboriginality is of far greater interest to Murcutt, when he discovers later that his roof profile bears resemblance to that of bark-covere structures. And again, his interest in Aboriginali is not related to the way the bark hut looks, but to the fact that these people are innately connected to the land, and seeking the simple rational solutions to the problems of shelter.

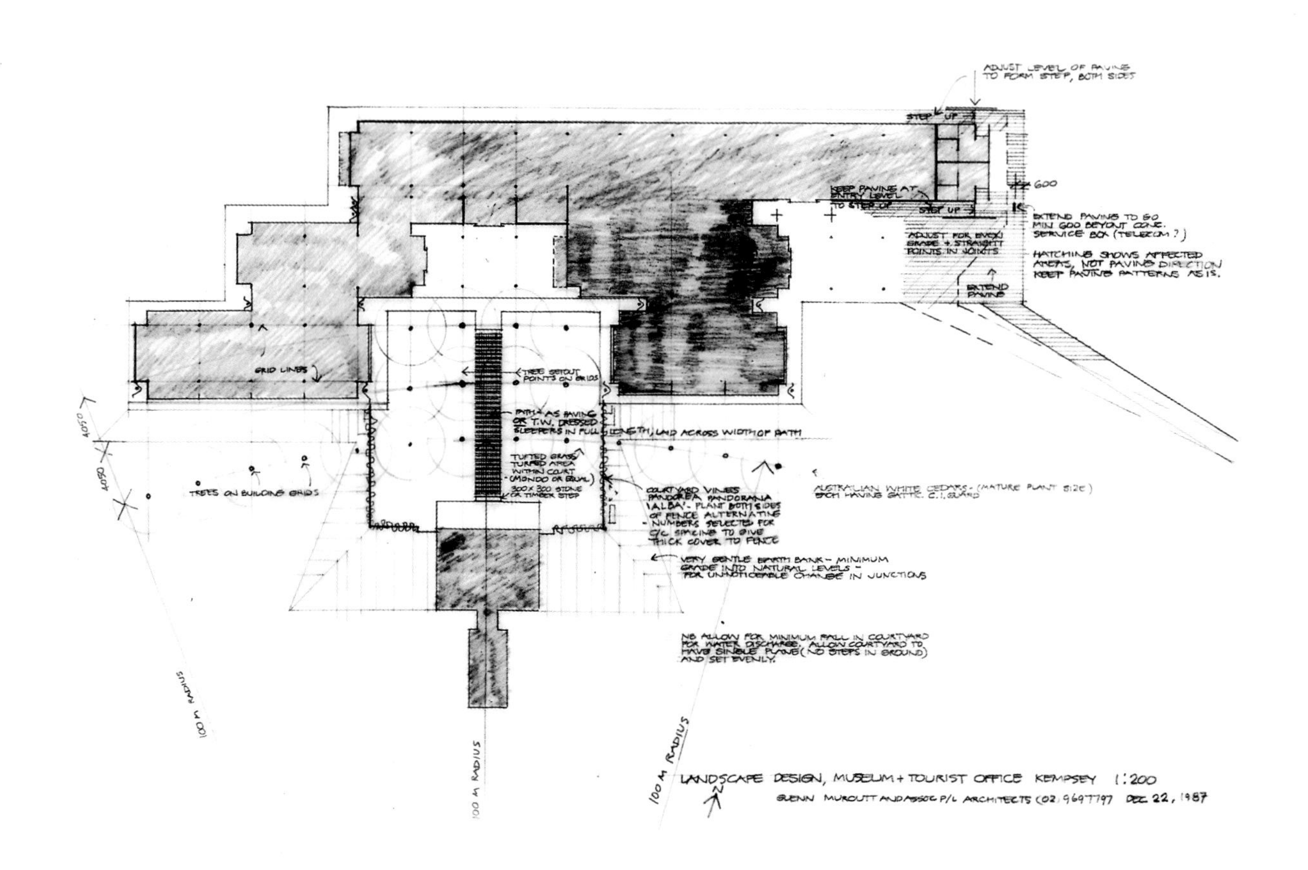

ıad been visiting Kempsey for many years. ıe local council had come to know me, ıd I also knew members of the town's various ɔmmittees of country men and women, such s Gwen Kemp, the local headmistress who also rmed. Gwen was the president of the historical useum, and the committee wanted a home r it. I told them: I have students and we an design several projects. You choose the site ıd define the brief, and I'll set the project for e semester at Sydney University. It was a nice aching project to give students experience of ɔuntry conditions. They presented their schemes the historical society.

eanwhile, the local council was aware that e historical society wanted to build a museum, ıd at the same time there was the possibility a government grant. The grant application quired a scheme, so in 1981 I agreed to act s honorary architect and develop an idea for the uilding. It included two historical houses to be assembled on the site. The complex and nding received approval. But we didn't yet have e land the museum was designed for. This site as next to the oval in the park in South Kempsey. /e were subsequently given the approvals ı use the site for Stage 1. Early in 1986, council ɔmmissioned me to develop a design for Stage which included a tourist office and extensions the museum. The plans were completed uickly, approvals given and tenders let: it was smooth job, with completion in late 1988.

ne contours of the land run east-west. There a gentle fall to the south and the site enjoys e north-easterly cooling breezes. By taking ıe Marie Short house as a model, I could build mple shed-like buildings. The region is flood-rone, so the building was designed for use as mergency accommodation.

The plan is flexible and the three independent programmes housed in the three wings can operate separately or together. The south component, the theatrette, can be used in isolation or as part of the museum or tourist office. The exhibition space is totally flexible. The 'garage' takes large machinery, such as the district's restored first fire truck, or an exhibition of historic bridal dresses.

The theatrette has to be simultaneously ventilated and blacked-out on occasions. The dark metal louvred doors and steel black-out louvres achieve this. Latticework set out from the face of the building lets in light and reduces the impact of the hot western sun. It also provides security and privacy.

The southern roof gutter of the theatrette sits above a diaphragm of patent glazing, allowing glimpses of tree tops: it is important not be completely enclosed all the time (compare with the house at Bingie Bingie). There are ideas here about sitting in the auditorium and seeing the sky and the trees, and ideas about good lighting and ventilation; and when the space is required to be blacked out, it still ventilates.

The ventilation roof system is the same as that of the Marie Short farmhouse, but the roofs are barrel vaults: it is very economical to use a single sheet of material and bend it. Cladding the exterior in galvanised iron – Zincalume – provides a very cheap waterproofing system.

The roof is a double skin. This is the first time I used corrugated iron inside as well as outside. The roof set on purlins forms flutes all the way around, allowing the build-up of hot air to clear.

The roof structure is steel pipe. It's a tin shed farming district. Farmers are adept at doing ingenious things with metal. Local farm buildings usually use pipe sections for structural steel framing systems; the steel pipe section allows complex junctions. The 75mm pipe columns read as fine elements and can be curved to form the top cord of the truss, creating the roof profile. A tension bar forms the bottom tie, and a hanging rod keeps the tie straight: very lightweight, almost under-designed, and each support column is tied to each brick nib set at the module points. The triangular bracing gussets between the pipe columns and pipe rails through the building are stiffeners; they are a measure of how lightweight the steel construction is. This is the language of farm buildings: everything cut down, stripped back.

The brickwork is single skin. The thin columns are stabilised by being tied back into the cross wall. Everything works together. It is reverse brick veneer, with the mass on the inside and waterproofing lightweight skin on the outside, and insulation between the two, protecting the mass, which becomes a thermal sink. The mass supports the lightweight steel frame inside. The structural system works in symbiosis and operates like muscles, sinews and bones.

It was necessary to increase the mass inside the buildings because there is no air-conditioning and the museum needs a generally controlled environment for the photographs, clothing and other pioneering paraphernalia on display. The ventilation system consists of Western rotary turbine roof vents, which are wind-driven air extraction units, lots of louvred openings, and high thermal mass to modify the sometimes considerable diurnal temperature variations. (The climate in the region of Kempsey is warm temperate but it can get occasionally below freezing on winter nights.) The roof vents exhaust the internal volumes and minimise any heat and humidity build-up inside. During winter, dampers in the ventilator shafts can all but close down the escape of the necessary warmed air. There are ventilation slots along the entire long facades, and horizontal louvres at doorhead height. The north facade is a diaphragm for light and ventilation. The concrete floors are pigmented brown/grey. In winter, sun penetrates, so objects needing to be screened are located in brick alcoves. The sun in winter warms the walls and the slab and limits the temperature differentials.

During construction of the museum, at night time some of the local Aboriginal people spent time in the incomplete building. They would light a fire on the earth and spend nights under the protection of the unlined outer roof. I was told they liked the shape of the roof form. In 1988, I was shown photographs of Aboriginal bark shelters, and the roof of the museum has almost the same profile as a sheet of draped bark.

Stage 1 of the museum was designed at about the same time as the Ball-Eastaway house.

Engineer: Engineering Department, Kempsey Shire Council

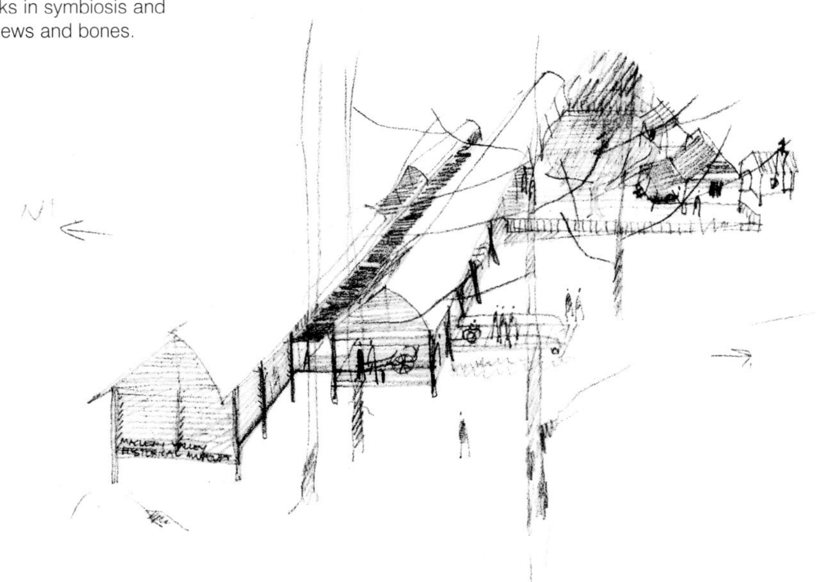

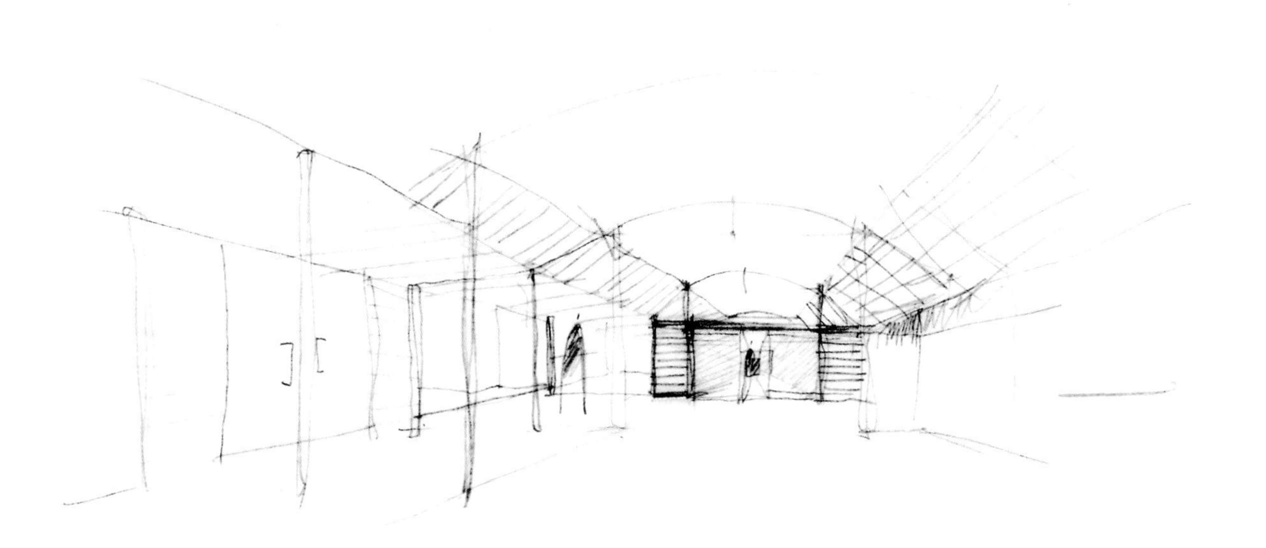

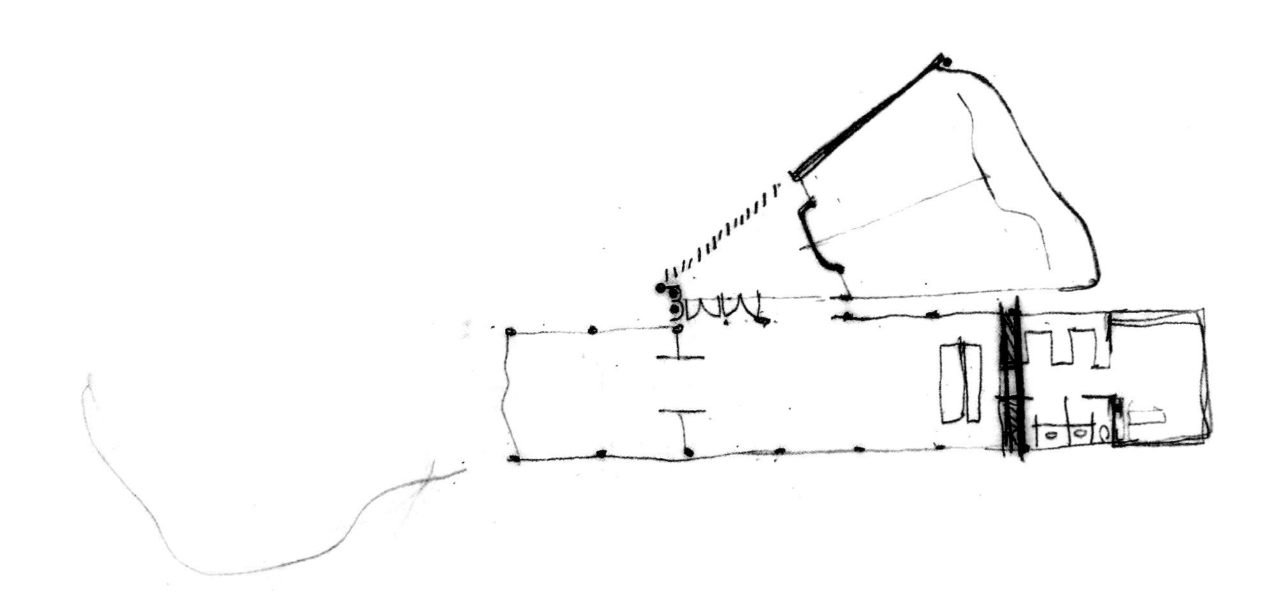

Ball-Eastaway house
Glenorie New South Wales
1980 to 1983

This house reveals the mature Murcutt.

In the Kempsey Museum, designed at around the same time, he is thinking hard about using the minimal amount of steel and articulating that frugality as an aesthetic, an idea still not fully resolved in the Museum. What now pushe him towards formal resolution in articulating this minimalism is an idea of the edges of things feathering down, a phenomenon that he observes in the way plants fine down towards their extremities. This is a formal idea that is appropriate to steel construction: the material implies an idea of tension, attenuation stretching. Feathering or fining at the edges gives an expression of this sense of stretching the metal. Murcutt creates the impression that the material could not have been reduced any further structurally: it seems to be right at its limits.

He pursues this minimalist, attenuated aesthetic in other ways. His details are ever mo crisp, light-handed, finer, drawn-out. From now on, all his buildings will have this delicacy You cannot imagine quite how they stand up: they look as if they could fly away.

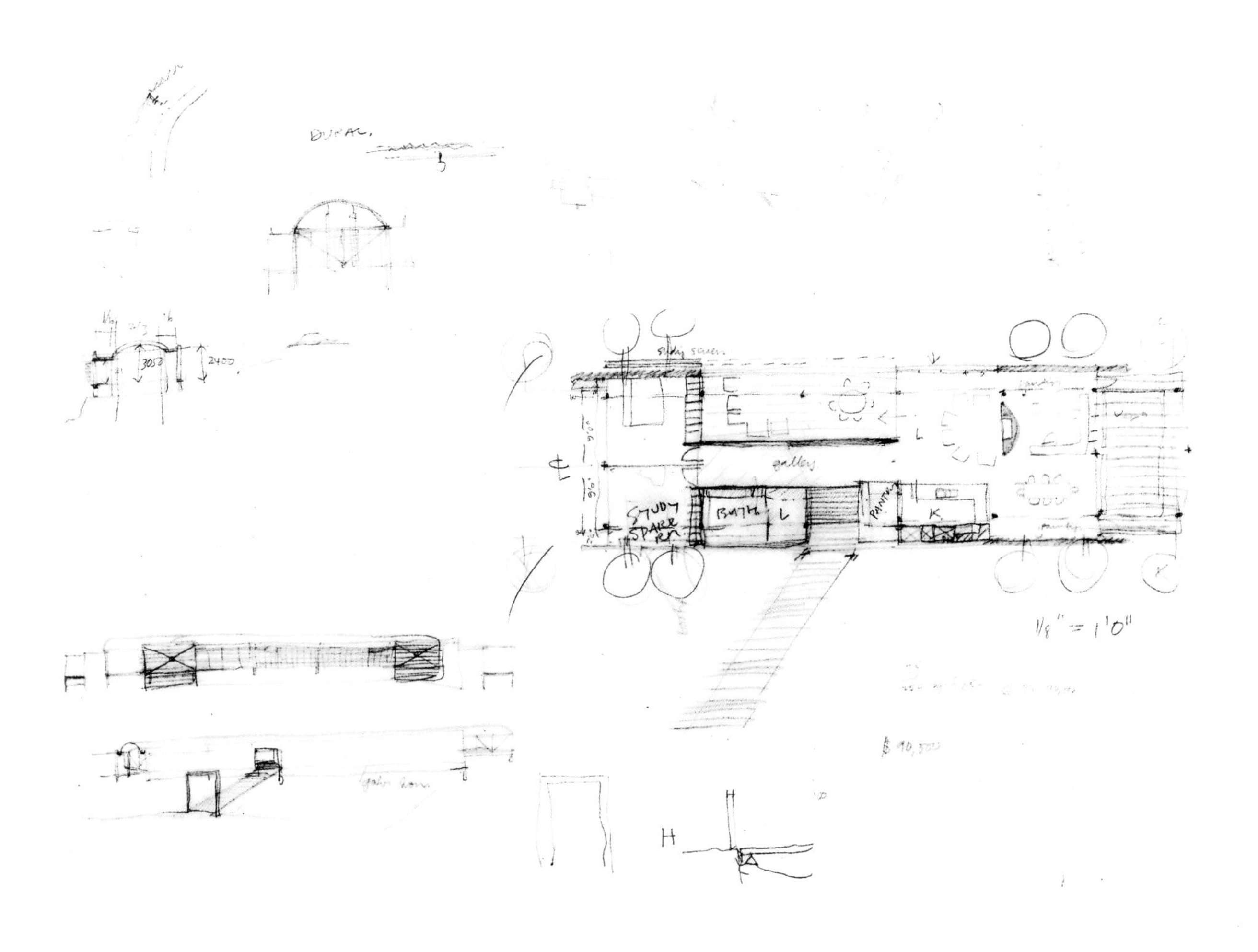

is house was designed for two painters. e now designed houses for a number of painters. d Ball was not long back from New York. Both and Lyn Eastaway were to relocate from their ner-city house and studios to an isolated bushland e in the area of the Hawkesbury River on the ndstone plateau a little to the north of Sydney. s tough country and has severe bush fires through e area in summer. Electricity is available but ere is no water. It can be very warm in summer nd cool in winter but generally enjoys a temperate mate. The site is ten hectares of beautiful bushland a high sandstone ledge with yellow bloodwoods, acias, grevilleas, banksias and hakeas. It receives me good cooling sea breezes.

ne house is like a building that has docked, put it its bridge like a ship, and is ready to go away. ried to reduce the impact of this building on the nd. It is set clear of the ground and makes inimal connection with it. We drilled 100mm holes r the column supports, filled the holes around e steel support columns with cement, and added ushed rock to the cement for the top section. is difficult to see where we have done the boring; nd if you took the house away, you would hardly now where it had been.

ne house 'slides' along a rock shelf just below large shelf of sandstone. For the final siting, e builder made a string profile of the plan, and ur people held the corners to ensure all flora as retained and the support points in relation the rock shelving were appropriate. There was o destruction of plants.

ne construction is fire-resistant, with large ardwood members for the support of floors. xposed timber members are painted with fire-esistant paint. There is a sprinkler system, and ater storage tanks are located next to the tudios; the water pumps are under the house. ne sprinklers on the ridge spray across the roof rea and gutters, and sprinklers along the eaves pray the sides of the building and the urrounding bush. The system delivers inundation. dditionally, the water can be reused to fill fire-ghting knapsacks: by placing a plumber's lug in the outlet end of the rainwater pipes, ne 'used' roof water can be retained. Releasing ne plug allows stored water to be collected in uckets to fill fire-fighting equipment.

here can be long periods without rain, and then deluge. The eucalyptus leaf is a phenomenal locker of rainwater pipes. Over three months the ccumulated leaves weave a fine mat, and most raditional gutters and downpipes don't work. On this roof, the leaves are tipped vertically via ne 45°-wide cone truncation at the top of the ownpipe from the 1-metre-wide gutter and go traight through the downpipe: there are no lockages. The water moves down centrifugally nd a beautiful, bird-like nest of leaves is eposited on the ground.

Why a box gutter? It's not just a water collection ystem. It's as much about the space, the section. The box gutter extends the column-defined space o provide alcove areas for hanging small paintings. Here the lower scale and columns define spaces nd allow each painting to have its own place. n contrast, the entry hall gallery provides a larger pace with higher walls where a painting of 6 by 3 metres can hang. This area extends into the lcove/box gutter space, allowing people to stand nd view larger works in their entirety. You can see a painting in a gallery, but here I wanted to change he scale. It was also an experiment to define a space with another quality – compare it with he Kempsey Museum section: instead of holding ne space, it is expanded.

The size of the gutter is in proportion to the part of the roof that it services.

The client required a place for meditation. A space was developed overlooking the valley. The deck looks westish; the aspect on the other verandah is north.

The only timber in the house was for the floor construction and the flooring. The rest of the house is steel. The wall section is steel studs with plasterboard lining, clad externally, like the roof, in corrugated iron.

The side walls project beyond the enclosure of the house to reveal the volume as a series of planes that develop the spaces. I always considered the finishing of the ends of walls difficult. Turning a corner in corrugated iron can be so clumsy. In this case I've stopped the corrugated iron short of the ends to sit proud of the wall frame, clearly expressing the wall thickness and fabrication: this makes plain that which is structure and that which is cladding.

A tough landscape produces delicate flora: plants that grow in shallow leached soils, where rains intersperse with long periods of drought, develop in such a way that the leaves and branches feather towards their extremities. I was interested in how one can make buildings finer at the edges. The feathering in this house is expressed by tapering the steel purlins, by the deck to the north where the floor peels away at the point closest to the ground, also by expressing/revealing the construction of the floor, and by the floor joists that feather to their edges. There are little 'ears' on the top of the box gutters, like the Kempsey Museum, which is an attempt to articulate edges.

I am making many building elements as light as possible, similar to a machine/shed aesthetic and language. This is becoming increasingly refined. I am pushing the formal possibilities of how one deals with the edges of building elements. I used to design and build model aircraft and boats and build 4-metre racing skiffs. Both disciplines develop an awareness of the importance of edges.

Assistant on this house: Graham Jahn

Engineer: Taylor Payne McDonald

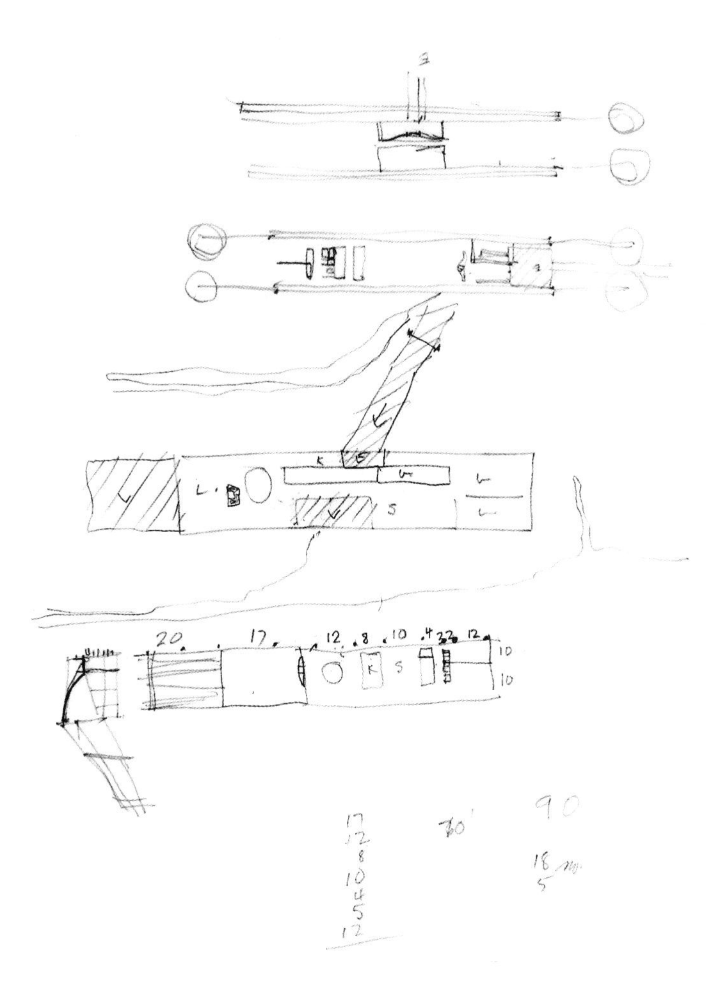

Fredericks house
Jamberoo New South Wales
1981 to 1982

This is the latest timber-framed house Murcutt has designed (aside from the little guesthouse at Kempsey, which is a remodelling of an existing timber-framed structure).

The quest for precision and perfection in construction is essential to Murcutt. It is evident in the way he details his buildings. In conversation he observes that the level of carpentry in the house is so fine and the jointing details so exquisitely resolved that the workmanship is almost closer to timber boat building than house construction. With the exceptional level of precision craftsmanship in this house, he is able to perfect his aesthetic of timber construction.

Around this time he calculates that he can achieve such fine precision in timber construction only rarely, since it is a very expensive form of craftsmanship and there are few left who can still produce it. Timber by its nature is not a precise material. It moves constantly. It is difficult to cut precisely: tolerances of many millimetres are generally accepted in timber framing. But Murcutt knows that he can go to any small steel fabricator and attain precision with tolerances down to about a millimetre, and it is a much cheaper system than timber. Consequently he shifts across into the development of steel framing as the structural system for most of his buildings since the Fredericks house. This move towards steel is driven as much by economics as aesthetics. Most of his houses do not have luxury budgets but are built to a price.

The Fredericks house is one of very few buildings by Murcutt where an upper level overlooks the main habitable spaces (the Muston house in Seaforth of 1988–92 is another). This is not something that he sets out to do: the overlooking upper level here results from a modification set by the clients when they decided to live in the house themselves and needed more volume. Murcutt provides the necessary additional space, but one senses an element of reluctance on his part. Why should this be so?

The upper level overlooking habitable space introduces a dynamic spatial condition that disturbs the serenity Murcutt typically seeks in his buildings. He states that serenity results from 'dimension', that is, the generosity of spatial conditions. Yet there is more than the length of a space or the vista it encompasses at work here. The serenity of Murcutt's buildings results fundamentally from a static spatial model, that of the cave or cell, which allows a sense of refuge and prospect to be experienced at the same time, and which he develops to enable both conviviality and withdrawal to take place, even within the same volume. With an upper level that looks down onto habitable space, this duality (communal activity centred on the kitchen, dining and hearth areas contrasted with the ability of the individual to find isolation and comfort in the cell) is lost. The space is in a constant state of 'convivial' or 'communal' mode owing to the capacity for it always to be overlooked.

Murcutt works fundamentally in plan and section. In planning his buildings he is constantly drawn between the tension of two extremes: on one hand is the universalising quality of the grid, and on the other the particularising of each place as a bay within the grid. The play between these two spatial conditions – the long view (prospect) and the refuge – is basically what interests Murcutt in spatial terms. He has no desire for the dynamic vertical diagonal present in the work of Le Corbusier or Charles Moore.

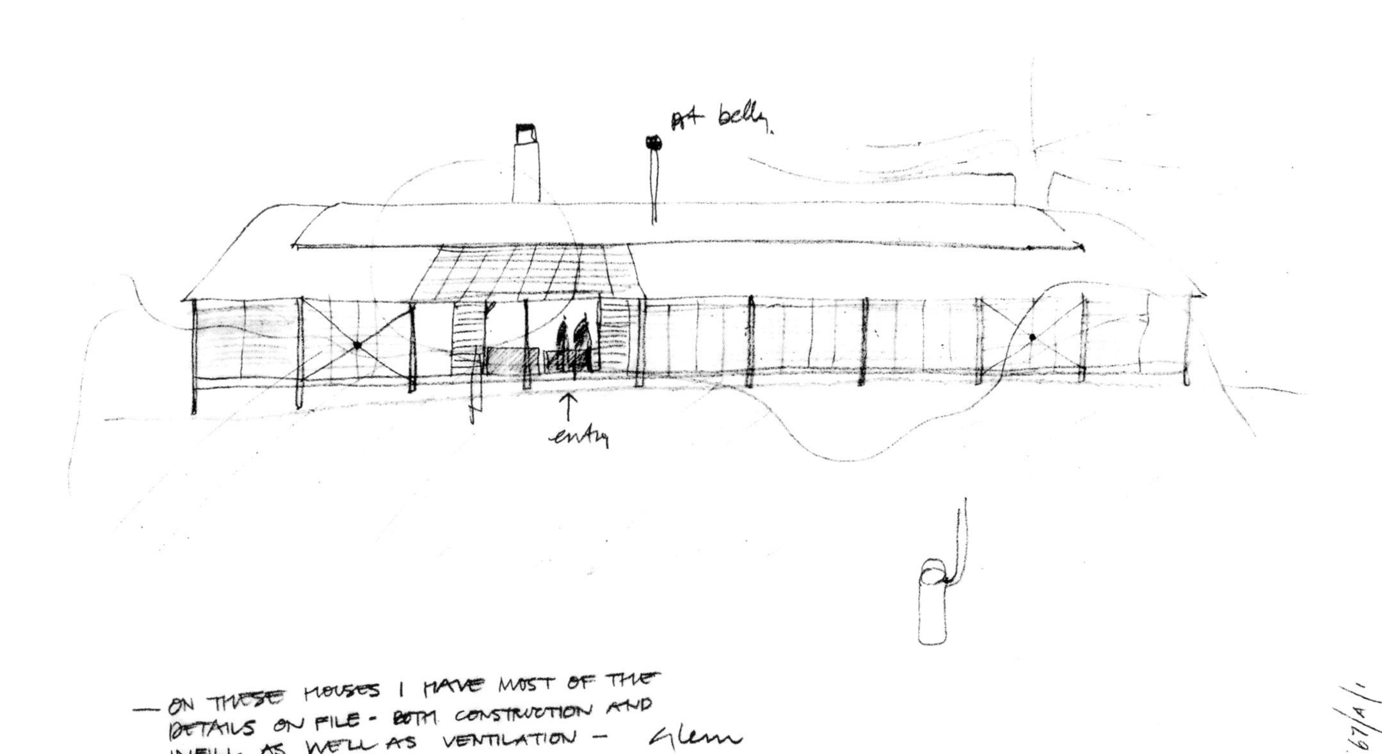
entry
— ON THESE HOUSES I HAVE MOST OF THE DETAILS ON FILE - BOTH CONSTRUCTION AND INFILL AS WELL AS VENTILATION — Glenn
— TO DOCUMENT THIS, I WOULD NEED 2-3 WEEKS - IT'S WORTHWHILE I FEEL —
G. MURCUTT
OCT 81
FREDERICKS
PXD 728/Roll 67/A/1

ıis house is built around an existing fireplace ɔimney left standing from an old farmhouse ılldozed in the 1940s. The north-facing site is ɜautiful, with an escarpment behind and good ılcanic soils. It's a remarkable location, ırrounded by New South Wales south coast ıinforests. The outlook to the north has long-stance valley views.

ıe clients responded to the Kempsey farmhouse ıd both the Mount Irvine houses. They very ıuch liked the idea of a timber house. The matic conditions are different from both ɜmpsey and Mount Irvine. In summer the site ıtches the prevailing north-easterly sea breezes; ınters can be cool.

ıtially, the house was designed for the edericks' dairy farm manager. Circumstances ıanged, a house was purchased for the farm anager, and the Fredericks pursued the design this house for themselves. I was well down the ıck with the design when their new requirements ɜcessitated changes such as extra space, ɔssibly above the second bedroom, and also the ırage/laundry spaces. These changes affected ıe profile of the house because of the need for ıanding room in the loft and space for a stair.

A diaphragm to the sky in the north-facing roof plane of the fireplace area brings winter sunshine into a large part of the room. On a cold day you sit in front of a big fire on the southern side, with the sun from the north pouring onto your back and also lighting up the fireplace breast.

The same sunshading principles as used in Kempsey are applied, but the blades tilt to provide an additional control mechanism. The blinds are on the outside. The window sunshading system consists of external adjustable aluminium louvres which pull up, tilt, drop, turn: it's very flexible. The sunshading panels are 3 metres wide and 2 metres high. Behind them I used double-hung windows rather than louvres; I thought louvres would leak too much air. The windows have seals and standard clip-on insect screens.

This house has a very ordinary plan. It's a one-sided corridor, like a railway carriage. The plan is 5 metres wide, a metre wider than many of my plans. Making the house 4 metres wide takes a certain courage. It works only by developing spaces which are pushed out beyond the 4-metre-wide space and framing system, such as bay windows and sleeping alcoves. (Compare it with the Marika-Alderton house.) The good thing about a bay at the ends of a disciplined, parallel framing system is that this turns the corner, instead of being chopped at what can be read as an almost arbitrary point. The purlins which taper at the eaves, and the eaves overhang, also help the termination. The same feathering occurs with the Ball-Eastaway house; it expresses: this is the end.

I often speak about being like a human ant in the landscape and a giant in the built environment. To observe, to know about place, we have to stand apart from it. A building removes us slightly from place, yet locates us within it. It is an existentialist idea of sharpening awareness, exposing people to things they hadn't perceived before.

The proportioning system in my buildings results from several factors: human scale, the scale of the landscape, available and appropriate use of materials, prospect and refuge, working with the site contours, the sun, wind, water, and more.

I use the post and beam structural frame for the long sides of this house as a formal ordering device. Combined with a platform, the system defines the framing of the landscape. To me it's a wonderful system which is really simple. It defines the edges. It establishes scale to the space one occupies.

I love buildings with order; I find chaotic buildings too close to my real nature. I am an untidy human; without a frame of reference, I'm like a bagperson. I get great pleasure in having a frame of reference that establishes what I can and cannot do. The zones developed by framing allow an ease of order yet can provide great flexibility. It's like structure in music, an order which the composer will develop as layers of complexity that add richness within the established order.

The southern side of the Fredericks house is almost all timber. There are few windows, only slit windows serving the kitchen and bathroom. There are windows to the eastern view, and floor-to-ceiling windows along the whole of the northern facade. Construction is timber frame with boarding both sides, well insulated. The structure is ironbark and the cladding western red cedar. The inside lining is pine.

The maximum span for a timber beam carrying floor loads is only a little more than 3 metres. Beams start to deflect under their own weight when spans exceed this.

The floor is cork on timber flooring inside, and boards on the verandahs. The cork floor is excellent insulation. These days I use tung oil and wax on timber floors. I am moving away from polyurethanes as much as possible. Tung oil gives a good seal and allows the full grain of the timber to be expressed. Wax has to be applied about every six months – whereas the polyurethane lasts about two years in a kitchen area before it requires sanding and refinishing. Tung oil and wax is an old system; it's what we used to do.

This house is like a boat: every rib is necessary. In North Alaska the Eskimos use driftwood in making their extraordinarily fine kayaks. By stretching animal skins over the frames and tensioning the skins they have developed a supremely beautiful, minimal structure. This pushing of elements to their limits is the ultimate. It occurs in grass, bamboo, reeds, trees, spiders' webs and the like. The immense cantilevers of the Moreton Bay fig are remarkable. Their joints are flexible to absorb varying wind pressures, on the same principle that aircraft wings need to be flexible.

This house takes my timber houses to another level of finesse. The workmanship is extraordinary: it won a national award for the builder.

Assistant on this house: Wendy Lewin

Engineer: James Taylor and Associates

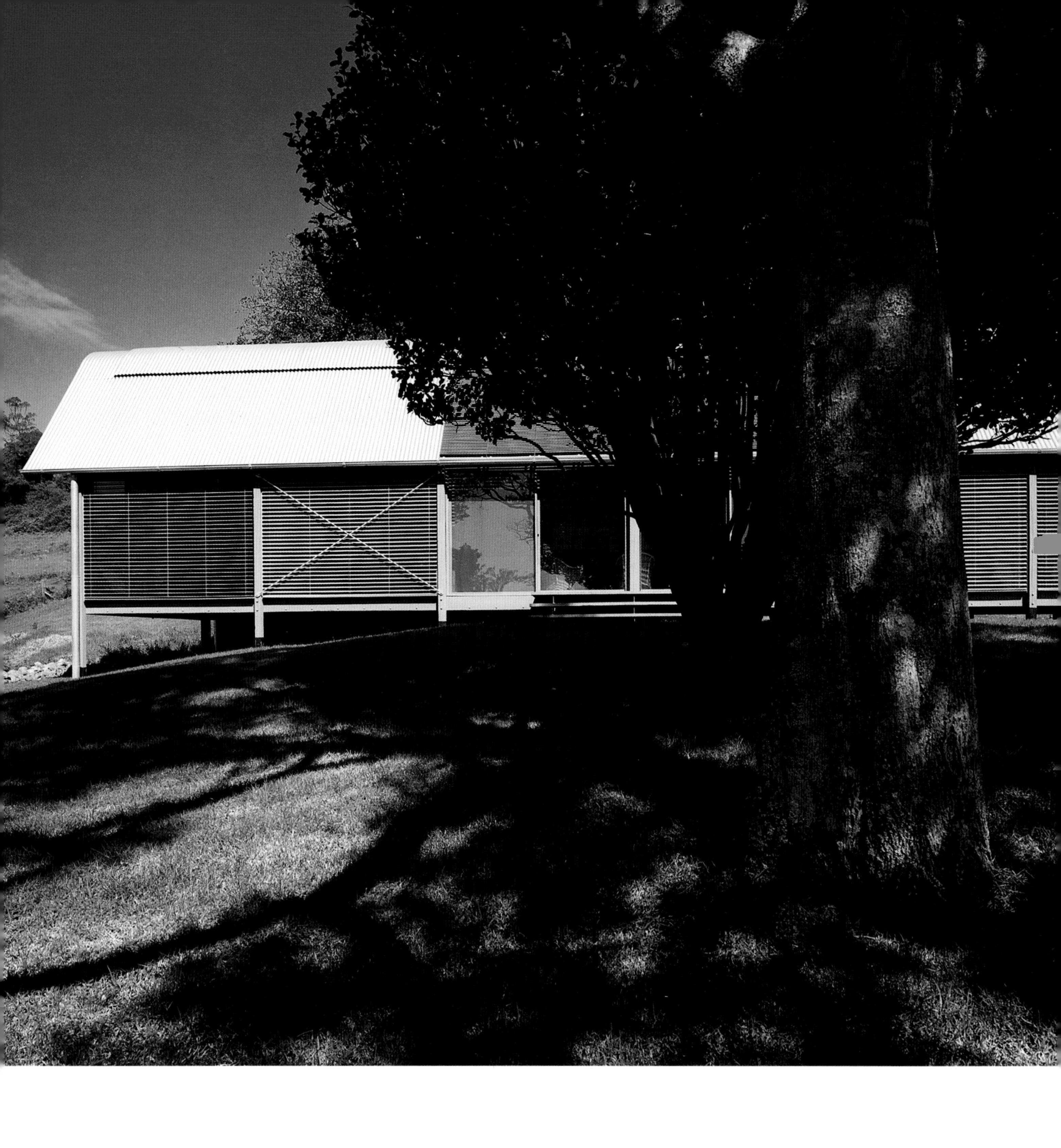

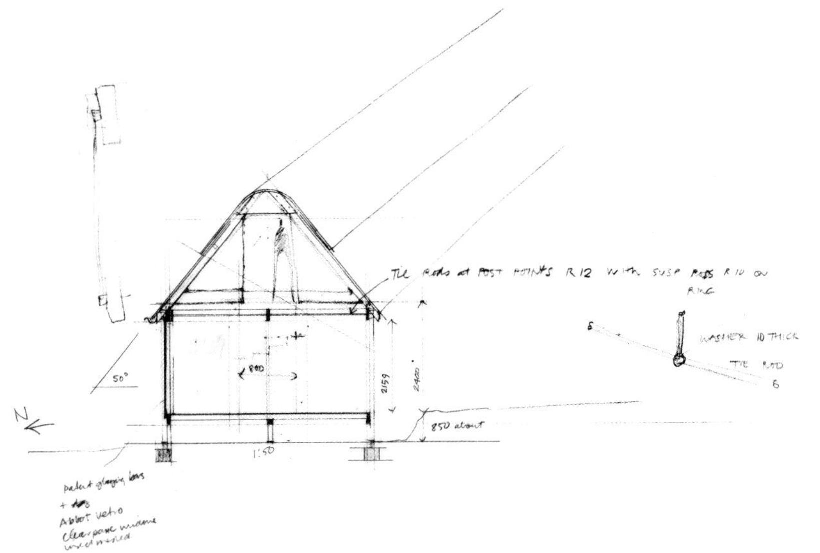
TIE RODS at POST POINTS R12 WITH SUSP RODS R10 ON RING
WASHER 10 THICK
TIE ROD
50°
800
2159
2400
850 about
N
1:50

Magney house
Bingie Bingie New South Wales
1982 to 1984

In the Kempsey Museum, Murcutt strips the structure back so far that he needs gusset plates to stabilise the junctions at the pipe column roof beams. The consequence is that the column-beam junction begins to assume a three-dimensional, spatial quality. Murcutt develops this idea in the Bingie Bingie house by attenuating the gussets into struts. He describes the result as 'skeletal', but it is actually more treelike: branches supporting leaves of iron. This is a clever detail: the eaves struts support a purlin, and the rigid corrugated iron sheet (rather than a further steel member) is used to triangulate the eaves structure. The struts are not on the same plane as the beams; here Murcutt is seeing the struts not only as utilitarian structure but also as spatial definers.

This vignette is pure Murcutt: as soon as he resolves functional or structural issues, he starts to give them an aesthetic reading in order to express the ideas of the building. The aesthetic here expresses not an idea of structure so much as place: gull wings, wind blowing, being open to the sky.

It is only in the project for his mother's house that Murcutt tests the Miesian idea of De Stijl space, with its overlapping planes that permit space to escape to infinity. But it is a spatial concept that he is never really wedded to, because fundamentally he is committed to the more Scandinavian idea of refuge and prospect. This produces space that tends to be static, bounded on three sides, open on the fourth to the prospect: the cave or monastic cell as refuge. Here Murcutt uses the structural grid to define each of these refuge volumes in the house. This spatial ordering is apparent also in the early works, but in the Bingie Bingie house it becomes a very clear way of articulating each place within a house. Also, he is now shifting away from the Miesian idea of the services as dividers between public and private zones and moving increasingly towards a more Kahnian idea of servant and served spaces. Murcutt clearly defines the circulation corridor and the services in this house: they have their own roof and their own minor expression in the section. The served spaces occupy the principal volume. While the roof defines the servant and served relationship, it is also the product of aerofoil design to control air movement within the house and to cope with the high winds.

Murcutt recognises that each building is a laboratory work, and he notes that this house is a chance to explore the skeletal frame. He is also testing air movement across the form of the roof. In this very windy location, the design of the skylight along the south wall, with its adjustable cross-ventilation, finely tunes the building. Murcutt is now able to control air movement consummately, setting up the systems that allow inhabitants to operate the house optimally.

Glenn Murcutt

This house pulls together ideas from earlier work; it also moves into new areas of thinking for me. The Fredericks house at Jamberoo clarifies a series of climatic, siting and spatial concerns. With this house I explore a formal poetic on the skeletal frame. The earlier houses were more related to the Miesian idea of structure as frame defining 'universal' space. Here there is a liberation in the frame through the section and roof form.

The site is five hours' drive south from Sydney on the coast. There are beautiful rocks and granite outcrops. There used to be cattle, but since their removal the native plants are growing back. A lake is to the north, the Pacific Ocean to the east, and mountains to the west. During summer the winds come from the sea, both north-east and south-east, tempering the heat. Winter brings cold south-westerly winds from the nearby snowfields.

The site is exposed and tough. The toughness appealed greatly to me, and I was excited by the prospect of designing a building responding to a landscape that was different from any I had worked with.

My clients and I walked all over the land looking for the right location; they said it was like water divining. We chose a flatter area rather than the most obvious place for a view: not on the top of the hill but on the brow – the approach to site selection advocated by Frank Lloyd Wright.

My clients had been camping on the site for years and they didn't want to lose the tent quality: lots of light, a minimal structure, and – like a tent – no formal entry. In a tent the occupier is vulnerable. At such a remote site, the occupier of a house is also vulnerable. But actually it's the arrivee who should feel vulnerable, not the occupier. The site is well removed from the public road. Visitors approaching the house by car are aware of being observed. On arrival it is not clear how to enter the house, but almost immediately the visitors are met and received.

The house is designed with one zone for the parents and the other zone for guests or family. The parents' section is to the east. In effect the plan works as two apartments, each with its ow kitchen and bathing facilities, sharing a commo verandah area open onto sitting, dining and kitchen spaces – the verandah thereby hugely extending the daytime living spaces.

At an early stage of the design process I sensec the scale of this landscape was much larger tha the scale of the sites at Kempsey and Jamberoo By using steel I realised the module could be expanded to 5.4 metres, increasing the scale of the building in response to the larger scale of th landscape.

I planned for the northern view and light. From t kitchen one perceives the topography as a sectic the hill and the land falling to the lake. The roof acknowledges the falling ground line. The angle of the roof struts is set to suit the equinox sun angle. Between seasons, blinds (which are s from the floor to the doorhead transoms) contro the sun; in winter they can be lifted to allow the sun to penetrate deeply into the body of the house; this system is used in many of my buildin It was important to carry clear glazing above the doors in order to see the sky and observe the weather changes.

This house departs from the segmented curves and pitched roof geometry to investigate curves drawing wind patterns to develop the section. I had not done a free-form curve previously. It ca be wondrous to encompass in the section of the building the site falling away to the north and the big sky.

The Kempsey Museum roof is steel, and the Ball-Eastaway house has a tubular curved sectic Here it's the Kempsey structural system taken forward. The tube pipes give the structural sectic But I was not certain how to line the interior side of the roof. In 1975 I had done an alteration in Mosman where some plasterboard sheets were left outside overnight. They had sagged, then it rained and the sag had increased and set. I realised that I could wet plasterboard and rewc it. I started experiments and found the sheets would not bend as well along the short axis as t long for a tight radius. The plasterboard sheets were fully immersed in water, then put on the underside of each purlin and screwed while wet. When dry, the sheets were set to the form, then removed and glued and screwed finally into positic

The roof profile is lifted off the transom datum. It is airy and light, like gulls' wings. The building possesses a tent-like quality in its lightness. It is a house where one goes to bed early and gets up at sunrise.

The zone developed above the southern bathing and kitchen functions admits south lighting and gave me the opportunity to develop a vent system. This horizontal vent set at the doorhead height encourages a very efficient air flow throug the house in summer. On really cold days with vents shut down, the spaces are static air cul de sacs which are filled with sun.

ere is a lot of glass to the north: I wanted to bring sky into the house. I also worked on thermal nfort. As in the Kempsey Museum, I used erse brick veneer for thermal reasons. The dark y tiled concrete floor is bathed in sun in winter; akes the sting out of the cold. Concrete is ood thermal mass when insulated. The open has a heat exchange cavity, providing a fairly cient form of heating. The external blinds help luce heat loss, and the potential is there for er insulated blinds. However, it's amazing how rm the house is with the present installation.

ents always play an important part in the sign process. When I design in front of them, y must work hard and make decisions. Finite king drawings can be intimidating because ents can feel they can't change them. But my awings generally are as rough as bags. I make m not to seduce clients but to get them thinking: ere is always room in them to imagine, and ople feel they can make changes and really y what they think.

gineer: James Taylor and Associates

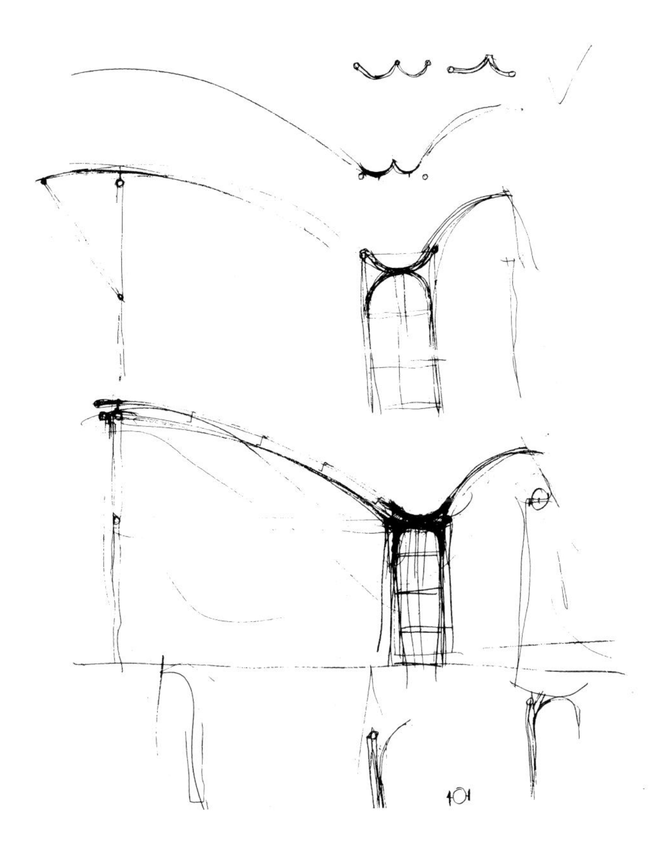

Magney house

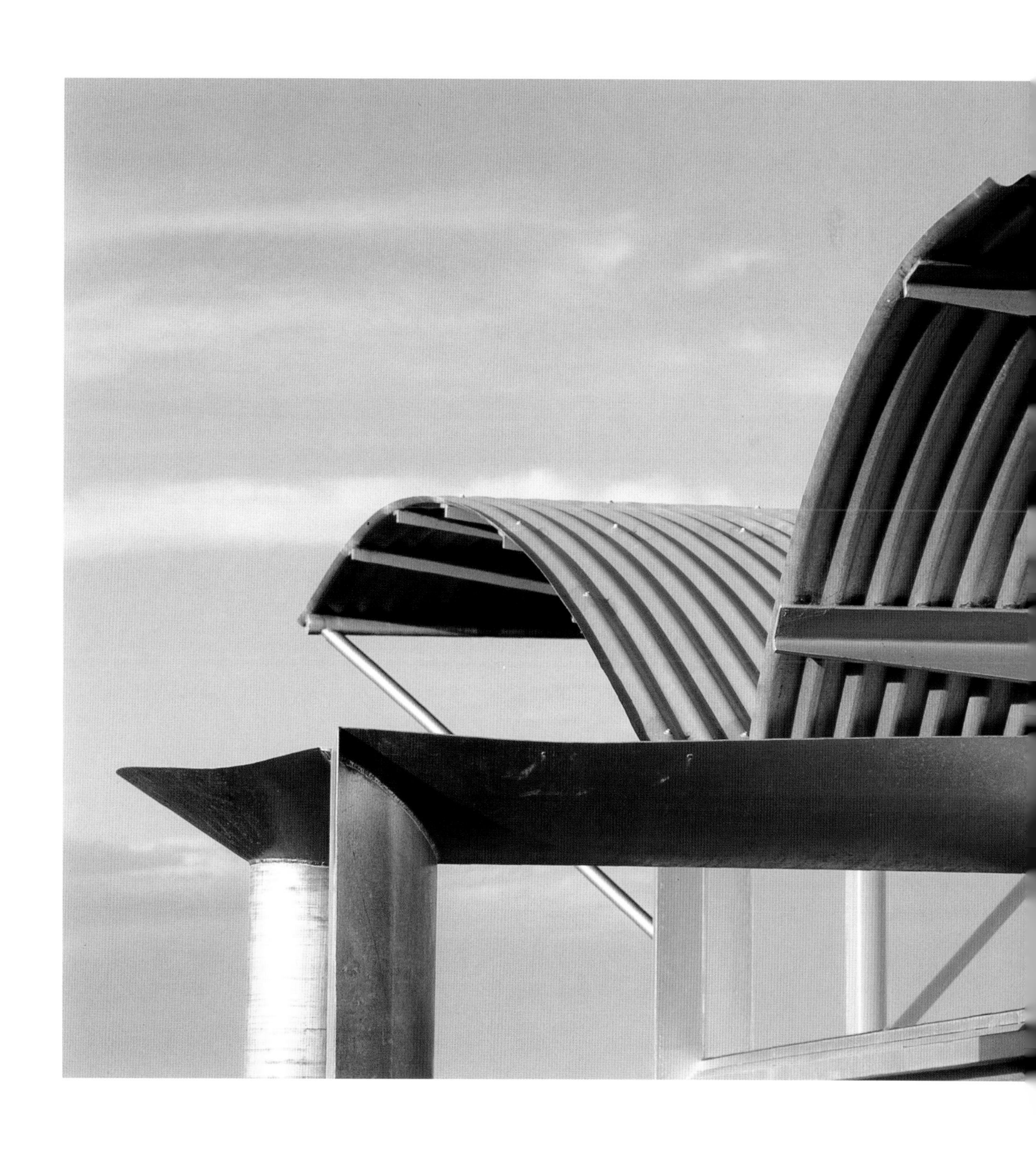

Magney house

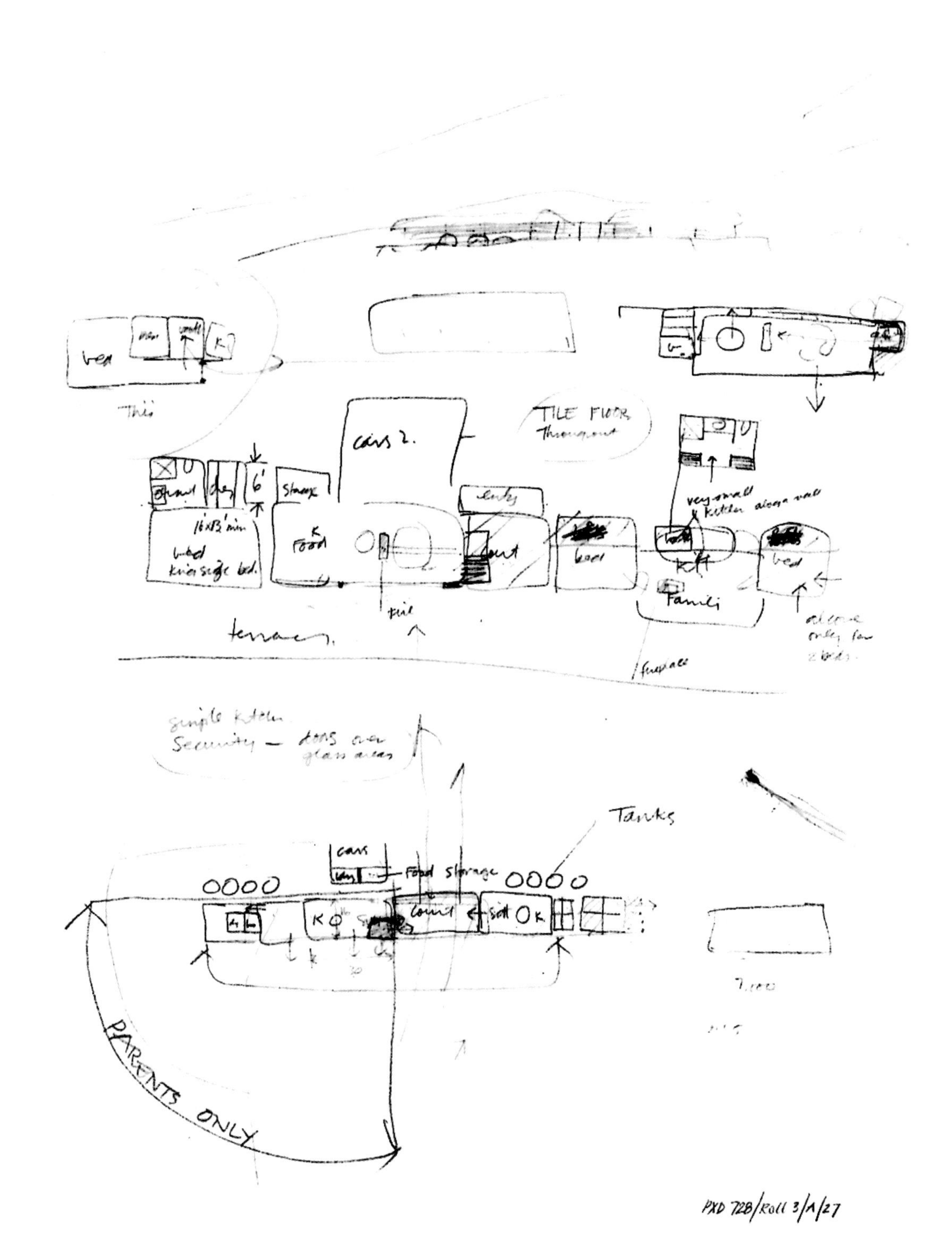

Aboriginal Alcoholic Rehabilitation Centre
Kempsey New South Wales
1983 to 1985 (unbuilt)

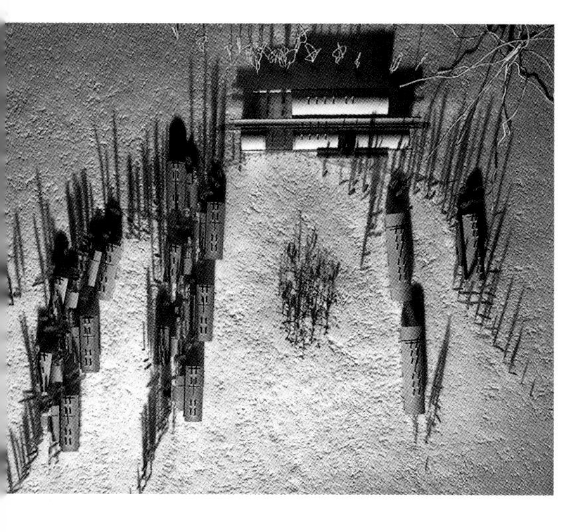

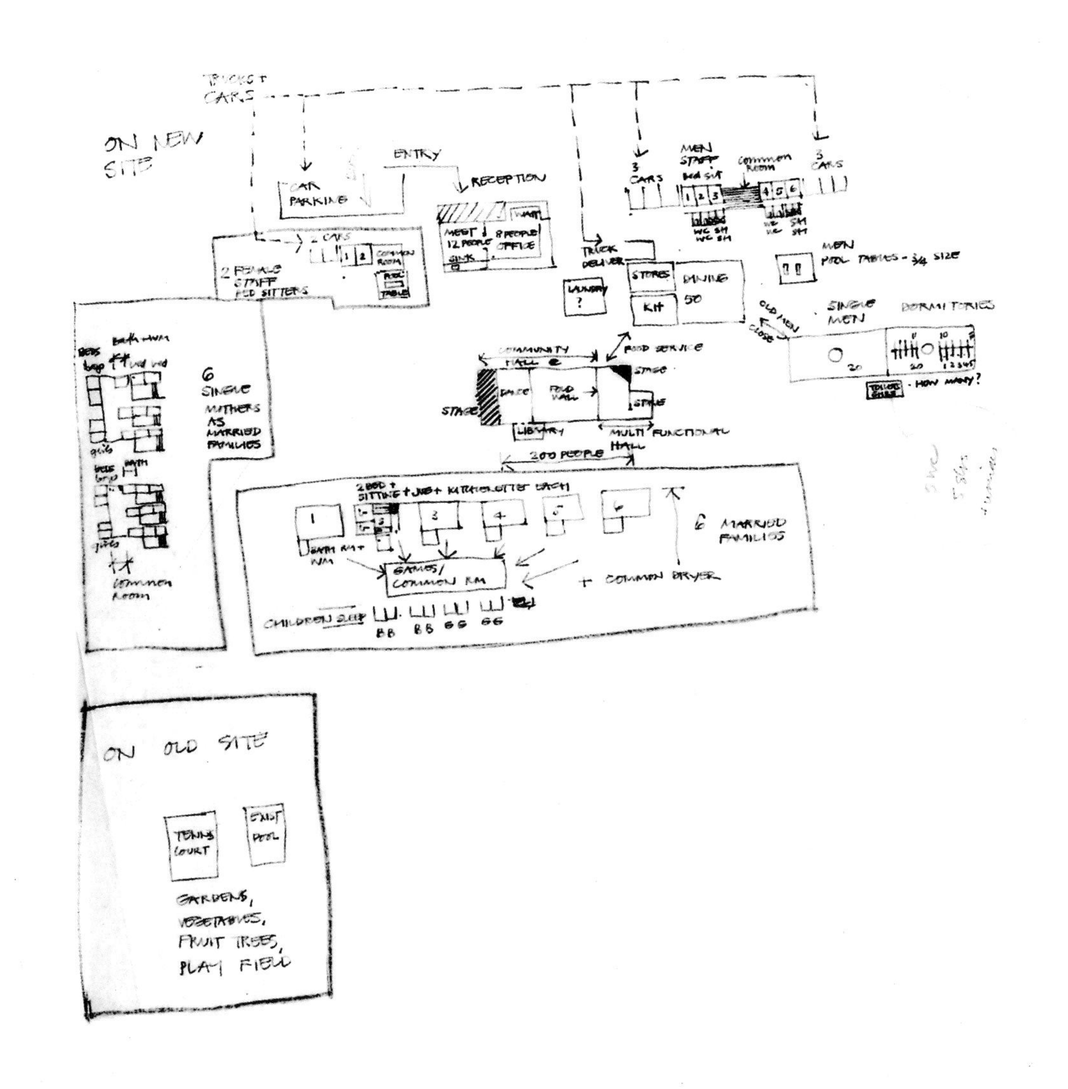
ON NEW SITE
TRUCKS + CARS
ENTRY
CAR PARKING
RECEPTION
MEET 12 PEOPLE
OFFICE
2 CARS
2 FEMALE STAFF BED SITTERS
COMMON ROOM
3 CARS
MEN STAFF BED SIT
TRUCK DELIVER
STORES
DINING 50
KIT
LAUNDRY ?
SINGLE MEN
DORMITORIES
MEN POOL TABLES - 3/4 SIZE
COMMUNITY HALL
FOOD SERVICE
STAGE
LIBRARY
MULTI FUNCTIONAL HALL
200 PEOPLE
6 SINGLE MOTHERS AS MARRIED FAMILIES
COMMON ROOM
6 MARRIED FAMILIES
GAMES/ COMMON RM
+ COMMON DRYER
CHILDREN SLEEP
ON OLD SITE
TENNIS COURT
GARDENS, VEGETABLES, FRUIT TREES, PLAY FIELD

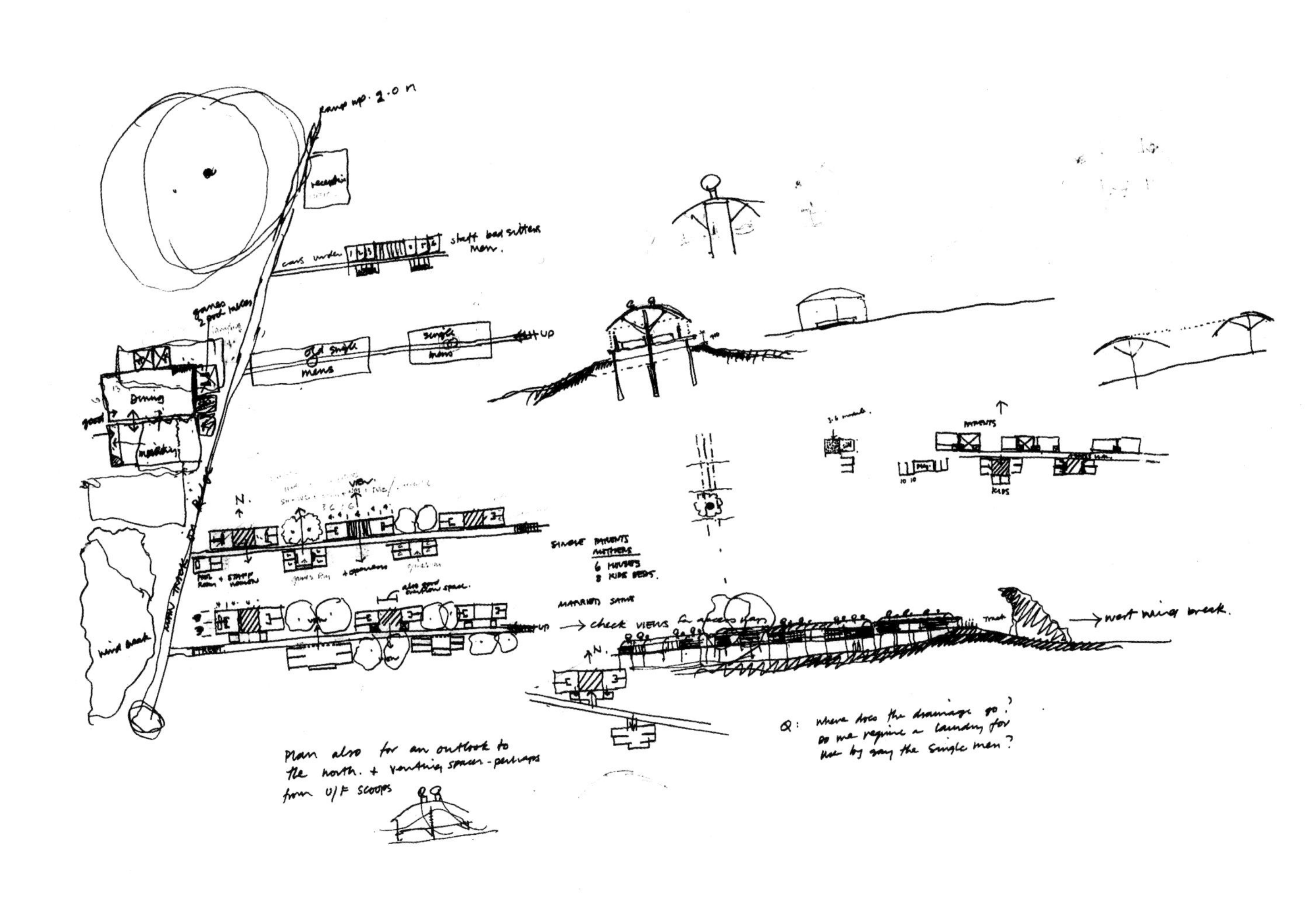
ramp up 2.0 m
staff bed sitters men.
cars under
Dining
N.
SINGLE PARENTS MOTHERS
6 HOUSES
8 KIDS BEDS.
MARRIED SAME
→ check views
→ west wind break.
wind break
Plan also for an outlook to the north. + venting spaces - perhaps from U/F scoops
Q: where does the drainage go? do we require a laundry for use by say the single men?

Murcutt finds in his Indigenous clients an ideal source of the complexities he likes to encounter and overcome through design. His favourite clients are those who bring him the most detailed and poetic programmes.

In the Alcoholic Rehabilitation Centre, he enjoys the direct involvement of the clients in developing the brief. For him the clients' participation in the design process is critical; and the more complex and difficult the design puzzle they present him with, the more deeply he engages, seeking solutions that are both programatically and formally satisfying: finding a single solution that serves many purposes is at the heart of his minimalist aesthetic, and he discovers the necessary leverage for design in the limitations and constraints of the brief. Working with Aboriginal people, the process is even more complicated because there are many voices to be heard, as well as cultural subtleties to be understood. It demands patience to work slowly through issues and arrive at consensus.

In this project Murcutt also revels in the opportunity presented in the programme to design many different kinds of spaces to answer the range of cultural requirements.

It is also an opportunity to develop his understanding of the land. Until now, his observations of the land have been essentially those of an ecologist. When he encounters Aboriginal clients, he begins to appreciate the land also in terms of its Aboriginal significance. Aboriginal people have lived in symbiosis with the land for as long as perhaps 60,000 years, and as hunter gatherers, have minimised the impact of their inhabitation. Their thinking is close to his own philosophic position as an environmentalist, with a desire to minimise the impact of habitation and to reduce the consumption of finite resources. Murcutt finds great accord with Aboriginal people whom he sees fundamentally as environmentalists *par excellence*.

He also begins to incorporate an Aboriginal cultural reading of the land: the way the building makes contact with the ground, and how it is approached obliquely, not on axis. These are ideas he will return to in the planning of many subsequent buildings.

The site is on the northern New South Wales coast. There already was a well-regarded Aboriginal alcoholic rehabilitation centre operating. The project was to design a new facility. The clients were familiar with the Kempsey Museum.

An Aboriginal alcoholic rehabilitation centre is a complex series of spaces and relationships. There is reception, consulting rooms, areas for sleeping, kitchens, dining, a meeting place, as well as a games room and theatre for projection – all various sized spaces.

It is important to understand Aboriginal cultural patterning: the relationship of mothers and kids, of fathers and kids, of single mothers and kids, of single mothers and single alcoholic men. Alcoholism in the Aboriginal community is regarded as a family issue and not just an individual's.

The areas are segregated: young single men, older men, etc. The idea is that young single men filter through the area of the older single men to the clinic, and on the way care for them. These people respect their elders. Single mothers have kids over twelve nearby, sons on one side and daughters on the other. There is an area for married couples. Staff are placed so they can ensure that single men respect the single women.

The planning system required varied spaces that people would feel comfortable in. Some preferred cell spaces and others big dormitories. Many spatial options had to be considered and planned.

This was my first contact working with Aboriginal people, although I was raised to the age of five by four national New Guineans, whom I feel had similar cultural rhythms. Initially we spent an extraordinary open day of discussions. I took notes in drawing form. People popped in, many participated. They contributed enormously to my understanding of the brief, and I appreciated the immense importance of having spatial and visual connectedness between inside and outside, having areas where people can easily enter and where, inside, one is not excluded from the landscape.

Movement in the complex must work as a continuum. It is important not to end up at dead ends. The buildings have no enclosed corridors; routes through them lead into the landscape, and all paths lead into the landscape. Generally the walkways do not run directly into a building; instead they come up alongside. Entry paths are slid in obliquely. The path allows someone at a tangent with the medical facility the choice of either wandering into the landscape or of stepping off the path as a decision to enter the building and pursue rehabilitation.

The main building is on a slab on the ground on the highest part of the site. There is a clear step onto it: it is a conscious choice to get on board.

The buildings needed to be above ground because of the floodplain siting. There are jetty-like platforms that become places to sit. The buildings sit or rest on the subtle ridges to each side of the spine walkways.

The housing is oriented north. The dormitory apartments are little versions of the bigger building. There is a common area in the centre, as well as sleeping spaces. It is based on the communal organisation of family structures. I hadn't realised at the time of designing this project that traditionally children are not placed to the west of parents sleeping: they should sleep on their parents' east side.

The long axis of the main facility – unlike the sleeping quarters – runs north-south, with roof lighting set over the access spine and courtyards. All day, sunlight enters and is bounced into spaces and the access route through the building. The Kempsey Museum roof section is developed here. The construction is steel frame and timber.

The costings were done: it was a super economical hospital facility but the state and federal governments of the day refused funding for the project. The scheme did not proceed.

Reg Lark assisted with the design development and made the model.

Littlemore house
Woollahra Sydney New South Wales
1983 to 1986

This house – as well as others on inner-urban and suburban sites – challenges a popular misconception that Murcutt builds only in the bush. Of course he builds in cities just as readily and applies the same theoretical propositions. This house contains his typical experimentalism, aestheticisation of details, and interest in adapting manufactured components.

Murcutt here returns again to the Miesian courtyard type, fusing it with the terrace house type common to the suburb.

In a high rainfall area, water must be discharged quickly from the roof: the shelving roof form achieves this and gives aesthetic expression to the task.

In the detailing and expression of materials, Murcutt displays a sense of craft reminiscent of the Maison de Verre; this is not a homage to Chareau, but the result of taking similar pleasure in the highly crafted detailing of manufactured elements. For instance, Miniorb on the ceilings is a material out of context, but appropriate both to the need to deal with acoustics and a desire to enhance the poetics of light.

Glenn Murcutt

The site is in an inner-city suburban context, an awkward narrow block of land with its northern side boundary abutting a small park. It is the only house that fully overlooks the park, embracing the realm beyond the site. The park was a difficult, hardly used or enjoyed open area off a back lane. Construction of this house has made it a less vulnerable space to be in.

We wanted solar gain and a ground floor where the interior and exterior spaces have an easy flow. That meant putting bed lofts upstairs. The building regulations required glass to be set back 900mm from the side boundary; we could build to the boundaries as long as there was no glazing. There is vacant land next door on the south side. Of course I wanted to glaze along the park-side boundary. We went to the Land and Environment Court because the local council was not able to approve a building with glass on the boundary; however, they submitted a report that supported our proposal, and the court approved the design.

The site is about 5.2 metres wide, a tight dimension. To maximise the visual dimensions, I made the ground floor as attentuated as possible: it has a narrow, axe-like plan, with the blade containing the living room, services and staircases.

Access is difficult. The ground floor level is a floor above the street. The level below is for the garage and entry lobby. Privacy was important.

The plan is related to the Bingie Bingie house, but on two levels. It has the same strict ordering of the service spaces. The idea of a zone of services is evident in the Nicholas house in Mount Irvine as well as at Berowra Waters Inn and the Ball-Eastaway house.

The design sets out to reinterpret the terrace house, which is seen in the section. Miniorb ripple iron on the bedroom level balustrade is set behind glass blocks, giving an abstracted sense of the cast-iron tracery of balconies on a traditional terrace house.

There are zones for parents and children as well as a music room.

The materials are brick and steel. Brick is used for the service zone, the north spaces of the house are framed in steel. The ceilings are metal: Miniorb. I could have used plasterboard for the ceilings, but there is so much music played by the children, I felt that corrugated metal would give a better distribution of sound. This corrugated profile also gives texture and light to the ceiling.

The doors are framed. It is a traditional joinery detail in terrace houses. I felt in this context a flush door would be inappropriate. The entry door is steel.

A double-layered and a triple-layered skillion roof abut a gable roof over the services. The northern face of the gable has roof windows that allow light into the hall. There was a limit to the incursion of height allowed along the south side boundary.

The roof form is the forerunner of the Broken Hill Mining Museum: each plane becomes steeper the closer it gets to the gutter, in order to discharge water quickly. Flooding is avoided by keeping the runs short and stepping the roof. I also needed a generous internal volume that a straight, single-plane skillion would have denied me.

Working drawings assitant: Wendy Lewin

Engineer: James Taylor and Associates

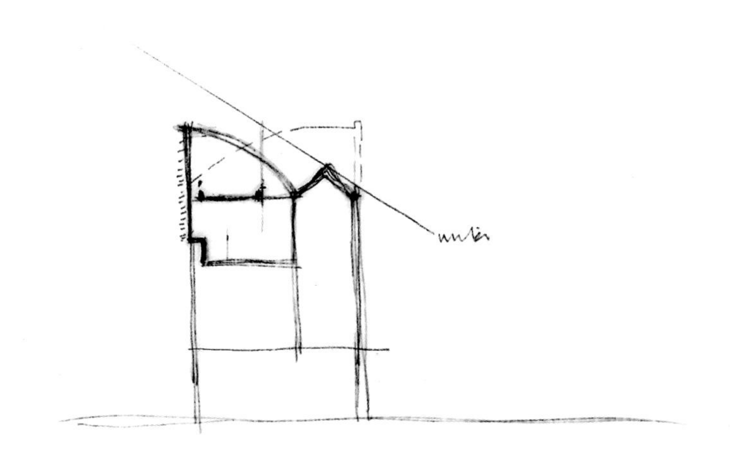

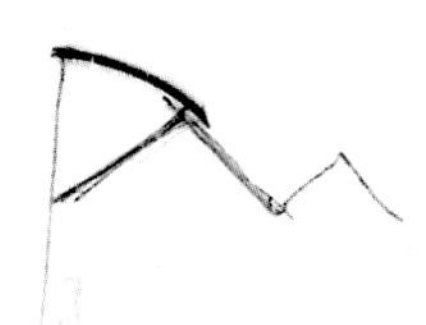

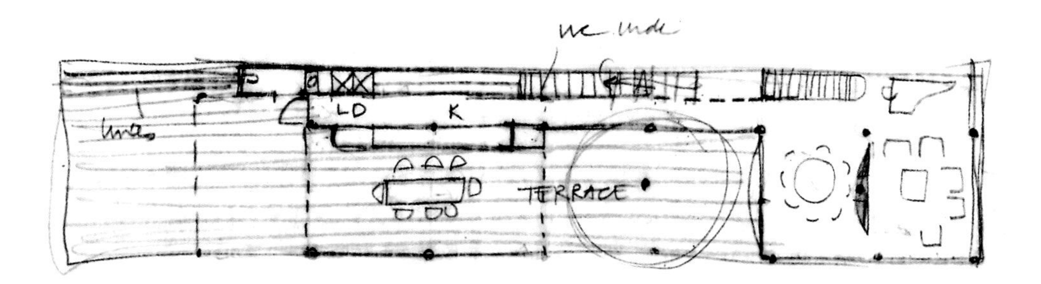
LD
K
TERRACE

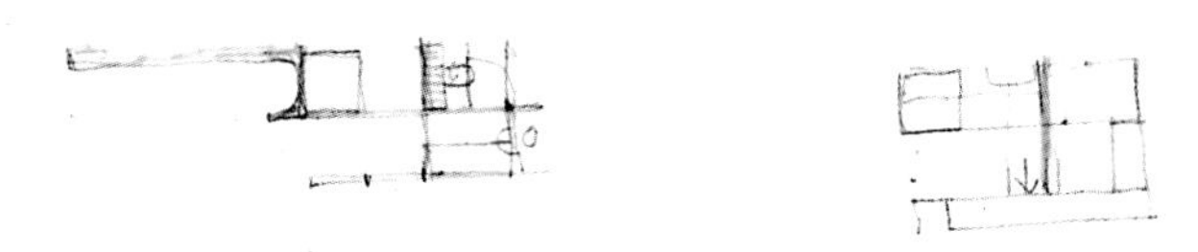

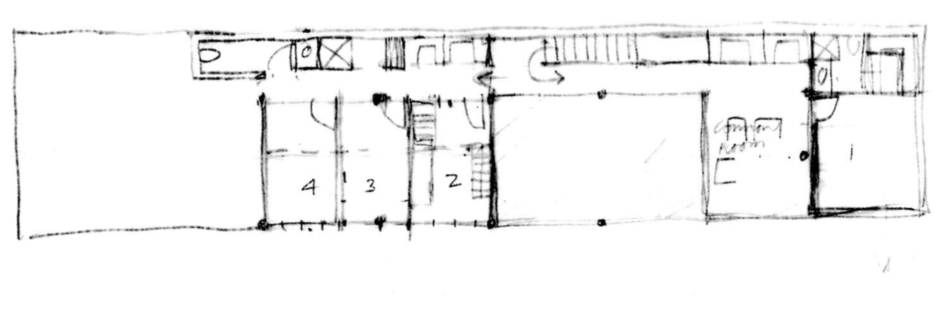
4
3
2
1

N

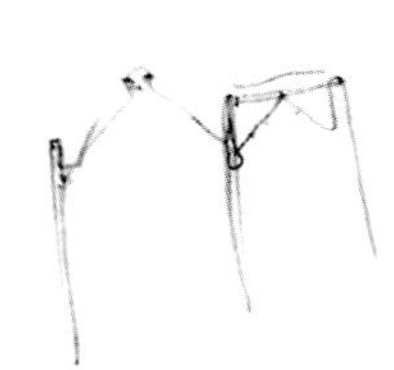

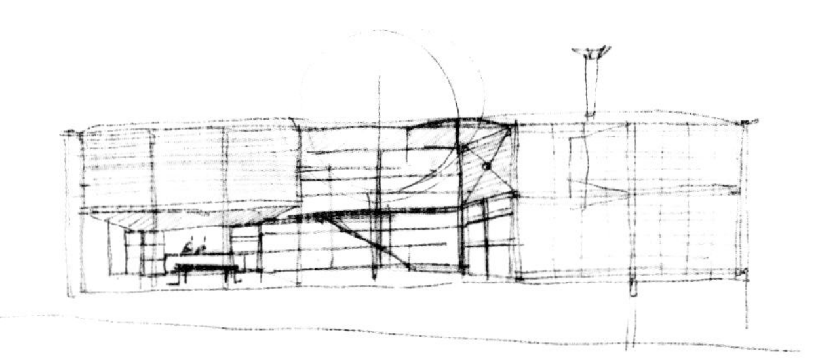

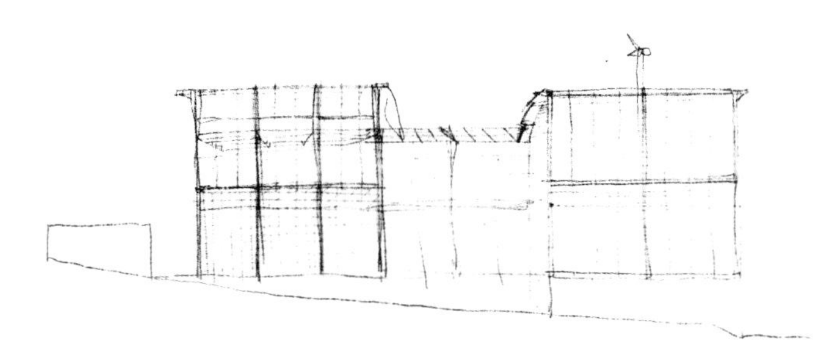

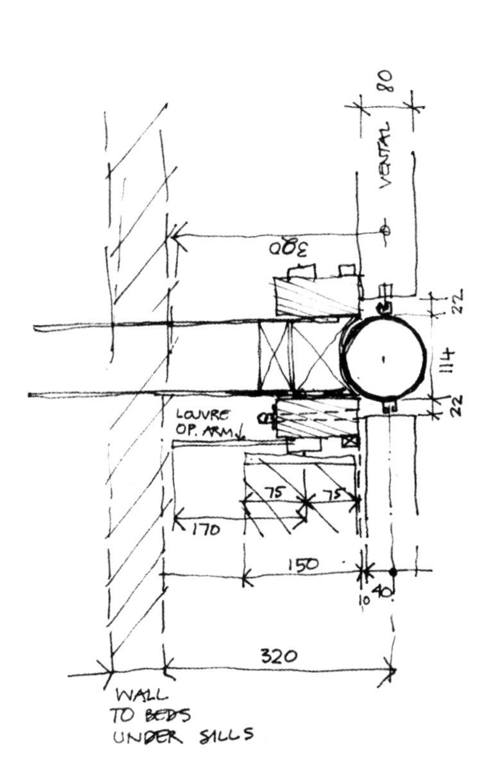
80
VENTAL
300
22
114
22
LOUVRE
OP. ARM
75
75
170
150
10
40
320
WALL
TO BEDS
UNDER SILLS

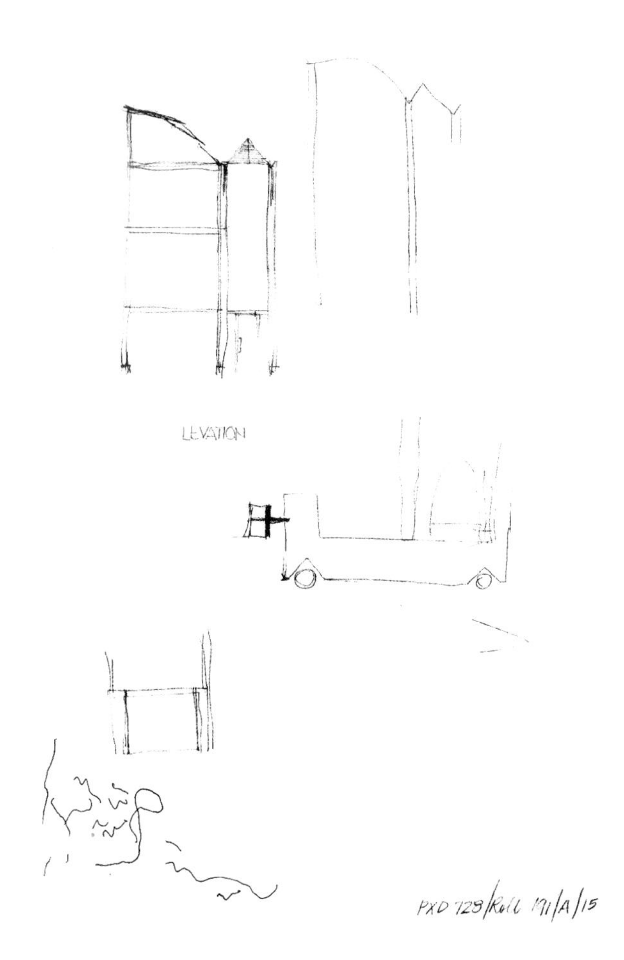
LEVATION

Magney house
Paddington Sydney New South Wales
1986 to 1990

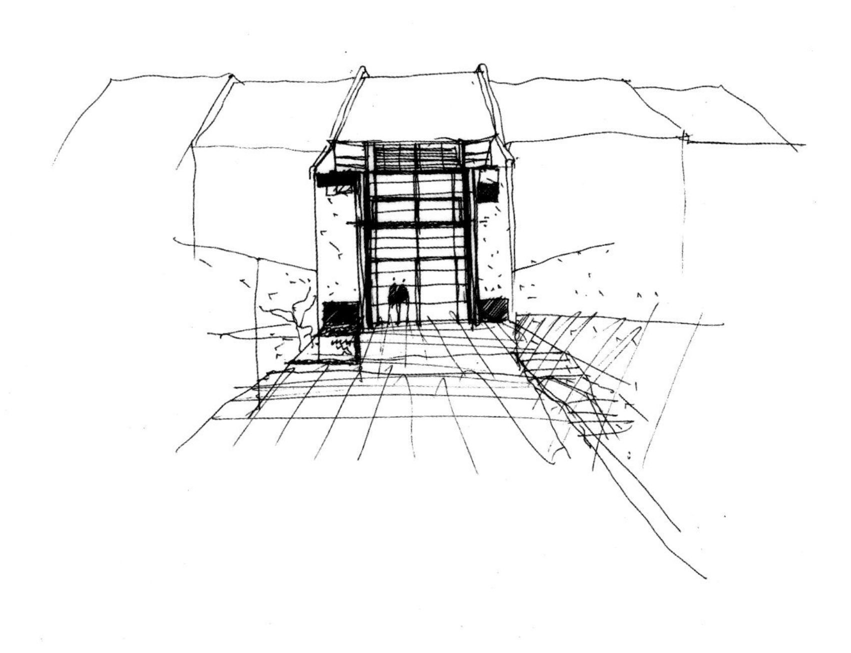

Murcutt has always tended to work with relatively lightweight materials. No doubt this emanates in part from his regarding the grid as a conceptually ordering schema for the pla which translates directly into the tectonics of the frame and suggests the use of lightweig constructional technologies.

When he designs the Ockens house (1977), even though it is a masonry building, Murcutt do not give it a mass expression: instead, the bri walls are stretched over the building within an detailed to achieve a planar, skinlike condition and the reading is lightweight. Yet at Berowra Waters (1977) Murcutt builds a rendered mason wall in the garden and explores the idea of mas and especially how the penetration of mass gives expression to its tectonic quality. He rea is deeply impressed by Barragan and the idea in his work of the true expression of a materia abstracted planes, minimalism and stillness.

In the Magney house Murcutt explores the ma tectonic. The rear elevation is in many respect a return to the formal development of the Ockens house, but now the Miesian expressio is completely gone.

The expression of mass enables Murcutt to establish the cell, the cave: that refuge. The mass also enables him to play a game of contrast between roof plane and wall: the roof plane is a lightweight floating steel frame and the wall is rooted in the ground, as well as being separated out from the roof to clarify the distinct condition of each.

The living room is abstracted to create the sense of a sheltering parasol roof – with clustered, cavelike spaces – and the floor plan stretching out to the prospect. There is a reference here to the Laurie Short house of 1972, in which – working within a Miesian vocabulary – the house is reduced to the most essential expressions of shelter and prospect. In the Magney house Murcutt abandons the Miesian expression and finds his own languag for these issues: abstraction of the elements that enclose dwelling.

This house is a key moment in the developme of Murcutt's design language. He broadens his repertoire for making architecture. Increasingly he will now mix lightweight and mass, taking pleasure in the tensions created in the plays between the two.

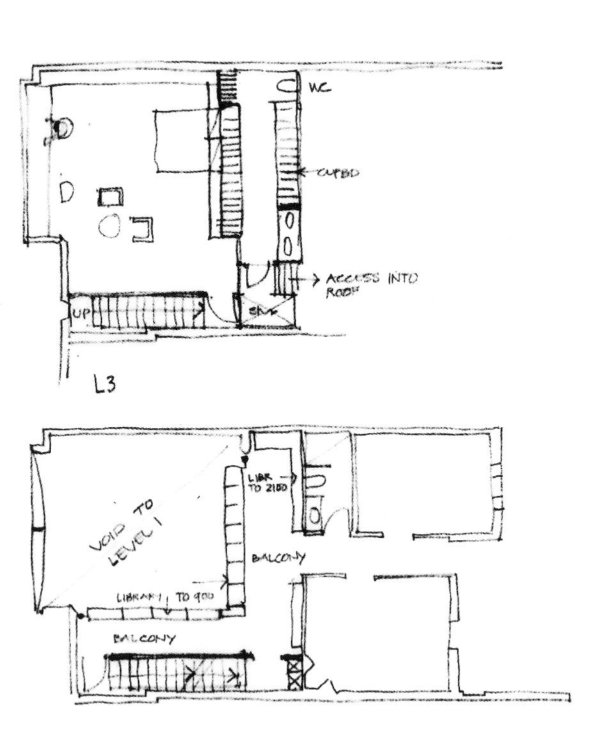

L2

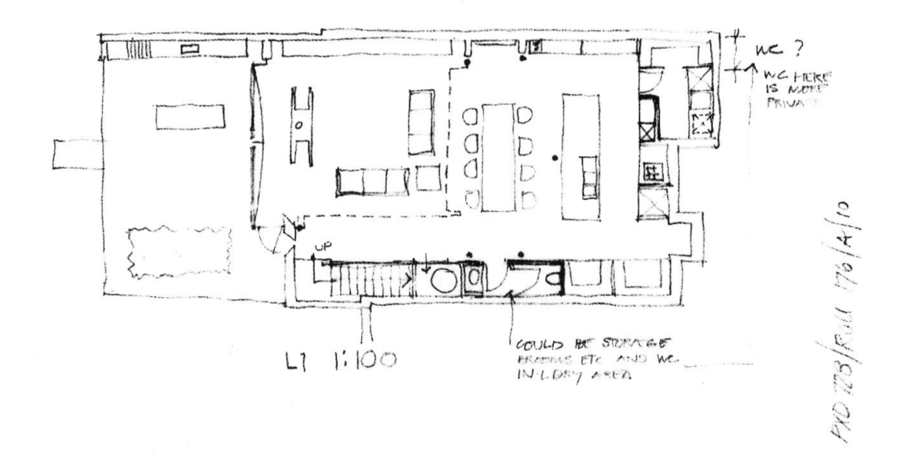

clients wanted to build in Paddington, nedium-density inner suburb. The back of the e needed to face north to receive the sun and th-east summer breezes. In Sydney it is an vantage to enter a house from the cool, shady uth side and move towards the sunlight. ht can generate wellbeing, and lack of light n be depressing. I personally prefer to walk vards brighter light.

clients and I looked at about three sites and aid: buy this one. It was a ramshackle eteenth-century terrace house, a terrible plan h long thin dark rooms. The site slopes down nsiderably to the rear and north. I produced o designs: the first was too big and expensive d I had to make cuts.

ept the roof profile and also the shell: side walls d the historic street facade. In understanding e planning of the original house, I retained e projecting street bedroom as the reason why e street elevation has a kick in it. The bathroom d bedroom spaces at the street level were t replanned.

e entry and associated spaces needed a better atial quality, and it was important to develop a it between the entry level and the re-established per main bedroom level in order to reveal e sitting/dining and kitchen level below. The entry ace looks much wider than the actual width the house, which is an illusion.

rmally I would use a round column, but here id not.

nost often use circular steel columns because ey are good for developing the curved roof section, d the junctions are easier to work. A round lumn can free up a space; a square column n be heavy. At Kempsey Museum I used round lumns abutting bullnosed brick piers to iculate the junctions. Here I thought it important at the entry platform to the bedroom feel as ough it 'floats' and is not contained at the open rner with a solid supporting element, so I made column spatially open.

the back, I used square steel H sections, wo-storey-high frame that supports the cantilever the roof plane. The steel columns are separate m the two-storey flanking brick reveals. is heightens the sense of both the mass of e brickwork and the lightness of the steel frame d the roof it supports.

e masonry is thick enough to give the sense at it can be carved, as at the back courtyard race wall at Berowra Waters. The masonry wall penetrated by angled slots opening to the ews. This is a traditional way of making openings mass walls, and used by Luis Barragan.

designing a building in an existing, well-tablished environment, I had not only to respond climate and place but also typology, morphology, ale, materiality. I wanted to achieve a rhythm the back elevation that reinforces the rhythm the terrace houses. The clients desired some tdoor privacy from the adjacent neighbours. e flanking reveals establish the vertical scale d rhythm of the adjacent houses and provide r outdoor living space, as well as privacy.

The two sitting room pivot doors on the ground floor sit within the column zone when they are open, clear of the brickwork.

The supporting poles for the lattice shade cloth are stored when not in use in the back of the H columns: the two rods in the H of the column add richness to the details of the columns.

The western side of the house is a zone for pedestrian movement, the eastern side is for the water element and bathing.

The back of the house faces north. The northern balcony off the main bedroom provides an outside intermediate zone. The raised floor level in the main bedroom allows the living room below it to enjoy a higher ceiling, admitting northern winter sunlight and a slot for through-ventilation.

The window at the end of the reflecting pool bounces beautiful light inside. As the day progresses, the light effects change. The sun in winter creeps into the back of the room, right up to the kitchen bench. The lightwell at the rear of the kitchen, which rises in the front garden, operates as a through-vent system, particularly important for suction venting in summer.

The roof light above the shower opens, so that while showering, one can experience the quality of the day. The window in the shower alcove, which has its sill set at chest level, also opens for added ventilation and for enjoying the views straight down Sydney Harbour in complete privacy. The shower is almost an outdoor space.

Working drawings assistant for the first design: Wendy Lewin

Landscape architects: Sue Barnsley and Andrew McNally

Engineer: James Taylor and Associates

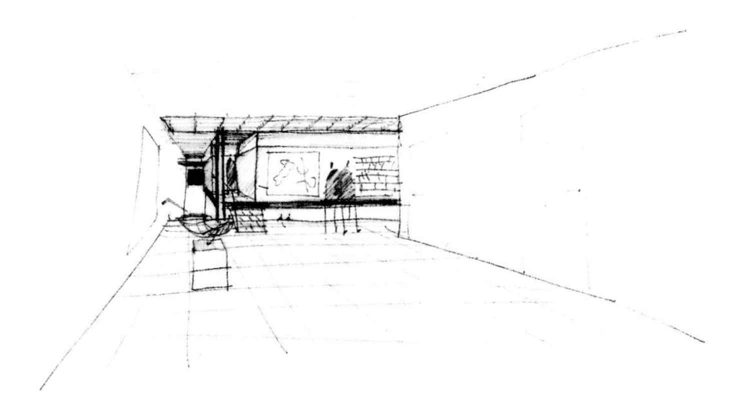

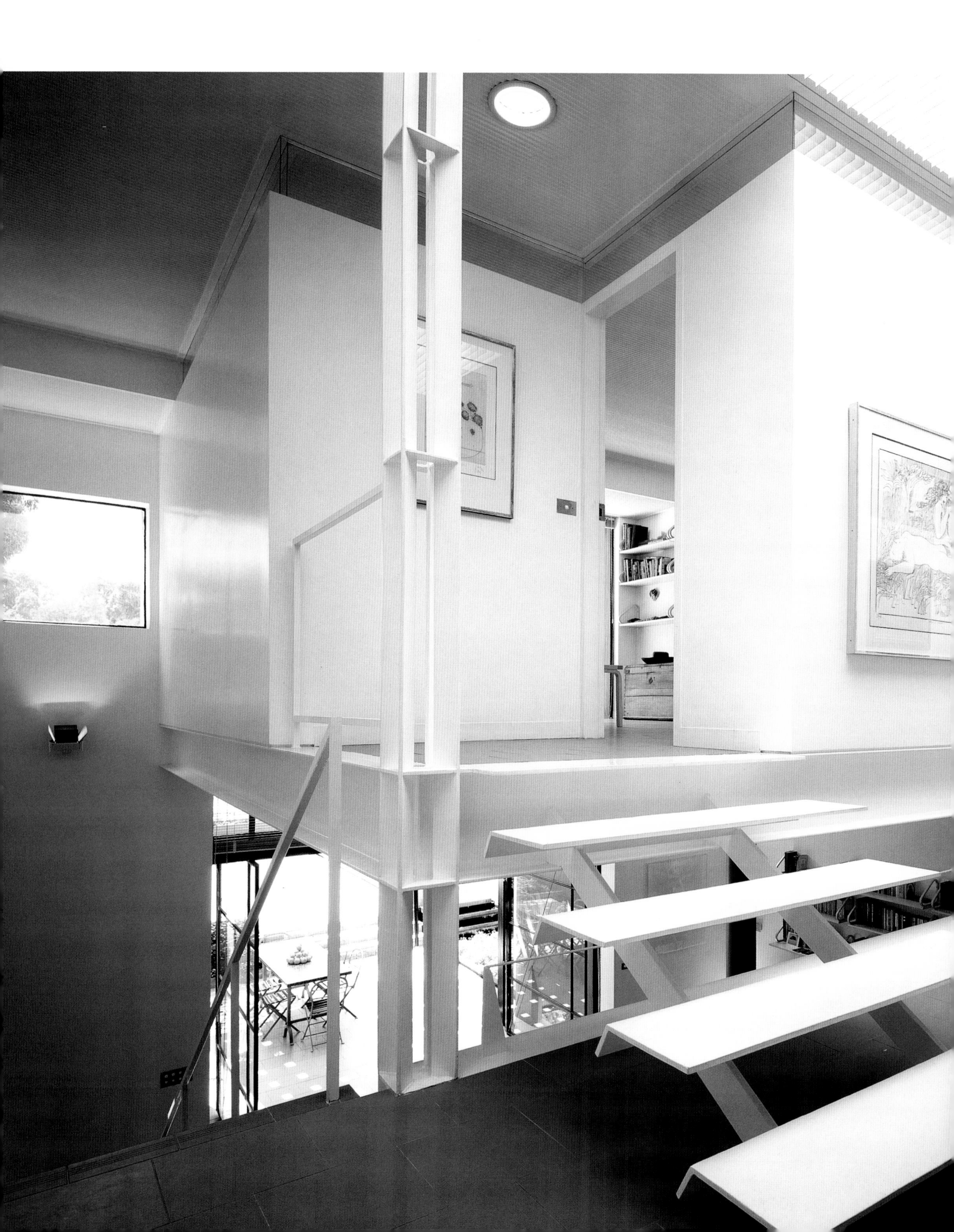

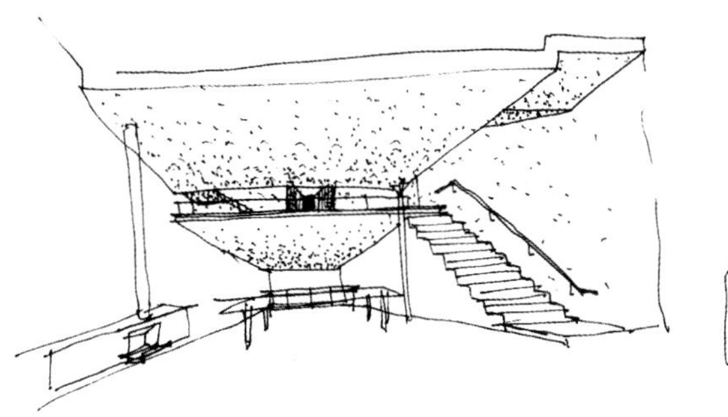

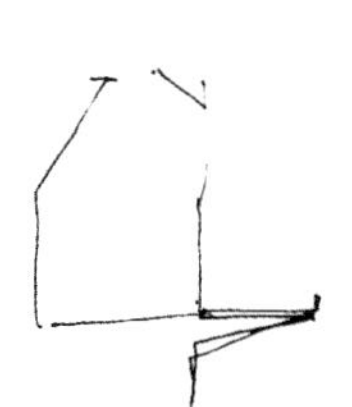

WEST

Done house
Mosman Sydney New South Wales
1988 to 1991

Following the Magney house and Broken Hill Mining and Minerals Museum, Murcutt is presented now with a perfect opportunity for a design based on the tectonics of mass. He sets out to make a courtyard house, an inevitable consequence of the suburban site being bounded on three sides by streets. But because the site slopes, the Miesian courtyard type – based on the notion of an abstracted horizontal ground plane – is inappropriate. In addition, the quality of the harbour views to the north militates against an inward-looking courtyard type focusing on interior outdoor space.

Murcutt returns to his experiences in the Greek islands and to ideas and observations that he made twenty-five years previously concerning the courtyard, the site and views.

The courtyard is a miniaturised homage to Barragan.

There are little references to art: the owner is a painter. The game of turning the corner slit windows into 'pictures' is carried through outside, where a window in the courtyard has a raised reveal around it, read 'picture frame'.

The house is full of tension and contrasts that serve to heighten awareness of creative oppositions in play. In an overtly mass building, Murcutt subverts the notion of mass and enclosure by drawing light into rooms through narrow slit windows placed right in the corners (normally the darkest parts of a room). At these points, the thickness of the wall disappears to a razor edge, so at the very moment that you might appreciate how heavy the building is, you actually perceive the enclosing walls as almost floating planes. Similarly, the roof is dematerialised. It is an insitu concrete vault with turf on top, yet inside, perception is of a floating curved plane. To achieve this, Murcutt draws light in at the ends of the vault and provides a little recess at the junction of the roof and the walls, so that the ceiling appears to float. There is no hint of the weight above.

Murcutt talks about dematerialising the roof and the wall. Underpinning this is an idea about abstracting the roof and the walls into planes. The transformation of the roof into a conceptual as well as a physical expression of shelter is a consistent theme throughout his work, and the roof plane always floats. In this house Murcutt goes a step further and desires to abstract the idea of the wall in the same way. The practical effect of this is to bring light into the room. The gesture is also both an ironic comment on and an affirmation of the massness of the building.

Glenn Murcutt

The site is relatively small and constrained, with roads on three sides. It has views north to Middle Harbour. Such a tight site – roughly 30 by 15 metres – suggested a courtyard type.

I had known the clients for a long time. They wanted to achieve a great deal through their brief and the site: a pool, a sun area, a courtyard, three bedrooms, a gallery for paintings, sitting/dining and a verandah. The proposition was exciting.

With roads on three boundaries, the site is extremely exposed. And having a street above the living level produces an uncomfortable and insecure feeling. So it was appropriate to look for a solution giving privacy and outlook, refuge and prospect.

A steel framing system at each end of the house braces the two-storey ends, thereby reducing the mass at these points to allow vehicular entry at the street and outlook to the north.

It was important to get all the spaces facing north. The bedrooms below street level and the floors above all have north-facing aspects. The lower rooms do not feel like spaces that are underground.

The entry access way is a roof-lit gallery for paintings and sculpture, serving two levels. The stair is widest at the top. The harbour view is only gradually revealed as one moves into the house: deliberately I did not disclose it all.

The entry hall skylight runs the full length of the access way down to the living room. The roof light is a central gutter with opal glass each side, with sun control adjustable screening outside the glazing. Over the dining room there is a similar system but here clear glass is used: we wanted to see the sky.

With sculptures and paintings in the entrance gallery and many other places, it was important that the light levels were adjustable.

The rib structure elements vaulting over the entrance gallery, supporting the big gutter, span 2.4 metres. At the end of the gallery I avoided placing a window to the view. There is good lighting at that end, and the view reveals itself as one moves towards the north.

The vaulted profile of the living room ceiling allows light in at the edge of the roof, allowing it to read as a suspended element and not structure. You never have the sense of its being heavy. The shallow barrel vault is made visually lighter at both sides by the recesses, and the ceiling is seen to float. The full-height glazed corner recesses and vaulted floating ceiling dematerialise the mass. At night the effect of dematerialisation is intensified.

A suspended concrete slab roof garden overlooks the courtyard. The deep blue swimming pool becomes more a landscape element than a pool. At night it is lit and seems almost suspended in space.

This house is not a lightweight structure. (The reason is not so much to do with climatic issues as with the general use of masonry in the area.) The design of the building is as though I have taken a solid and carved it. With many buildings, I have put a skin around a frame and developed structure as planes. In this case, the spaces are conceived of as having been carved out of the block on the site. Walls and corners are bevelled to direct circulation or to frame particular views. Within the courtyard there is a large frangipani tree. To frame the tree I opened up a tiny window with a splayed sharp edge on the inside of the wall opening. The opening appears frameless, and the view to the tree could be mistaken for a painting; further, the slot reveals the mass of the wall. These piercings dematerialise the walls. They also thrust the inside space out into the views, some of them stolen from beyond the site.

From the courtyard a stair leads to the secluded top terrace. From here the relationship is revealed of the harbour and Chinaman's Beach to the terrace and the pool: the cutaway, sloping wall opens the view to Middle Harbour. The terrace overlooks the garden roof of the living room. The upper terrace wall is bevelled to prevent immediate contact with what is a big drop. From within the courtyard, no other house is visible, just the clean edges of the roof cutting the sky, and the framing of sky and clouds.

Reg Lark assisted with the working drawings and details and site inspections.

Landscape architect: Marcia Hosking

Engineer: James Taylor and Associates

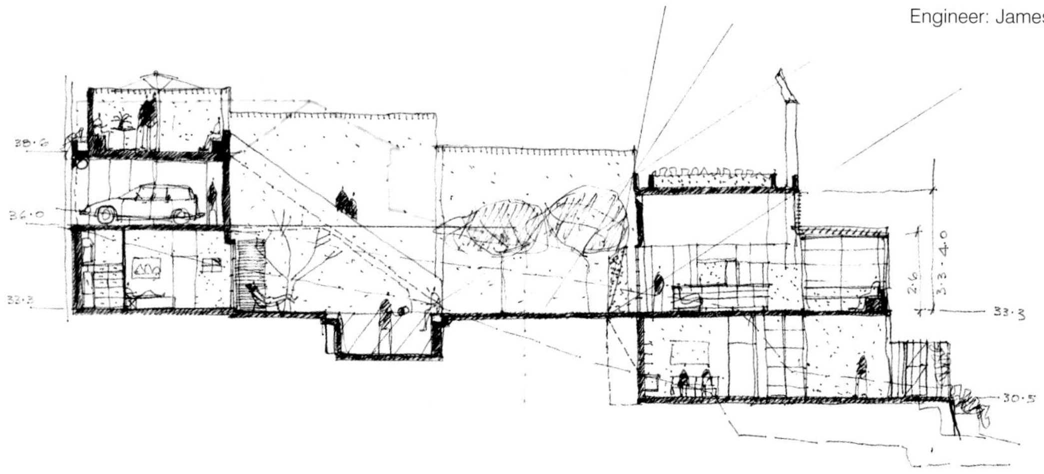

SECTION 1:100

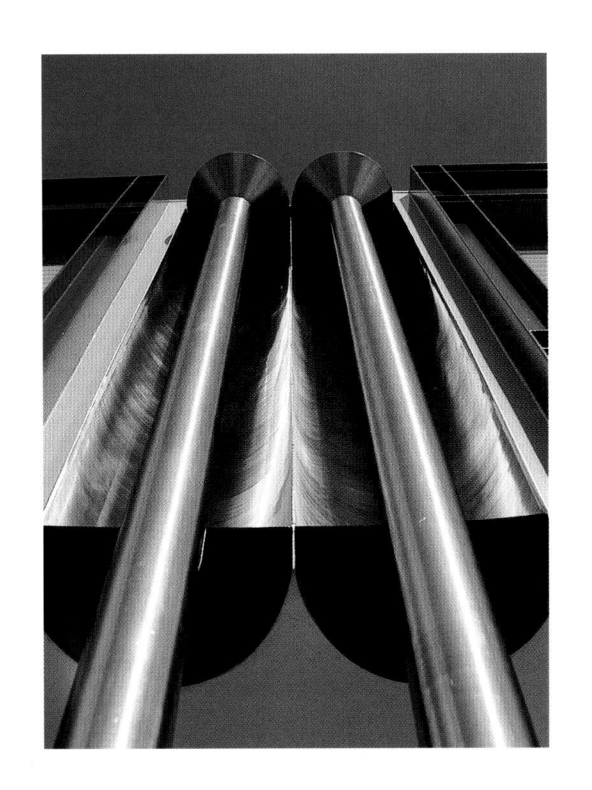

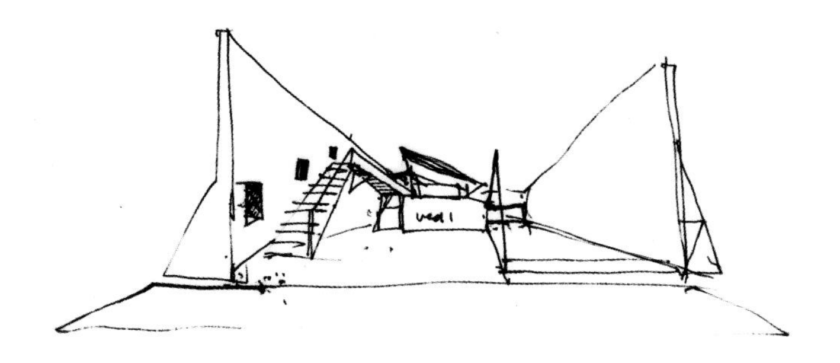

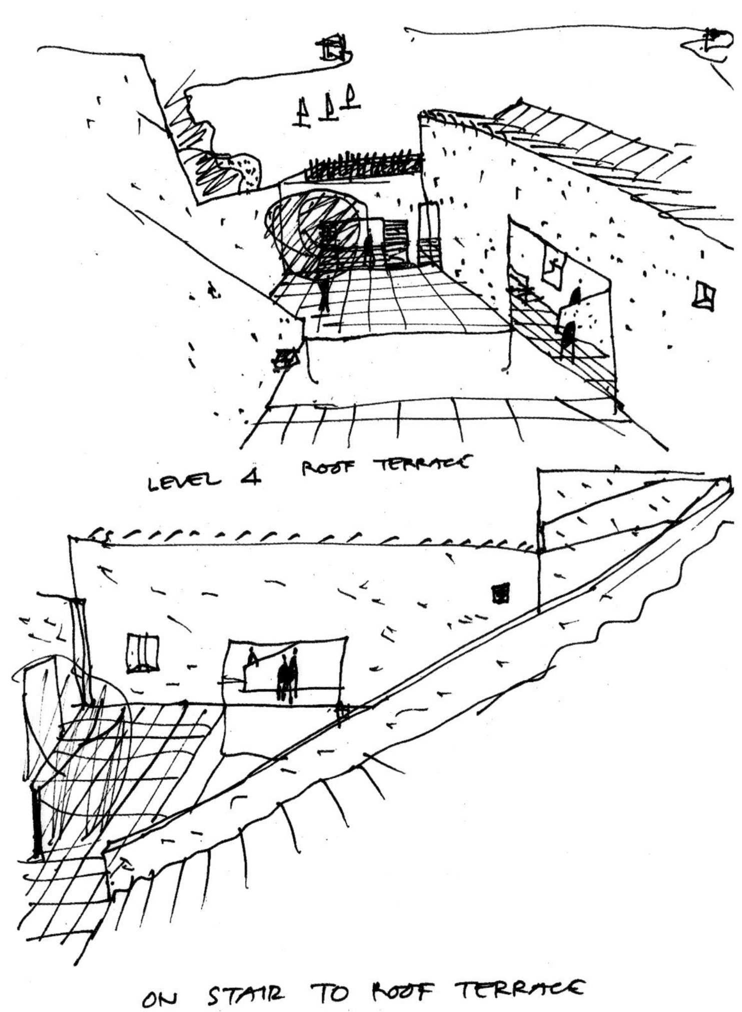
LEVEL 4 ROOF TERRACE
ON STAIR TO ROOF TERRACE

FROM LEVEL 1 TO LEVEL2 ON STAIR

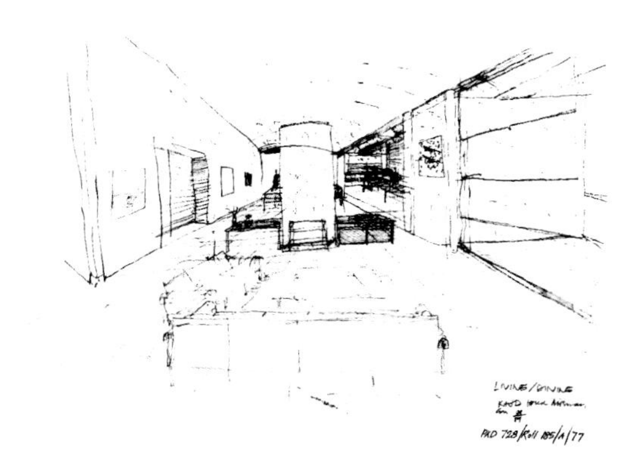
LIVING/DINING
PKD 728/Roll 185/A/77

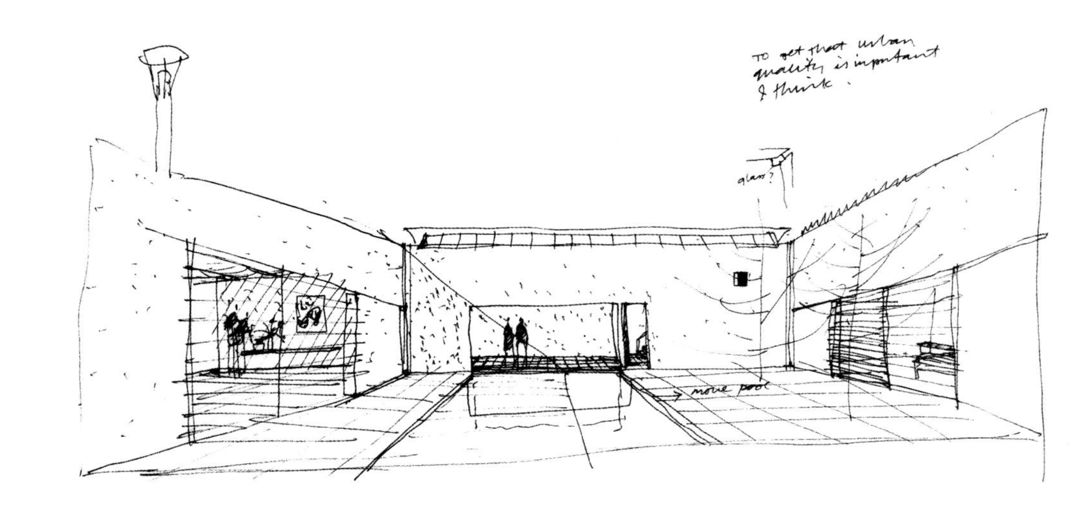
TO get that urban quality is important I think.
glass?
move pool

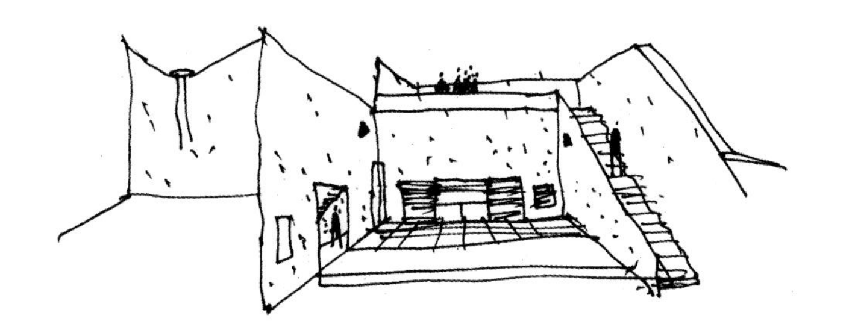

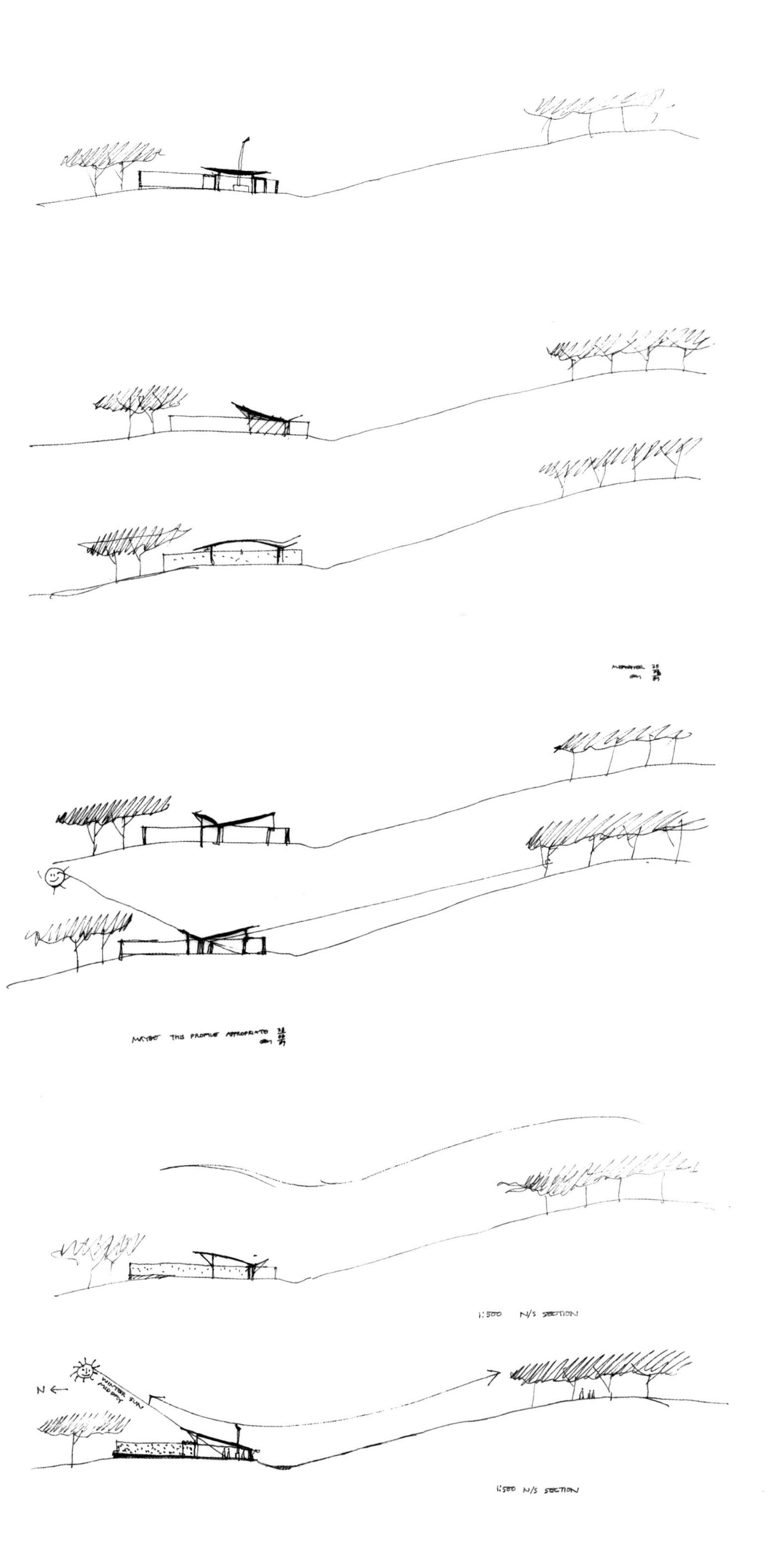

Murcutt takes pleasure in the mass tectonic because the expression of mass relates to enclosure and being grounded, which are central to his conceptual and formal readings of the house.

Invariably he sees the roof as a floating plane. In the early designs for this house, a butterfly profile swooped up to the south to allow views up the hill and to establish the roof as a floating concave plane. Murcutt relinquishes this idea because it would leave the dwelling too exposed and thus interfere with a notion of refuge. But he carries the butterfly roof profile over into the study, where it signifies the status of the little building as an independent pavilion.

When Murcutt details this building – and this is true also of most of the houses that will follow – the steel frame that supports the roof is expressed as being independent of the mass expressed masonry walls, and roof and walls are physically separated out in the same way as in the Magney house in Paddington. Here he places a steel frame with a skillion roof inside the masonry box.

In detailing the steel structure of the roof, Murcutt has long abandoned the expressive logic of timber framing. In this house it is most evident at the corners of the eaves, where the same steel 'rafter' profile turns through 90° – an impossibility in timber construction but a pragmatic solution with welded steel connections. Murcutt is exploring how steel might find its own expression, the processes of fabrication becoming part of the aesthetic.

House
Southern Highlands New South Wales
1988 to 1992

e Southern Highlands of New South Wales
n be hot and dry at times in summer, with low
nperatures and occasional frosts in winter.
e site is beautiful and exposed, receiving cold
nter high winds from the south-west. A large
ur to the south has magnificent views,
d other parts of the site are sheltered. There
s a question of building on top of the spur,
til one day during the high winds we went there
d realised a house would whistle like a flute,
y and night. Also, placing a building on a ridge
n so easily destroy the landscape integrity.

a country house. My client required good
orage, a protected courtyard and places to hang
intings. There are living areas, three bedrooms,
very private study, garaging and a site for a
ure tennis court. All the rooms enjoy north light.

e site is at the base of a spur and hill. It is wet:
ter run-off from the hill is collected along the south
le and fed into the dam. The double skillion
ovides space between the two layers of the roof
receive the gutter along the bottom of the larger
of for drinking water collection. I could have
n the roof as a single big plane, but I wanted to
t it back over the entrance, to reduce the scale
ong the entries and access spine.

e entry is discrete, planned as an extension
a major access spine. Within the airlock,
nall windows are placed to give glimpses of
e hillside and courtyard. Access to the external
udy is via a covered pathway and pergola.

e butterfly roof over the study opens to high
ws of the spur to the south, behind the house,
well as to the north. The windows have insect
esh and battened timber sliding shutters,
owing the entry of dappled light and ventilation.

ery much like sliding slatted window walls. They
eak down the obviousness of the view, modulate
e light levels, and reduce the fatigue of looking
t. They create an intermediate zone, yet when slid
ay, allow for uninterrupted views.

e fireplace adjacent to the entry is curved,
nphasising the direction of the corridor and defining
more intimate space for the sitting area in front
the fire. The arms of the fireplace are for stacking
ood, and a hollow at the other end houses the
evision when it's not being used.

The sitting, dining, kitchen and court is a steel box, in essence, alongside a masonry case. The big long south-facing wall is a double brick cavity wall set against the cold south-westerly winds.

The living room has a big window box to one side. Masonry walls flank the living room 'courtyard'; the corners are splayed. Holes cut in the flanking walls allow glimpses down into the garden and extend the courtyard space. The front open edge of the court is protected by the 800mm-high courtyard wall: cattle can graze to the house but cannot enter the external living areas.

The bay window seat in the south wall has tilted glazing to enable views up the hill to the mountain spur to the south.

The house is brick and cement-rendered masonry. Within the court the materials are brick, glass and steel. A dado set from the floor level to the undulating ground level is tiled in greenish slate: it formalises the ground and allows mud to be washed off the walls. Above the green slate, the walls are rendered and painted ochre.

Assistant with the sketch plans: Andrea Wilson

Engineer: James Taylor and Associates

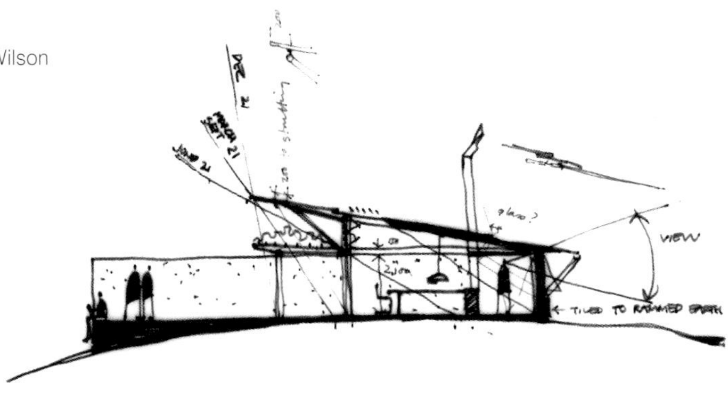

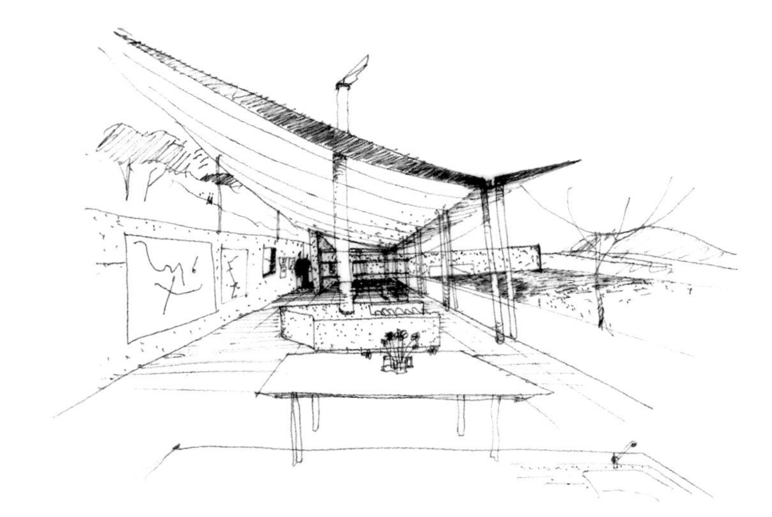

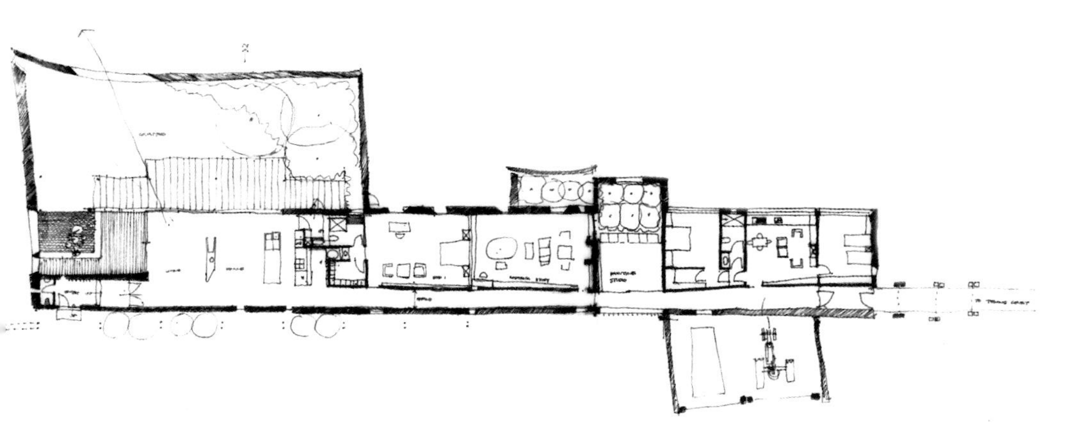

Simpson-Lee house
Mount Wilson New South Wales
1989 to 1994

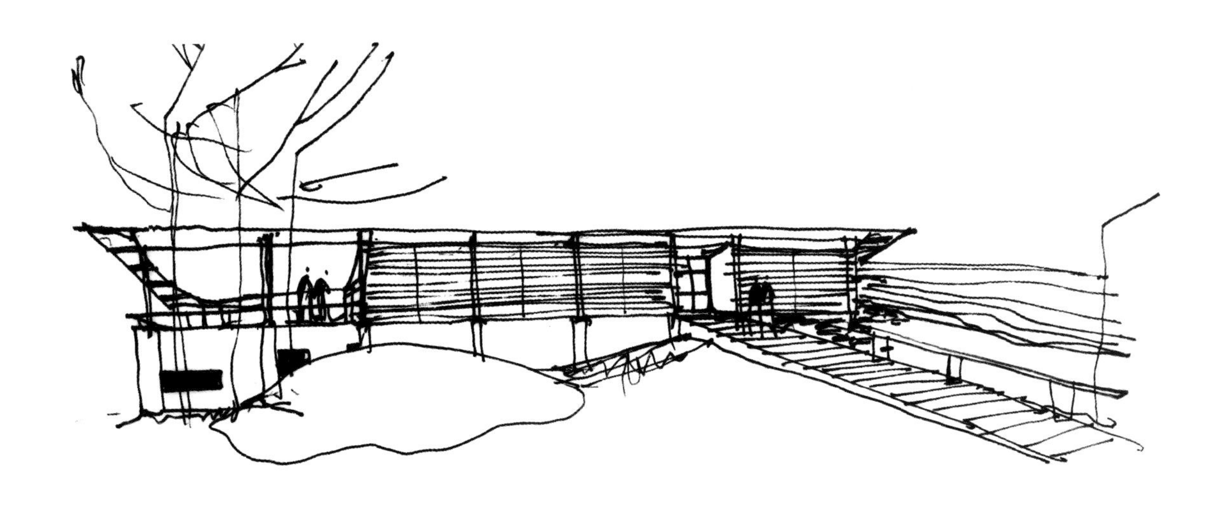

Murcutt himself thoroughly describes how this house came into being, and it is not difficult to infer from his comments that it might be his favourite house. Certainly the convergence in this project of exacting and enlightened clients, and the opportunity to resolve every issue and detail fully, gave him great satisfaction.

Constraint and restraint are central to Murcutt's design process. He needs constraint to develop the design idea, and he enjoys restraint as the mechanism for establishing his aesthetic. In this house, the clients constrained the design process with a clear and highly detailed brief embracing both the pragmatics and poetics of dwelling.

Murcutt's architectural aesthetic gives a uniformity to all his buildings, yet the aesthetic development of each is closely connected to the client's brief and the site.

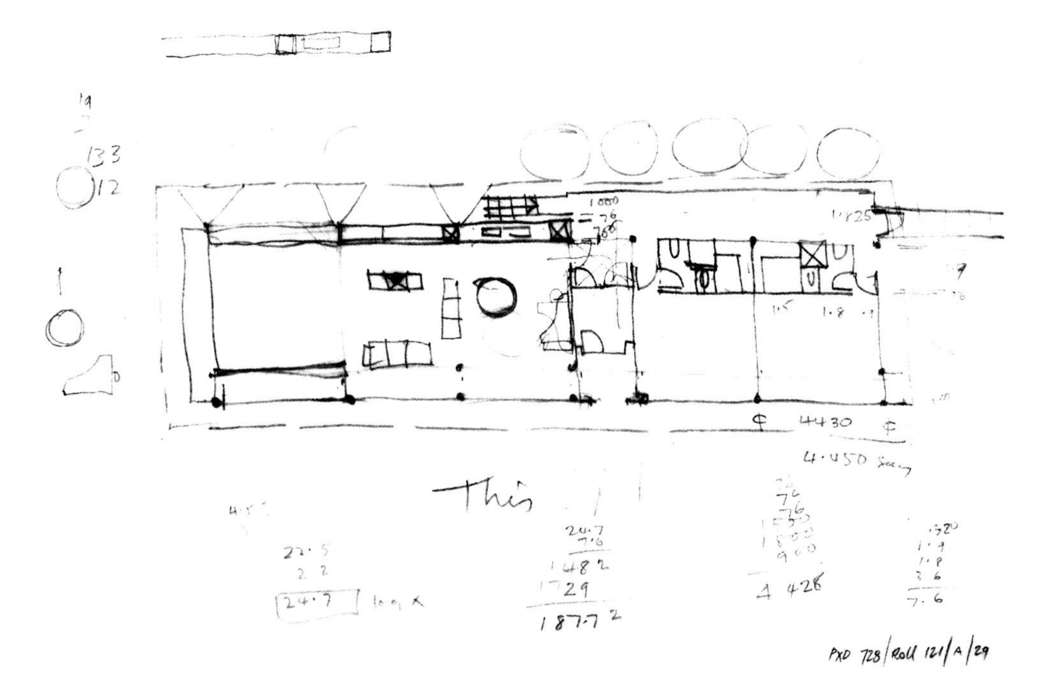

Glenn Murcutt

The clients wrote me a long letter. They wanted a house with a secular monastic quality. They ha owned land for a long time in the Blue Mountair west of Sydney. The climate is cool in winter anc it can snow. Summer temperatures have reache 40°C. It's dry with often hot high winds during summer and cool winds in winter.

The clients are greatly informed and deeply interested in architecture. They required a minim tough simplicity. And wherever possible, they wanted to use Australian labour and materials. (Apart from the Smeg oven and Finnish chairs, the house and its fittings are all Australian.)

It was my intention to make an exemplar of how modernism can ameliorate and benefit livin It had to ring true to modernism and also be of its place.

It took a long time to develop the design of this house, having lengthy discussions over a coupl of years, stage by stage, with the total involvem of the clients. All design decisions were made based on their understanding the practical and aesthetic reasons.

It finally took twenty-one months to clear the planning and building authorities. The area has a local environment plan which required all new work to comply with the early twentieth-century building models: timber, pitched roofs and smal divided windows. The Historic Buildings Council in New South Wales is a powerful body. It took them sixteen months to approve the house on th grounds that it was removed from the village.

The site is in sandstone country and immediatel below the volcanic soils. The flora includes big fern grasses, mosses, banksias, acacias and diverse groupings of native shrubs, as well as eucalypts and very tall trees. There are lyrebirds and an abundance of other wildlife. The site offered mar possible locations for consideration. We walked over the land and assessed different places for outlook and access. Building on the eastern side of the hill gave greater protection from fire.

We chose a site 30 metres back from the first escarpment and at the base of a big rock where the hillside flattens out. The contours of the site and profiles of the rocks established the relationsh of the house and studio garage. The location is very much like a glade between a large rock outcrop and the edge of the escarpment overlookir a deep valley. (It's hard to see the house from the valley.) This place provides relatively easy access to the valley, and was a path that would have been used by Aboriginal people. Since it was a path, there was an opportunity to re-establis it as the path into the house.

I had by this time experienced caves in northern Australia, and seen how Aboriginal people enter them from the sides, rather than from below or on a central axis, as one does with European civic architecture: I was learning that entry can be more subtle when made obliquely. These caves also confirmed for me the importance of spaces providing both refuge and prospect. All the caves I have experienced are lowest at their inside dept and highest at their edge. On this site, the fallen rocks provide a sense of refuge.

signed a datum at floor level and another doorhead height. It was important to me that building should connect with but also float r its site. The proportional system based on 9-metre module is developed throughout the nning. Relationships are established and the ering system to bring them together.

arriving there are many experiences: the arpment, the bush, the house. Visitors are eived under the protection of a large roof and gress through an airlock. This entry zone ntains the roof bracing system. The cantilevered f eaves system is a triangulated truss with only corrugated iron as the top cord. Bingie Bingie similar, though not as well developed. The tem is as thin and minimal as I could sonably make it. To construct this minimal piece structure, the builder had to prop the V struts in ir final position and fix the roofing. The roof ks in both compression and tension, pending on whether it has an updraught or owndraught.

e roof appears totally free of the building, nost as though it is about to take off. The above nsom glass is mitred where it turns the corners. dematerialises the corner of the building and plifies the lightness of the roof to the steel Ts d corrugated profile edge. The external insulated rugated iron cladding over the brickwork is ed between the vertical flanges of the H columns, nilar to the detailing of the doors.

e house is well insulated inside and sits on enclosed concrete block foundation. The bulk he building stands on a masonry base, with mm of styrofoam underneath for a well-insulated b. Insulation under the whole floor prevents the rmth from radiating down. There is also heating he slab: it's left on all the time during the ldest periods and runs at the rate of a 100-watt be: this takes the edge off the cold of the ncrete. A main fire heats the volume. The ceiling neavily insulated. The building construction everse brick veneer on the western side. There provision for a retractable insulated pocket blind the full height of the glazed wall, but so far as not been required. It is a translucent thermal nd. External blinds reduce the flow of cold air er the lower panels of glass.

e bare concrete floor has a water-based sealer h a slightly milky quality; it softens the colour the concrete while retaining the integrity of the aterial. Walls are bagged brickwork internally d painted. The ceiling is painted plasterboard. e steel is painted with silver aluminium paint – e colour of the bark of the local eucalypts.

The window in the kitchen kicks out of the vertical plane to about 90° to the angle of the hillside, and throws the eye up towards the rock face and landscape behind. That window and the strutting opposite are related. The strutting recalls the trees reaching out to the light. This building is pushing in the same direction as the trees, opening to the valley.

To the eastern side the access way is pushed beyond the foundation base and develops a lightness. The main living space seems to cantilever. The leading edge is fined down to the thinnest profile.

The sliding walls along the eastern facade allow the house to be closed or fully open to the landscape. They run the full length of the living space: the doors slide back into the zones of the airlocks at each end. When the doors are open the space changes its dimension dramatically, and it connects powerfully to the landscape. The room, for me, is reminiscent of the cave shelters of northern Australia, with their fallen rocks; I realise how much I have absorbed from those landscapes.

The large rock, which lies like a beached whale, rests only 1.5 metres from the eastern wall of the sitting room. It becomes an integral part of the room when one is sitting, and as one moves closer to the edge of the eastern wall, the rock appears to have shifted away from the house.

The risk of fire is high. Fires have already swept through on each side of this building. The sprinklers through the roof are connected to the water storage dam and pressurised by a petrol pump. The system was designed largely by my client. The large rock shelf to the east has deflected a fire; and as nothing grows against the house, the masonry, corrugated iron and cement sheet leave little to burn.

There is reasonable annual rainfall. The water storage dam is placed between the two buildings: the house plus the smaller second building containing the garage, laundry, overflow space and pottery wheel. The dam is a fire resource, with a huge volume. It takes the overflow collection from the seven water storage tanks. They are all set with the same top level, as tall as can be, relating to the fall of the ground.

The monopitch roof set with its fall to the higher side of the site resolves the potential problems of gutters and attending to them. A single pitch is easy to maintain.

The water surface of the storage dam bounces north sunlight into the house, and the light is further controlled by adjustable, retractable external louvred blinds. The bounced light ricochets through the house.

The detailing in this house is as good as I've ever done. This is most satisfying for me. This building has had thought to its siting, geometry, path, refuge, prospect and technology.

Engineer: James Taylor and Associates

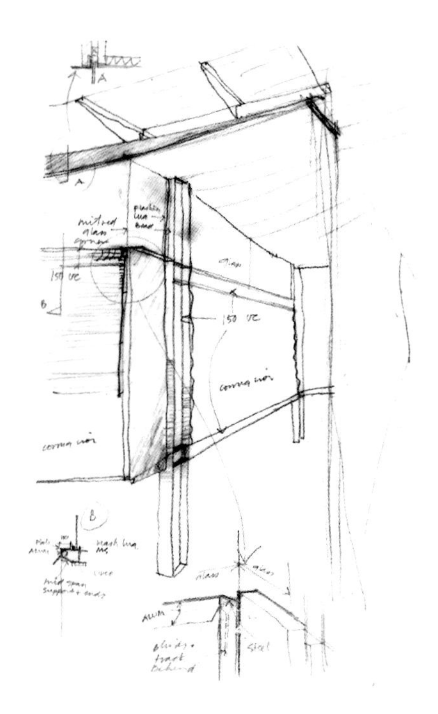

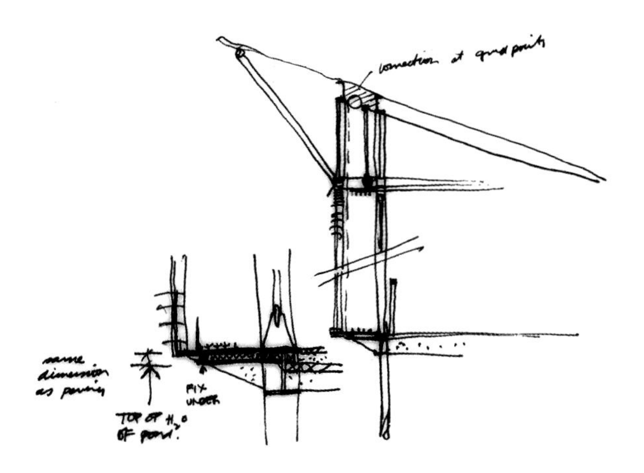

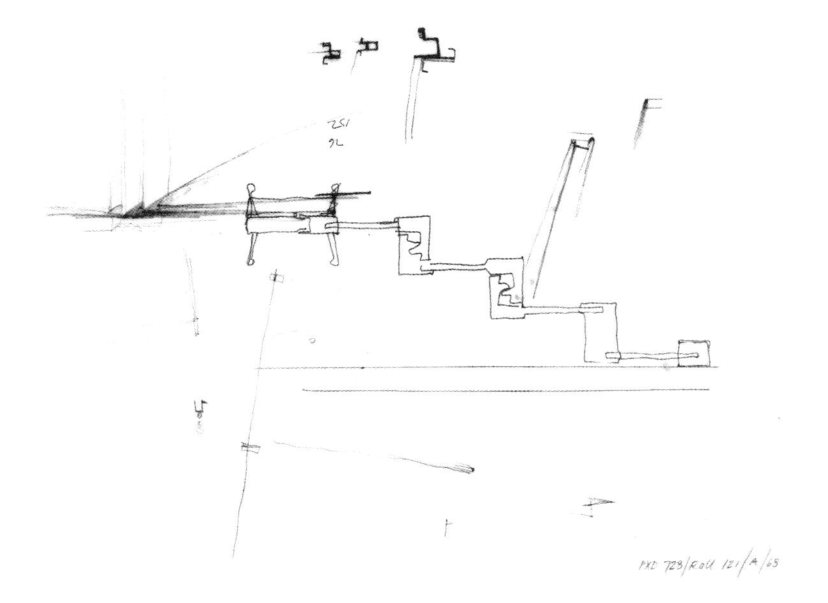

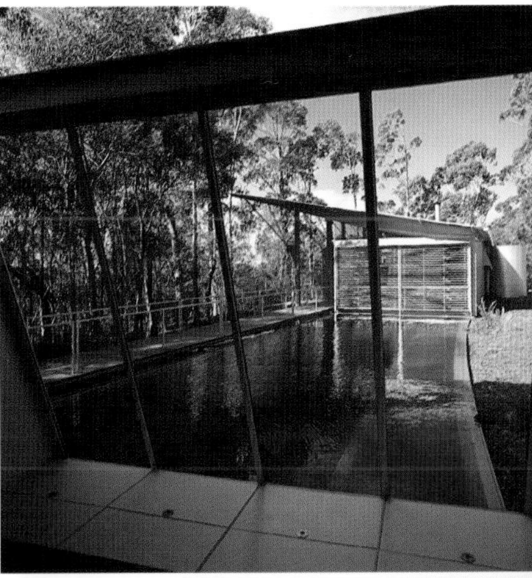

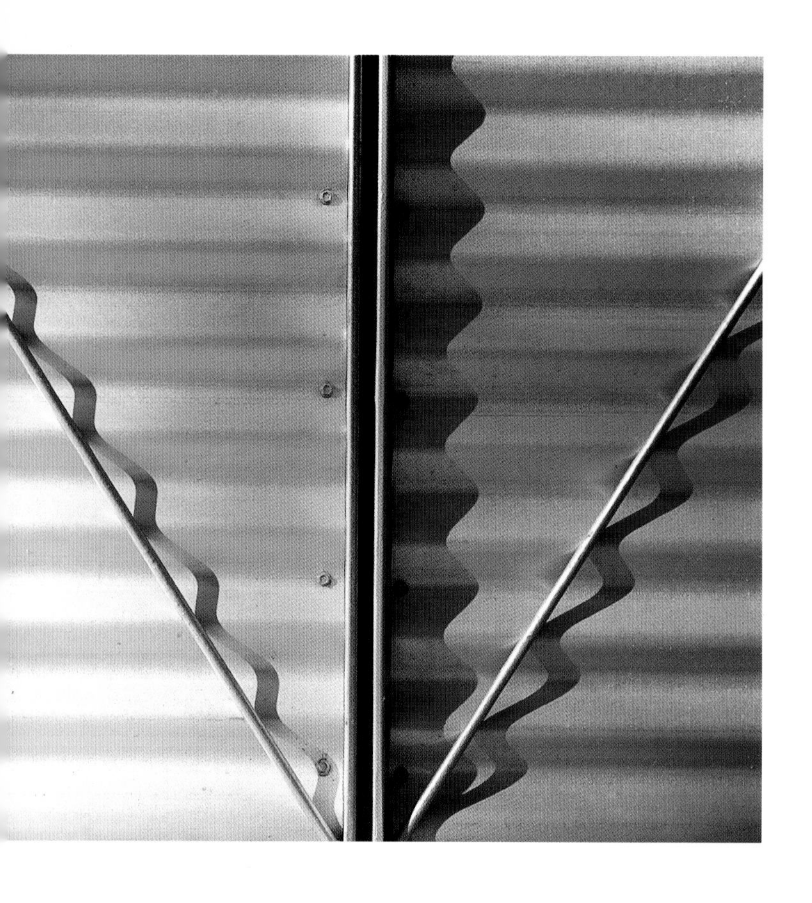

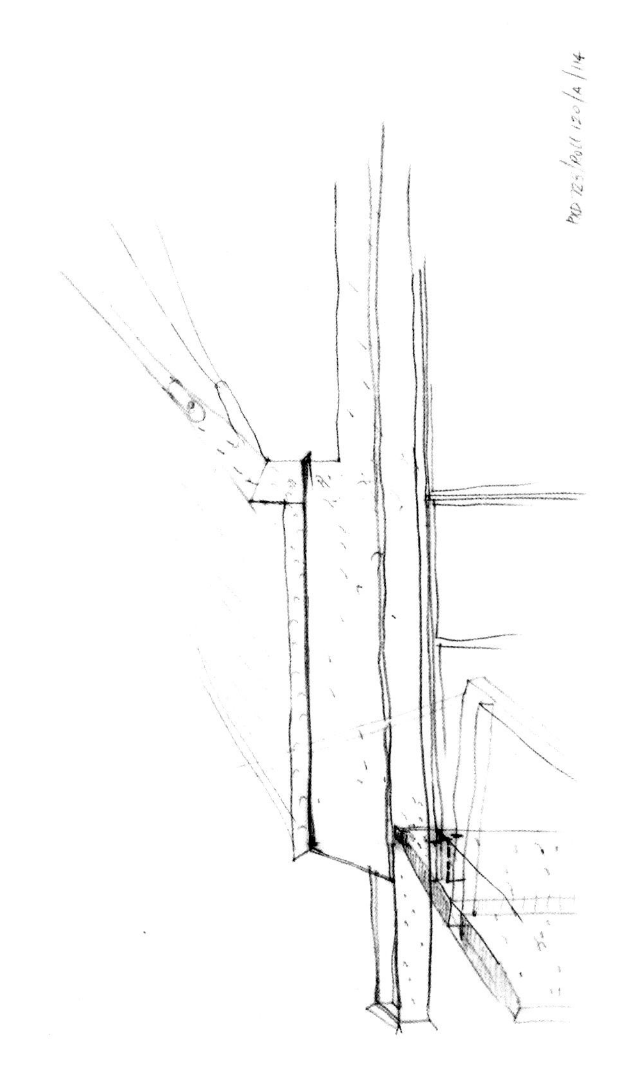

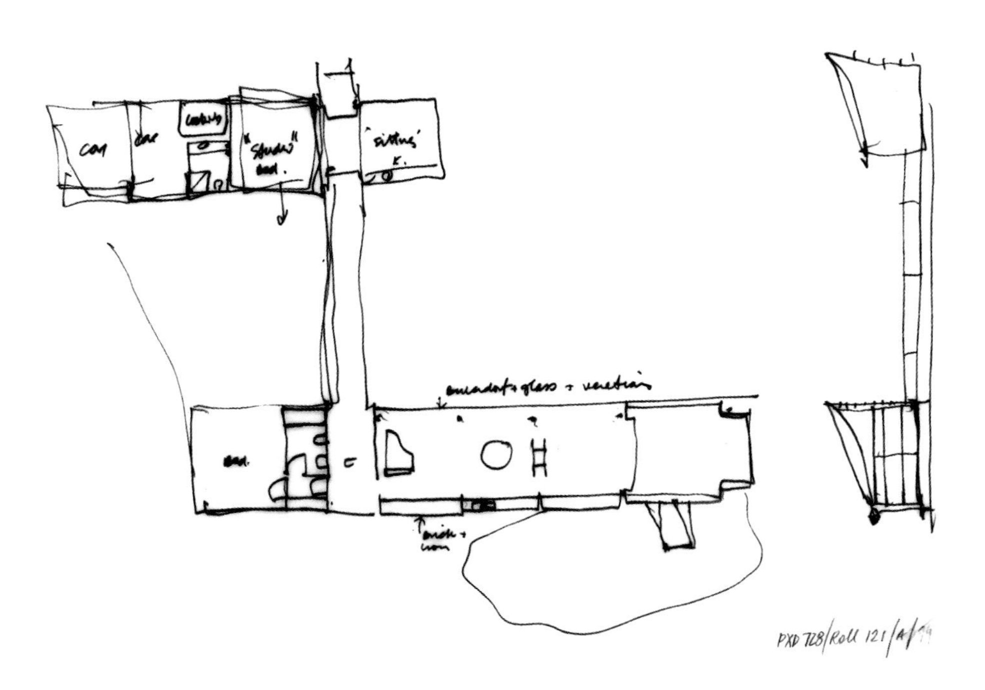
car
'sitting'
K.
PXD 728/Roll 121/A/

Marika-Alderton house
Yirrkala Community Eastern Arnhem Land Northern Territory
1991 to 1994

NEW HOUSE FOR MARIKA, YIRRKALA, N.T. EASTERN ARNHEM LAND

HOUSE FOR THE ABORIGINAL COMMUNITY

$12\frac{1}{2}^{\circ}$ S

MONSOONAL TROPICS CLIMATE

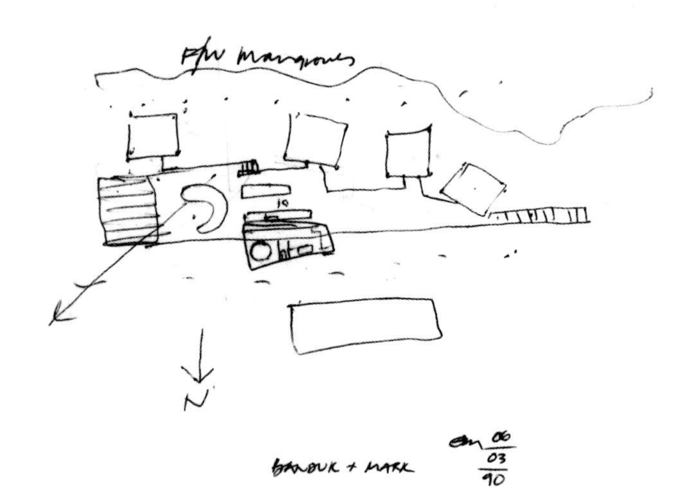

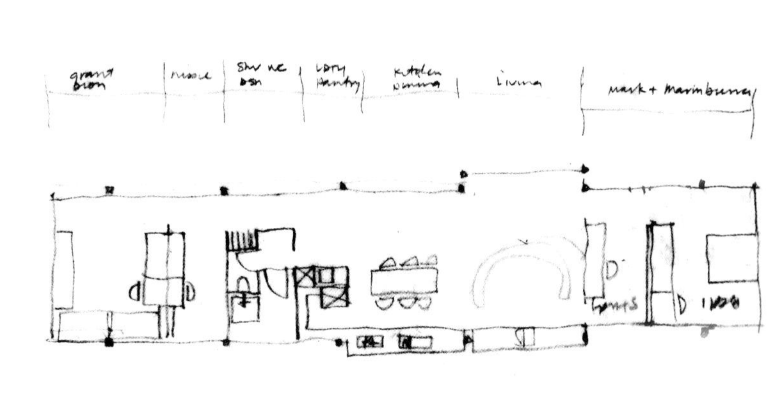

Winter winds SE - Dry
Summer " NW - Wet

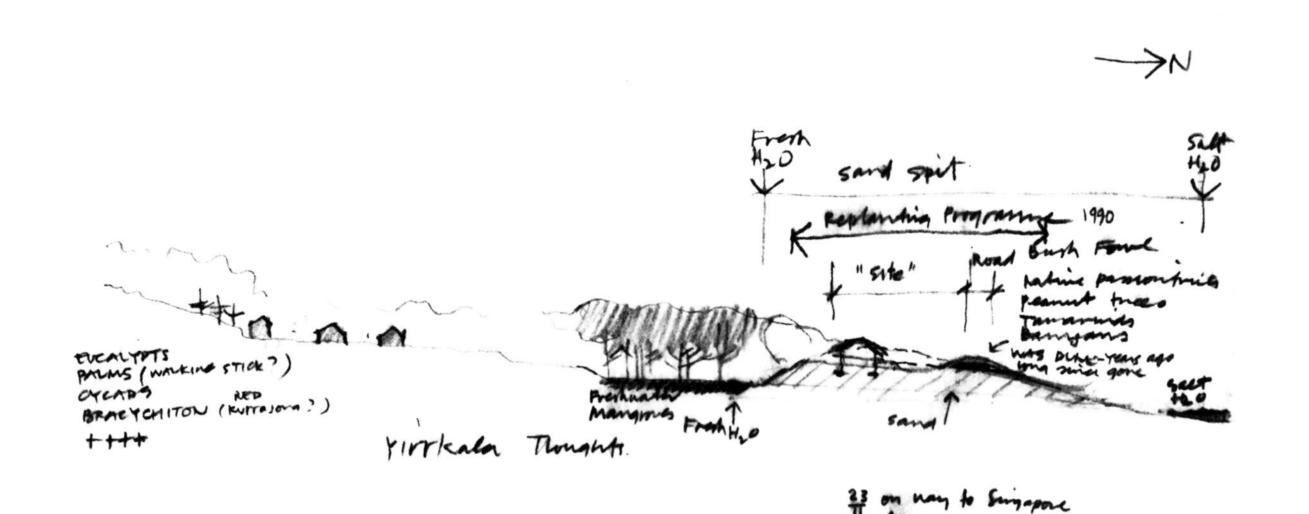

ıe Marika-Alderton house in the Northern
erritory represents the apotheosis of Murcutt's
eology and method, incorporating all the
rands of his experimentation over more than
irty years, plus his more recent considerable
ersonal investigations into Indigenous culture
nd way of life.

iis house is for an Aboriginal client whose
ilture is between 40,000 and 60,000 years old.
ıere is no tradition of house building – although
ere is a tradition among her people of elongated
unded bark-roofed raised shelters. The house
lopts a very similar form for the same rational
asons: it gives protection from sun, insects
nd the wet (up to half a metre of water can flow
der the building during tidal surges). And like
e bark shelter, the house is open at each end,
iented to the prevailing summer and winter
eezes; the long facades face north and south,
hich minimises sun entry.

ıe climate is tropical monsoonal. Summer
mperatures are in the 30°C range, with humidity
)–90%. The site, on Aboriginal land, is beside
beach. The surrounding natural environment –
nd and sea – provides food still hunted and
athered in the traditional manner.

iis house is highly experimental. It is one of only
handful of houses ever commissioned by an
original client and probably the first that is the
utcome of a detailed investigation of Aboriginal
ilture and customs. In this investigation, the
usband – who is European – was critical in being
ole to explain the cultural dimensions of the brief.

urcutt spent three years researching before he
esigned the house. During this period he stayed
th the clients' family on site for up to a week
a time, joining them in their way of life. He also
ad widely on Aboriginal culture and researched
e history of (white-designed) Aboriginal
ousing, discussing the reasons for its failure
th his clients.

'hat is most notable about Indigenous people
their deep, intimate and harmonious relationship
the land, which has spiritual, practical, social,
esthetic and cultural dimensions.

ıe house had to be prefabricated, with everything
eighted in. The cost was $A186,000, which
cludes on-costs of 100%, so overall the building
ould have cost at the time about $US70,000
nder normal circumstances.

is a composite structure of steel frame and
ustralian (non-rainforest) hardwoods. An elegant
stem of plywood and timber slatted flaps allows
e house to be opened up completely or partially
osed, modulating the ventilation according to
e weather. There is no glass in the building.
t times when the family goes away, the flaps are
osed up and the house becomes a locked box.

ıe programme is both quite ordinary and highly
ecific. It is a family house built to comply with
yclone building codes (wind velocities reach
)0 kilometres per hour) and modern standards
comfort, effectively cooled by summer and
inter winds, providing ample shade, as well
s shelter from rain without having to be closed
o. The cultural dimension of the programme is
ecial. Among the design objectives Murcutt lists
the need for people to move within the building
ithout being vulnerable to evil spirits: there is
o breezeway which might allow their entry.
ıe occupants had to be able to see the horizon
s well as culturally significant markers in
e landscape, and who's coming and going,
e weather changes and animal movements.
ıey also had to be able to see out without being
een, in order to avoid eye contact if necessary
nd so not have to welcome all-comers. The
ouse had to provide security, particularly while
ccupants are asleep. It also had to feel
omfortable for one or twenty relatives alike.

From the plan, this appears to be a conventional single family house with two bathrooms. However, the reason there are two bathrooms is culturally specific: one bathroom had to be well removed from public areas and located deep in the house, for women. (This is also the room that is reinforced for cyclone protection.) There are other culturally-driven aspects of the planning. Children's bedrooms are to the east, the parents' to the west, reflecting an Aboriginal idea of people's occupation of space corresponding to where the sun rises and sets. Aboriginal sense of space is very different from the Western tradition. It is subtle: you do not approach a building or space frontally, but from the sides.

The floor is open so that sand easily drops through, and also the cool air from below is drawn up into the house by Venturi-type exhaust fans in the roof. These also balance the air pressure inside during cyclones. (The extreme differential in air pressure between inside and outside during cyclones can cause houses to explode.)

The house has now been occupied for a number of years. The clients have replanted the surrounding area with local vegetation. They are happy and say the house works well within the context of their complex community culture, and they have not needed to make any changes.

Engineer: James Taylor and Associates

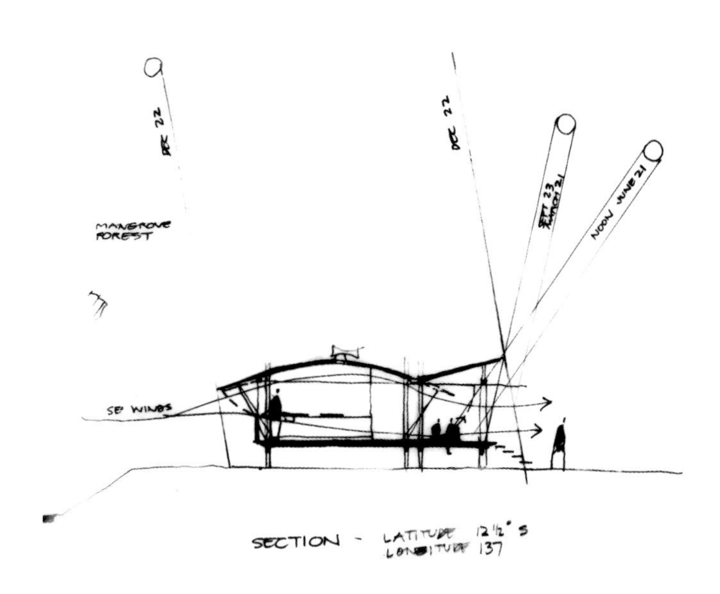

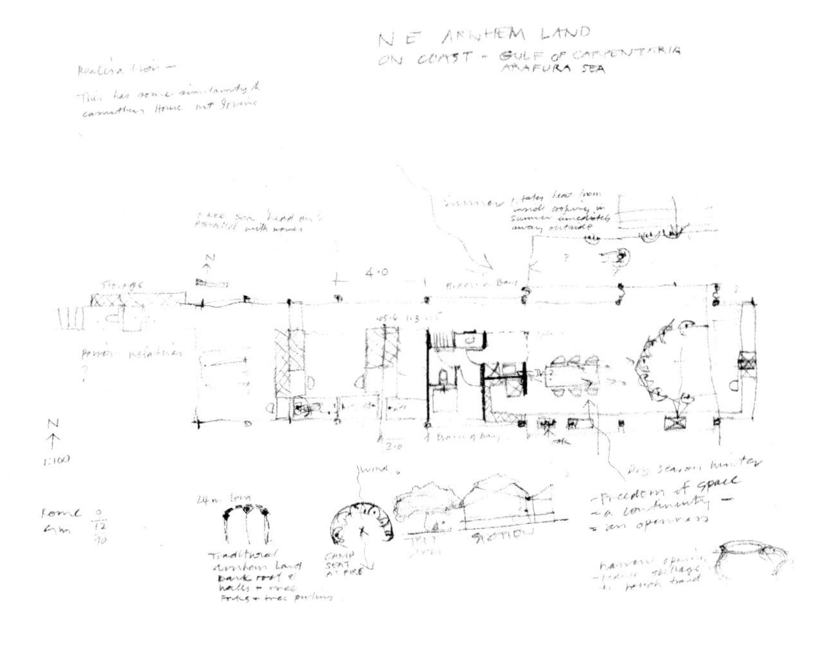

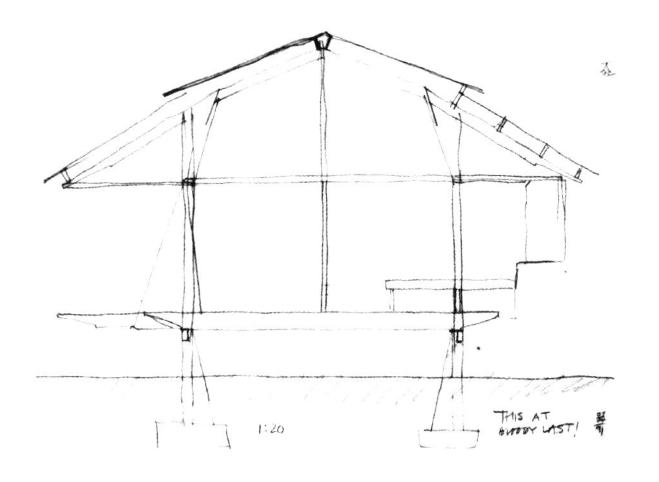
1:20
THIS AT
BLOODY LAST!

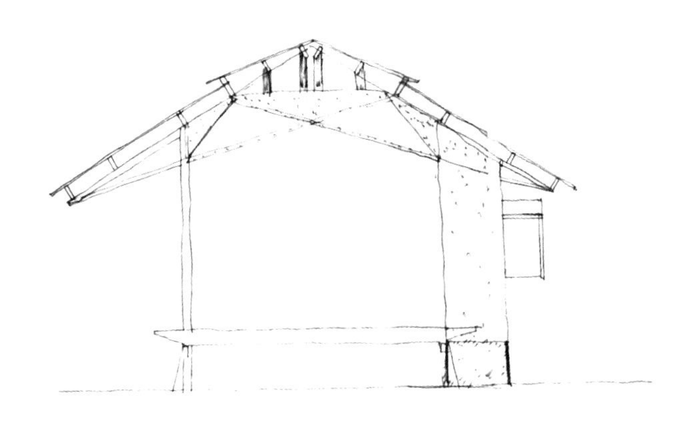

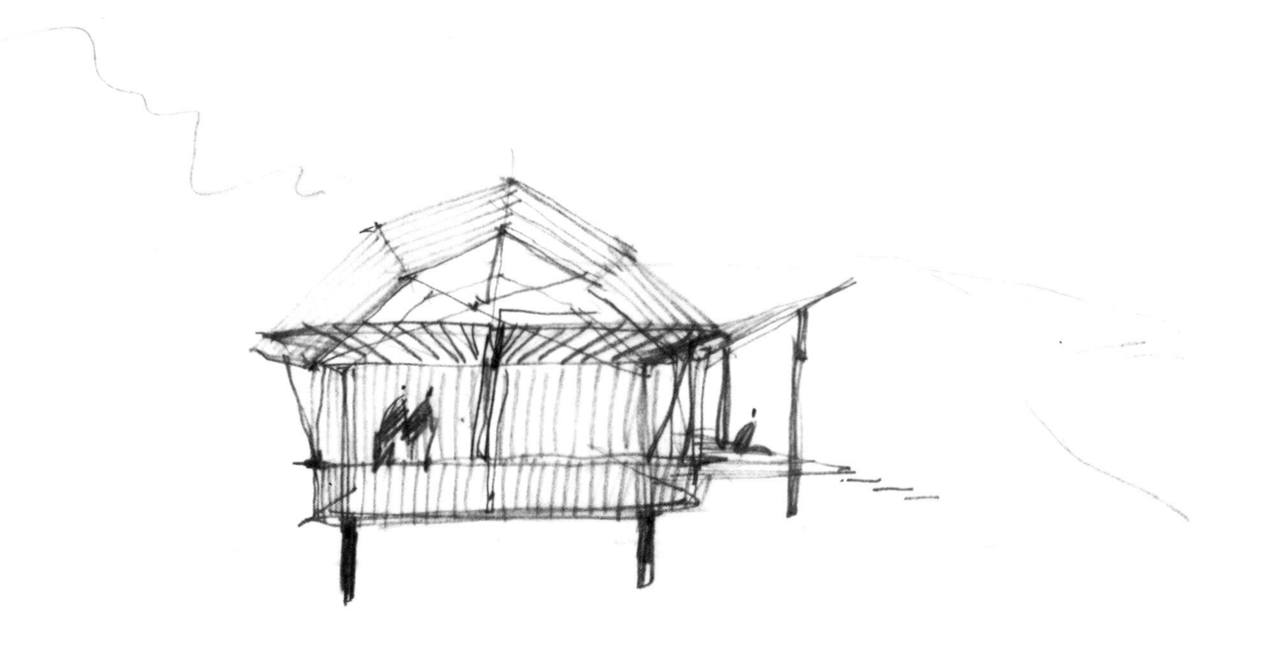

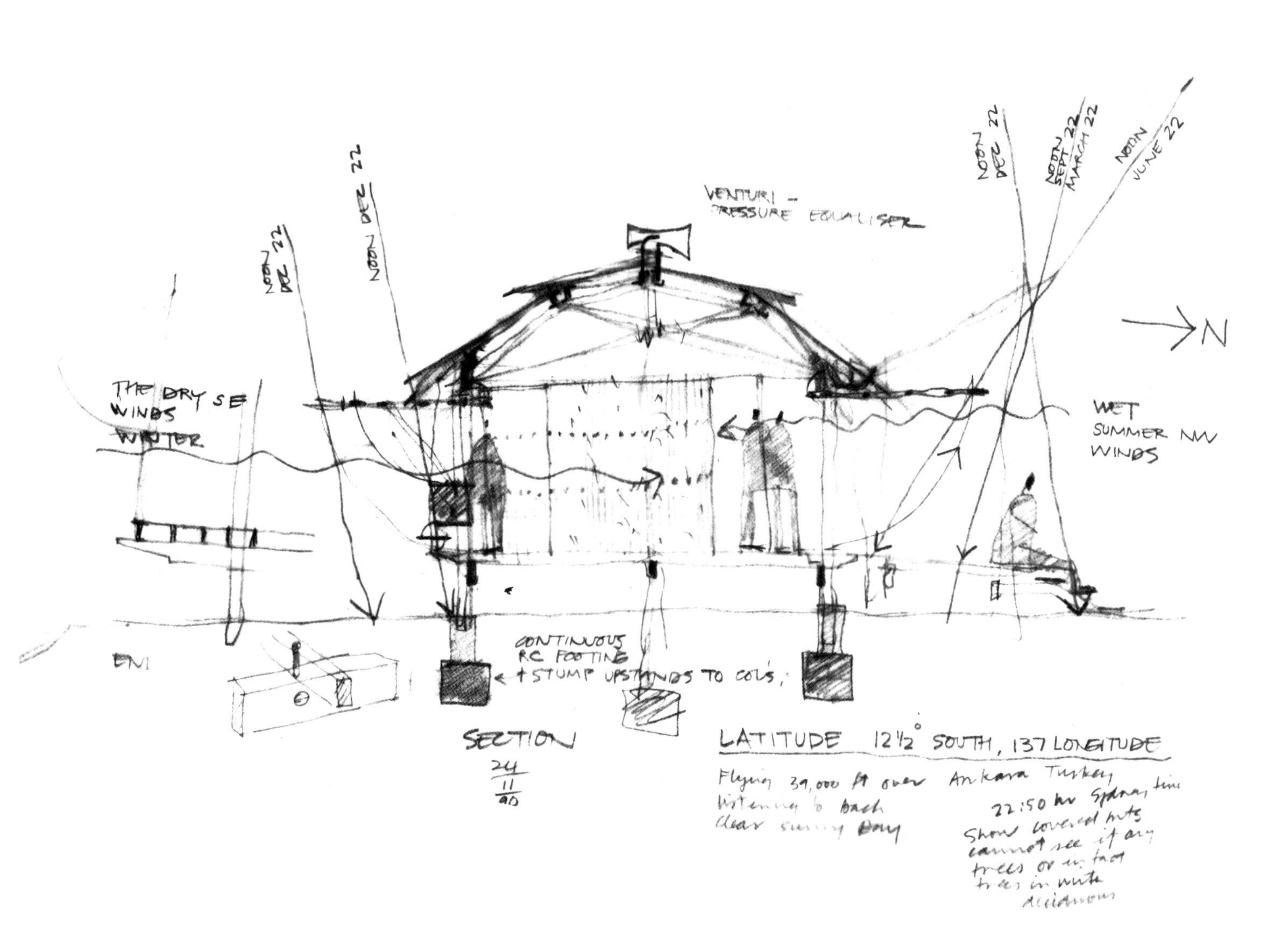
VENTURI - PRESSURE EQUALISER
NOON DEC 22
NOON DEC 22
NOON DEC 22
NOON SEPT 22 MARCH 22
NOON JUNE 22
N
THE DRY SE WINDS WINTER
WET SUMMER NW WINDS
CONTINUOUS RC FOOTING + STUMP UPSTANDS TO COL'S;
SECTION
24/11/90
LATITUDE 12½° SOUTH, 137 LONGITUDE
Flying 39,000 ft over Ankara Turkey
listening to Bach
clear sunny Day
22:50 hr Sydney time
Snow covered huts
cannot see if any
trees or in fact
trees in winter
deciduous

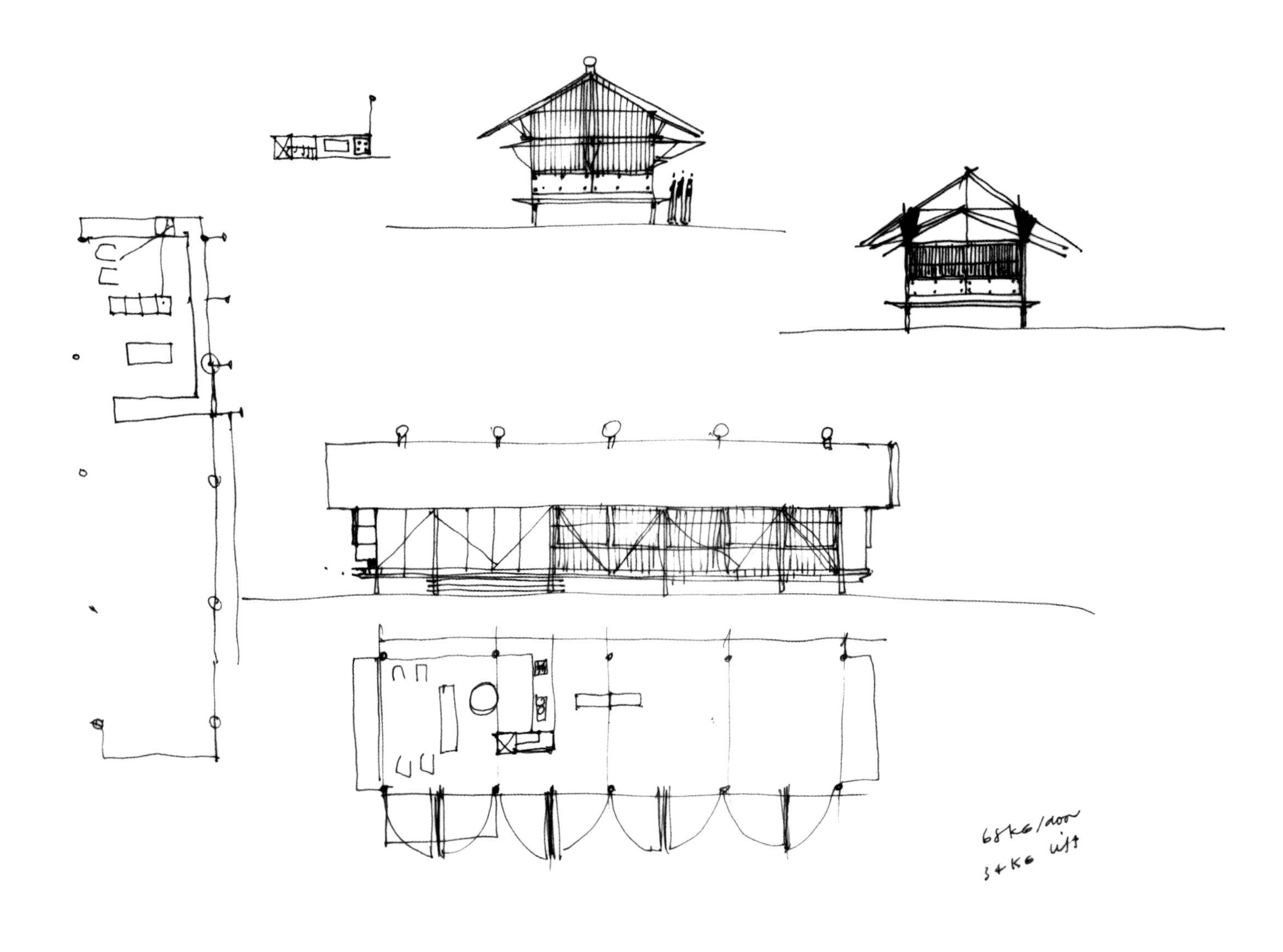
68KG/door
34KG lift

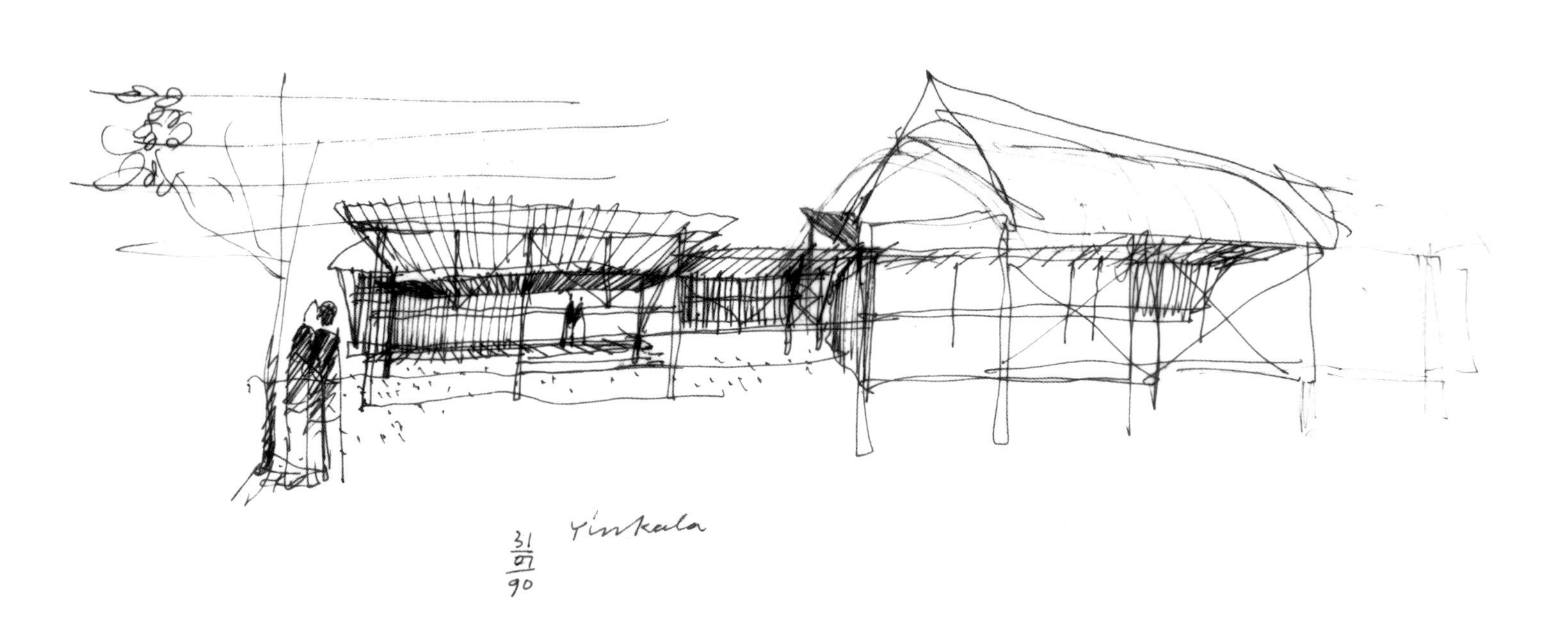
31/07/90
Yirrkala

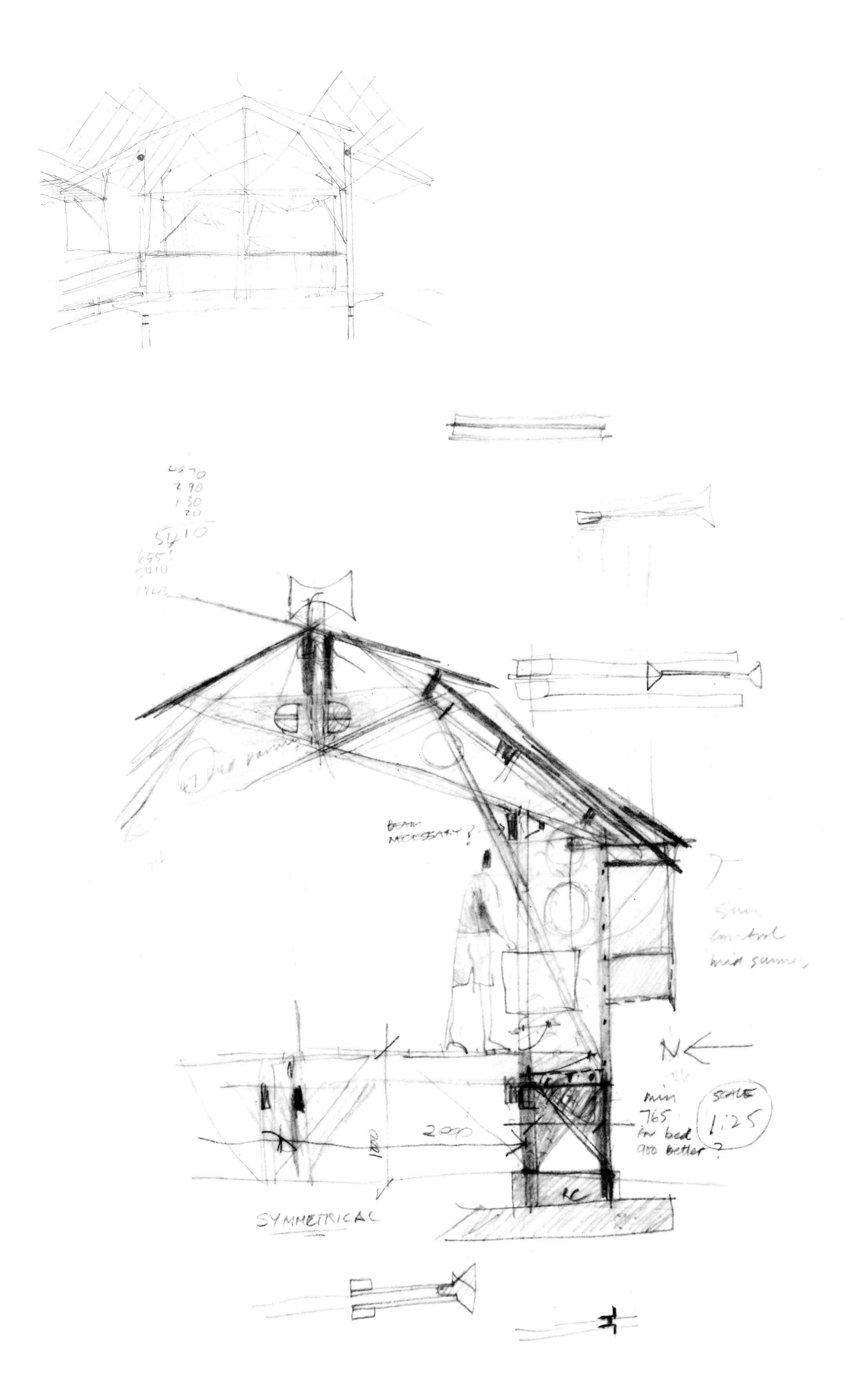
5410
BEAM NECESSARY?
N
min
765
for bed
900 better?
SCALE
1:25
2000
SYMMETRICAL

I LOVE THE BUILDINGS IN YOUR PHOTOGRAPHS

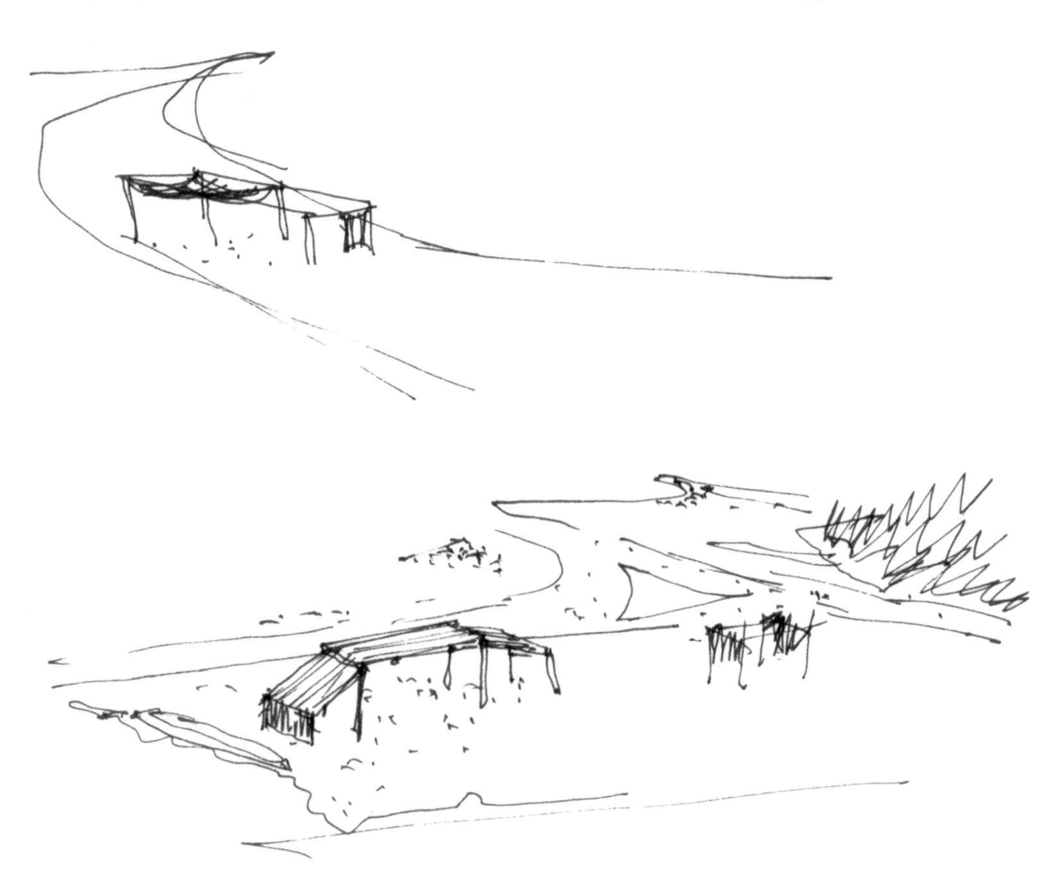

AND THE LIGHTNESS, DELICACY AND MINIMUM IMPACT IS JUST RIGHT FOR THIS AND MANY OTHER LANDSCAPES IN AUSTRALIA.

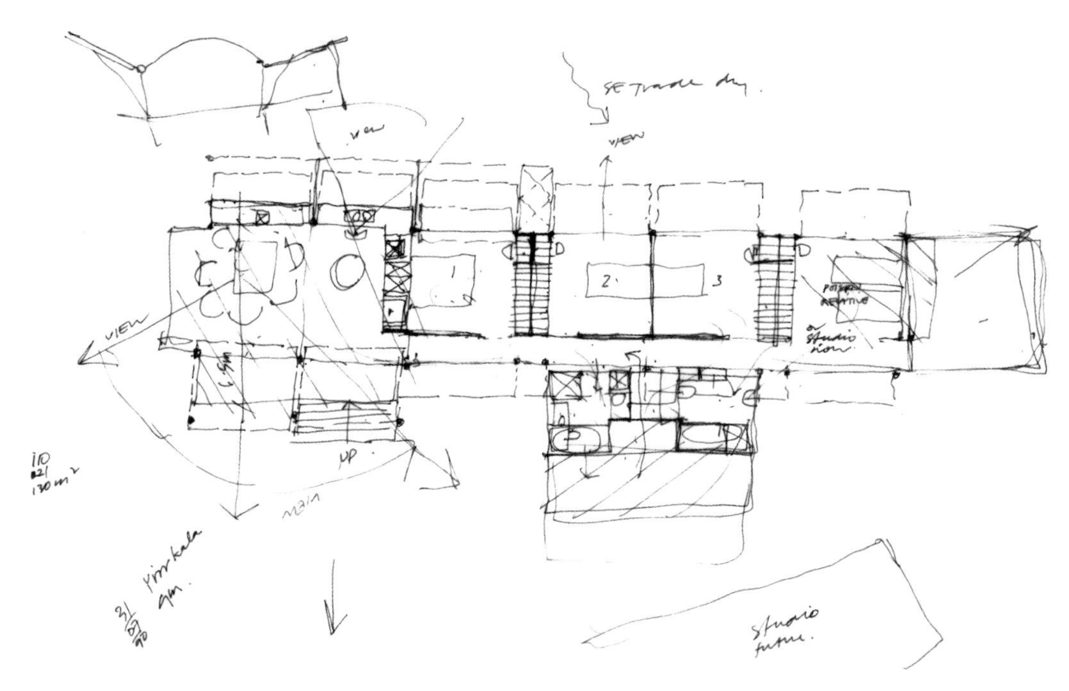
VIEW
VIEW
VIEW
UP
MAIN

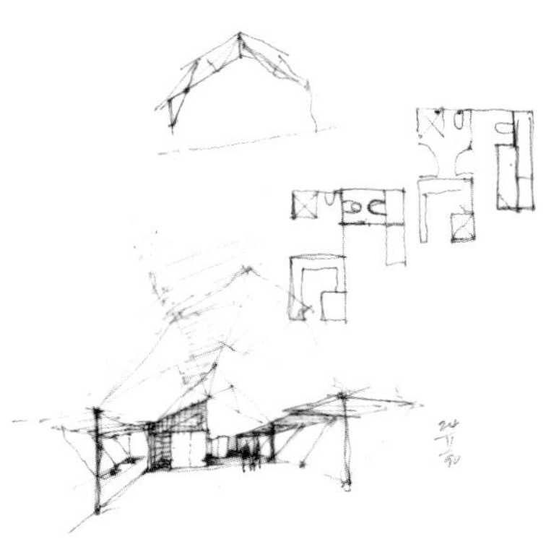

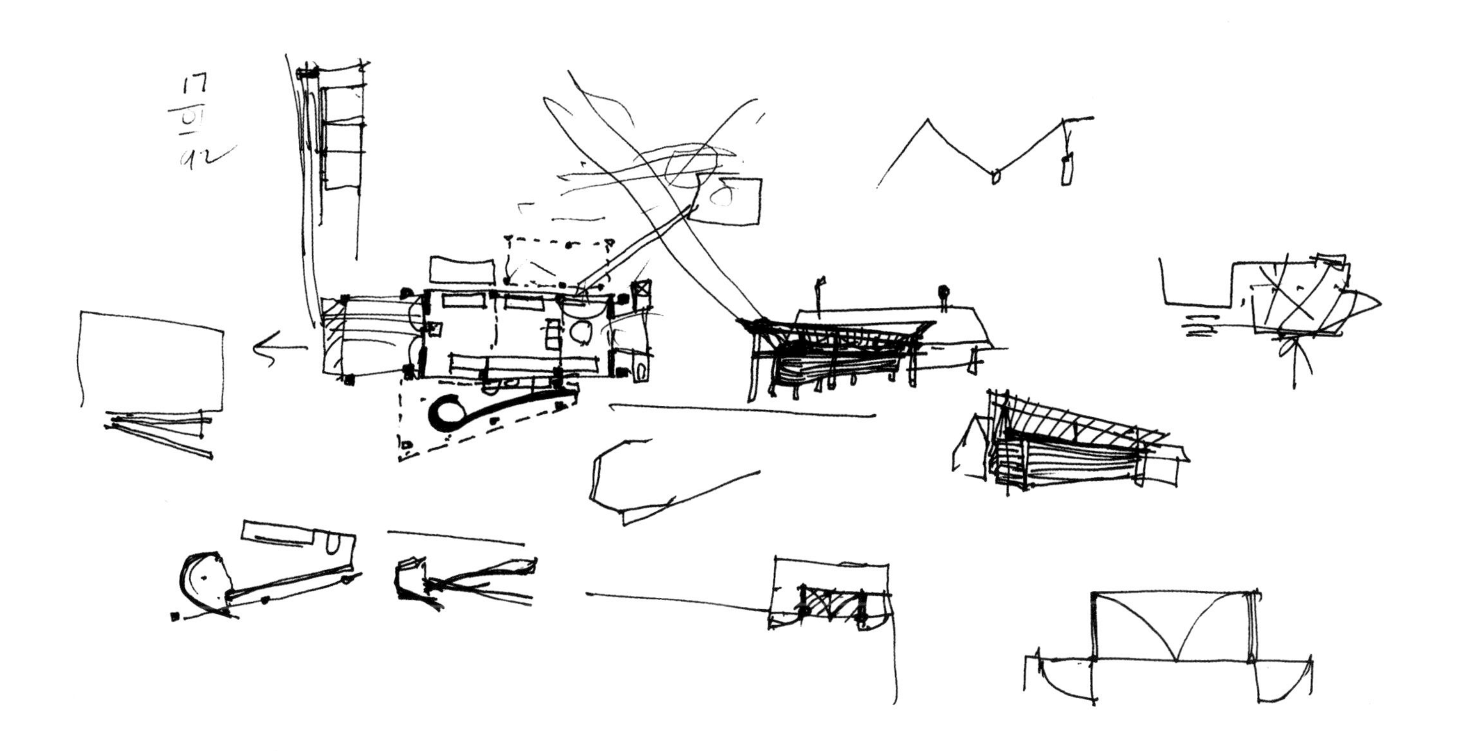

In renovating a rundown farm building (previously converted to a flat) on his property, Murcutt delights in consigning himself to the given constraints of the shed. He must retain its structure and fabric and use recycled materials. And he sets an additional constraint of making the building wheelchair accessible, even the bathroom.

It is of course a game. All the beautiful boards that form the external cladding were taken off, sanded on the inside, grooved to take the hoop iron strap weather/insect strip, and reassembled. He retains the rough essence of the timbers and sets them against the new elements. The oil-stained floor is contrasted with an Aaltoesque sideboard that contains the kitchen. (With such a small volume, a kitchen would seem to consume too much space; so he turns it into an apparently moveable piece of furniture and frees the space.)

The little servant wing bathroom is a separate element. When the shutters are folded back, the shower opens up to the outdoors. This is one of the first instances that a bathroom opens to the landscape rather than to the sky.

This pavilion is a casebook example of Murcutt's ideal of refuge and prospect. It is a cell with the prospect to the north: a perfect little villa.

Glenn Murcutt

I had kept the building as I thought that one day I might restore it, making planning changes. It was a rural worker's flat and tractor shed, located to the south and below the main house. At Christmas, this shed was the local dance hall. Some of the floor was propped in the 1930s and 40s. The old flooring boards are thick and oversized, with oil stains all over them. The shell was in a deteriorated condition.

The biggest aesthetic problem was spatially dealing with the timber bottom cords to the exposed roof trusses The bottom cords defined spaces. To have them fall above beds or in the centre of a zone would make for very awkward occupation. Taking these bottom cords as givens, I organised the plan into three zones, with the fireplace in the middle zone.

I very much enjoyed taking an existing seat-of-the-pants farm shed, reusing materials and restoring and reworking some elements. And it is still a shed, but now very comfortable.

All the material is reused from the shed or recycled from a pergola that was pulled down from the house. Inside, the original timber boards forming the walls have been sanded. A hoop iron strap tongue between each board allows for the movement of timber and prevents insects entering.

I renewed the roof. The roof framing is renewed in part, where the termites had inflicted damage. I retained the hand-shaped adzed timbers. The building can ventilate at each end at the ridge glazing.

Some posts were termite-damaged. New posts were bolt connected to the solid sections of the posts. New posts extended the existing posts and set up the skillion so that sun from the north penetrates deeply into the room in winter. The new posts taper back at the base.

The finesse in the kitchen and rawness of the other parts is a good contrast. The floor, with its different oil stains, has a beautiful sheen through the waxed finish. The window system is standard steel.

The small shower room and toilet are lined externally in Miniorb. The shower space works well. There is no corner mullion, and when the adjacent windows are open, the corner dissolves. With the windows open, you feel at one with the landscape.

I wanted to create as much space as possible and visually relate to the house and the landscape. For me there is an appeal in the minimalism which provides for the essence of living, using an existing shed with a clip-on shower room and toilet. It's just one room, simple.

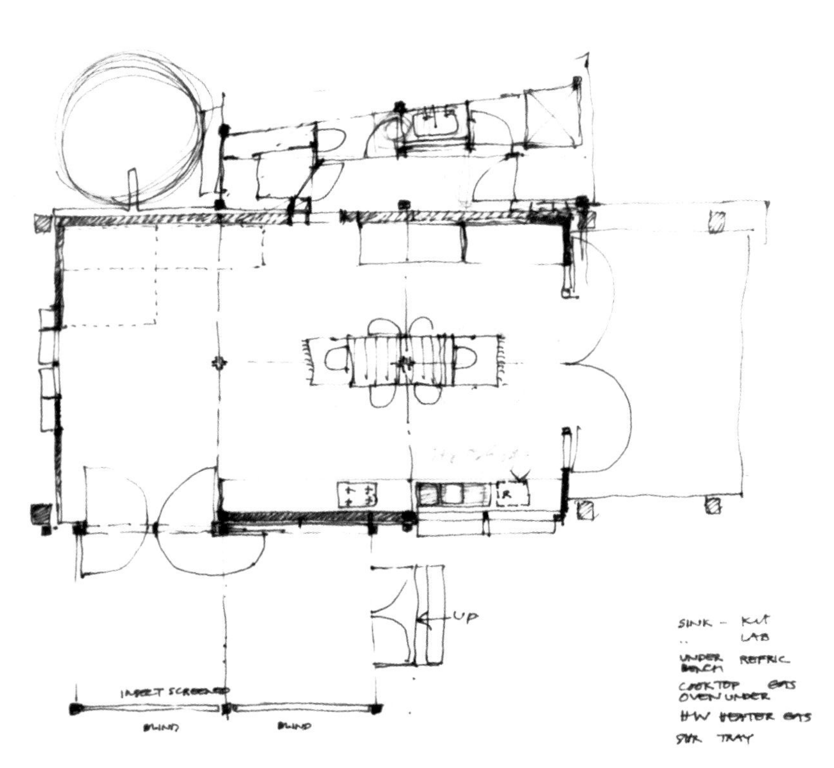

1:50 PLAN

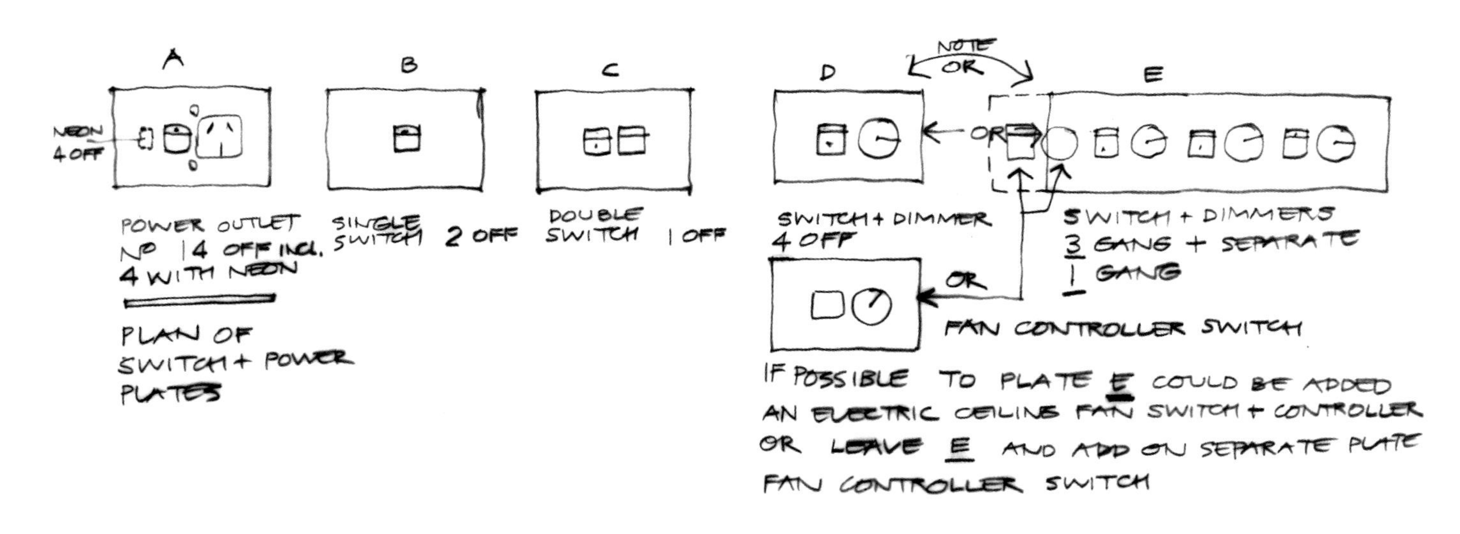

PLATES FLAT S.S, HORIZONTAL MOUNTINGS SS 788 POWER 114X70
SS 770

POWER OUTLETS WITH NEON INDICATORS
2 FOR KITCHEN SET AT 1125 TO ℄ ABOVE FF
1 FOR BASIN IN BATH " " "
1 FOR TUB IN LAUNDRY " "

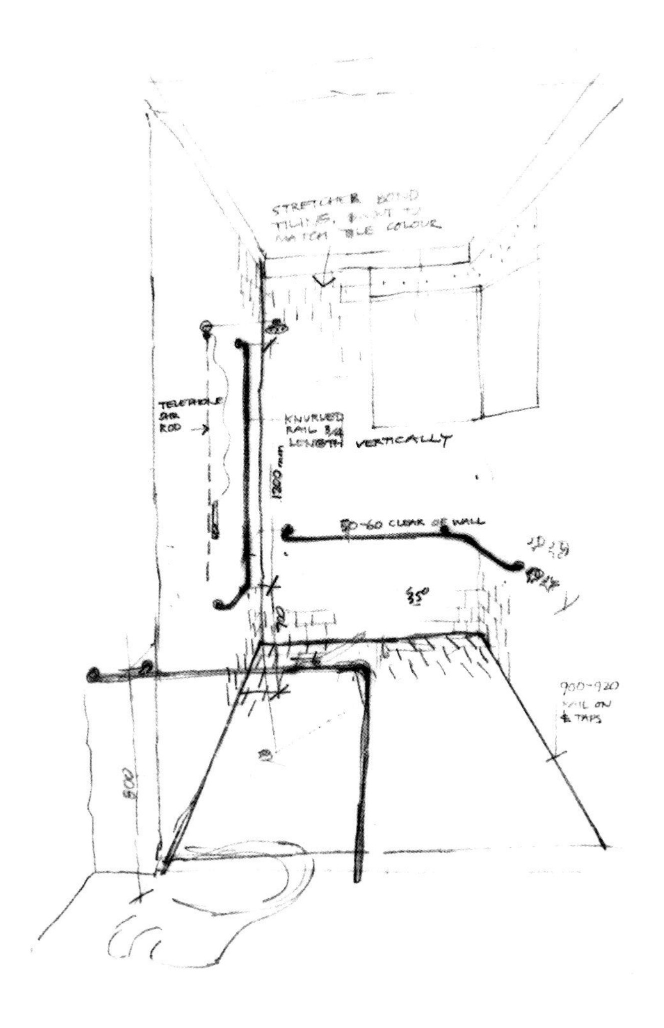
STRETCHER BOND
MATCH TILE COLOUR
TELEPHONE
SHR
ROD
KNURLED
RAIL 3/4
LENGTH VERTICALLY
1200 mm
50-60 CLEAR OF WALL
350
700
900-920
RAIL ON
TAPS
800

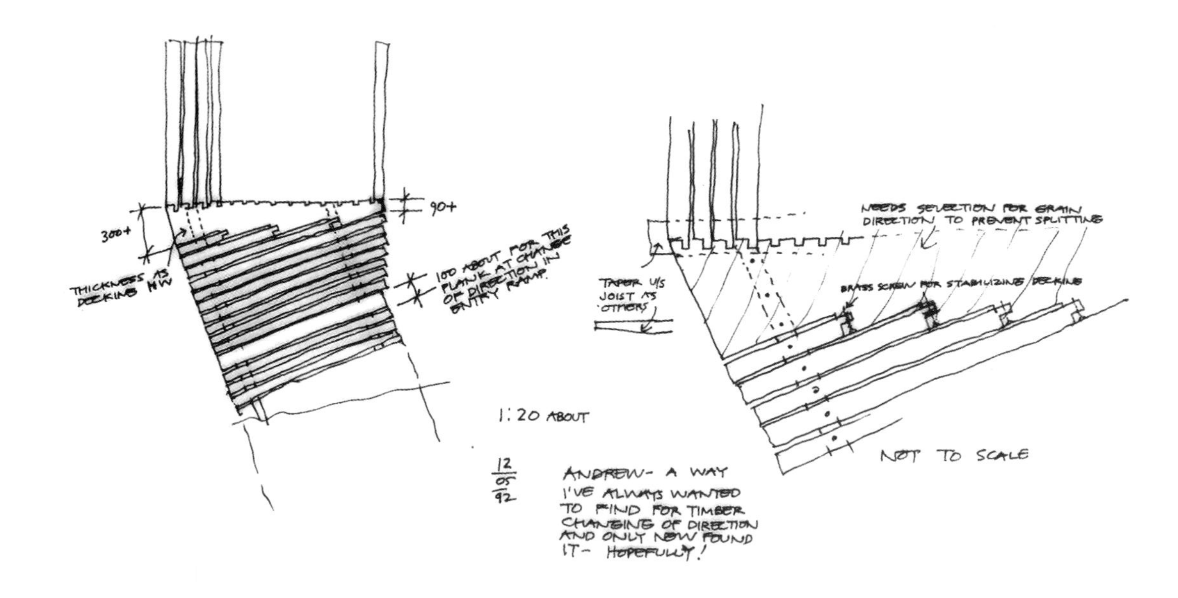
90+
300+
THICKNESS AS DECKING HW
100 ABOUT FOR THIS PLANK AT CHANGE OF DIRECTION IN ENTRY RAMP.
NEEDS SELECTION FOR GRAIN DIRECTION TO PREVENT SPLITTING
TAPER U/S JOIST AS 'OTHERS'
BRASS SCREW FOR STABILIZING DECKING
1:20 ABOUT
NOT TO SCALE
12/05/92
ANDREW - A WAY I'VE ALWAYS WANTED TO FIND FOR TIMBER CHANGING OF DIRECTION AND ONLY NOW FOUND IT - HOPEFULLY!

Schnaxl house
Bilgola Sydney New South Wales
1994 to 1996

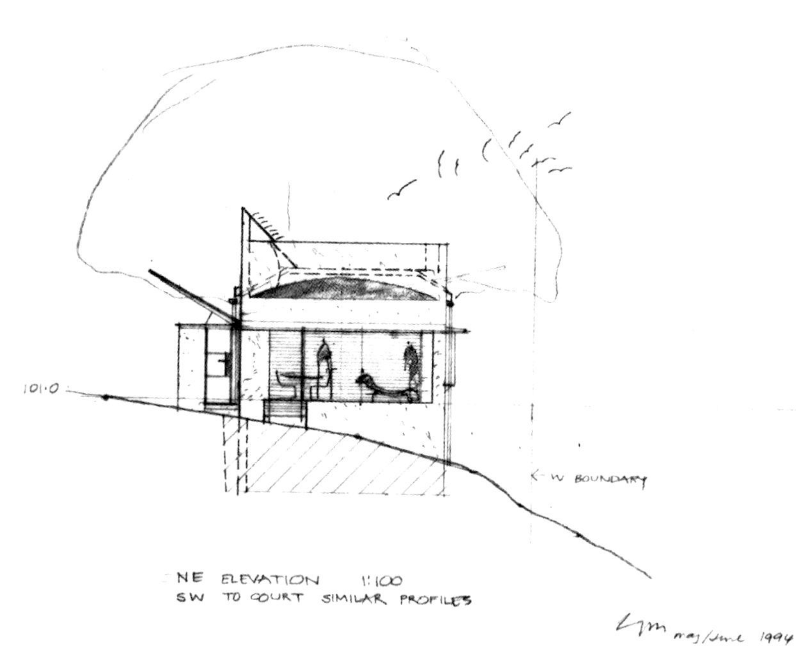

This is perhaps the most difficult site that Murcutt has had to contend with. First, there is a fall of almost 15 metres from the street frontage to the rear boundary. Second, stunning water views stretch along a north-south axis rather than east-west (which would have been ideal), so the house faces west rather than north.

Murcutt's working method is revealed in the way he addresses these two problems.

His design approach here bears comparison with that of the Minerals and Mining Museum at Broken Hill, which begins with an Aaltoesque accretion of the programmatic elements before becoming a linear plan. In both cases, Murcutt does not arrive at the linear plan from the outset. As he says of this house, his initial design explorations are generated by an idea of blocks stepping down the topography and forming a courtyard around the old tree. A double problem for this Aaltoesque solution is the location of the ancient angophera on the southern side of the site, making it difficult to bring sun over the building and down into the courtyard. Murcutt works very hard at this plan before he abandons the strategy.

Once he settles on the linear plan, which gives him the best access to the water views, the problem is to bring north light into the centre of the house. Murcutt does this with a very unusual roof section. It is framed up as a gable inside, but with a light monitor that draws north and east light into the central living area. On the northern end of the house he makes an indoor-outdoor room: with all the windows and shutters pushed back, it is a summer verandah, and in winter it closes up and becomes a glazed sun-trap. The bedrooms, which do not need north sun, are positioned to enjoy the views.

The poetics of the entrance sequence has its beginnings in the Ball-Eastaway house and Southern Highlands house (1988–92), and is further developed in the Simpson-Lee house. The entry sequence slides in at the side, allowing people to take in the landscape and experience the sense of place.

e site is a beautiful piece of land in the midst mediocre buildings of the last twenty years. s a difficult site, sloping almost west, with raordinary views to Pittwater and Scotland Island. ere was a preservation order on an ancient e, the angophora costata. I used it in the arrival quence to develop ideas about entry.

e house is located to the bottom, rear boundary the site, near a large sandstone outcrop. There e layers of rock shelves and fine opportunities landscaping the garden. The clients wished live on the edge of the site and to see the water yond. This siting makes possible the greatest mension in relation to the number of rooms that joy an outlook to Pittwater. The house sits on a ate plinth, which reduces the height of the building ually, especially from the Pittwater side.

ad problems with the local authorities about e location of the garage: they insisted on double garage for a three-bedroom house and apron for one car, creating a 7.5-metre setback ntage on an arc. The site has more than 1:4 fall. Driveways can be a maximum of 1:4. e 7.5-metre setback for the garage meant the rage would be at an immense scale. We cut e house to two bedrooms, therefore only a single rage was needed. I tried to make it as low and nall as possible. It was something I dismissed being obliged to do.

e entry sequence begins from a high level ong a path on axis with the angophora, which huge and gnarled. Four metres from the tree e path turns to face the door, returns under pergola and towards the view via a beautiful ck, and then down to the door. When the door pens, light floods in from above.

ere is a linear light monitor through the house, d also good bounced light. The timber roof embers are exposed and clad as a series of ribs the space. Summer and winter sun is controlled adjustable sun blades set above the glazing.

e zone of the pitched and flat ceiling defines e blade. Paintings are hung on walls which have een thickened to receive art works.

hen the sitting room doors are open, there a sense of being outside on the verandah while the living area. There is sun there all winter. the evenings in summer the space can be opened d protected with just the flyscreens.

e fin or corner of the house at each end ssolves, directs the view and also extends the mension of the view.

e verandah is both an inside and outside space. e corner opens up fully. Insect screens and nber screens can be pulled back. The site drops vay and one experiences a sense of being the edge of the building, poised over the view.

e space floats yet there is a very strong sense mass, security. Light floods in and reveals the ge end wall elements of containment. Deep-cut oping reveals to openings increase the perception wall thickness. Space flows and there is the ense of its being a bigger space than it is in fact.

e upper floor is the same level throughout, and in polished concrete. The walls are hard plaster. ternally the house is cement-rendered and painted Ionian White. Timber is stained dark oak. e ends of the purlins are tipped with bitumen.

The timber shading screen has become a system combined with sliding glass and insect screens. This provides increased security, with two major systems to penetrate.

The section is about compliances. I took a bay out of the house when we decided not to include a guest toilet. That gave more space for the angophora. The footings were designed so they do not affect the drainage to the tree's root system.

The end of the building is quite modelled, with bits pulled out and bits recessed. I needed to locate a stormwater detention tank. About 2000 to 3000 litres of water go into the tank. It is a municipality requirement designed to reduce the risk of landslides in a downpour, as so much rainwater comes off the roofs.

The big excavated underfloor space is not damp. The sewerage line is way up, more than 10 metres higher than the ground floor of the house. A cutter shreds the waste, which is pumped up to the sewerage.

There were some earlier versions of the house. The initial scheme was not a rectilinear box: instead, the building was staggered in response to the topography, boundaries and light. This initial idea driven by the topography lent itself to a courtyard arrangement, enclosing the big tree. I often start with ideas I want to explore, but eventually I am dragged back to important things. I had a sod roof, but it was too expensive in construction. Cost was an issue. I did lots of sketches, looking at sections, roof structure, elevations, plans. I'll often do lots and lots of drawings just to see the possibilities.

When a drawing is marked 'THIS', that's when I settle on an idea. Then it's let's get on and develop this. I often forget I've done things. I should go back and check but mostly I don't. It's a problem. But often I've touched on the idea some time back in the design process and passed it over.

Landscape architect: Schaffer Barnsley
Engineer: James Taylor and Associates

Deakins-Beckwith house
in collaboration with Nicholas Murcutt
Woollahra Sydney New South Wales
1994 to 1997

This tiny house is an exercise in very tight planning. It is almost like a yacht. The two children's bedrooms have the quality of cabins; Murcutt achieves the same feeling in the little bedrooms of both the Marika-Alderton house and the Boyd Education Centre.

The challenge for the architects is to give the house a sense of space and increased scale. To achieve this on the lower level, Murcutt reprises the scale-inflating effect of the flanking mass walls of the Magney house in Paddington. Upstairs, the very tight volume of the circulation is attenuated and given a greater sense of dimension by the layering of the wall planes, achieved by little projecting timber nibs that transform the walls into floating planes.

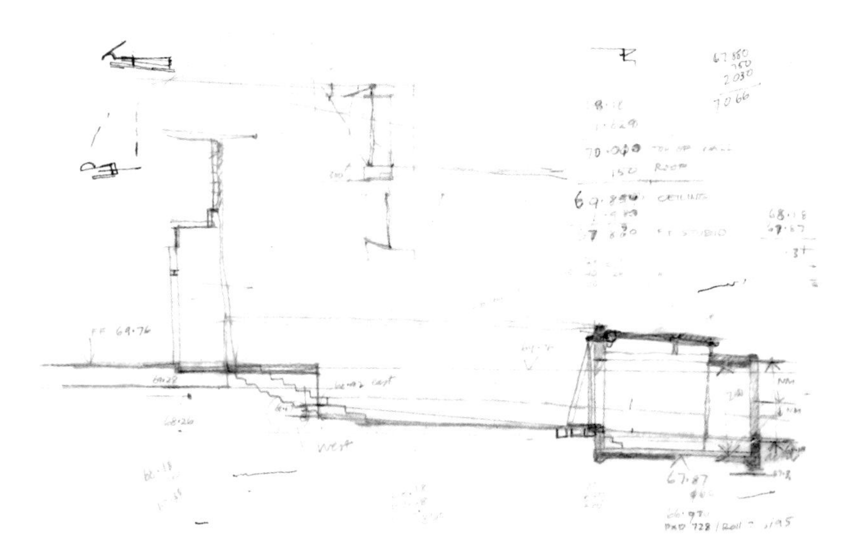

Glenn Murcutt

The project involved an alteration and addition to a small terrace in a group of three workers' cottages. Upstairs there were two private rooms and one walk-through room, and downstairs two rooms and a space at the rear for a quite primitive kitchen and bathing space, and an outside toilet. The rear faces north. Termites had attacked many areas and the house was close to being derelict.

But the front facade has a good stone wall and exposed brickwork from the second floor, with a projecting balcony. The street facade has been retained and restored.

The clients are a young family. They required good living spaces and bedrooms for two children, as well as a studio out the back. A service lane provides access to the rear.

The house is narrow: the clear internal dimension is just over 4 metres. The existing house was 6 metres deep. The addition increases the depth in effect by another 3.5 metres, on two floors. It is now a tightly planned three-bedroom house with a freestanding studio at the end of the garden. The garden is fully contained by the buildings and courtyard wall.

Light is brought into the middle of the house by a light trap which serves the bathing spaces on level two as well as the dining room on level one. The lightwell is ventilated and insect-screened. The roof light is screened.

The rear of the house has a vertical scale reminiscent of the Magney house, with a simple steel framing system with a big horizontal member – a modified steel C-section supporting the children's bed alcove window system. This steel frame holds the box of windows that projects beyond downstairs, creating a mirador effect that provides shading to the kitchen and eating areas from the equinox throughout summer. Blinds give privacy and shade to the bedrooms.

A vent at the bed alcove floor level reads as part of the door system to the kitchen below, increasing the scale of the lower floor. The ground floor looks bigger than it is and the tightness is achieved from the garden elevation.

The studio is built out to the boundary. It is a very stripped-down form, a little mass box with deep alcoves inside. It has a pitched roof and varied ceiling heights: two-thirds of the floor area is above 2.4 metres. The alcoves on the side boundaries have lower ceiling heights to achieve the maximum fence height on boundaries. The ceiling opens up to bring in northern light.

Designed with Nicholas Murcutt

Engineer: James Taylor and Associates

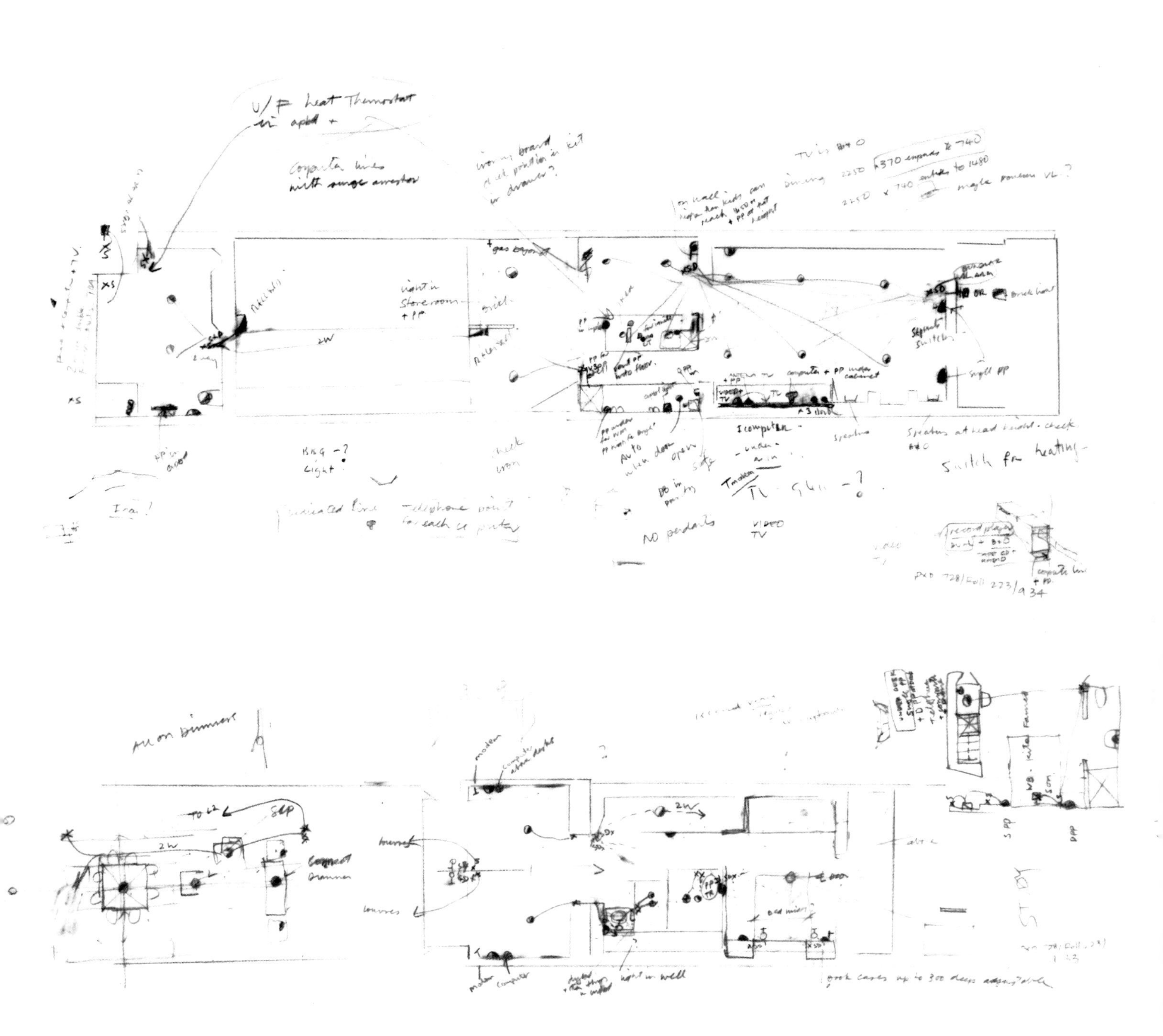
U/F heat Thermostat
Computer lines with surge arrestor
TV is B+O
Switch for heating
Speakers at head height - check B+O
single PP
NO pedals
VIDEO TV
All on dimmers
book cases up to 300 deep adjustable

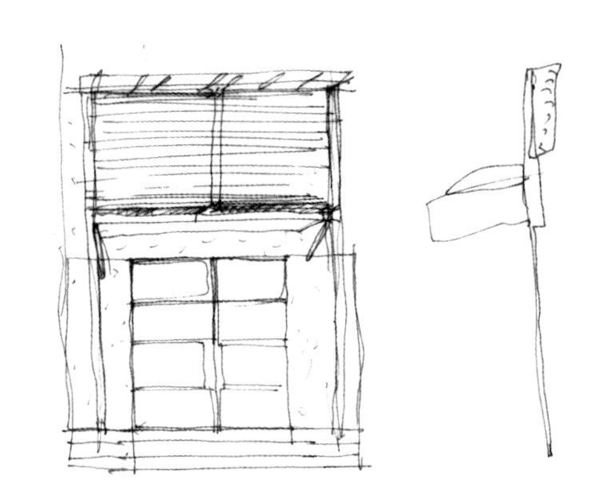

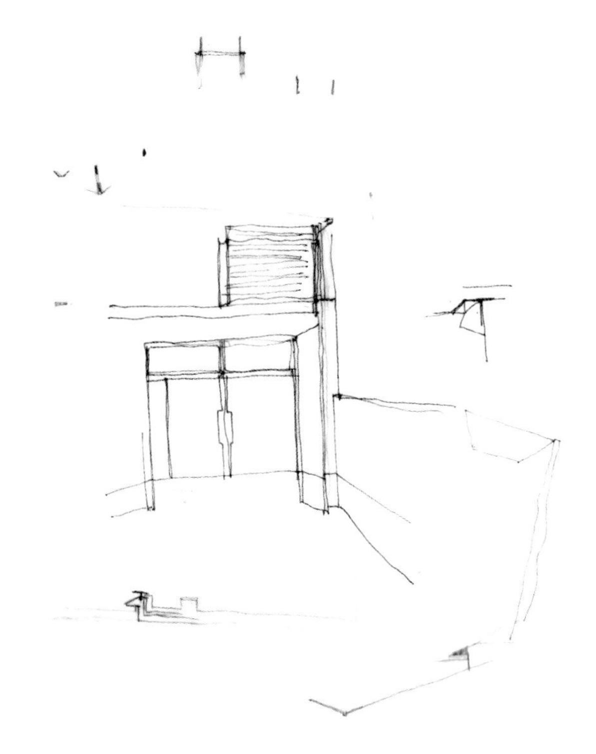

Fletcher-Page house
Kangaroo Valley New South Wales
1996 to 1998

SITTING / DINING / 'COUNTRY KITCHEN' —

EXPOSED TO VIEW — OVERLOOKING — TO THE SITE ABOVE.
ALL UP I THINK I PREFER SCHEME 'A'

IT LOOKS LIKE 144 M^2 IS AS SMALL AS I CAN MAKE YOUR BRIEF WORK AND STILL ACHIEVE GOOD SPACES. IT'S 15 m^2 - 20 m^2 MORE THAN I WOULD LIKE TO MEET YOUR BUDGET SO IT'S EITHER REDUCING SPACES OR UNDERSTANDING THAT THE $300,000.00 INCL FEES & BUILDING, NEEDS SOME 'TOPPING UP'!
WHAT DO YOU THINK? — I WOULD LIKE SOME DIRECTION SO THAT I CAN GET PLANS TO YOU THIS WEEK FOR COUNCIL D. A. SUBMISSION.

WHILST PLANS ARE IN COUNCIL, THE DESIGN CAN BE FURTHER DEVELOPED. I PROPOSE WALLS 'BAGGED' PAINTED BRICK INSIDE — BATTENED, INSULATED & TIMBER LINED OUTSIDE WALLS OIL STAINED GREY EXTERNALLY

ROOF GALV, CORRUGATED IRON - NATURAL TANKS

DOORS/WINDOWS LIDCO 1030 ALUMINIUM POSSIBLY FINISHED IN A GREY, SOME WINDOWS WILL HAVE SHUTTERS OF SLATTED TIMBER, OTHERS EXTERNAL VENETIAN BLINDS (IF ABLE TO BE AFFORDED)

I'M IN SYDNEY MONDAY PM, TUESDAY WEDNESDAY & THURSDAY AM.

REGARDS,
Glenn

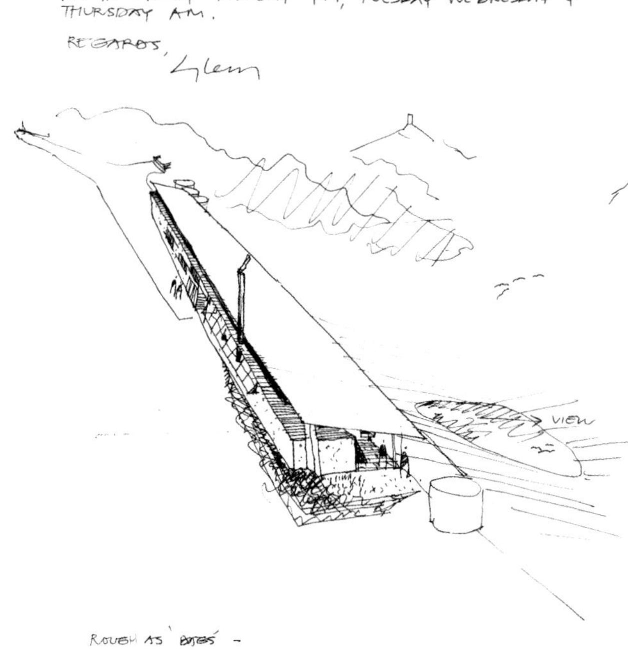

ROUGH AS 'BAGS' —

Glenn

the Southern Highlands house (1988–92), impson-Lee (1989-94) and Fletcher-Page ouses, we see a progressive reduction of the chitectural idea to two formal gestures: the ox and the roof plane. Increasing simplicity haracterises these works. Internally, the section never compromised spatially; and the plane the ceiling flows. The proportioning system the frame becomes less overt. Whereas e frame is explicit in the Bingie Bingie house 982–84), in these later houses the frame is ot expressed, and yet there is always the sense the rhythm it generates.

urcutt consistently works to attenuate buildings their edges, where they are typically stretched nd thinned down. But now also he increasingly retches the buildings themselves, achieving cale through the extended horizontal dimension.

/hile the more pronounced emphasis n abstraction and minimalism simplifies the uildings formally, the details become more omplex and exquisite, and materials more ensual. Murcutt directs attention to the elements the house that the body comes in contact ith. This duality of formal simplicity bstraction/mind) and enhanced tactility body) is inherent in minimalism. As architecture ecomes stripped of its visual, iconographic gns, the opportunity intensifies to emphasise s haptic, tactile qualities, and these have e effect of grounding inhabitants through the senses.

urcutt's detailing of the edges of things ecomes more expressively gestural – notably e windows and exterior doors in this house. the course of abstracting the wall plane, e dramatises the contrast between – and ngagement with – inside and outside by, aradoxically, thickening the openings rather an the wall itself. Windows become boxlike, most habitable spaces, with multiple layers shading and ventilation components; nd the doors too have many layers: insect creening, timber batten sun screening, glazing directly engaging inhabitants.

iven that the view is to the south and urcutt wants to open the building to the north r solar access, the house becomes very ansparent. It is in fact the most transparent all his buildings. The living room is now ss cave-like, yet it still manifests the sense f containment that is fundamental to Murcutt's nperative for refuge. Here he explores ways generating the requisite sense of refuge while creasing transparency.

is an idea that he began to explore – but bandoned – in the initial design for the outhern Highlands house, using a butterfly oof to increase the building's transparency.

Kangaroo Valley is 190 kilometres south of Sydney. The site is in a beautiful valley falling to the south. My clients wanted a very simple house, with living, dining and kitchen together, a separate area with a bedroom, bathing and dressing, and a small verandah off the bedroom, a separate studio for painting and another for writing and to double as a guest bedroom, with a bathing space nearby.

The house is sited as near as I could locate it along the contours, which provide a wonderful outlook to the escarpment. There are good breezes in this escarpment area.

Winters can be cold, so the house is built with reverse brick veneer, like the Bingie Bingie and Mount Wilson houses (this house is clad externally with timber), and there are laminated glass doors, heating, a fireplace, and concrete floors providing thermal mass.

The double concrete floor has insulation between the slabs as well as cable heating. The 80mm top concrete slab is a thermal sink: it expands and contracts over a Styrofoam base. The concrete can move in all directions against expansion felt set against the walls. The concrete is steel-trowelled and given a latex finish. It is a simple monolithic floor.

The proprietary firebox built into one of my surrounds is a simple, honest-looking unit. It is a combustion/heat exchange system: air is drawn in at the floor, passes around the fire, is heated and discharges through the top. I modified the jacket around the firebox and put gravel around it for additional thermal insulation. It is a box within a box.

It was very important to capitalise on the northern light to the rear of the house. The excavated earth was reworked to create a flatter terrace in front of the living space. Sun penetration in mid-winter is excellent. The projecting northern window bay and external adjustable retractable venetian blinds provide summer sunshading. Sliding timber screens to the northern studio windows provide shade, privacy and security.

It is one of my objectives to design openings to function in multiple ways. The openings have insect screens and outside sliding screens providing both security and ventilation. The sill panel ventilation is the same system as Mount Wilson, where ventilation is still available when it's raining.

The windows to the north side also have separate ventilation panel systems for the bedrooms. The insect-mesh timber-grille vents have hopper panels internally for air control. They can be fully open to closed.

The main shower enjoys privacy and a beautiful outlook. The corner window pulls right back to give the shower a feeling of being outside, like the Kempsey guest studio.

It is a warm grey house sitting in a lush environment. The timber siding is 200 by 25mm western red cedar stained grey.

The endgrain of the timber rafters is exposed to weather. A saw-cut ensures the water drips off. The end is painted with bitumen to reduce further the potential damage to timber by wetting and drying.

The roof pitch is 11°, similar to the angle of the fall of that part of the site.

Like many other country buildings I have designed, there is no town water to the site. Drinking water is collected and stored in tanks. The corrugated galvanised roofing and water storage tank materials were initially a problem for the council. We submitted a dossier on why the design should be approved: it was not affecting anyone or causing glare. Council changed policy as a result and removed its blanket clause preventing the use of galvanised iron materials. Galvanised iron has become a basic part of our cultural landscape in Australia: it takes on the light and colour of the surrounding elements and the sky.

The kitchen is a convivial, old country-type kitchen, with the dining table included. The kitchen, dining and sitting room bench tops are stainless steel. The cupboards below the bench are painted timber, all white. The built-in cabinetry for the hi-fi, TV and video has venting, either slotted or drilled holes. The speaker boxes are integrated in the walls.

Most elements have been worked out.

Working drawings assistant: Nick Sissons

Engineer: James Taylor and Associates

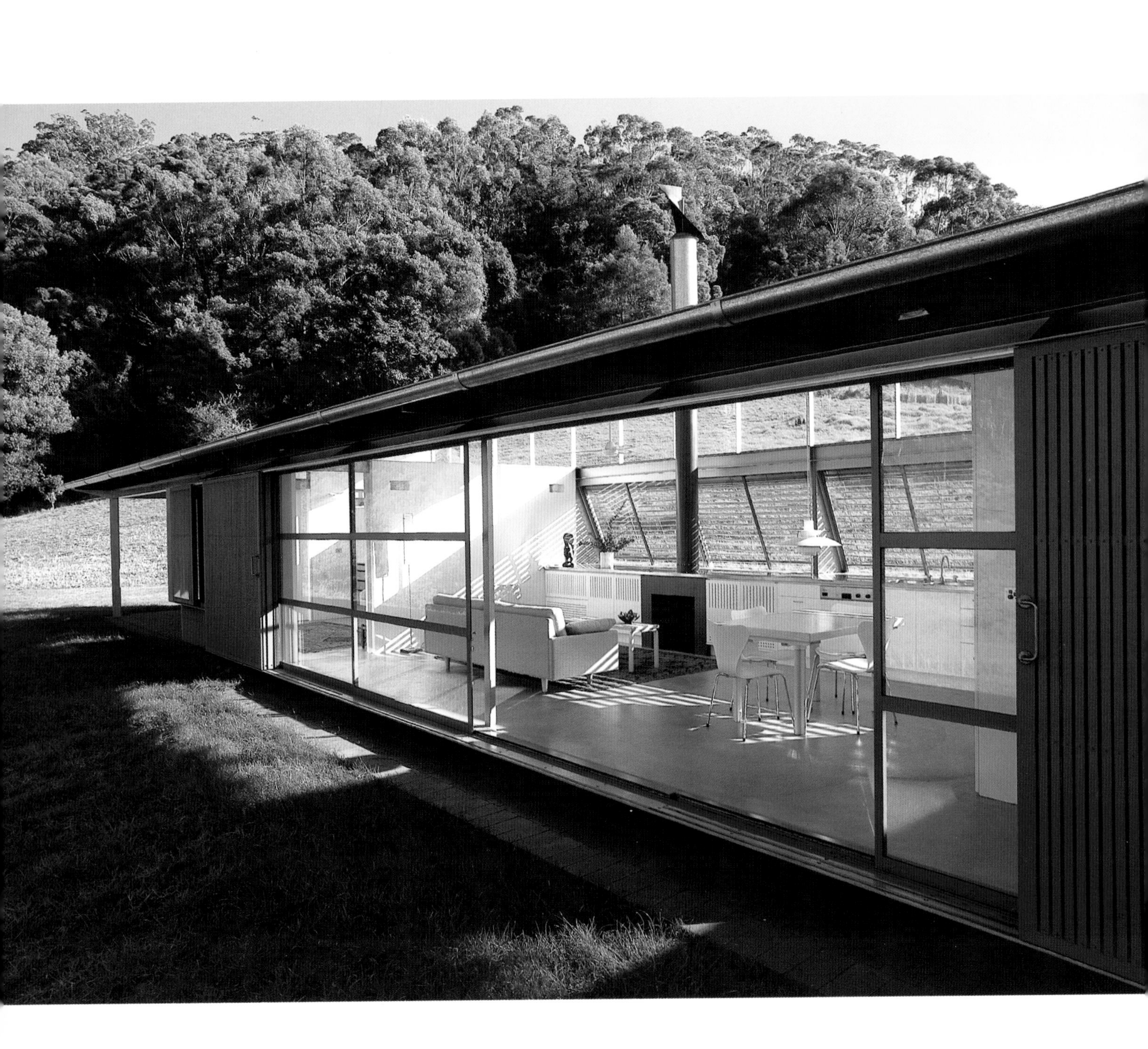

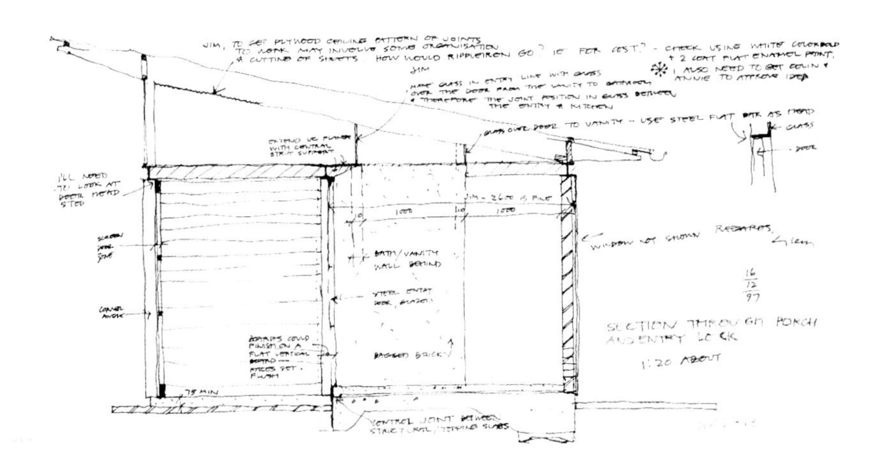
JIM, TO GET PLYWOOD CEILING PATTERN OF JOINTS TO WORK MAY INVOLVE SOME ORGANISATION & CUTTING OF SHEETS. HOW WOULD RIPPLEIRON GO? IE FOR COST? – CHECK USING WHITE COLORBOND + 2 COAT FLAT ENAMEL PAINT.
I ALSO NEED TO GET COLIN & ANNIE TO APPROVE IDEA
JIM
MAKE GLASS IN ENTRY LINE WITH GLASS OVER THE DOOR FROM THE VANITY TO BATHROOM & THEREFORE THE JOINT POSITION IN GLASS BETWEEN THE ENTRY & KITCHEN
GLASS OVER DOOR TO VANITY – USE STEEL FLAT BAR AS HEAD
GLASS
DOOR
EXTEND UC PURLIN WITH CENTRAL STRUT SUPPORT
I'LL NEED TO LOOK AT DOOR HEAD STOP
JIM – 2600 IS FINE
1000
1000
WINDOW NOT SHOWN
REGARDS, Glenn
BATH/VANITY WALL BEHIND
STEEL ENTRY DOOR, GLAZED
CORNER ANGLE
BOARDS COULD FINISH ON A FLAT VERTICAL BOARD — PIECES SET FLUSH
BAGGED BRICK
75 MIN
CONTROL JOINT BETWEEN STRUCTURAL/TOPPING SLABS
16/12/97
SECTION THROUGH PORCH AND ENTRY LOCK
1:20 ABOUT

House
Mount White New South Wales
1996 (unbuilt)

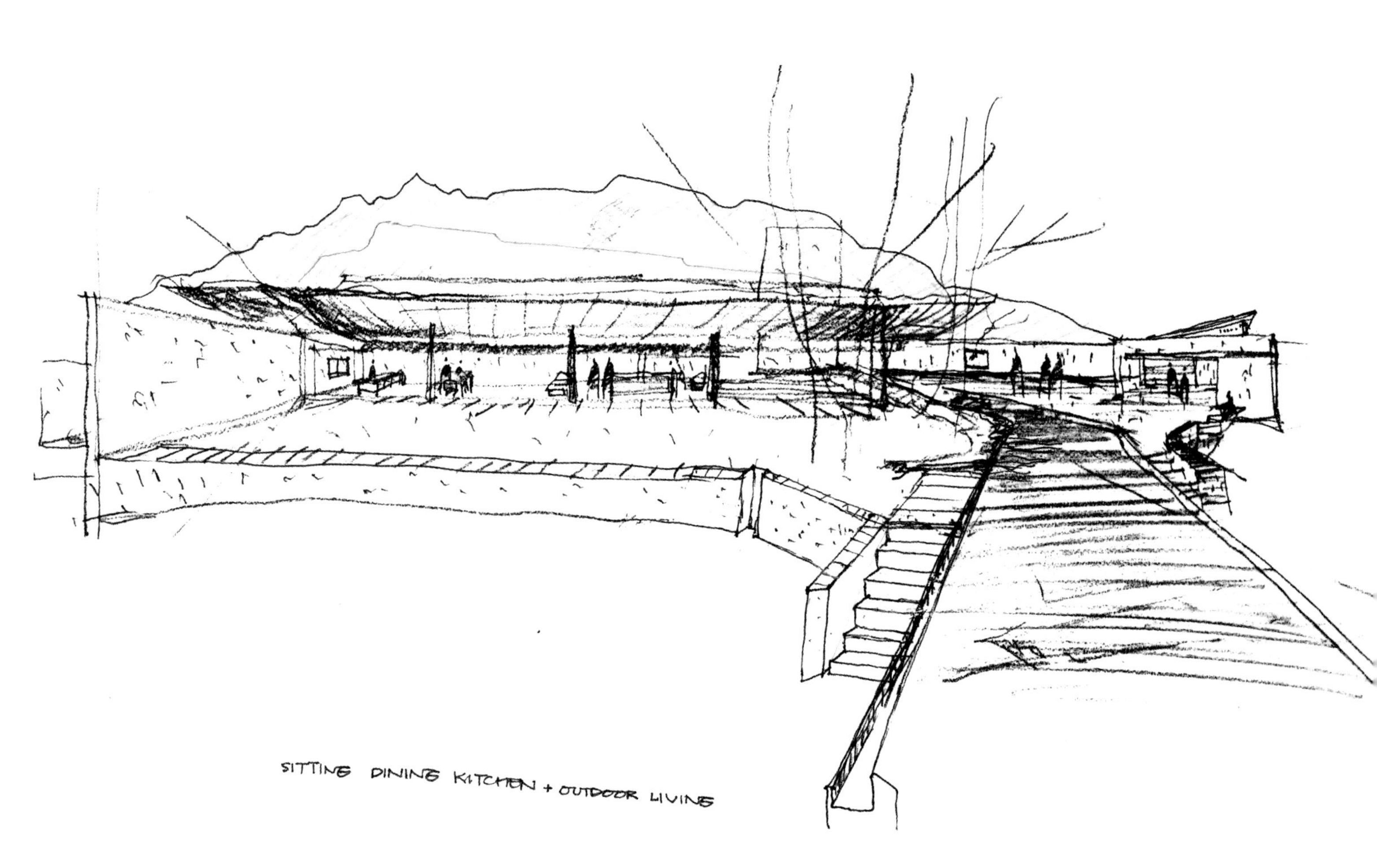

nall houses, awkward sites, constrained briefs, nited budgets, difficult solar access, the oblems of suburban overlooking, the threat bush fire, the necessity to collect rainwater, e urgency to discharge it from roofs: these e the challenges that Murcutt deeply enjoys ontending with, and the stuff that he makes s architecture from. A big luxurious house is oblematic because it has few of the defining onstraints of smaller projects.

ith such a very large house Murcutt has the ption of two design approaches for managing e inflated scale: one is to fragment the rogramme into several buildings, the other is to retch the building. The last two houses published ere, this and the Carter house, demonstrate ese two contending approaches. With this roject he breaks the programme into separate arts and builds a family compound; with the arter house he stretches the building.

he risk with a large house lies in inflating the omestic scale to the extent that the building kes on an institutional character. (Unlike Europe, ustralia does not have the palace as a model or the very large house.)

ere Murcutt manages the scale of what in the nd is simply a four-bedroom house. He uses ttenuation as the mechanism for overcoming e problem of inflated scale by pulling the bits f the building apart. In effect he makes three uildings. They are each given expression, hich prevents the overall conglomeration from ecoming too big.

lurcutt makes use of the scale and programmatic aterial of this house to really investigate an Aalto lan, something he has been longing to do for irty years. First he follows an Aalto idea of using e contours of the land as a form generator. he building is big enough to inscribe the sweep f the contour (whereas a smaller house would imply be lodged into it). Thus the house xpresses the topography.

lurcutt extends this topographical idea the Aaltoesque organicism of the children's edrooms, interpreting them as elements the landscape. In the development of the rief, it became clear that the bedrooms were equired to have a measure of independence om each other: that functional prerequisite ecomes the key for an organic interpretation f the bedrooms as 'boulders'. There is a fine ttle Aalto plan, with the negative of the sitting pace giving meaning to the positive of the nree bedrooms.

formal equivalence exists between the rganisation of this building and that of the Arthur nd Yvonne Boyd Centre. The forecourt, living and hildren's bedroom wing foreshadow aspects of e formal and planning organisation of the Centre.

lurcutt's work now exhibits much greater evels of sensual expression. It is as if he is more elaxed, less constrained, less driven by utilitarian ecessity. He feels at ease with those issues and s more willing to develop the sensual, experiential ualities of his buildings. It is no surprise that rchitecture has long been considered to be n 'old man's' occupation: design demands he suppleness of mind that comes only from ecades of life experience and sustained formal nd technical experimentation and reflection.

This site is in the bush fire-prone, sandstone country west of Gosford, an hour and a half north of Sydney. It has a quality akin to living in the wilderness. The vast scale of the landscape breaks down into smaller-scale elements of rock outcrops to the north-east of the site.

Entry is from an access road to the south. The landscape shelves up on either side, producing a feeling of being in the middle of an amphitheatre. The house is deflected to follow the contours of the site. There are rock outcrops with many beautiful views. To capitalise on the views I've placed the spaces in a way that reflects the topography: where the scale of the site is smaller, I've broken down the scale of the components of the building. Every room has a different view and a different relationship to the landscape.

The property supports a horse stud. The programme took a while to establish; it changed and developed and the brief expanded, to the point where the final drawing sheet size had to be increased greatly to fit the expanded scheme.

The materials are earth, stone, concrete and metal, chosen to withstand fire. Walls are rammed earth. I first wanted to use rammed earth for the Minerals and Mining Museum at Broken Hill, and I then had the opportunity to use this material in the Northern Territory in a project with Troppo Architects, and I had also planned to use it for my brother's house in South Australia, but it was more expensive than brickwork at the time. I like the idea of earth in a fire-prone area. Rammed earth also gives a beautiful finish, almost like travertine. The colour can be anything from grey to purplish brown to a straw/sandstone.

The concrete base to the building is clad in bluestone to the underside of the ground floor slab. The walls to doorhead height are formed in rammed earth, and above that are a concrete beam and projecting soffit to protect the earth wall below. The rammed earth walls need protection from direct driving rain. The control joint between the concrete and rammed earth has a stainless steel 2mm angle and drip, which sheds water beyond the earth walls where they are exposed.

The house has three parts: children, entertaining, parents. The parts are separated by a covered verandah and a terrace off the sitting room.

The lap pool – 25 by 2.4 metres – is on axis to the mountain peak a few kilometres away. The mountain is reflected in the pool when seen from the bathroom, main bedroom and study.

The three children's bedrooms each have dressing and bathing areas. The bedrooms have louvres and insect screens inside, as well as timber batten sliding sun protection screens.

The children's sitting area is an interior space with a large roof light, with views out from the gaps between the bedroom blocks. Each gap offers an exit to the landscape, without having to go through the middle of the house. It is like walking down among the big rocks on the site. I wanted the land to come up and meet the floor level.

The parents' bedroom has its own dressing, bathing and sitting spaces. The shower enjoys 280° vistas.

The living room doors fold back and stack against the powder room and entry foyer, expanding the room from 5.9 by 8 metres to approximately 14 by 8 metres, a grand entertainment space. The north-facing doors slide out of sight against the laundry at the eastern end, creating one vast outdoor living space. Since it is just under a metre off the ground, there is no requirement for handrails.

The main living area has a gentle arc to the underside of the roof. It is convex to the space. I did this too at the Simpson-Lee house. It is a way of making a low space feel larger, creating a visual expansion of the volume.

At the end of the terrace, the stair down to the ground level splits. I could have had a single stair, but the formality would have been too powerful and directional. The stairs arrive near smaller elements of the landscape, therefore I wanted to break the down scale of the staircase and also suggest with one of the flights a move in a different direction.

The stone paving patterns take up the different geometries of the house, with the pattern near the children's sitting area being less formal.

At the junction between the terrace and the pool house there is a step up onto a bridge: it's like getting off or on a boat.

There is no town water but a good bore water supply. All the rainwater from the roofs is collected. A sprinkler and a concrete gutter system are designed for collecting water, with 350mm of gravel on the roof to allow the water to move slowly through into huge storage tanks below the building. The gravel also provides thermal insulation. The roof really is a vast box gutter. An overflow from the storage tanks goes to fill the lap pool.

Overflows for the roof gutters are set out at module points. Glass at the module points allows the entry of a narrow strip of sunlight, animating each column support.

Engineer: James Taylor and Associates

House

Southern Highlands New South Wales

1997 to 2000

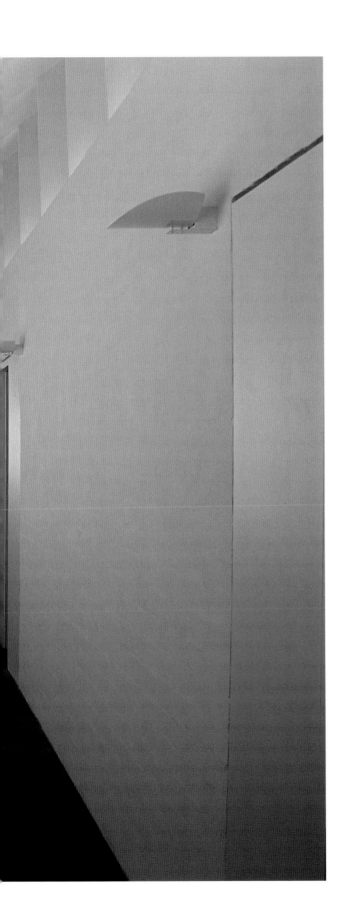

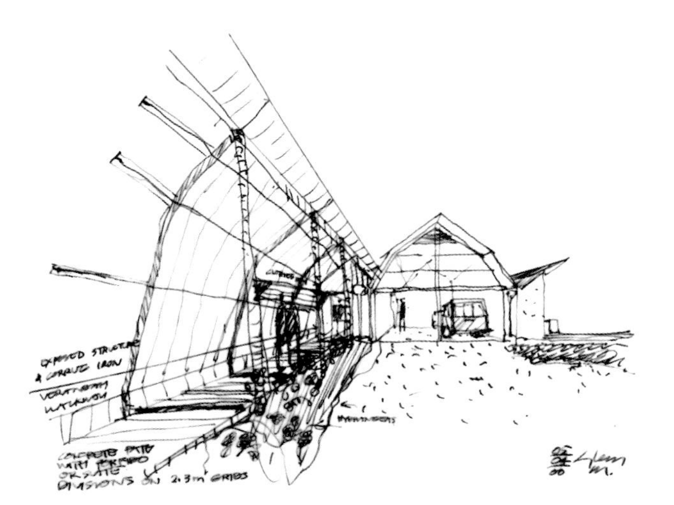

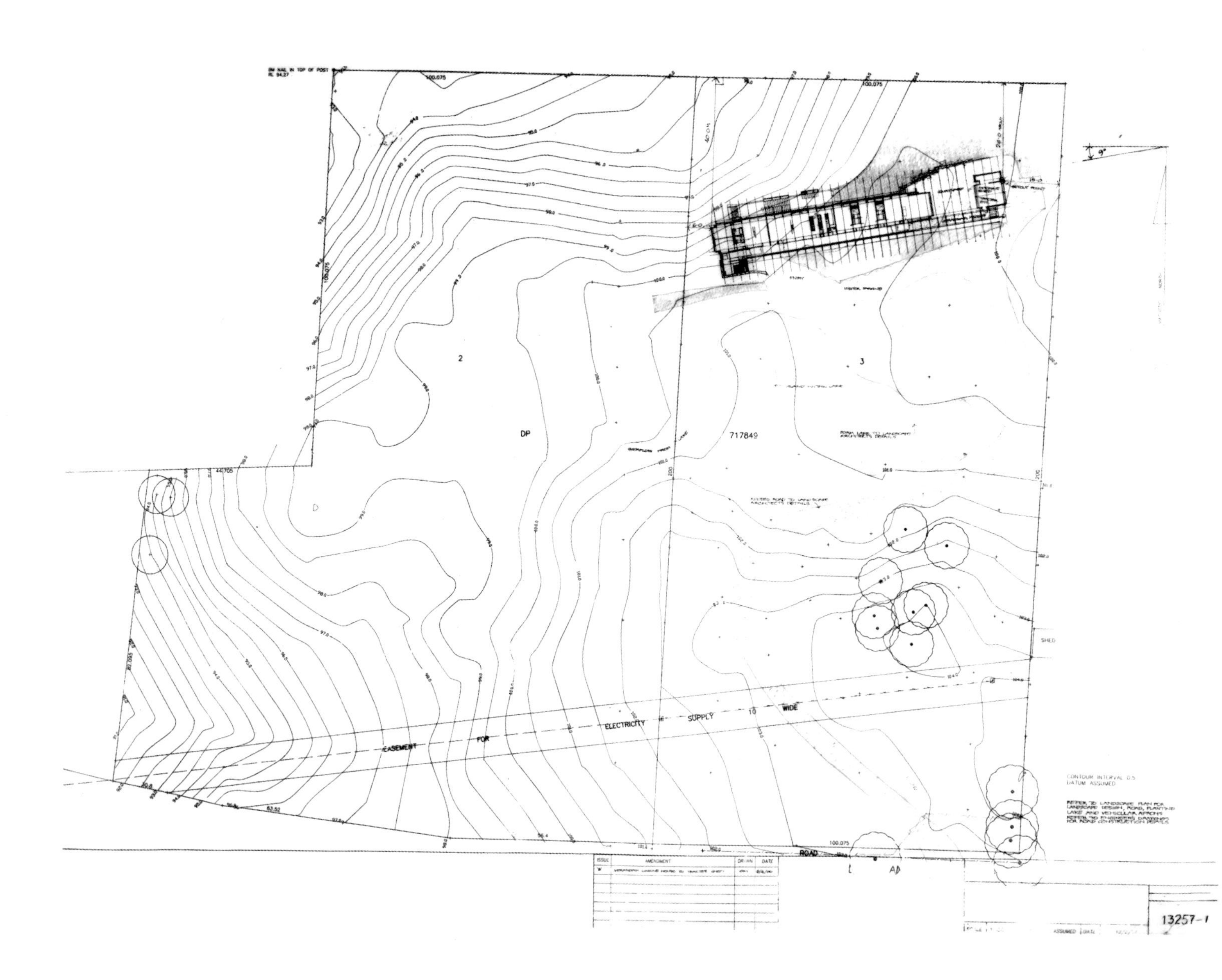
BM NAIL IN TOP OF POST
RL 94.27
100.075
2
3
DP
717849
EASEMENT FOR ELECTRICITY SUPPLY 10 WIDE
ROAD
SHED
CONTOUR INTERVAL 0.5
DATUM ASSUMED
ISSUE
AMENDMENT
DRAWN
DATE
13257-1

nis is a very big house that achieves grandeur rough the scale of the cross section. The Dutch able profile is the product of Murcutt's desire achieve a steep pitch to induce high winds flow effectively over the roof. It is also a tested chnique of his for increasing the velocity of inwater run-off from the roof. Together, these nctional constraints help determine the terior volume.

contrast with his tactic in the Mount White ouse of fragmenting the plan to manage the rge scale of the building, here Murcutt employs tenuation and repetition. The building is like train, with carriage after carriage, each crisply ticulated by slatted timber screens along the orthern side. The house pulls a caboose along ith it, the tractor shed at the far end: in all continuous line of building 80 metres long.

unning the length of the house along the outhern side, some 50 metres, is a beautiful all. It is an elegantly detailed, separate little steel ructure in the form of a light monitor bringing north light that is washed across the curved rofile of the hall wall. The house is essentially ne room deep, with all the rooms facing north nd opening to winter sunlight. In moving cross the house towards the southern hallway, habitants encounter sunlight again in the hall. he effect is magical: in winter the entire internal outhern wall of the hall is bathed in sunlight.

he ground falls away to the north, and Murcutt llows his now almost standard way of dealing ith the mud and grime of rural sites since the outhern Highlands house (1988–92) by building stone-clad plinth that the house is seated on. his is a mechanism for both reducing the eight of a big building and also grounding it.

is interesting to see just how far Murcutt has ome in the use of steelwork since the Kempsey luseum (1976–79). This house demonstrates e fruits of twenty years of investigation into the xpressive detailing of exposed structural steel.

It is full of other thoroughly thought through details. The exterior cladding of the hall wall is corrugated iron that flows up in a continuous curving plane to form the roof: the wall becomes the roof.

Murcutt uses the zone of the thickened wall (containing the storage cupboards) between the hall and the rooms to locate the vast box gutter necessary for rainwater collection. This is a technique he first explored in the Bingie Bingie and Ball-Eastaway houses.

A gutter detail running the length of the southern wall is suspended 150mm above the ground and pulled out from the structure so that the entire wall plane, some 50 metres long and 4 metres high, appears to float.

Murcutt develops his idea of how to enter a house. He does not make a direct axial entry but structures a route that takes in the length of the building, passes through an entry court and zigzags in an S pattern before entering the house proper. In the course of entering the house, the inhabitant/visitor gets a double take on its immense length, snaking back into the lobby and looking down the length of the hall, now inside and bathed in sunlight.

There are ideas in this house that indicate the refinements of twenty-five years of investigation and experimentation.

This house is located in the Southern Highlands, south of Sydney, a beautiful region of undulating country, rich soils and productive farming. In winter the prevailing high winds from the south-west are very cold; but during February it can become hot.

The rural setting will be restored in part with forest species that are native to the region, and a lake formed for water collection and attracting wildlife. The lake will also be a new visual element experienced on arrival to the house.

The axis of the building is east–west, providing ideal orientation to true north for most spaces.

A large hedge shields the house from public view and forms the first line of defence against the cold winter winds. The public and work entries are both protected by a courtyard and a sloping wind-deflecting wall that houses the main access gallery serving all rooms. This wind deflector is a response to my observations and experience with pressure differential. Wind from the south-west is driven up and over the roof; the terrace roof resolves eddying on the negative pressure plane: and together these measures provide a stable and calm zone to the northern-facing sitting room terrace.

The form of the main access gallery suggests the wind-shaped trees. The landscape is visible at both ends of this gallery, and the roof profile, glazed to the north, allows for winter sun and summer shading.

The roof pitches and overhangs shelter window openings and walls during summer, and in winter allow the sun to penetrate deeply into all rooms. The climate demanded good thermal mass. Floors are insulated reinforced concrete and finished in stone or carpet. Photovoltaic cells and inverter provide electric underfloor heating and supply/take power from the grid.

Outside shoes are removed at the main and working entries, in the traditional Japanese manner.

The five bedrooms and two living rooms allow flexibility when members of the family and friends gather, enabling them to be together or have independence by opening or closing connecting spaces.

The bathing zones for the main house are generous, and showering precedes bathing. Windows the length of the bath alcove are set at the bath level so that the bather gazes at the landscape.

The kitchen/dining/sitting room relationship is similar to that at the Kempsey farmhouse. Here, doors to the sitting rooms slide fully out of view, enabling a strong connection to the northern terrace and undulating landscape beyond: this area develops into one large indoor/outdoor space. When the native deciduous trees fully develop, with their canopy covering the terrace, the outside space will work as a room filled with green light filtering the strong summer sun.

Since 1995, I've used the tripartite system of sliding slatted timber screens, insect screens and glazed doors. This allows for many options, and the layers can be adjusted to accommodate varying climatic conditions.

Externally, walls are either lined with grey slate or are a cement base painted dark warm grey. Timbers are stained with deeply penetrating oils. Reinforced concrete columns and all corrugated galvanised sheet wall linings and roofs are left natural. The structural steel elements are generally painted in protective metallic 'natural grey' system. Aluminium windows and doors are powdercoated. Paving is grey slate and porfido. Internally, the walls and ceilings are painted white, cupboard doors clear-finished timber veneered in satin texture, and stone floors are porfido.

House
Southern Highlands New South Wales

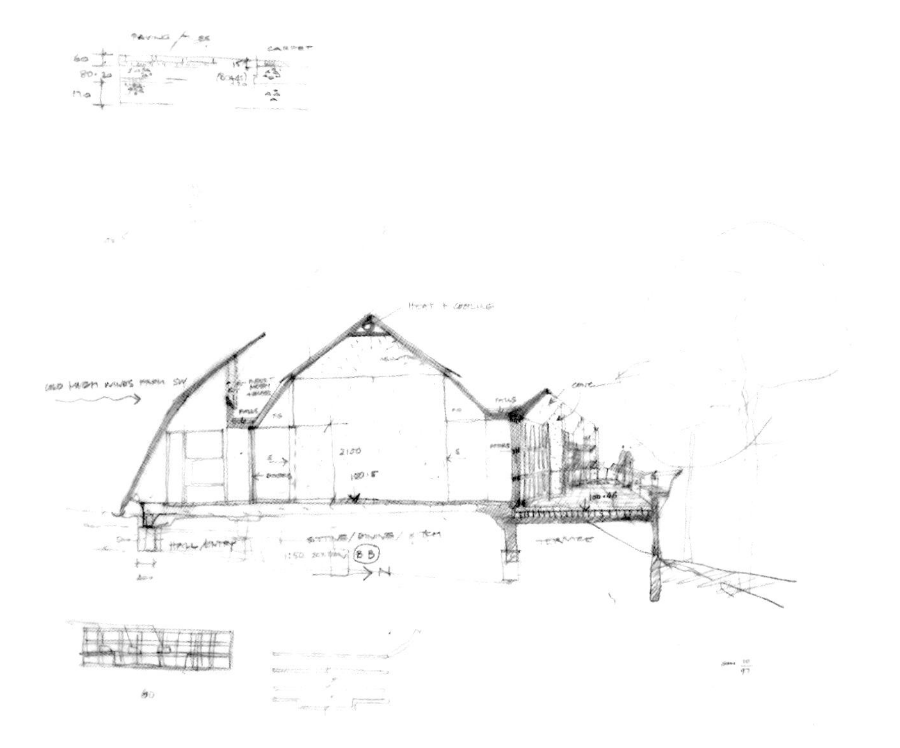

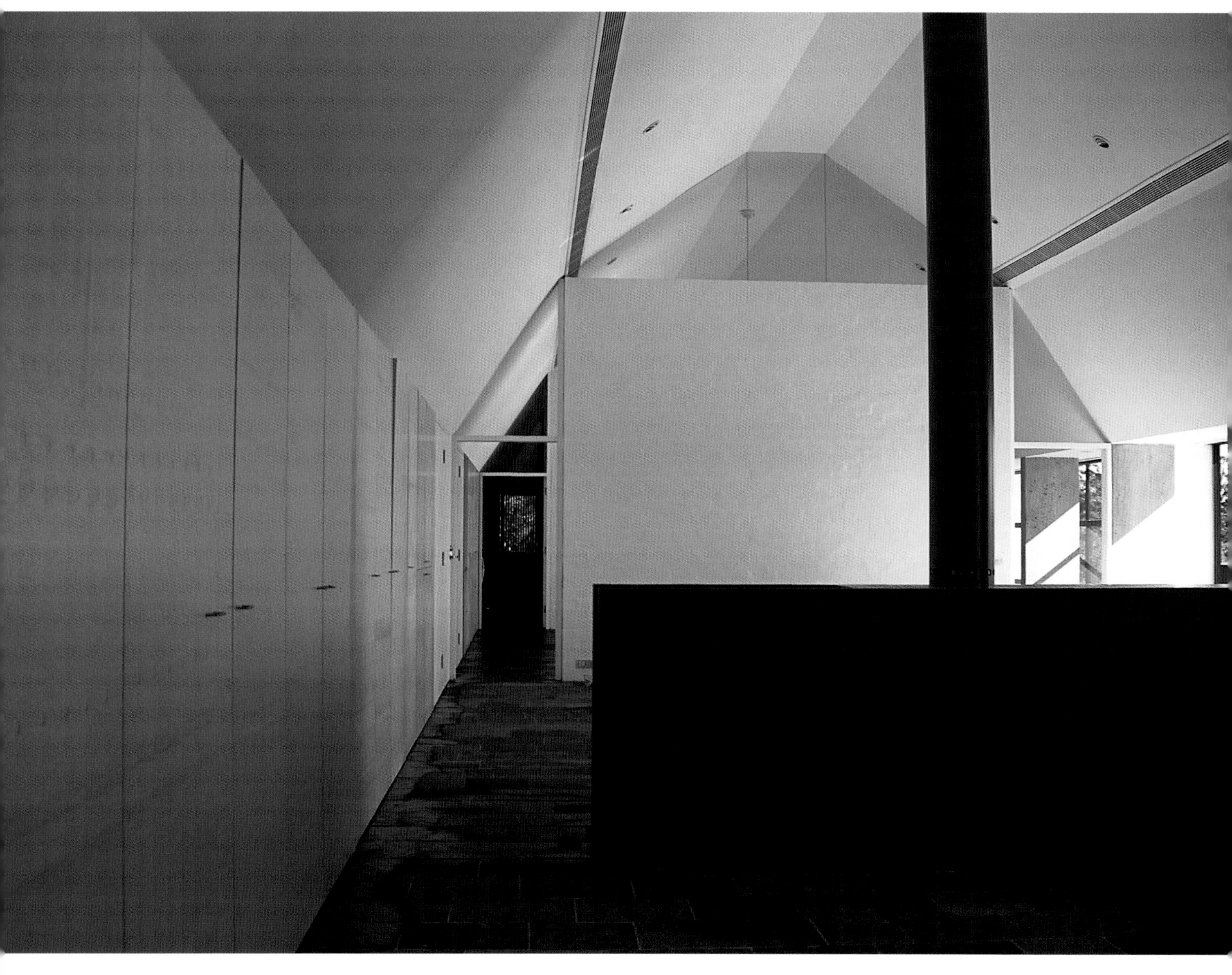

1:50 SECTION

House
Southern Highlands New South Wales

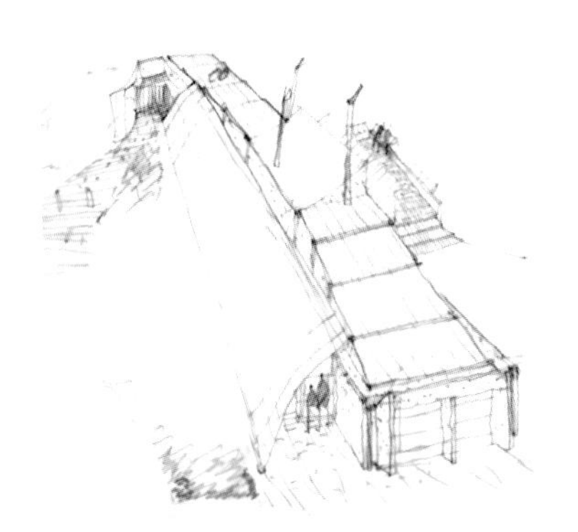

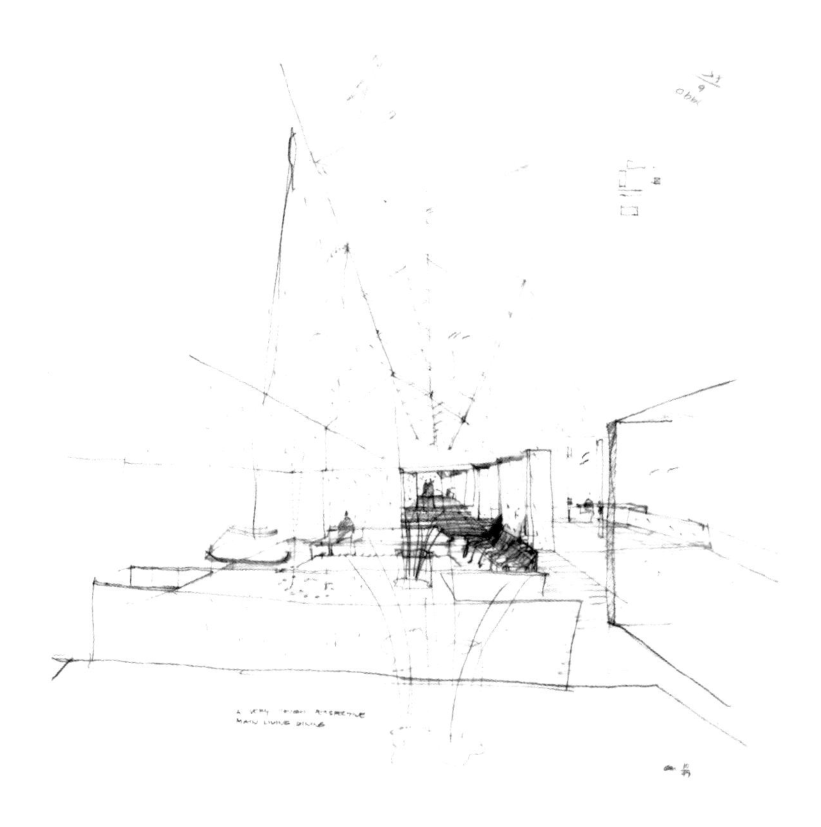

Arthur and Yvonne Boyd Education Centre
in collaboration with Wendy Lewin and Reg Lark
Riversdale West Cambewarra New South Wales
1996 to 1999

Haig Beck and Jackie Cooper

Arthur and Yvonne Boyd's rural property, Riversdale, on the Shoalhaven River is the site of a building complex housing their education foundation, completed in 1999 just months before Boyd's death. The complex consists of a large hall and accommodation for up to thirty-two students staying for several days at a time. The site is glorious, on a rise surrounded by hills and overlooking the broad river that has served famously as Boyd's muse. It is farming country interspersed with extensive tracts of bushland.

Prelude

Two schemes were done before the location and design were ultimately settled. These projects removed the new building from the existing cluster of farmhouse cottages in order to ensure that artists in residence were not bothered by the noise and activity of visiting student groups; but during the process of negotiating the brief, thinking shifted towards the idea of relocating the artists in residence programme largely to an adjoining Boyd property upriver (both properties are gifted to Australia), and allowing the new building to relate to the cottages.

'You can select an architect without having design ideas already worked out. The way to design a building is through discussion and negotiation between client and architect. You work with the architect to select the site, develop the brief, sort out the budget.'

The brief had to be tailored to a budget that had to fund substantial infrastructure for on-site water storage, water filtration and sewage treatment works, and landscaping.

The requirement was for simple accommodation – 'more like camping than a five-star hotel' – and a dining hall to seat eighty, doubling as a theatre and concert hall for a hundred. The kitchen was to have a separate access point for students collecting their lunches.

Murcutt notoriously maintains a one-man practice. But he is also an enthusiastic believer in collaboration, and this project was undertaken in association with Wendy Lewin and Reg Lark, both of whom have been his collaborators on previous projects. 'We did the design together. There were lots of breakthrough discussions and everyone was involved in all the decisions – not like a committee, but having a shared idea of what we were doing.'

True to a rationalist way of practice, the design doesn't just fall out automatically. Instead, it is a process of many trials and experiments before things finally come together. Murcutt and his colleagues constantly endeavour to distill the programmatic requirements and mesh them with environmental, poetic and constructional ideas that they feel strongly about.

Murcutt has a tendency to want to stick to a material; this is another of the constraints he sets himself, to explore the idiom of the material and construction technology and push them to extremes. In this project the three architects start to look at off-form concrete for the first time, and also at using composite structural members of timber and steel.

Discovery

Three modest timber and stone cottages – one Boyd's paint-spattered studio – are retained (an ugly shed was demolished). Indeed the cottages establish the setting and point of entry for the new complex, which is only discovered by degrees as one penetrates the site.

After negotiating the tortuous driveway track down through the bush, cars and small buses arrive at the timber cottages. 'It's like arriving at Boyd's old place, virtually unchanged.' Visitors are unaware from here of the new building. They filter through the domestic-scaled verandah passageway of the upper cottage (Boyd's studio), to be released out onto the large open terrace serving the new hall. This terrace – which Murcutt refers to as 'the silent space' – announces the hall-and-dormitory complex and constitutes the performance platform for an amphitheatre (yet to be built) large enough for a full-sized orchestra, with seating for three hundred and fifty terracing up into the hill; this amphitheatre acts as a hinge between the new and old buildings. From the terrace there are uninterrupted views downriver.

Between

The ample terrace is perceived as a floating plane lodged midway on the hill that rises gently behind the long building and in front rolls down towards the river. The building is poised between two landscape experiences: the native bush of banksias, cycads and turpentine looming above it, and below it the manicured and cultivated river flats. This dichotomy reflects Boyd's own oscillation between the landscapes of Australia and England, drawing his inspiration from this place and returning to complete his paintings in Suffolk.

For the architects it was important that the building frame both the native and the cultivated landscapes. The simple linear parti promotes awareness of the land, as visitors contemplate the sumptuous views over the river and then turn round to find the bush.

Long

The linear form holds the landscape together and makes it legible. Yet the building as line between the two landscapes was not an immediate first premise. There was much preliminary analysis of the geometries established by the existing cottages, as well as attempts to configure the building in various ways. 'We could have stepped the bedroom modules down the site and we also looked at a dog-leg, but there is a weakness with both ideas because the building would be too close to the site boundary, the terrain is very steep, water comes through the site, and the quality of light wasn't so good. The long building was right. We felt we wanted to keep the bedroom modules pulled apart rather than packed together. And with the thinness there is minimal impact on the site.'

Comet

The building is like a comet, with the hall and kitchen as the head, and the tail containing the dormitories. It could have been designed as three linked units or pavilions, but the continuity of the mass material produces a strength. The building is like an inhabited wall, the scale heroic when seen frontally from below and in conjunction with the soaring roof form of the hall. From other vantages, it takes on an almost domestic scale of small elements, the fins and blades articulating the linear wall plane.

Blades

Murcutt used blades first in the Marika-Alderton house in the Northern Territory, essentially for early morning sun control and privacy. Here they serve a similar purpose, as well as bring extra light into the bedrooms, catch the breezes and frame views. Their effect on the exterior is to feather down the scale and texture of the building mass. The large sliding doors to divide the bedrooms are housed in the larger blades, enabling an exceptionally tight floor plan – only 2 metres wide – to feel generous; the protruding bed boxes cantilever beyond the floor.

The bedrooms face east over the wide river, at dawn a luminous shimmering plane. Getting the kids up early was a design issue: the fins bounce in the morning sunlight.

Recycled

The floors, bed supports, and windows of the bedrooms are in natural timber. The brushbox floors are pink. Doors, cupboards and ceilings are yellow hoop pine ply. Sills and joinery are russet. The cotton duvets are white.

The deep window sills are bevelled – framelike – making the edges finer, which, in addition to containing the views, affects the way the timber takes the light and also discourages clutter.

Except for plywood, which is a plantation material, recycled timbers are used throughout the building. Columns are brushbox. Beams and purlins are blackbutt. The big doors of the hall are old growth oregon, many recycled timbers forming the jambs. The door slats too are oregon; and the natural brass door rails are bound in leather where the hand grasps or pushes – a finish that recalls Aalto. 'Everything is to be received nicely by the body. You understand about materials, but things are also easy to use.' Steelwork is finished in black micaceous paint: 'it gives the burnt bush quality we were after'.

Despite the building's utilitarian character, there is finesse in the details and resolution of junctions of materials. Steel flitches lighten the framing of doorways, refining the depth of the section. Beams and purlins use a composite construction of timber and steel, exploiting the nature of steel to work in tension and timber in compression. 'The two elements work with each other, like muscles and bones. It is very economical.' The steel cores of the beams are visible between the timber cheeks.

There is pleasure taken in such measures of economy. This is a bush building incorporating frugality and ingenuity.

Fire

Stringent fire regulations require that a two-hour fire rating apply throughout the building, despite there being a 3.7-metre roofed courtyard separating bedroom modules – when buildings 3 metres apart are not subject to such a fire rating. However, even though the 250mm hardwood purlins would not sustain any flame, the continuous roof meant that this was deemed a single building and the regulations applied. The fire rating between bedrooms called for 150mm of concrete or brickwork. 'It was the first time in our lives, for all of us, that we had built in concrete. There were potential problems of cracking and dirt, and it was a challenge.'

The building and its site possess a monastic quality which the severity of the concrete expresses. Also, the material presents continuity in the long form and, in a painterly way, a big field, and it works too in terms of colour and light.

Breathing

The bathrooms are the classic three-way holiday design: toilet, shower and hand basin can all be used simultaneously. Each is a little 'outdoor' room. Eight people share a single unit. Given this intensity of use, the bathrooms have to breathe. There is plenty of ventilation. The shower has no glazing but timber venetian blinds that tilt for privacy or open for views: steam easily escapes, and the effect is of taking a shower outside.

A slatted roof section over the basin brings in light and reduces reliance on electricity. At night the toilet module, with its translucent glass, glows like a lantern when occupied. The bathrooms are supplied with bore water.

Framing

'The building is an instrument of framing place. Just as a painter would frame a scene, so we have organised the building to look at different parts of the landscape.' The framing of the landscape is created not only in the large openings and smaller window views, but also in the actual siting of the building and in its roof form. On approach, the first view of the building is end-on, looking down its length to the bush beyond; by its location on the site, visitors immediately apprehend the lie of the land. The portico roof extending over the terrace forms a commanding frame to the majestic views of the Shoalhaven River, and the portico roof also funnels the eye deep into the hall; from inside, the roof captures the nearby hill and river and brings them right into the hall.

Throughout the building, glimpses of the landscape are framed by each opening and window. In the bedroom units, each bed box has its own special frame, a composite window with a fixed glass panel below an opening timber screen. This screen can be closed right down, leaving just a ribbon of view, or progressively pushed open, first as flyscreened frames and then even further for complete openness to the outside. 'The view opens up but only when you open the plywood sash. It's like a tent opening out.' The little articulated timber panels within the screen invite use, just as an intricate box does, adding a playful yet practical character to these otherwise plain and spare bedrooms. Similarly, the rooms themselves can be closed up or made transparent and open.

Scale

The framing of views is a preoccupation of the building, and operates from the large scale to the very intimate views available from each bed space. The scale of the building encompasses heroic and domestic. 'The breaking down of the scale is important in what could have been an overly-scaled building. We kept breaking down the scale into smaller elements, and developed ways of dealing with the views, and ways of changing elements, materials and using screens to break down light levels and vistas. It is what we've learned from Aalto as well as Japanese and Indian architecture.'

Roof

There is a butterfly roof over the hall and kitchen, with the section over the kitchen continuing down the length of the building to cover the bedrooms. This skillion is tipped up along the western side towards the bush views; there is no fear of sun penetration because of the steepness of the hill and the shade of the forest. Over the bedrooms, the skillion is layered in two planes, with a small glazed gap along the eastern side over the bed boxes; this brings in light across the ceiling and defines a subtle spatial territory. The prevailing north-easterly breezes are funnelled up under the open ends of the corrugated roofing to ventilate the roof space.

The hall roof – the other wing of the butterfly – is a skillion tipping up to the east in response to the views of the river and the morning light. The trick is to turn the east-facing skillion through 90° and allow the portico to open to the north, bringing winter sunshine deep into the hall. This is an inclusive gesture that addresses the views to the hill and the long reach of the river, and connects the new building to the existing cottages.

Many designs were done for this hall roof, using models to resolve the complex geometries. The solution is an inside-out hip: a valley that folds the pitch back towards the big central gutter and channels the rainwater. (All drinking water is collected and stored in huge tanks underneath the building.) From inside the hall, the roof appears as a single plane: there is no sense of the valley cutting diagonally across the portico.

The roof is heavy-duty corrugated iron, 'big stuff', all the way around, silver to match the cottages. The main roof expanse aligns with the front edge of the columns, then a further 'eyebrow' is supported by projecting steel jack rafters. It presents a light edge and releases wind pressure on the facade. Wind can flute through the gap at the base of the eyebrow flap, instead of fluttering the roof edge. The structural effect of this edge is to produce a holding-down quality.

Plane

The building floats on its platform: there is a shadowline recess step down to the ground. The columns are seen to pin the building to the ground. The floor floats out beyond the interior space to encompass the terrace. The paving establishes a single surface throughout, with strong lines in bluestone in the long direction. The paving is in purply-brown-mushroom bricks, 'the colour of the tree trunks'.

The columns of the new building and the existing cottages, as well as the trees, set up a rhythm of verticals that is in contrast to the flat planes of the river and the sky.

Prospect

Prospect is made up of the elements that are beyond where one is or what one knows: prospect highlights one's vulnerability. Always it needs to be modulated by refuge, a place of withdrawal. A refuge can be quite flimsy: just a tent on a platform in the bush. The porch, verandah or terrace is the refuge to the vast landscape, and also the transition between inside and outside; and it alters scale by breaking it down. In the hall, the availability of sweeping views is modulated and the range of spatial experiences varied as screens, doorways and then whole walls either dissolve or enclose. The hall is a verandah.

Sacred

The character of this building is very powerful. Its stillness conveys the idea of monasticism. The sense of a temple is invoked both by the setting, which invites the idea of shrine, and by the monumental scale. A building of such scale and simplicity is neither domestic nor institutional.

A temple is almost emptied of programme: only quietness is critical to the act of contemplation; everything extraneous is pared down and removed, or it slides away. This quality comes naturally to Murcutt. A temple is the refuge of the gods. In the immensity of the Australian bush, he creates a temporal place of refuge. There is also an obvious – if unintended – formal connection with the Greek Acropolis in the arrival sequence. It is not something the architects set out to achieve, but results from a sensitivity to an Aboriginal idea of oblique approach. Just as you arrive at the main forecourt and are presented with the elegant peristyle form of the hall, you sense it's almost sacrilege to walk directly into it; and you are drawn down the side. This is sacred and profane space.

Designed in association with Wendy Lewin Architect and Reg Lark Architect
Landscape architect: Schaffer Barnsley
Engineer: James Taylor and Associates
Water supply and waste management engineers: Woodlots and Wetlands

This text first appeared in UME 10, September 1999.

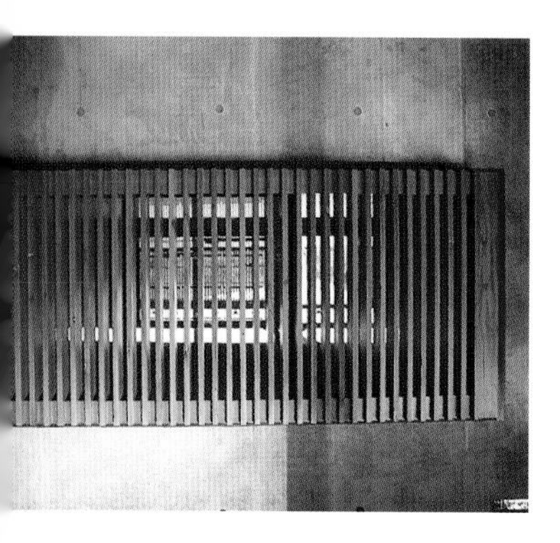

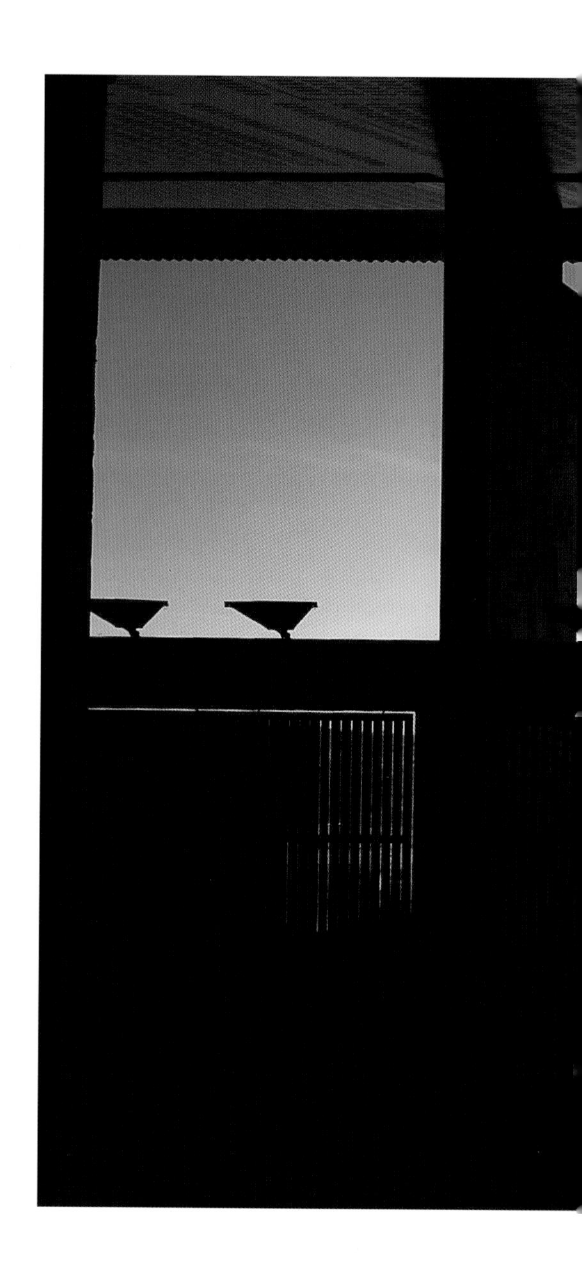

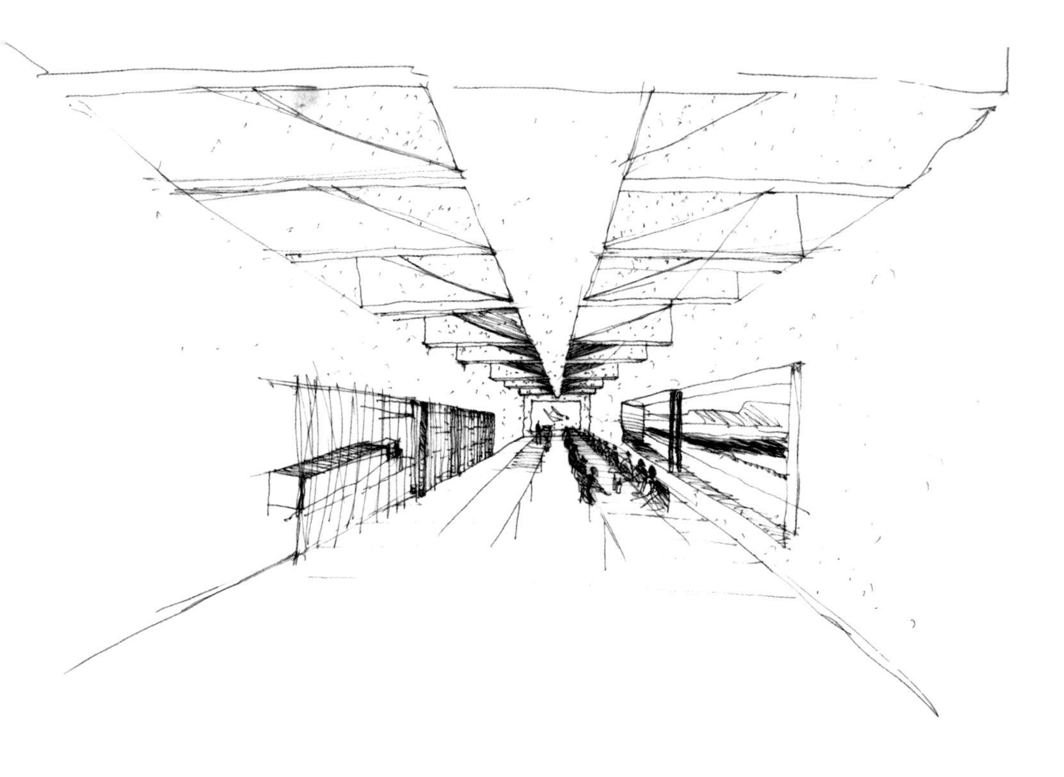

Daphne Murcutt house
Seaforth Sydney New South Wales
1968 to 1972 (several designs, unbuilt)

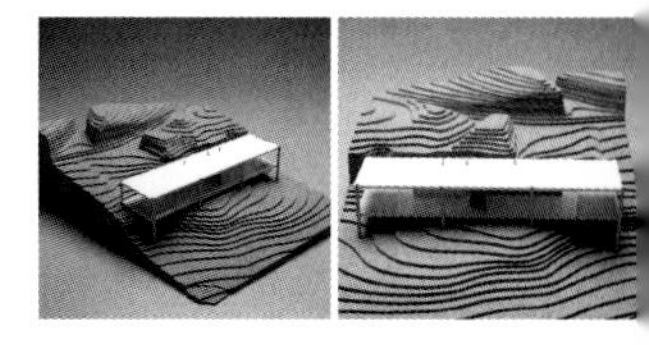

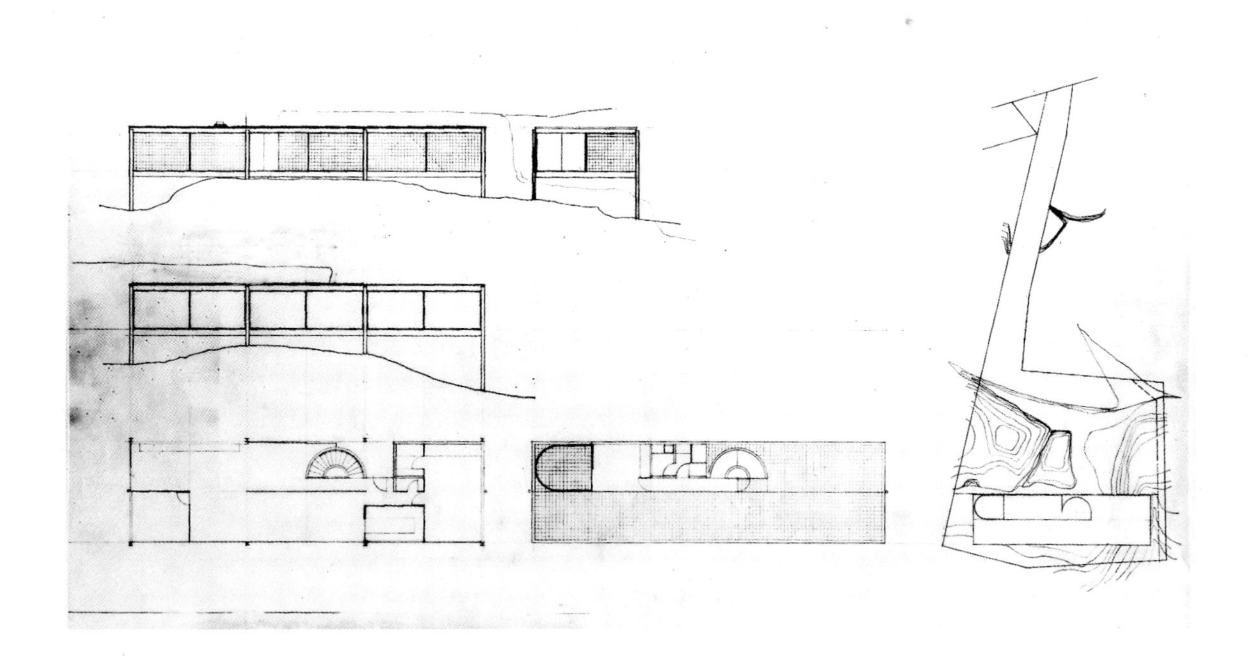

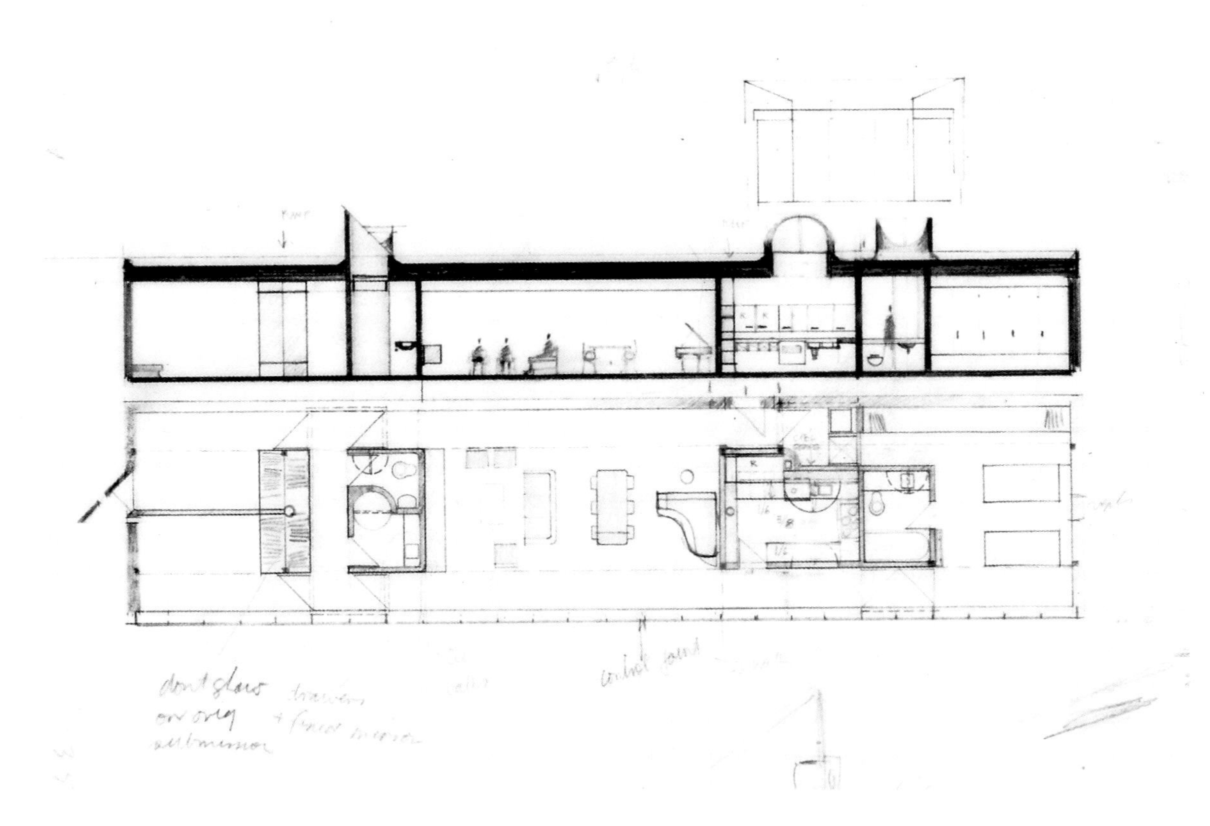

Doug Murcutt house

Belrose Sydney New South Wales

1969 to 1972

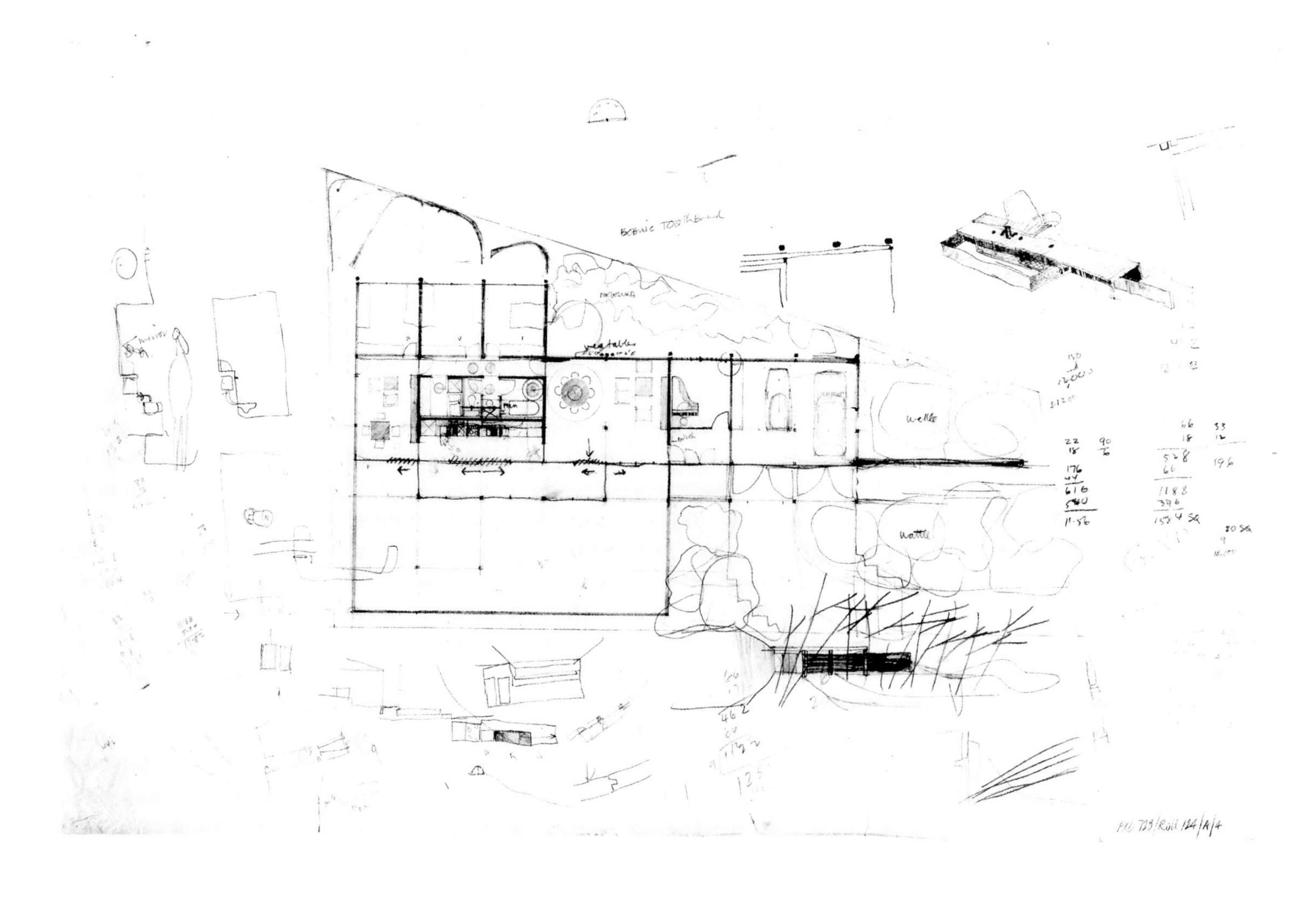

Laurie Short house
Terrey Hills Sydney New South Wales
1972 to 1973

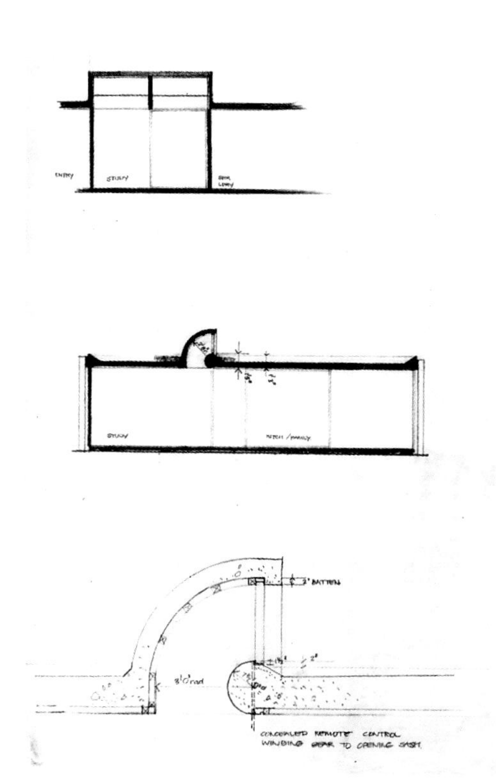

concealed remote control winding gear to opening sash

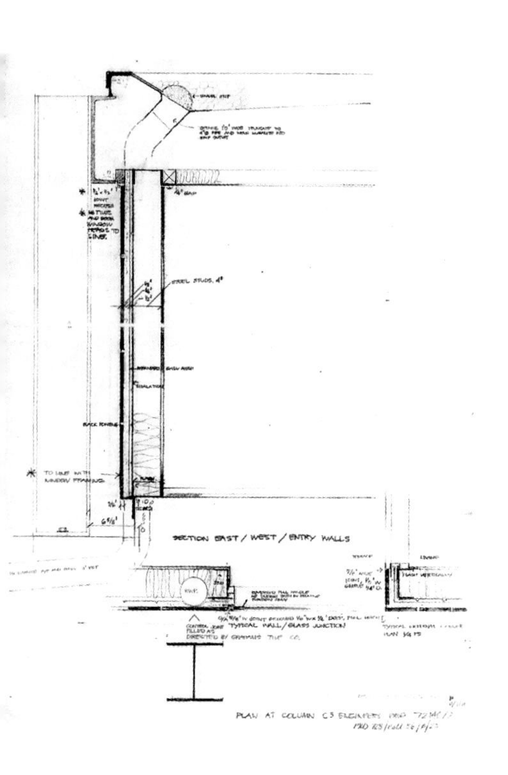

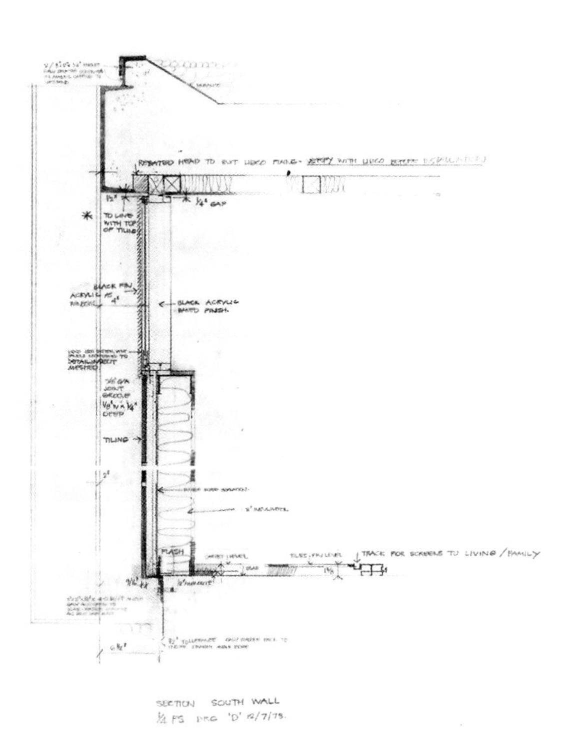

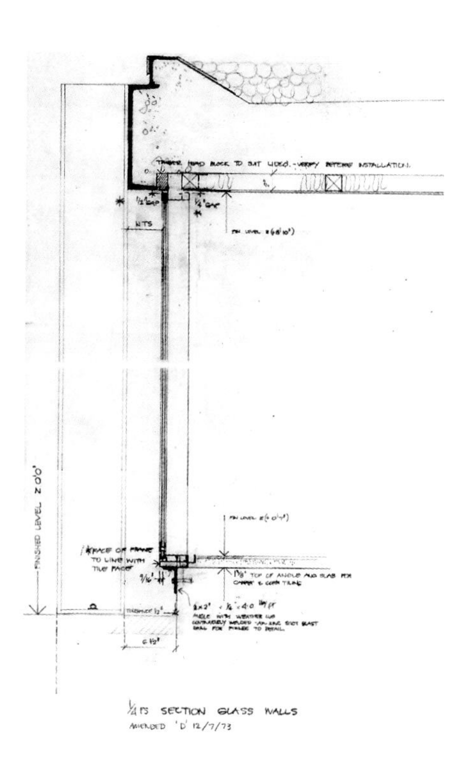

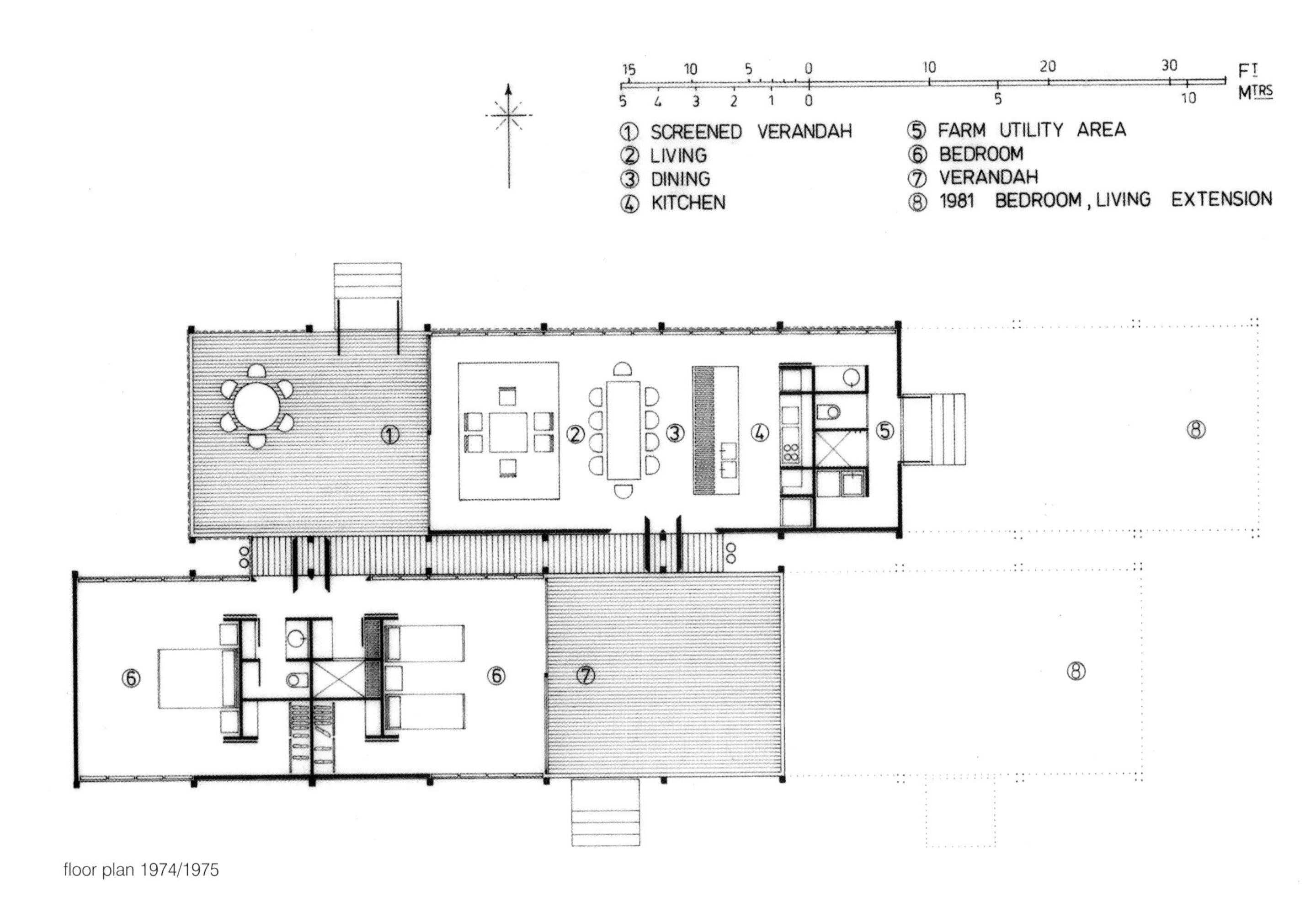

floor plan 1974/1975

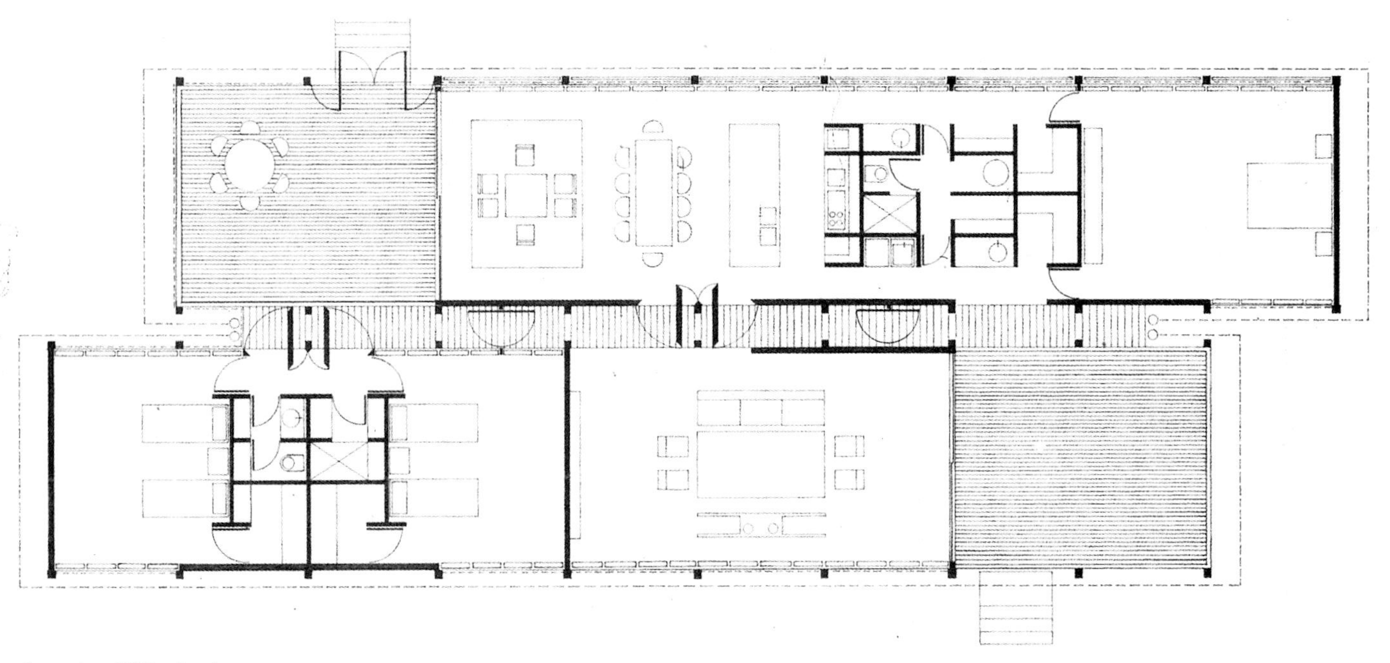

floor plan, 1981 extensions

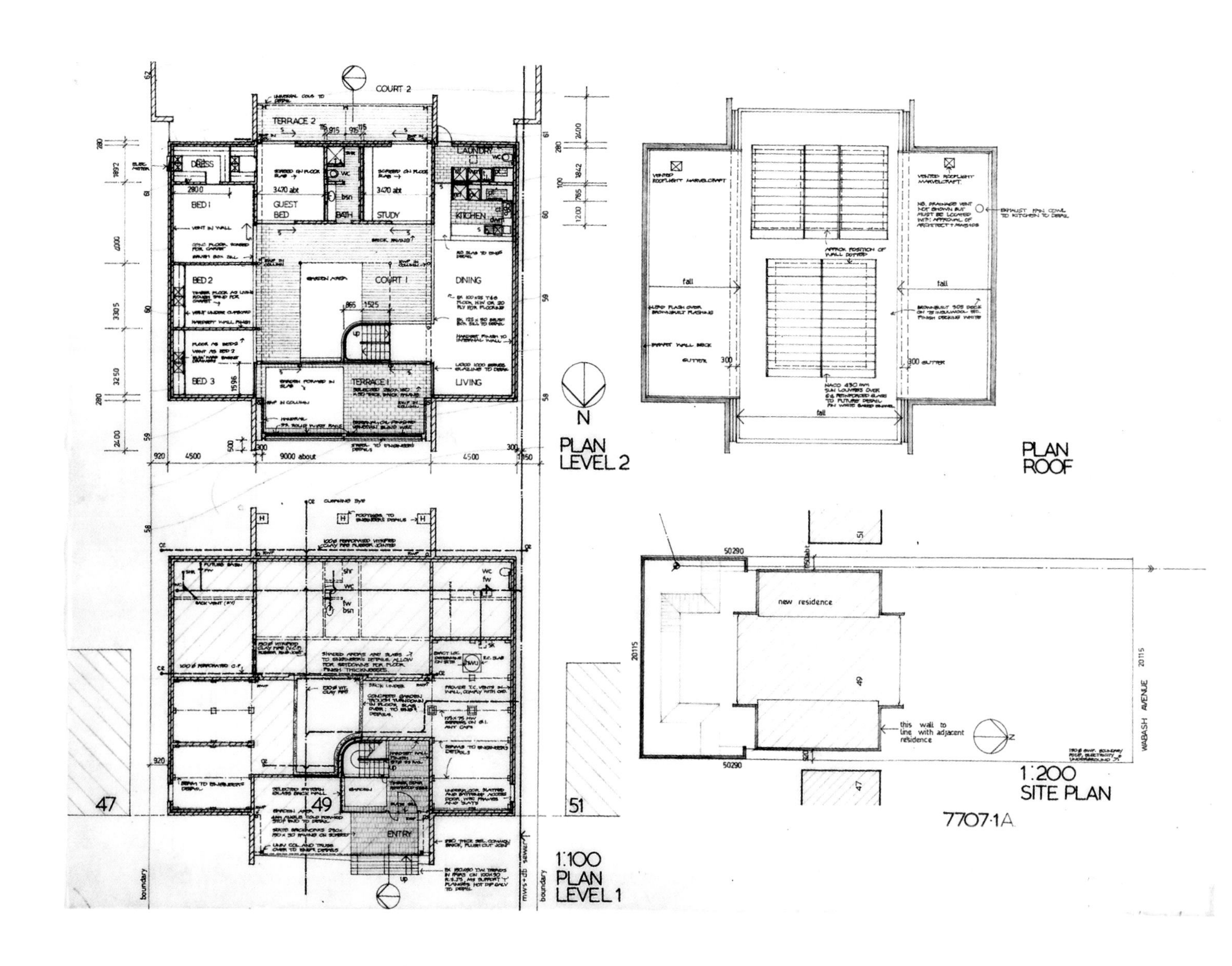

COURT 2
TERRACE 2
DRESS
BED 1
GUEST BED
BATH
STUDY
LAUNDRY
KITCHEN
BED 2
COURT 1
DINING
BED 3
TERRACE 1
LIVING
N
PLAN
LEVEL 2
9000 about
4500
4500
PLAN
ROOF
fall
new residence
this wall to line with adjacent residence
WABASH AVENUE
50290
1:200
SITE PLAN
7707·1A
47
49
51
ENTRY
boundary
1:100
PLAN
LEVEL 1

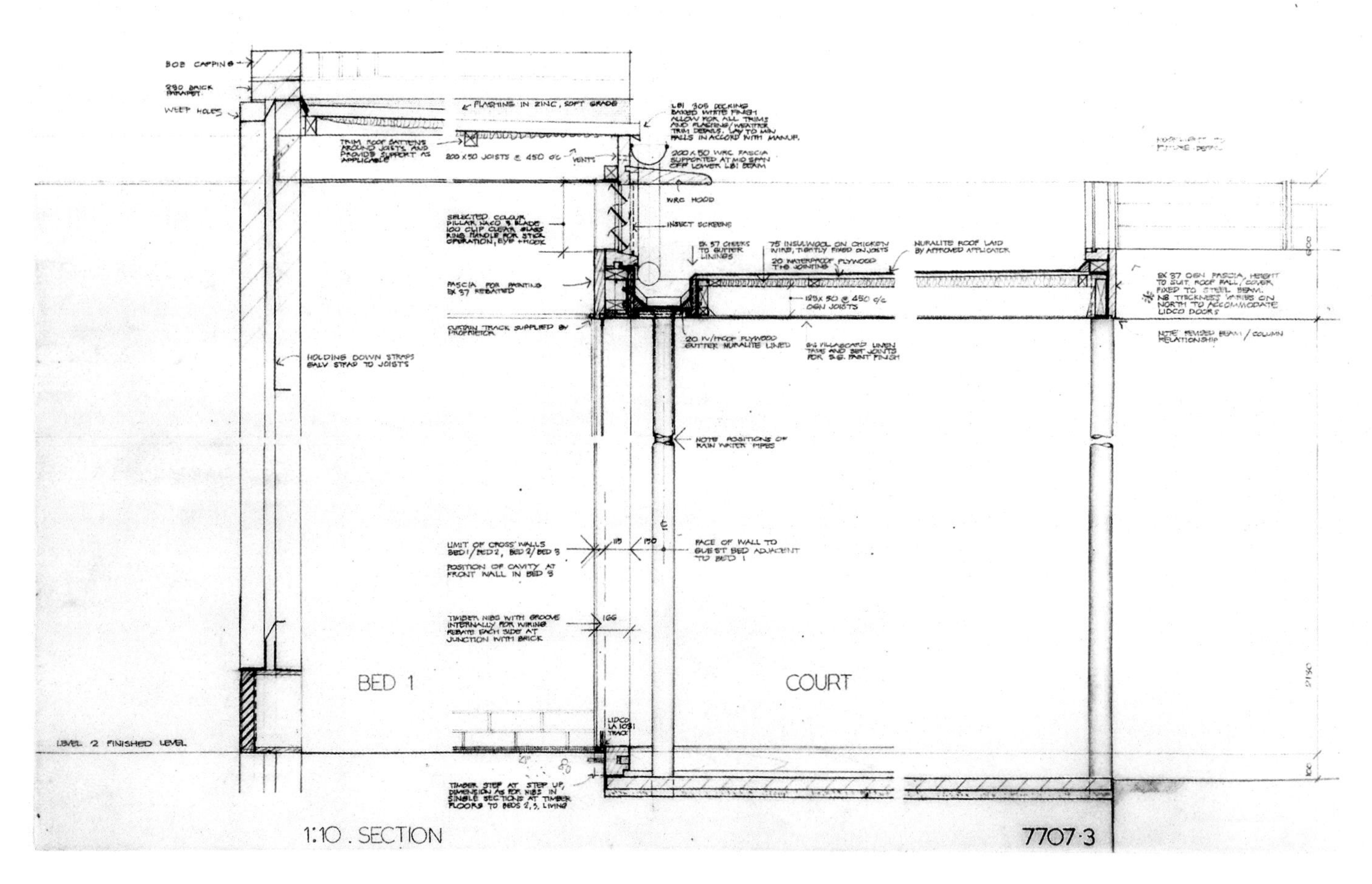

BED 1
COURT
LEVEL 2 FINISHED LEVEL
1:10 . SECTION
7707·3

Ockens house

Cromer Sydney New South Wales
1977 to 1978

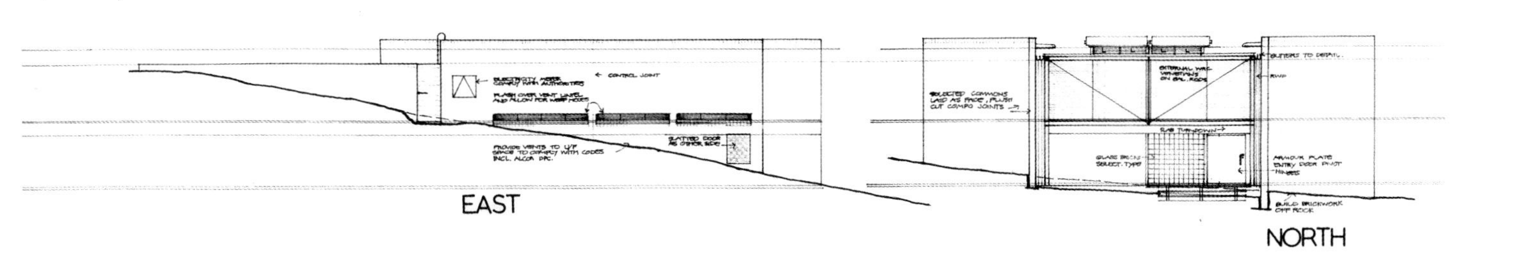

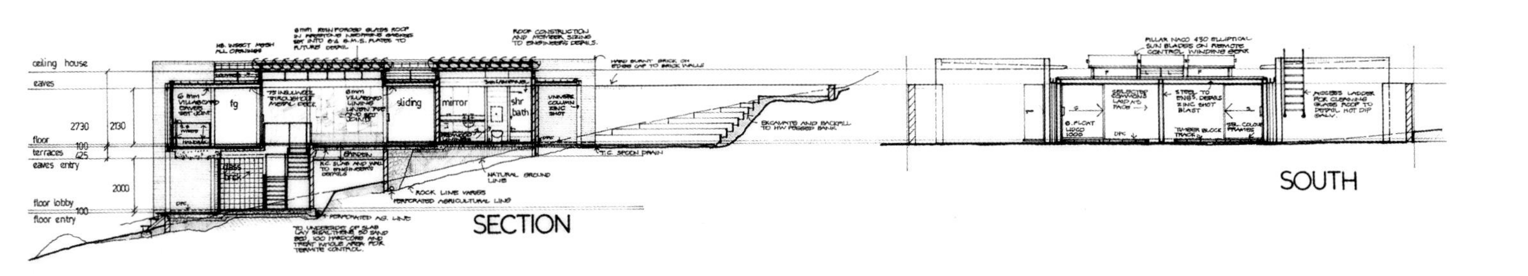

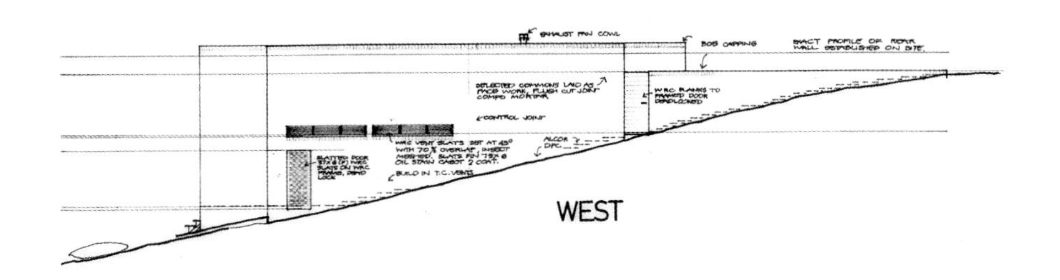

Museum of Local History and Tourism Office
Kempsey New South Wales
Stage 1: 1979 to 1982; Stage 2: 1986 to 1988

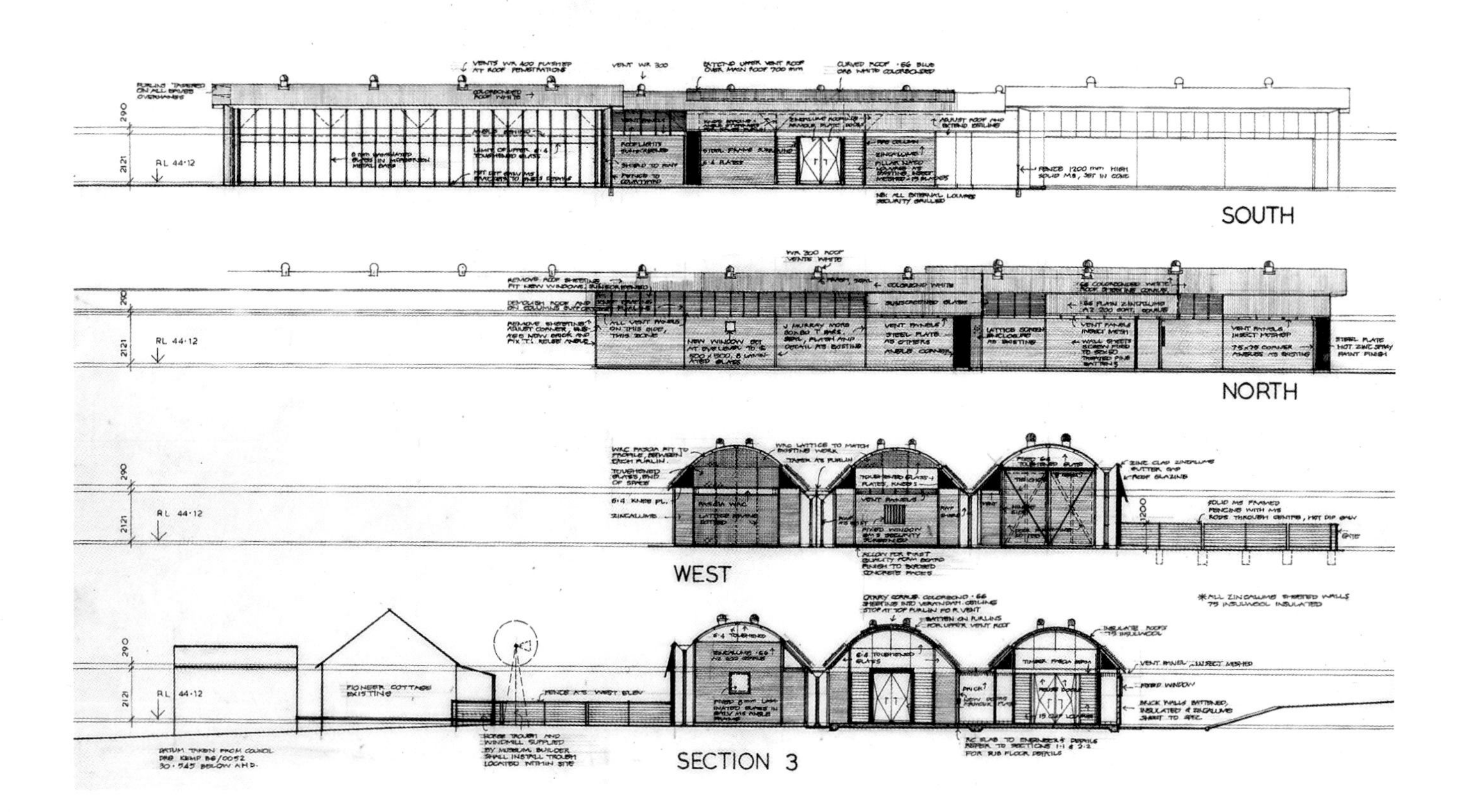

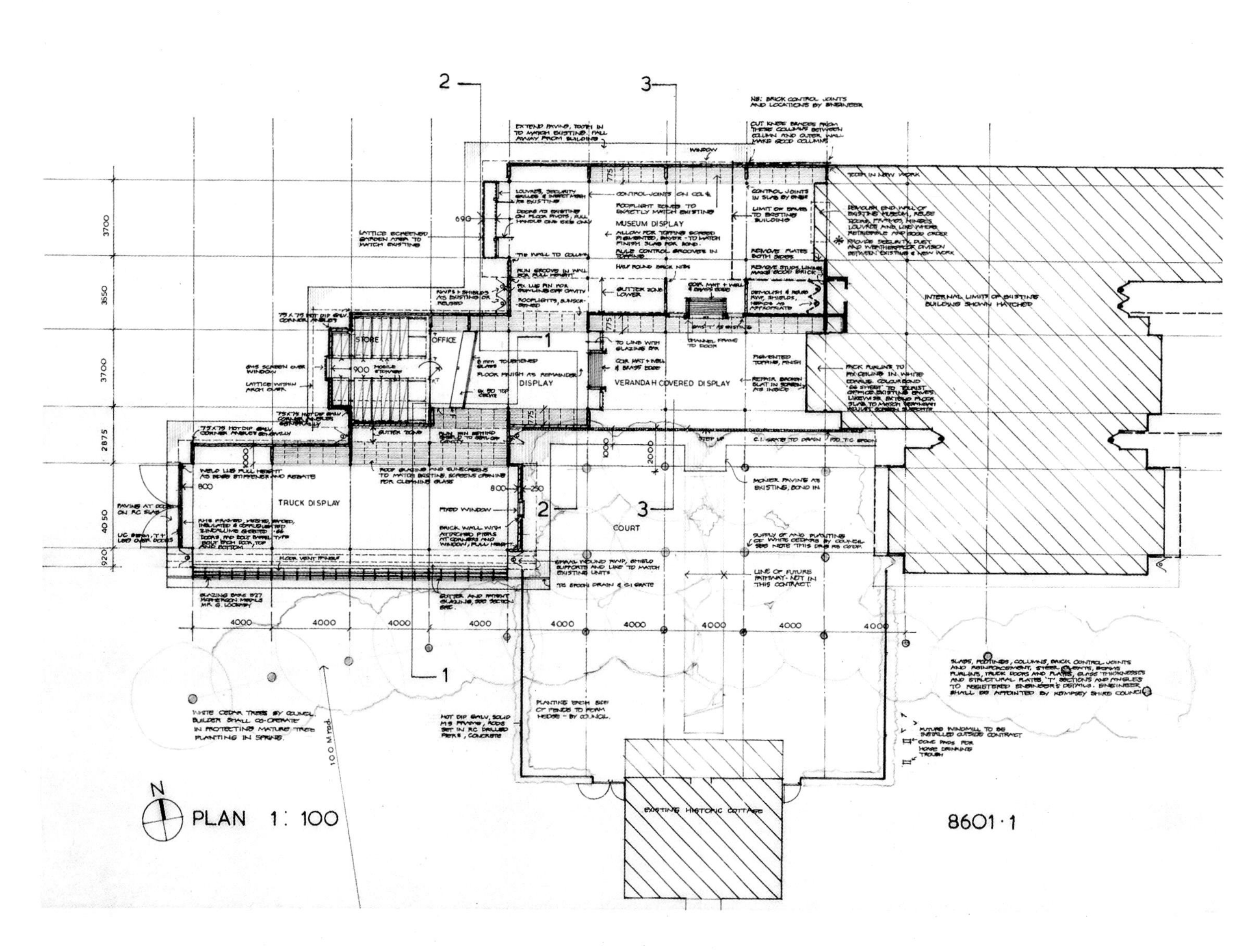

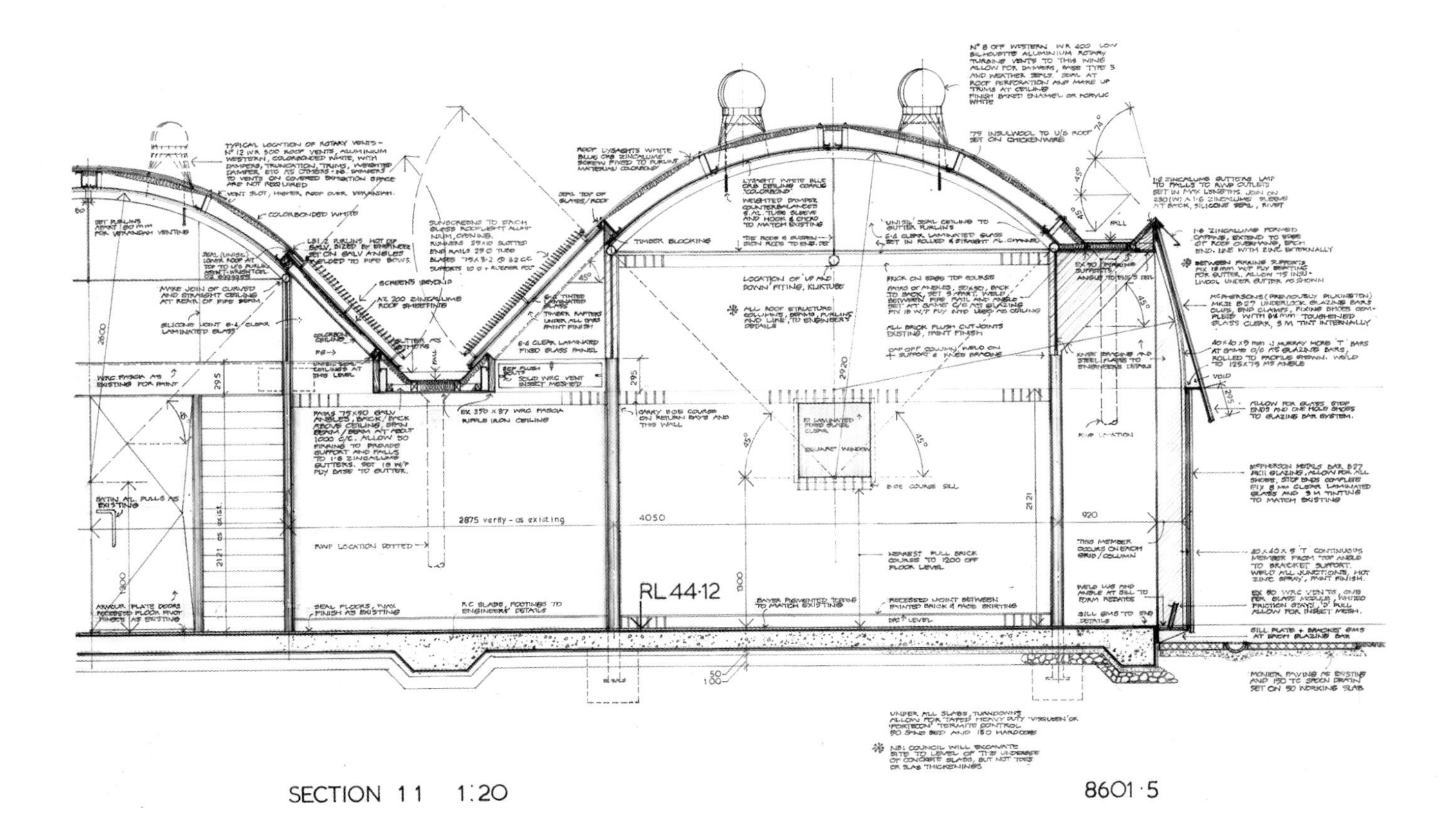

SECTION 11 1:20

MUSEUM
THEATRETTE TOURIST OFFICE
4000 4000 4000 4000 4000 4000 4000 4000 4000
A
CONTROL JOINT
LOUVRES AS AT ENTRY
GRANOLITH FINISH
VERANDAH
WRC LATTICE IN GABLE END OVER
MAT SINKING, SURROUND AND DOORS AS ENTRY
POT BELLY STOVE
FLOORS CONCRETE FINISH GRANOLITH
WALLS 115 BRICK PAINTED
EXHIBITION
ROOFLIGHTS OVER
ENTRY
ARCHIVES
GLAZED WALL TO DETAIL
STORE
urinal
men
women
5250
WRC LATTICE IN GABLE END OVER
GLASS BLOCK WALL AS OTHERS
FINISH FLOOR AS ENTRY VERANDAH
SIGHT LINE CUT OUT FOR VISION CUT
230 1500 910 1362 100
115
TRUNCATE GUTTER TO FORM RAIN WATER HEAD TO DOWN PIPES
CRUCIFORM STEEL GUTTER COLUMN SUPPORT
exhibition alcove
cupboard over
tea
DOWN PIPE HEADS AND SURROUNDS TO DETAIL
LOUVRE WINDOWS + SECURITY GRILLES
LATTICE IN GABLE END OVER
office
SHELVING TO DETAIL
desk
RECEPTION
ENTRY
ROOFLIGHTS OVER
3700
MAT SINKING BRASS ANGLE SURROUND
DOORS STEEL TO DETAIL
CHANNEL FRAME
6·4 LAMINATED GLASS IN LOUVRES, SECURITY GRILLED
GRANOLITH FINISH TO SLAB
verandah
PATHS, SITEWORKS BY COUNCIL
SLAB EDGE
KNEE BRACE OFF COLUMN TO PURLIN
display
display
chair store
store
CORRUGATED LYSAGHTS ZINCALUME WALL CLADDING
PILLAR NAGO METAL LOUVRES, SECURITY GRILLED
FUTURE POND LOCATION
FUTURE WIND MILL PUMPS
FUTURE TANK
FLOOR GRANOLITH TO CONCRETE SLAB
SCREEN NOT IN THIS CONTRACT.
COLUMNS TO ENG'S DETAILS
ROOFLIGHTS AND LOUVRE BLACKOUT OVER DOTTED
theatrette
4050
GLAZED SCREEN TO PROJECTION ROOM
INTERNAL WALLS, NIBS PAINTED BRICKWORK
projection
EAVES LINE DOTTED
WALL BRICK WITH 230 x 115 ATTACHED PIERS, STUD FRAME AND INSULATE + CORRUGATED ZINCALUME LINE
FORM GUTTER GUARD TO PROFILE AROUND RWP
WINDOWS DOTTED VENT SLOT OVER
250 600 165 600 250
B

8009·2A

N

PLAN 1:100

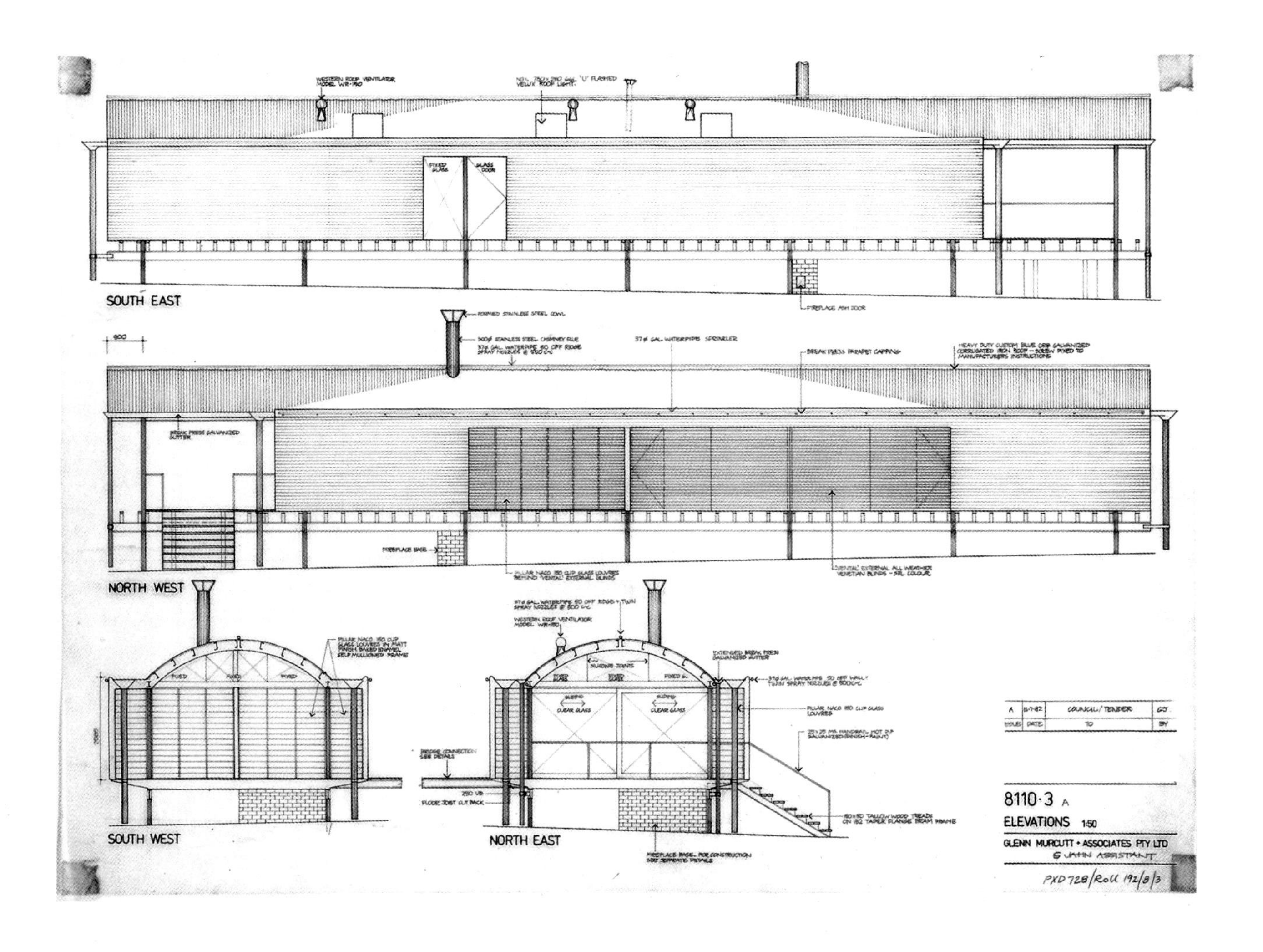
SOUTH EAST
NORTH WEST
SOUTH WEST
NORTH EAST
A
COUNCIL / TENDER
GJ
ISSUE
DATE
TO
BY
8110·3 A
ELEVATIONS 1:50
GLENN MURCUTT + ASSOCIATES PTY LTD
PXD 728/Roll 192/8/3

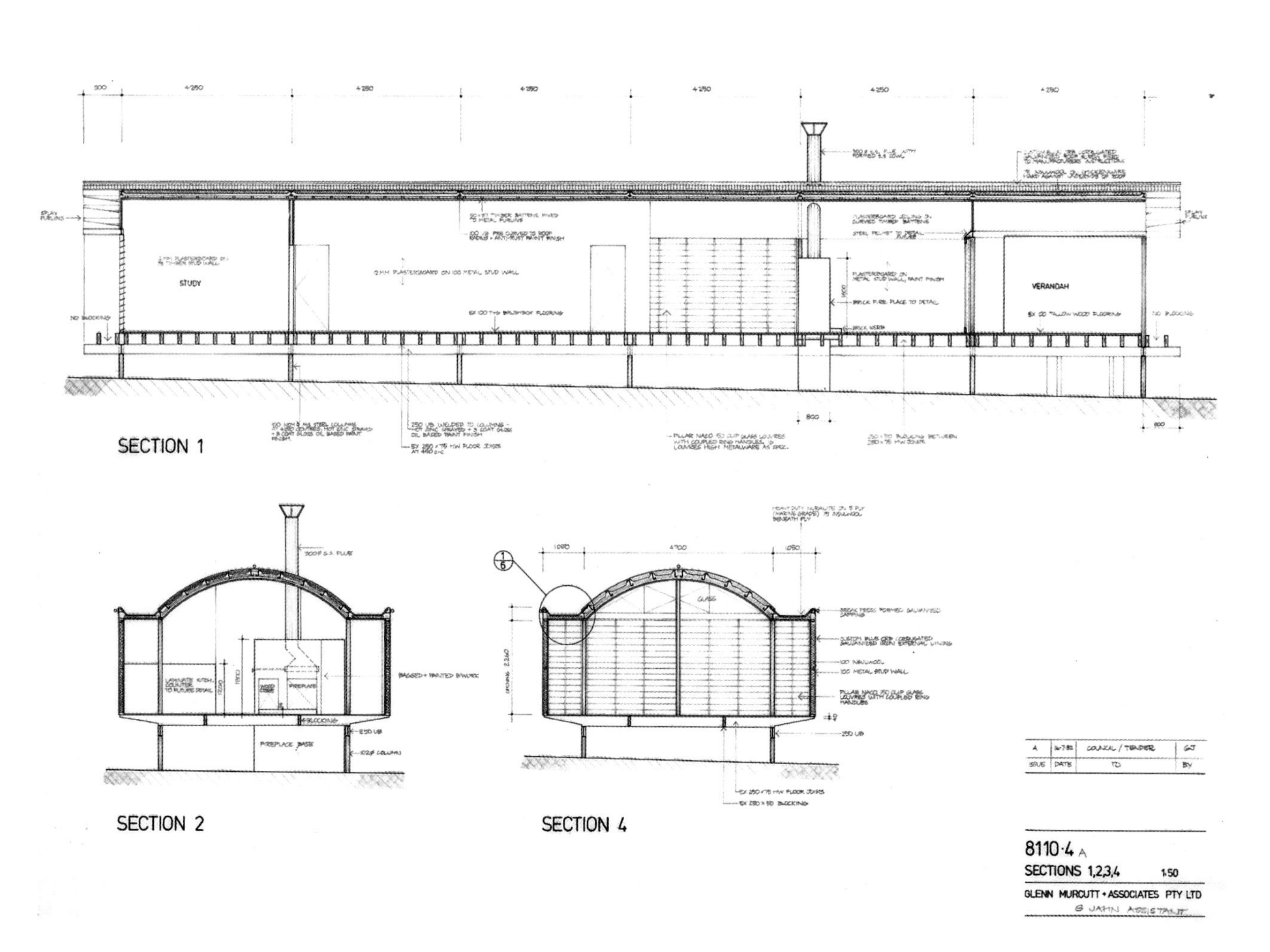
STUDY
VERANDAH
SECTION 1
SECTION 2
SECTION 4
A
COUNCIL / TENDER
GJ
ISSUE
DATE
TO
BY
8110·4 A
SECTIONS 1,2,3,4 1:50
GLENN MURCUTT + ASSOCIATES PTY LTD

Ball-Eastaway house

Glenorie New South Wales

1980 to 1983

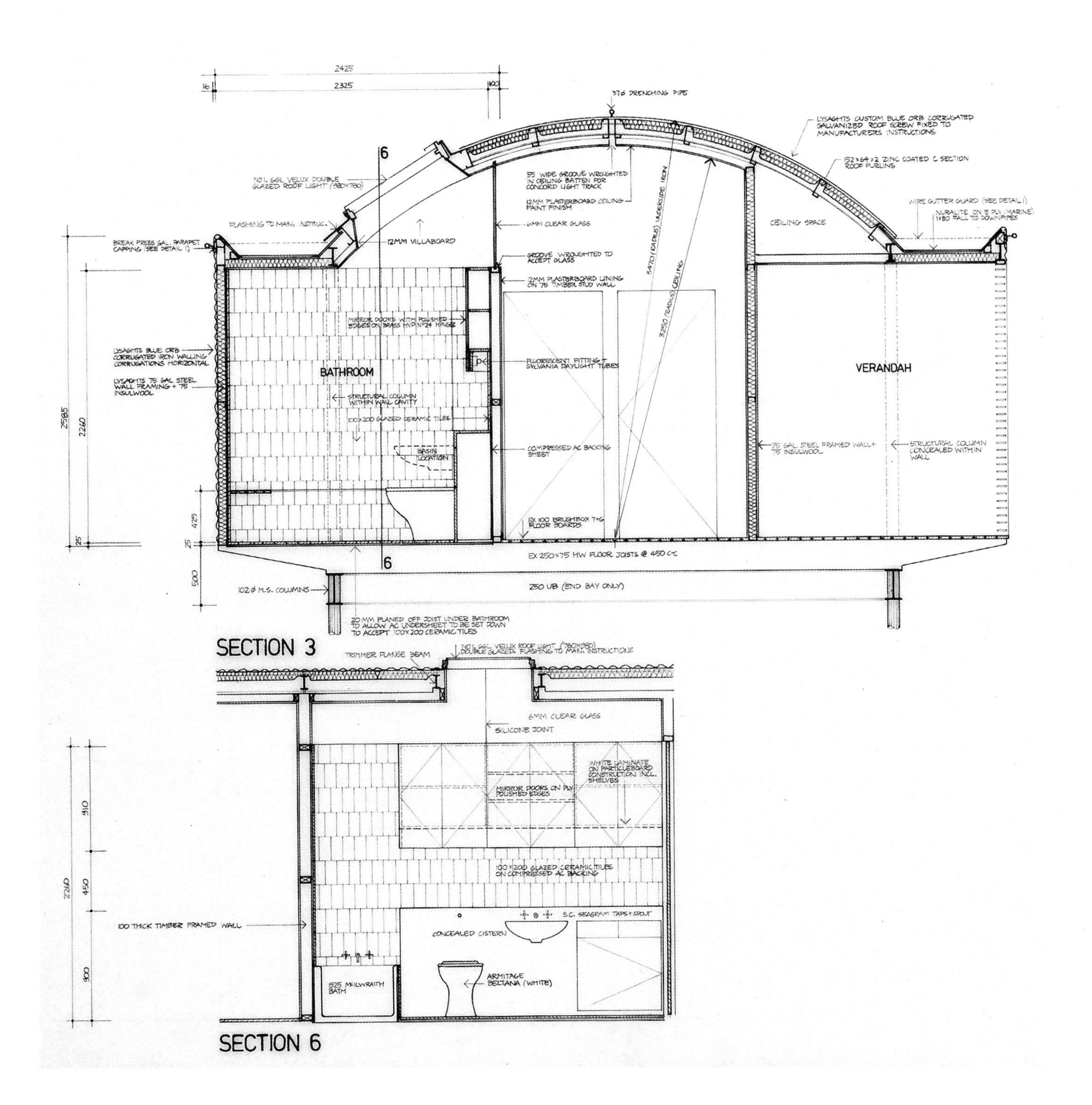

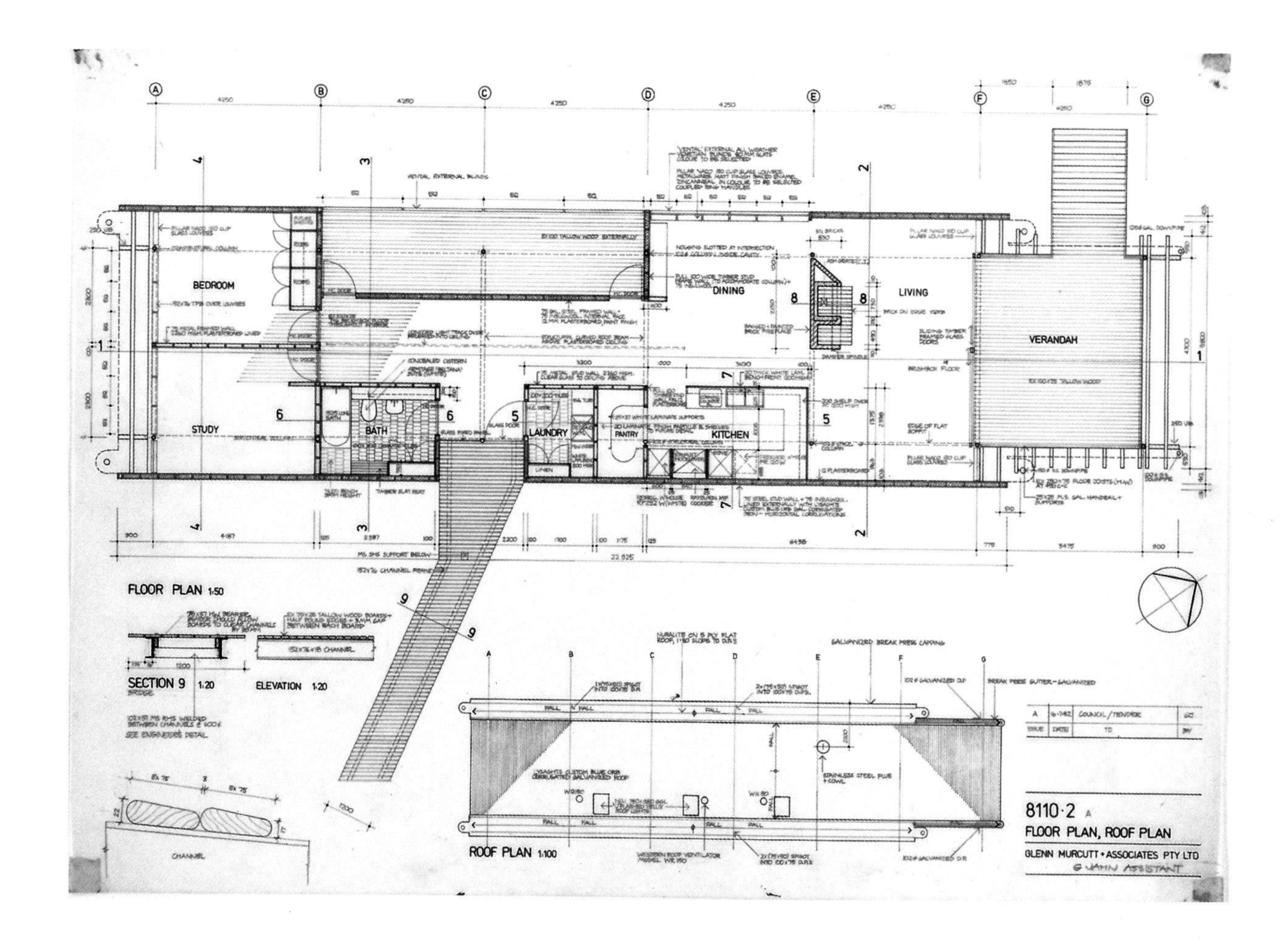

BEDROOM
STUDY
BATH
LAUNDRY
PANTRY
KITCHEN
DINING
LIVING
VERANDAH
FLOOR PLAN 1:50
SECTION 9 1:20
ELEVATION 1:20
ROOF PLAN 1:100
GALVANIZED BREAK PRESS CAPPING
8110·2 A
FLOOR PLAN, ROOF PLAN
GLENN MURCUTT + ASSOCIATES PTY LTD

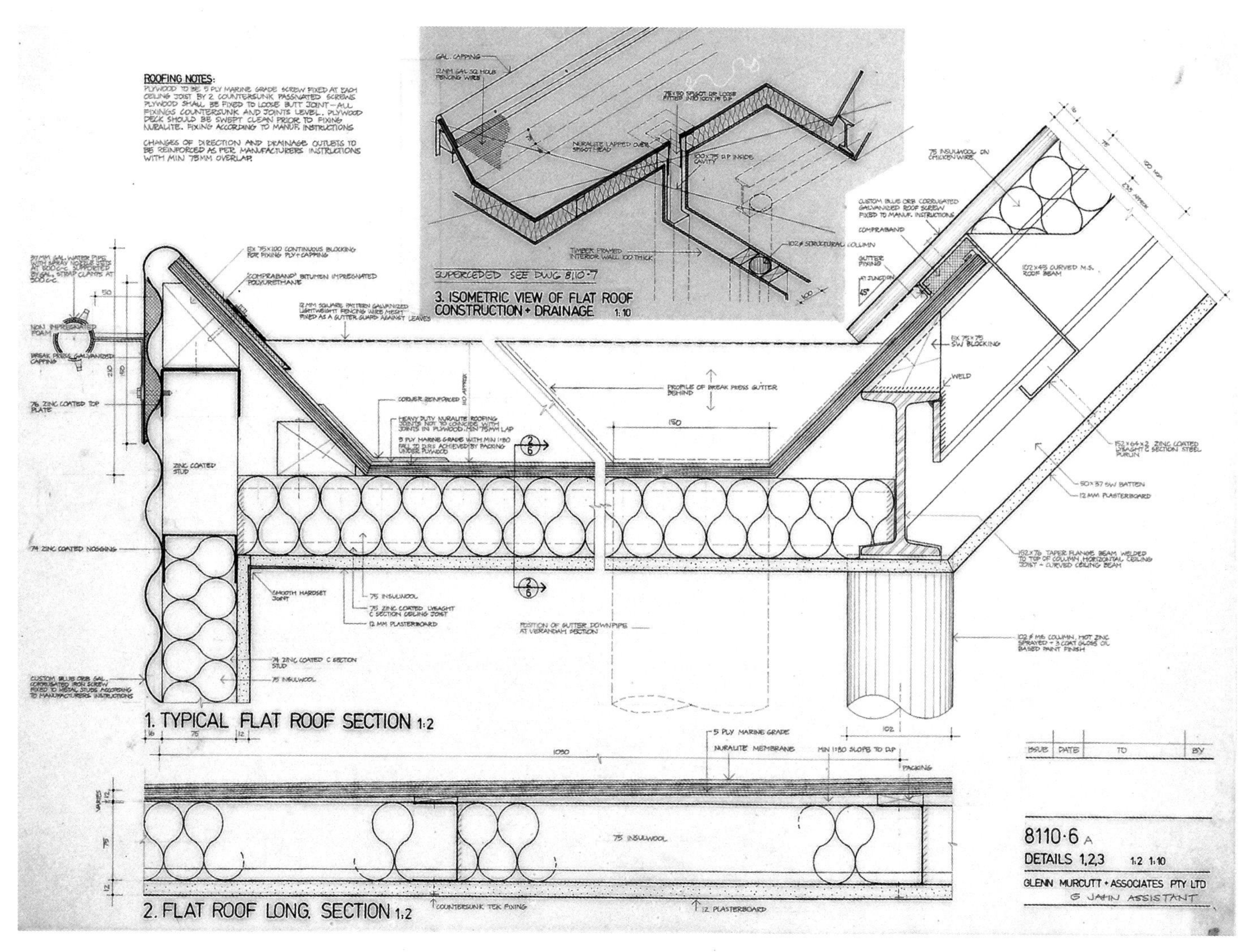

ROOFING NOTES:
PLYWOOD TO BE 5 PLY MARINE GRADE SCREW FIXED AT EACH CEILING JOIST BY 2 COUNTERSUNK PASSIVATED SCREWS. PLYWOOD SHALL BE FIXED TO LOOSE BUTT JOINT — ALL FIXINGS COUNTERSUNK AND JOINTS LEVEL. PLYWOOD DECK SHOULD BE SWEPT CLEAN PRIOR TO FIXING NURALITE. FIXING ACCORDING TO MANUF. INSTRUCTIONS
CHANGES OF DIRECTION AND DRAINAGE OUTLETS TO BE REINFORCED AS PER MANUFACTURERS INSTRUCTIONS WITH MIN 75MM OVERLAP.
SUPERCEDED SEE DWG 8110·7
3. ISOMETRIC VIEW OF FLAT ROOF CONSTRUCTION + DRAINAGE 1:10
1. TYPICAL FLAT ROOF SECTION 1:2
2. FLAT ROOF LONG. SECTION 1:2
75 INSULWOOL
5 PLY MARINE GRADE
NURALITE MEMBRANE
12 PLASTERBOARD
COUNTERSUNK TEK FIXING
8110·6 A
DETAILS 1,2,3 1:2 1:10
GLENN MURCUTT + ASSOCIATES PTY LTD

Ball-Eastaway house

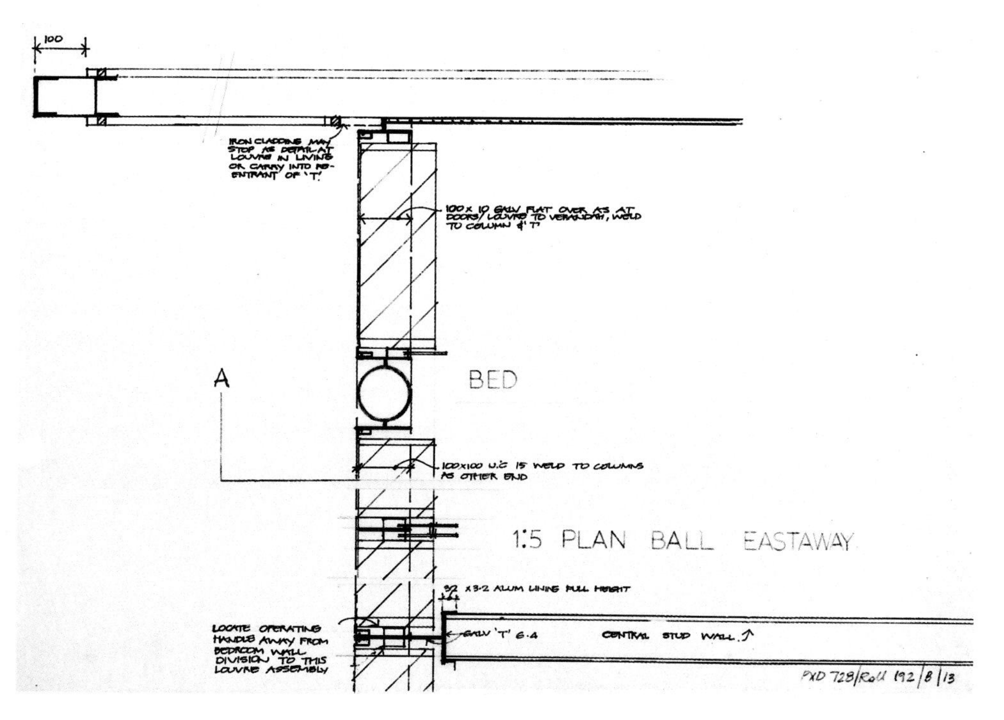

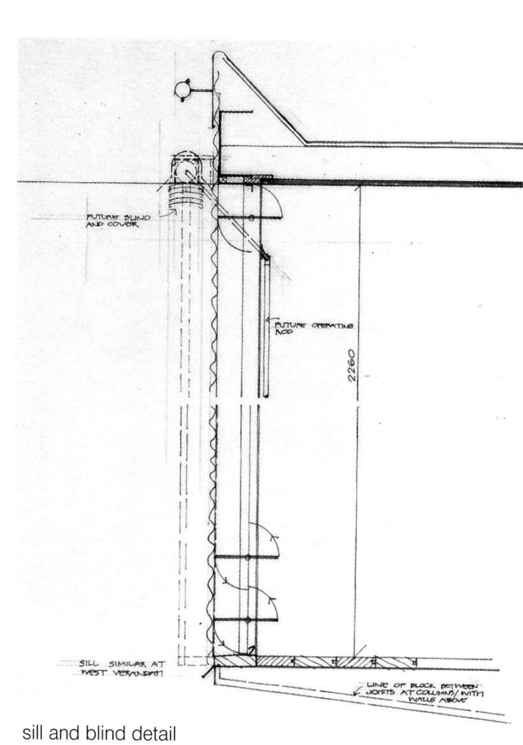

sill and blind detail

BREAK PRESS GAL.STEEL CAPPING

CORRUGATED GAL STEEL ROOF

CONICAL STAINLESS STEEL RAINWATER HEAD

W.R. CEDAR BLOCKING

150 PILLAR NACO GLASS LOUVRES

STAINLESS STEEL DOWNPIPES

102 ø STRUCTURAL STEEL COLUMN

CORRUGATED GAL WALL

END ELEVATION

150 102 APPROX 60 102

1050

CAPPING

FLAT TRAY FITTED UNDER NURALITE

45° 45° 45°

POSITION OF EXPOSED FLOOR JOIST BELOW

150ø GAL DOWNPIPE

45°

CORRUGATED ROOF

PLAN 1:5

CORRUGATED ROOF

ROOF EDGE

BOTTOM EDGE OF 152x76 TAPER FLANGE BEAM

250x75 HW JOIST

STAINLESS STEEL CLAMP BRACKET

SIDE ELEVATION

60 150

100

A	16.7.82	TENDER	GJ
ISSUE	DATE	REVISION/TO	BY

8110·7 A
GUTTERS + DOWNPIPES 1:5
Glenn Murcutt + Associates

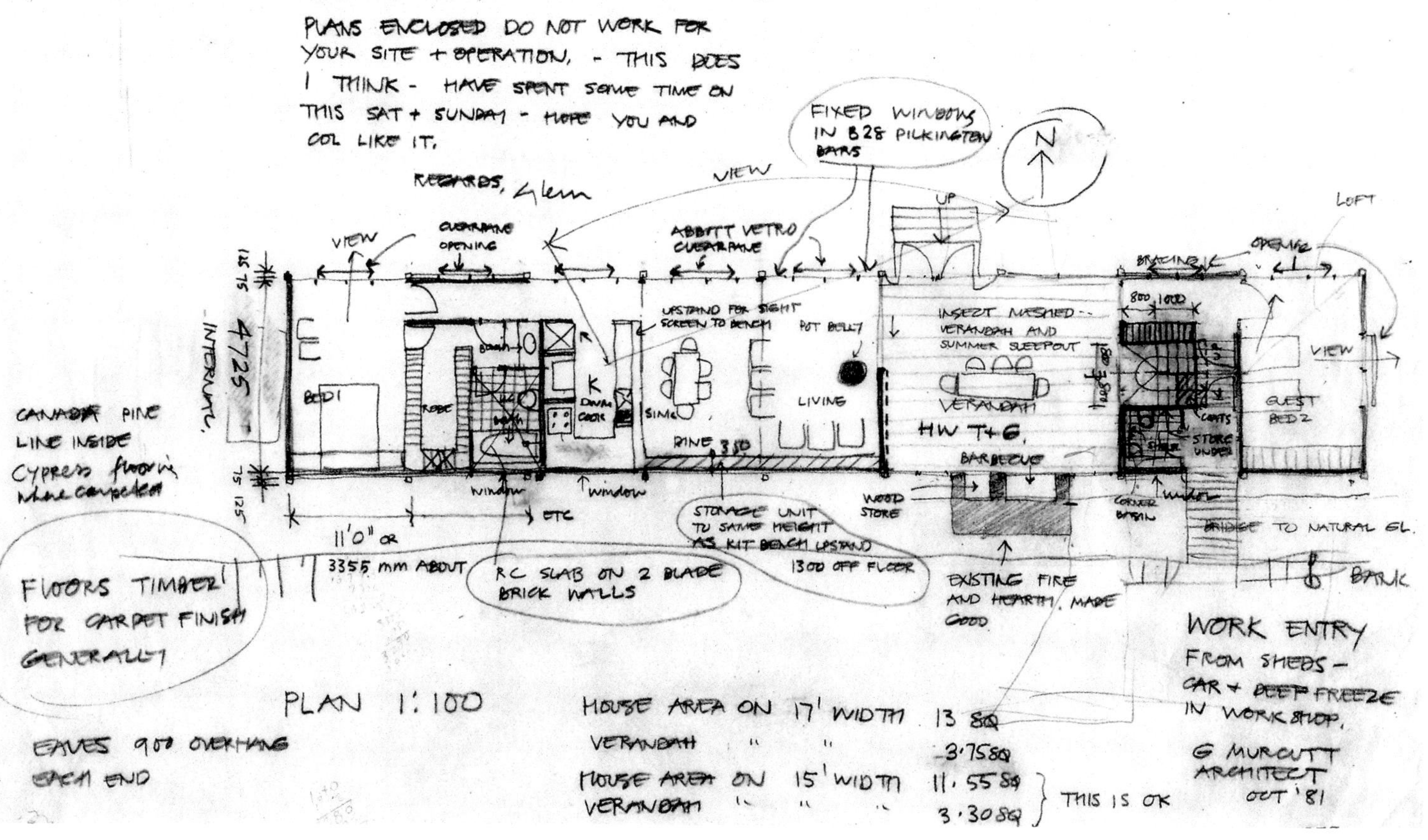
OCT 26 '81
NEVILLE + JILL,
PLANS ENCLOSED DO NOT WORK FOR YOUR SITE + OPERATION, - THIS DOES I THINK - HAVE SPENT SOME TIME ON THIS SAT + SUNDAY - HOPE YOU AND COL LIKE IT.
REGARDS, Glenn
FIXED WINDOWS IN B28 PILKINGTON BARS
N
VIEW
UP
LOFT
VIEW
CLEARPANE OPENING
ABBOTT VETRO CLEARPANE
BRACING
OPENING
800 1000
UPSTAND FOR SIGHT SCREEN TO BENCH
POT BELLY
INSECT MESHED VERANDAH AND SUMMER SLEEPOUT
4725
INTERNAL
BED 1
ROBE
K
SINK
LIVING
VERANDAH
VIEW
GUEST BED 2
CUPBDS
STORE UNDER
HW T+G
BARBECUE
DINE
CANADA PINE LINE INSIDE
Cypress flooring when completed
window
window
ETC
WOOD STORE
CORNER BASIN
BRIDGE TO NATURAL GL.
BANK
11'0" OR 3355 mm ABOUT
STORAGE UNIT TO SAME HEIGHT AS KIT BENCH UPSTAND 1300 OFF FLOOR
RC SLAB ON 2 BLADE BRICK WALLS
EXISTING FIRE AND HEARTH, MADE GOOD
FLOORS TIMBER FOR CARPET FINISH GENERALLY
WORK ENTRY FROM SHEDS - CAR + DEEP FREEZE IN WORKSHOP.
PLAN 1:100
HOUSE AREA ON 17' WIDTH 13 SQ
VERANDAH " " 3.75 SQ
HOUSE AREA ON 15' WIDTH 11.55 SQ
VERANDAH " " " 3.30 SQ
THIS IS OK
EAVES 900 OVERHANG EACH END
G MURCUTT ARCHITECT OCT '81

Fredericks house
Jamberoo New South Wales
1981 to 1982

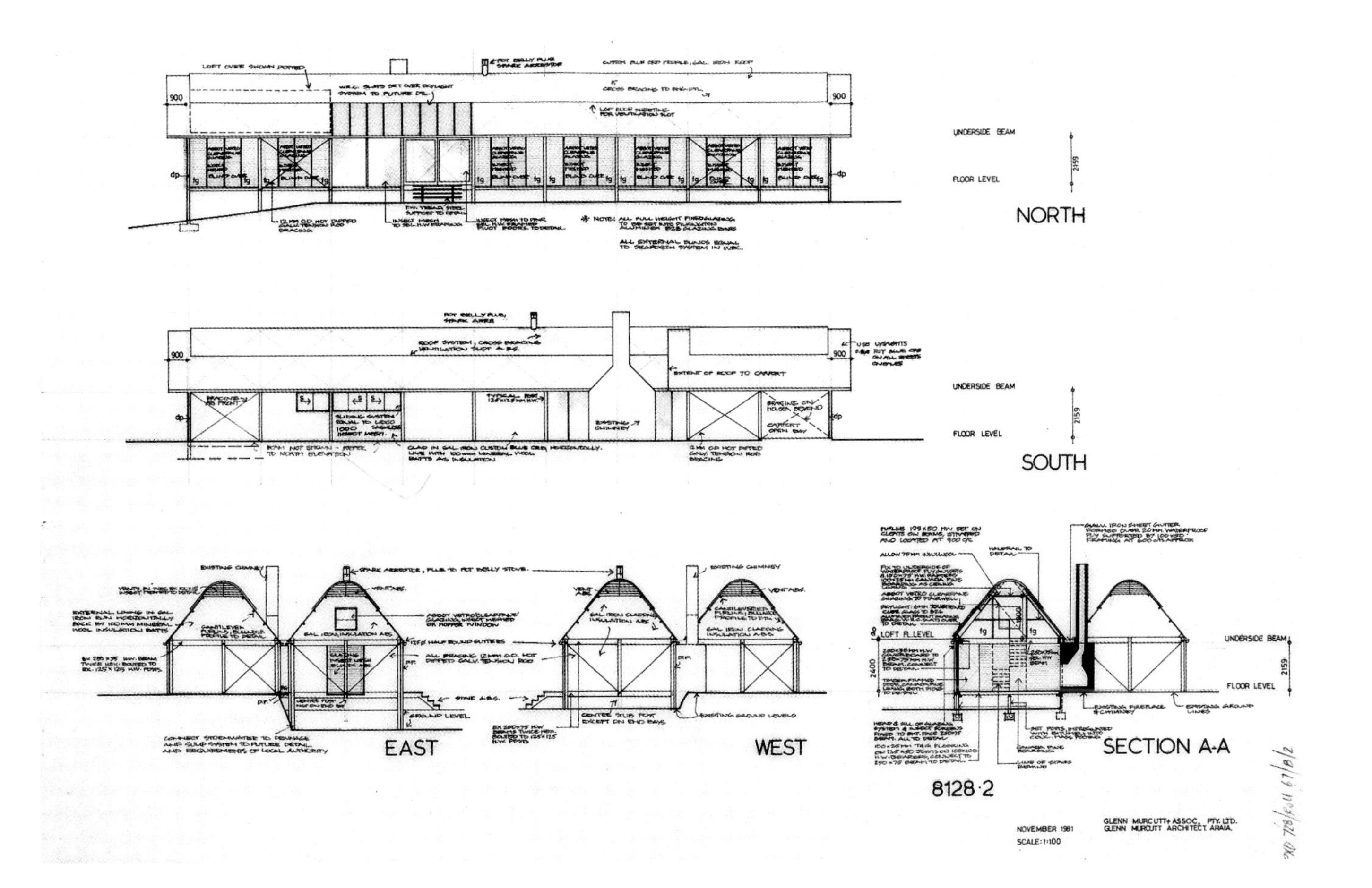

Magney house
Bingie Bingie New South Wales
1982 to 1984

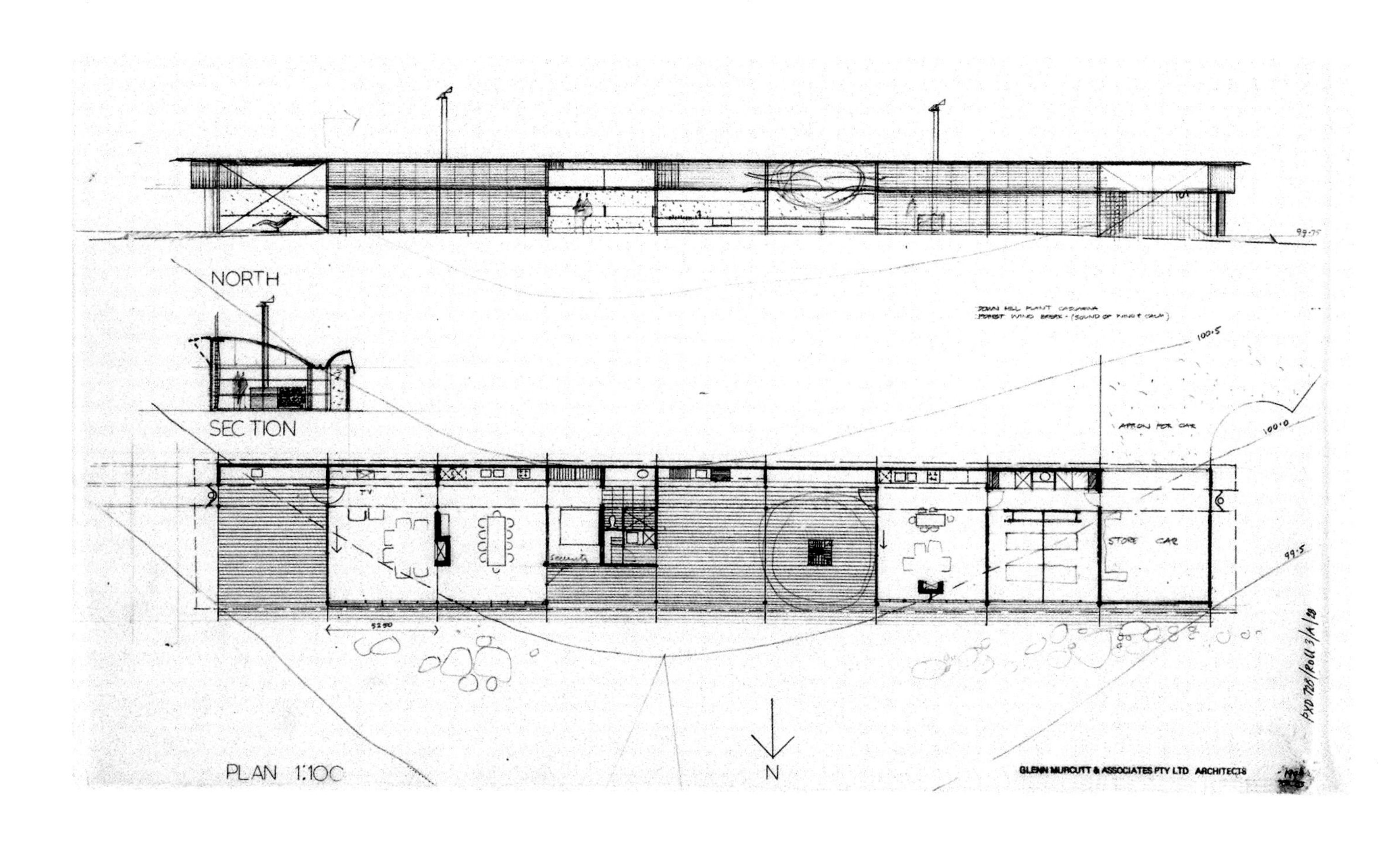

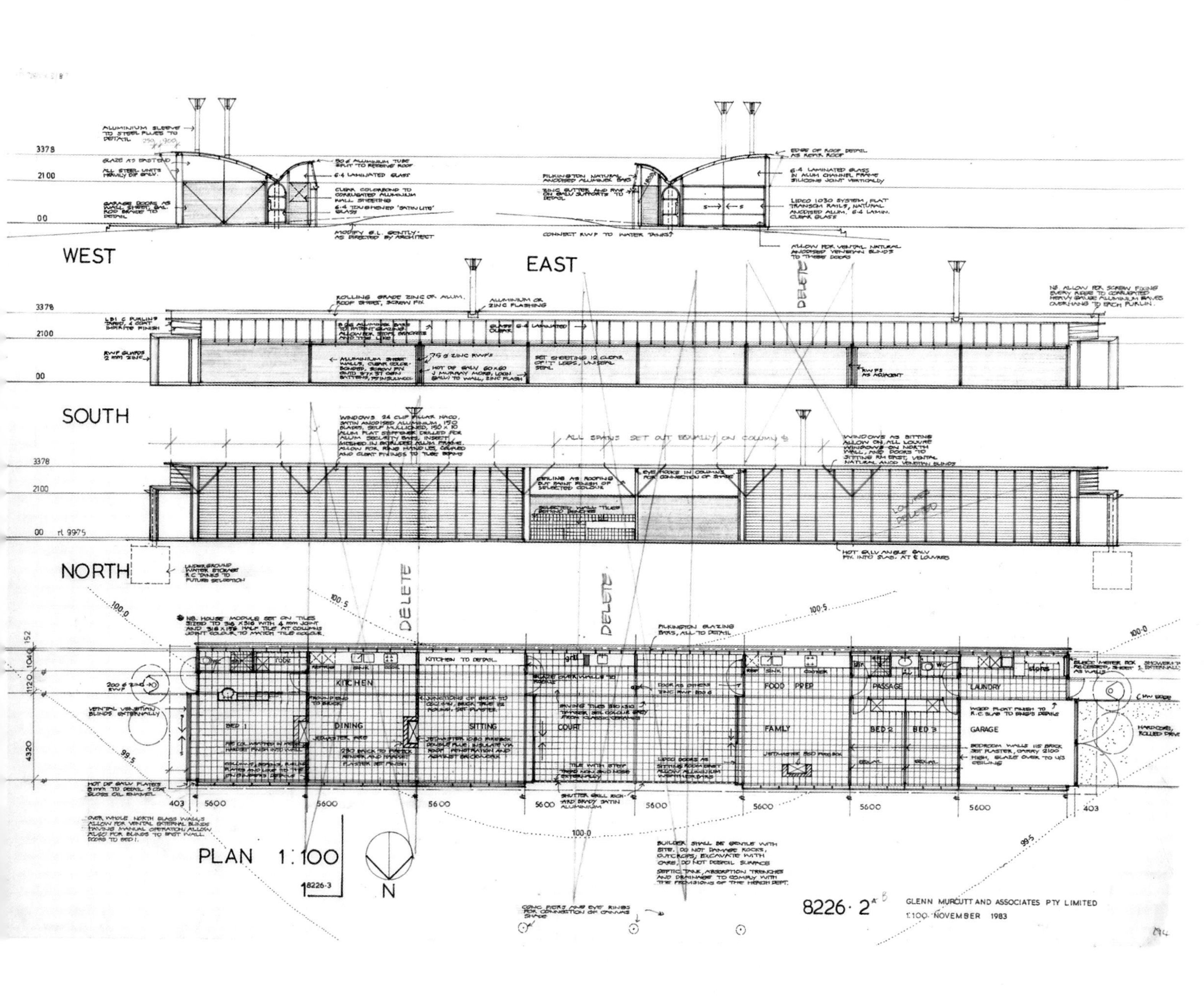

WEST
EAST
SOUTH
NORTH
DELETE
KITCHEN
DINING
SITTING
COURT
FOOD PREP
FAMILY
PASSAGE
BED 2
BED 3
LAUNDRY
GARAGE
BED 1
PLAN 1:100
N
8226 · 2
GLENN MURCUTT AND ASSOCIATES PTY LIMITED
1:100 NOVEMBER 1983

Magney house

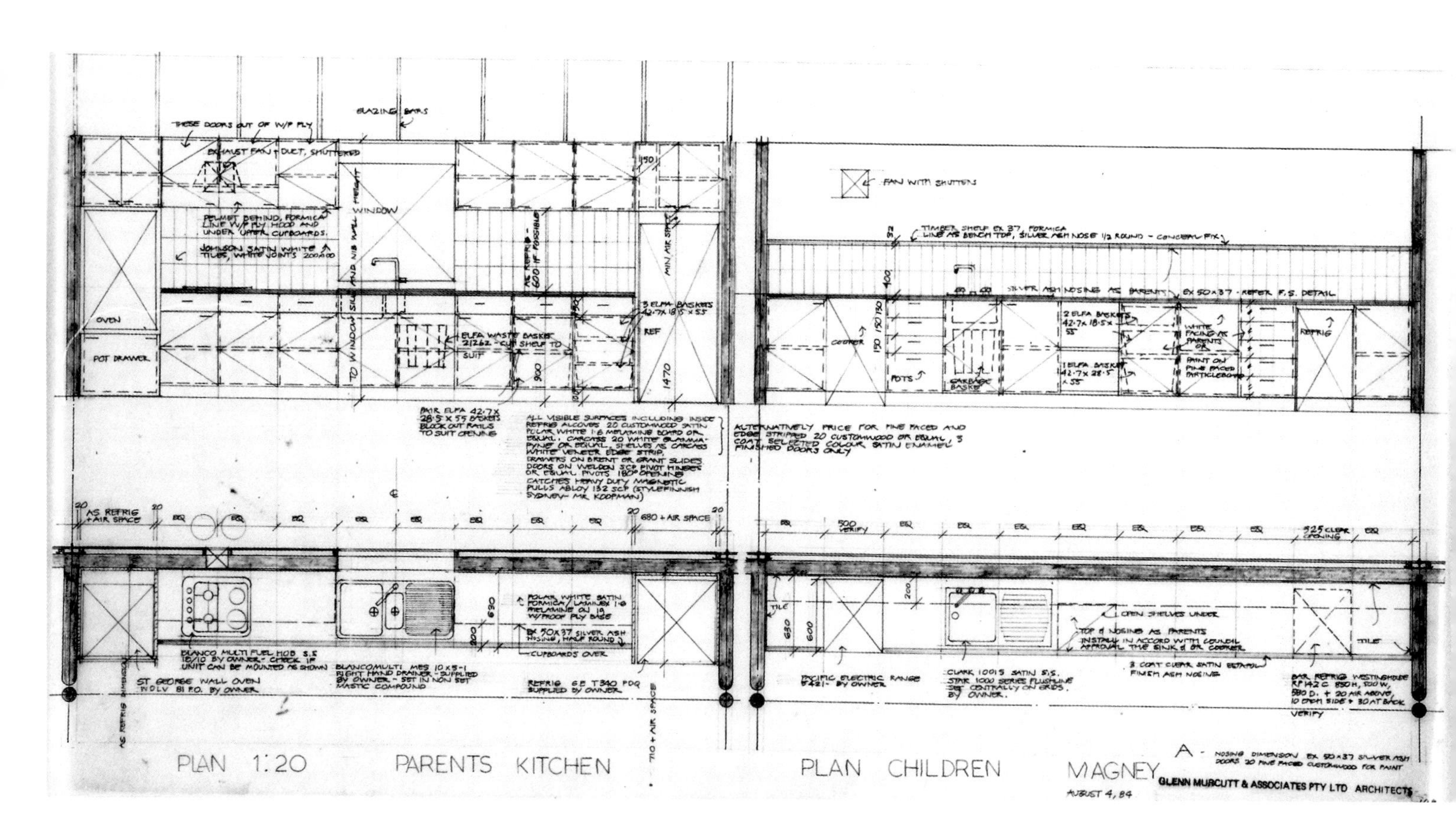

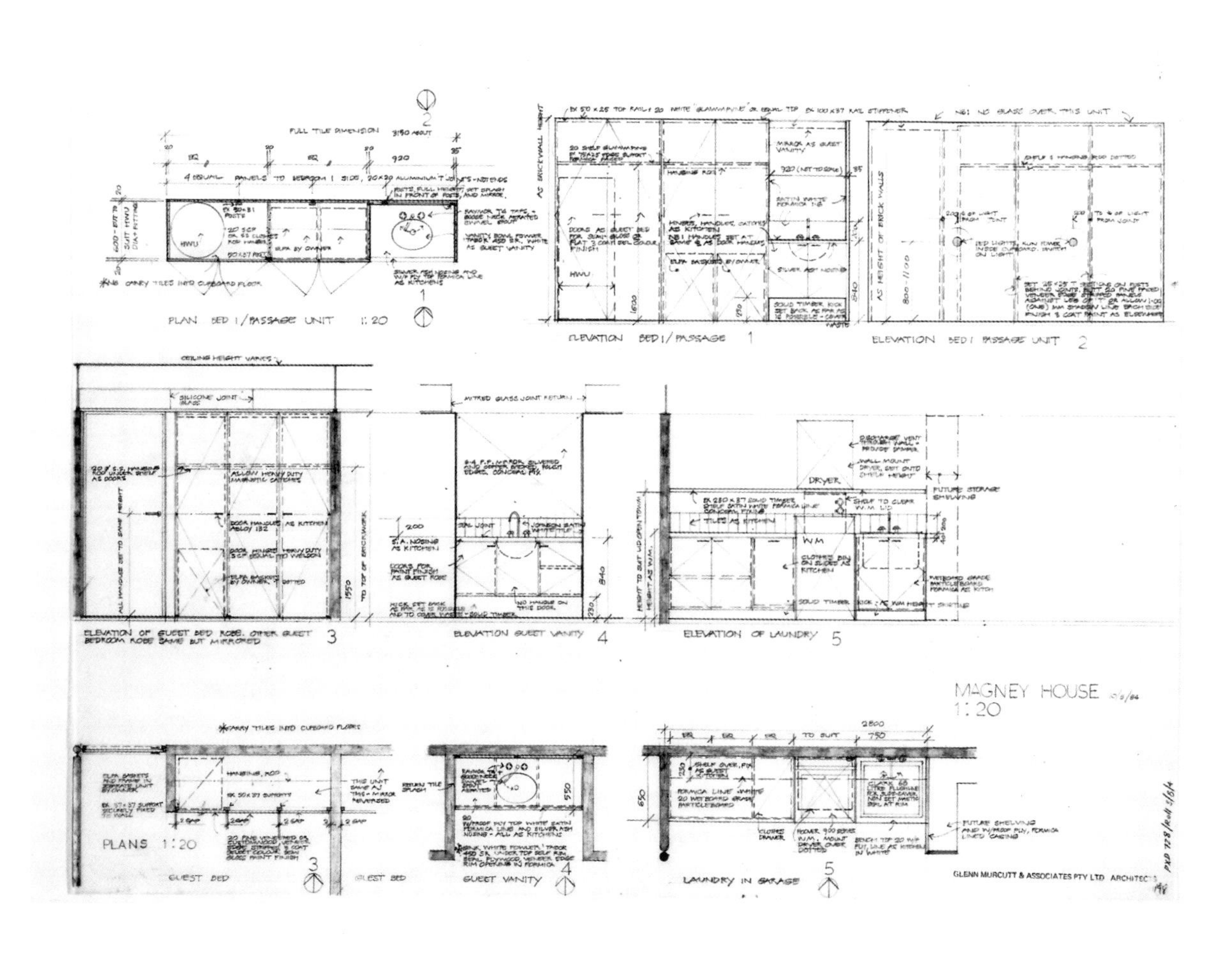

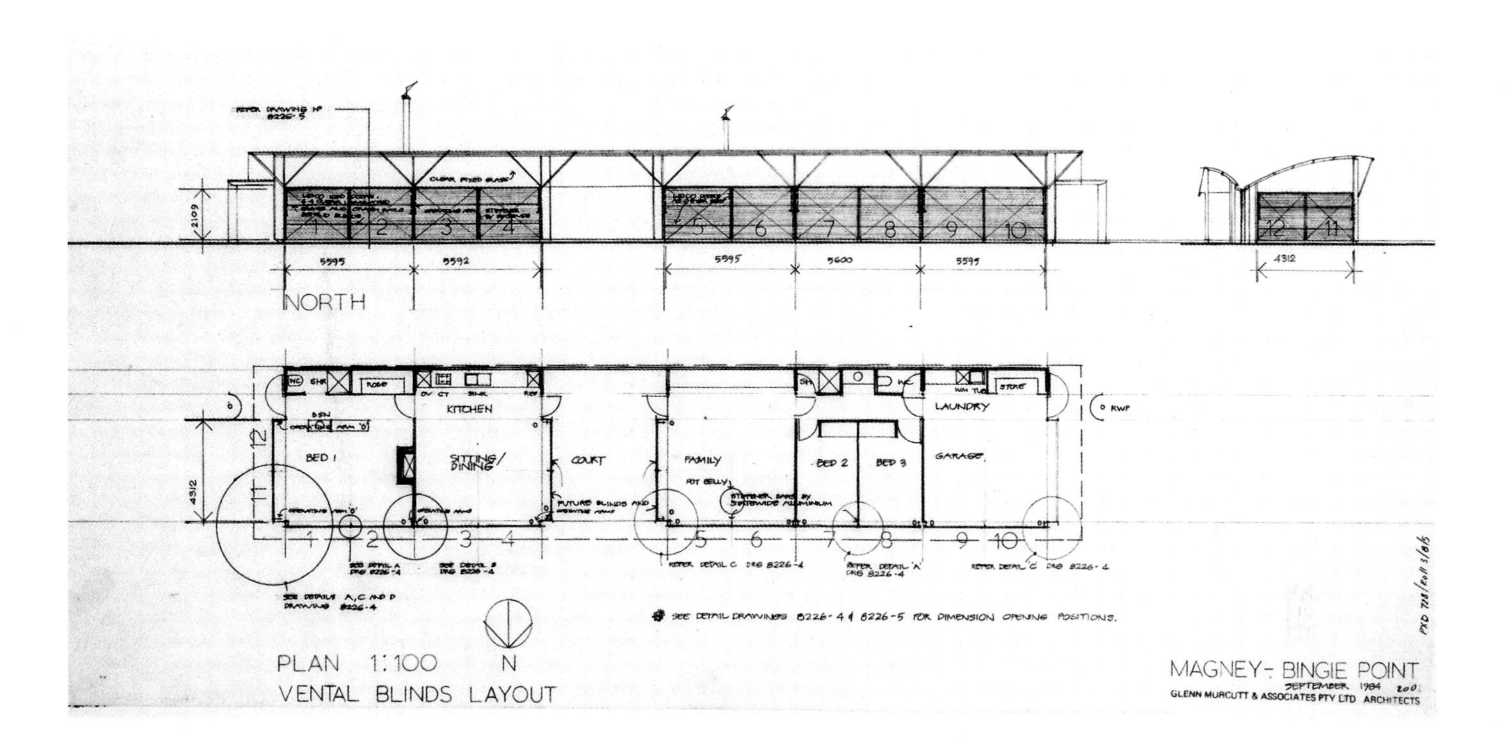
NORTH
KITCHEN
BED 1
SITTING/ DINING
COURT
FAMILY
POT BELLY
BED 2
BED 3
LAUNDRY
GARAGE
5595
5592
5595
5600
5595
4312
2109
SEE DETAIL DRAWINGS 8226-4 & 8226-5 FOR DIMENSION OPENING POSITIONS.
PLAN 1:100
N
VENTAL BLINDS LAYOUT
MAGNEY - BINGIE POINT
SEPTEMBER 1984
GLENN MURCUTT & ASSOCIATES PTY LTD ARCHITECTS

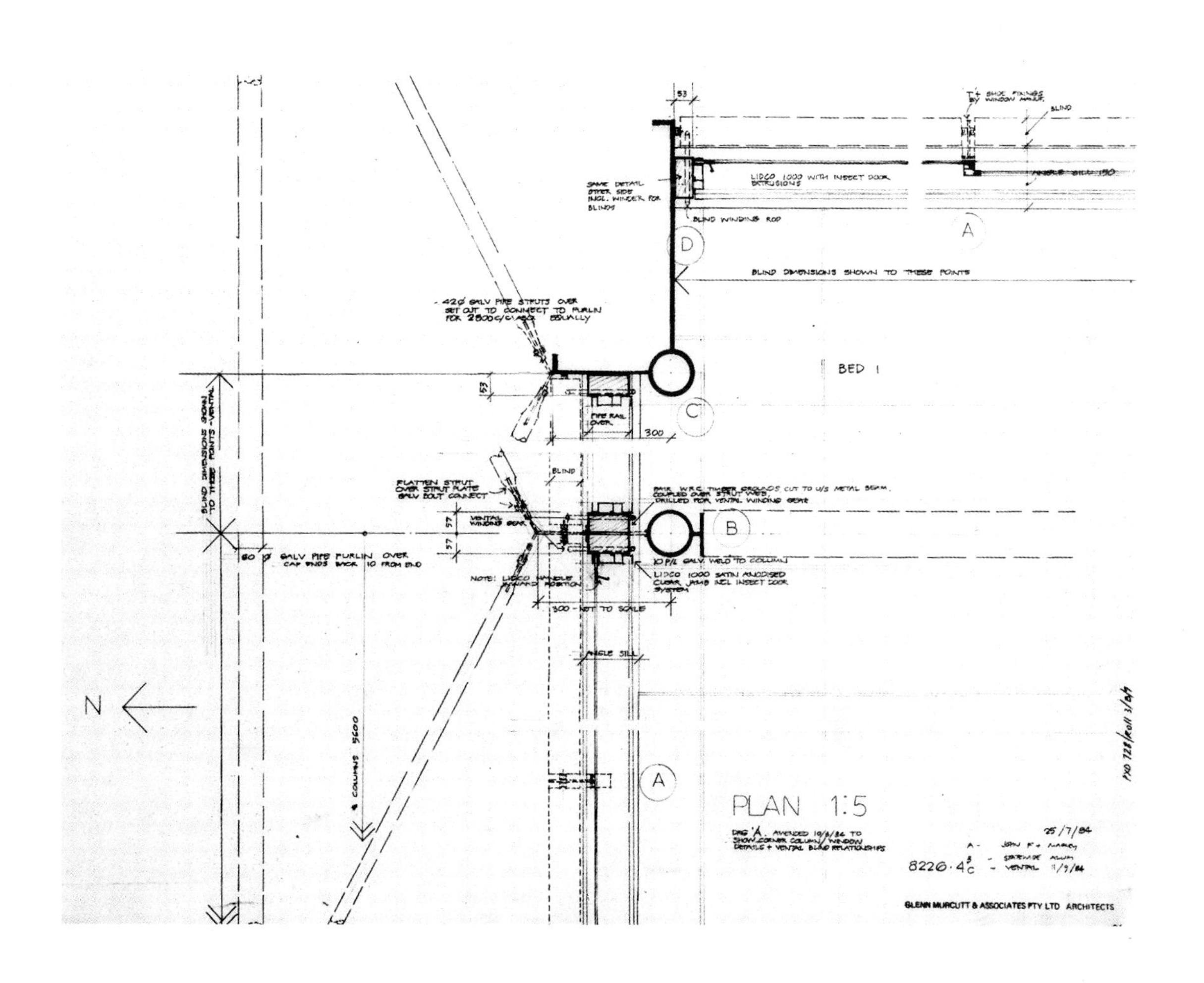
BED 1
BLIND DIMENSIONS SHOWN TO THESE POINTS
BLIND WINDING ROD
N
PLAN 1:5
300 - NOT TO SCALE
ANGLE SILL
GLENN MURCUTT & ASSOCIATES PTY LTD ARCHITECTS

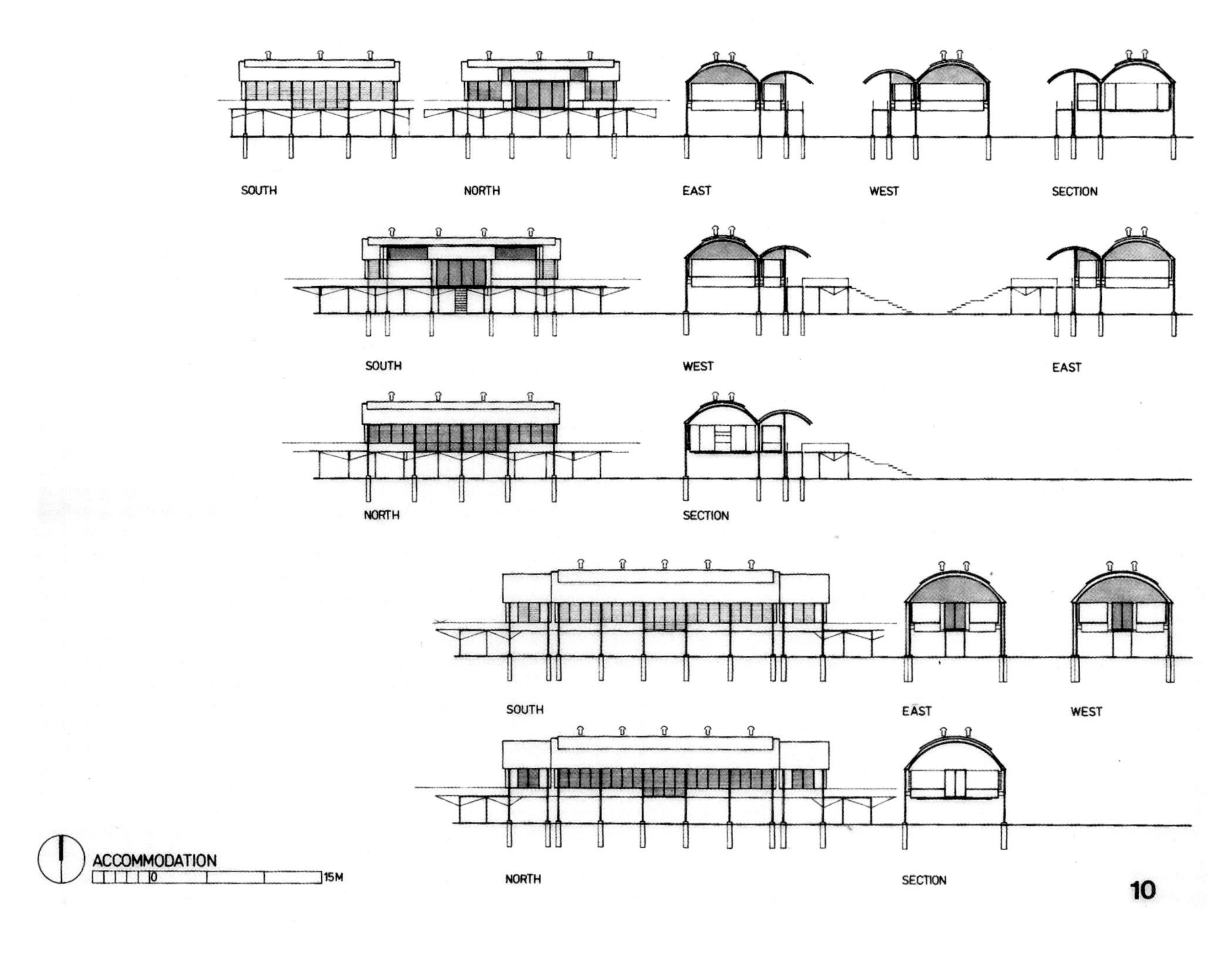
SOUTH
NORTH
EAST
WEST
SECTION
SOUTH
WEST
EAST
NORTH
SECTION
SOUTH
EAST
WEST
NORTH
SECTION
ACCOMMODATION
0
15M
10

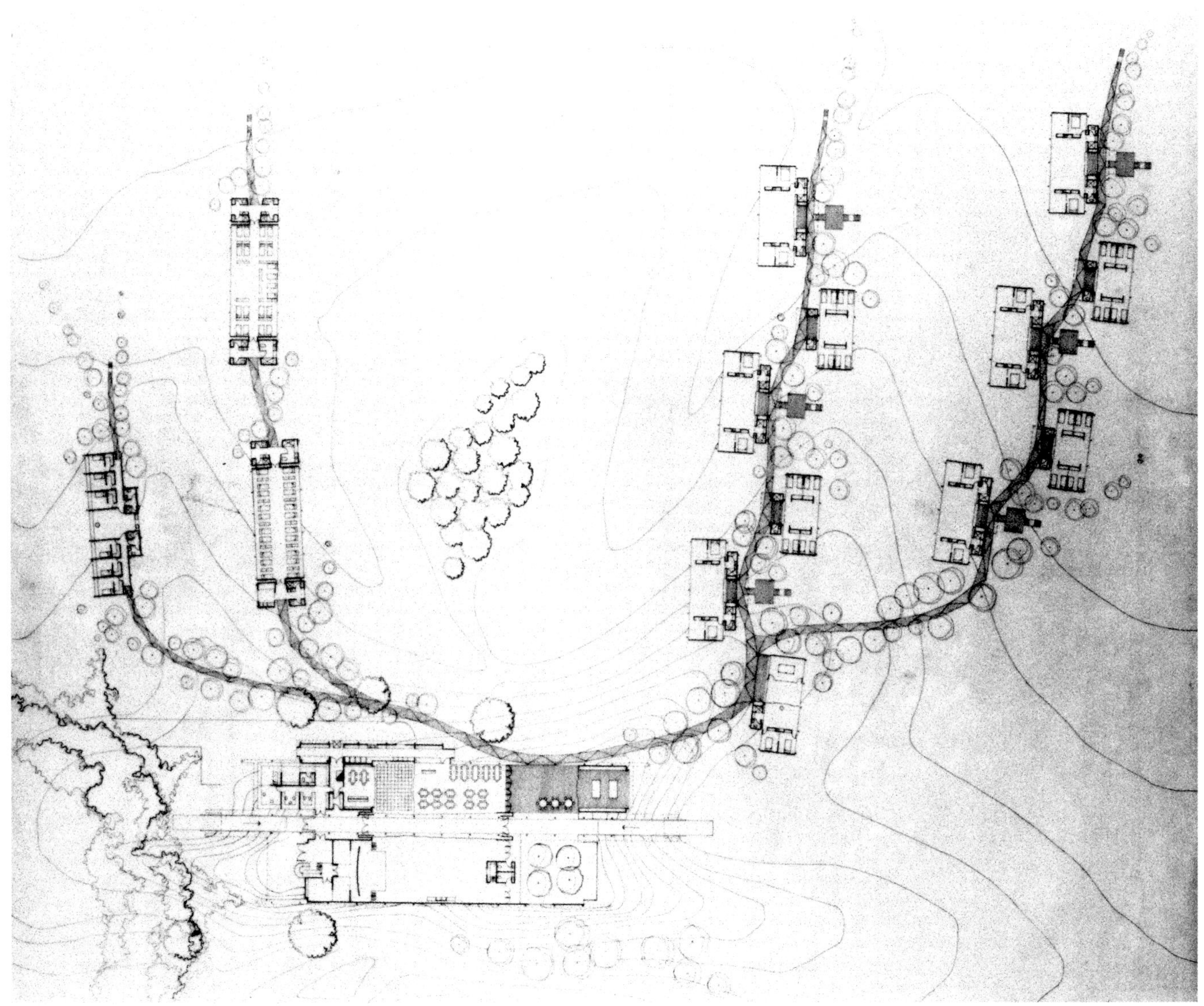

Aboriginal Alcoholic Rehabilitation Centre
Kempsey New South Wales
1983 to 1985 (unbuilt)

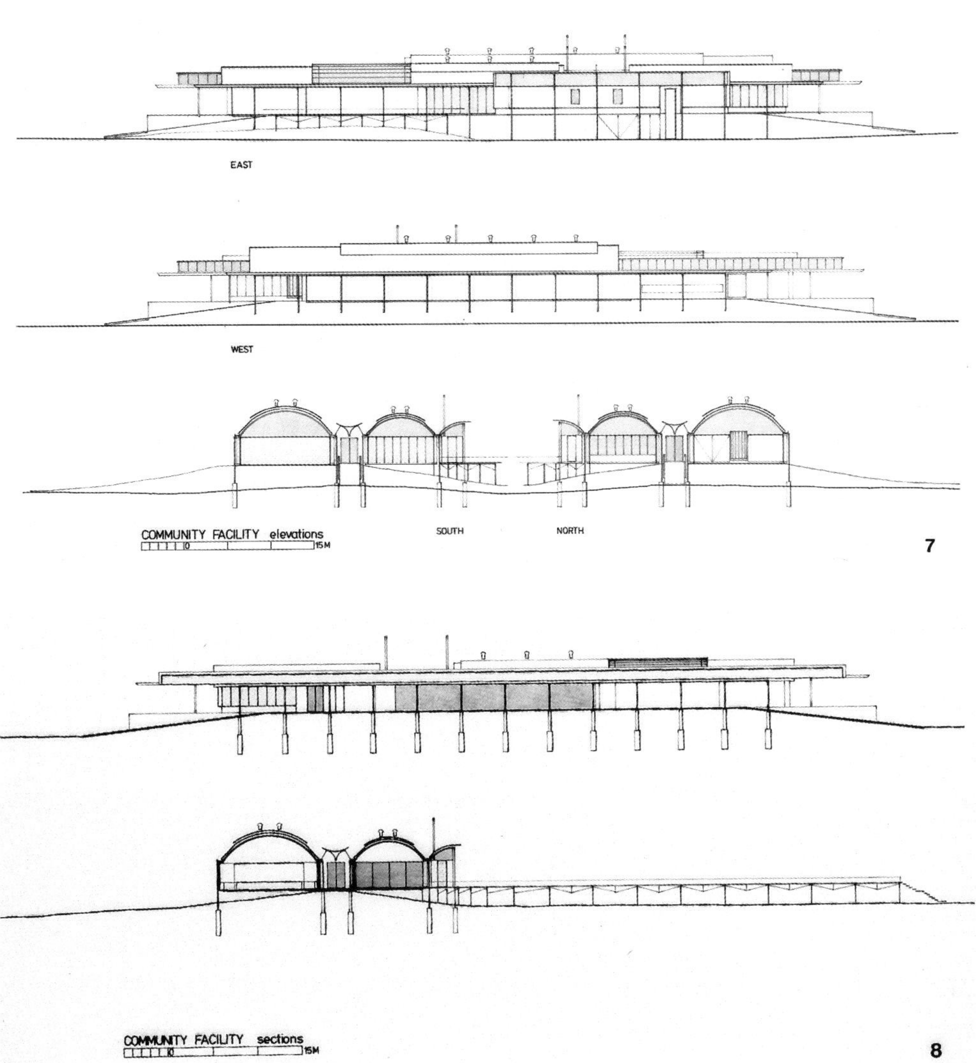

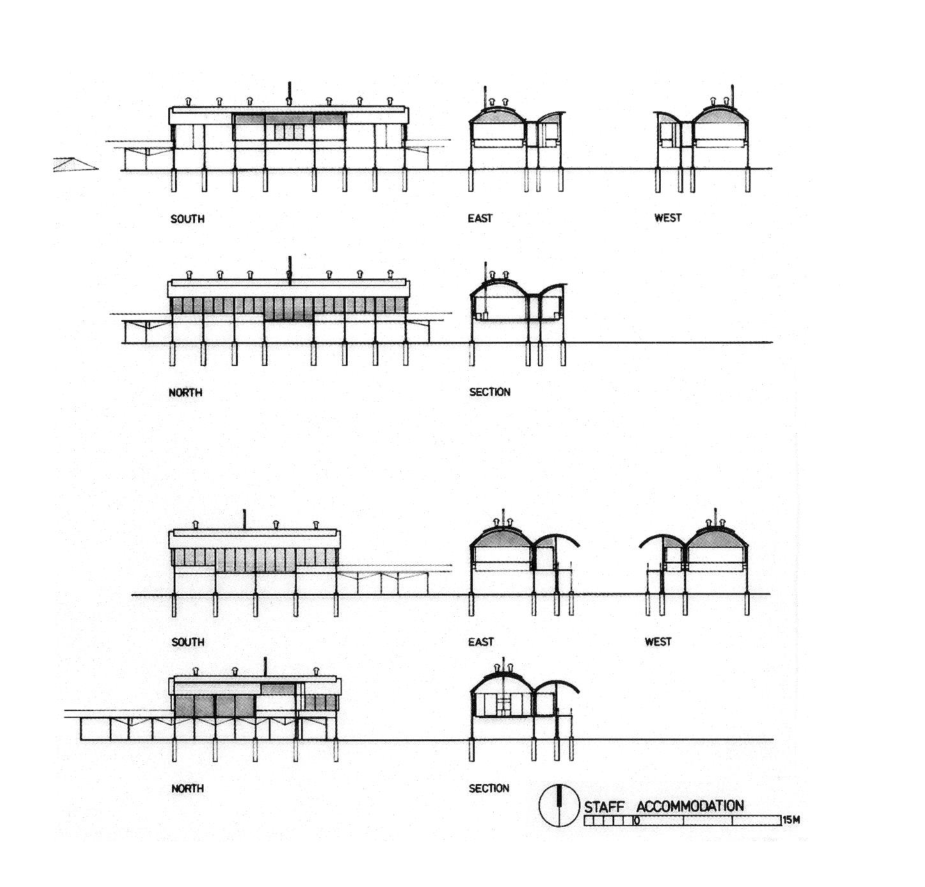

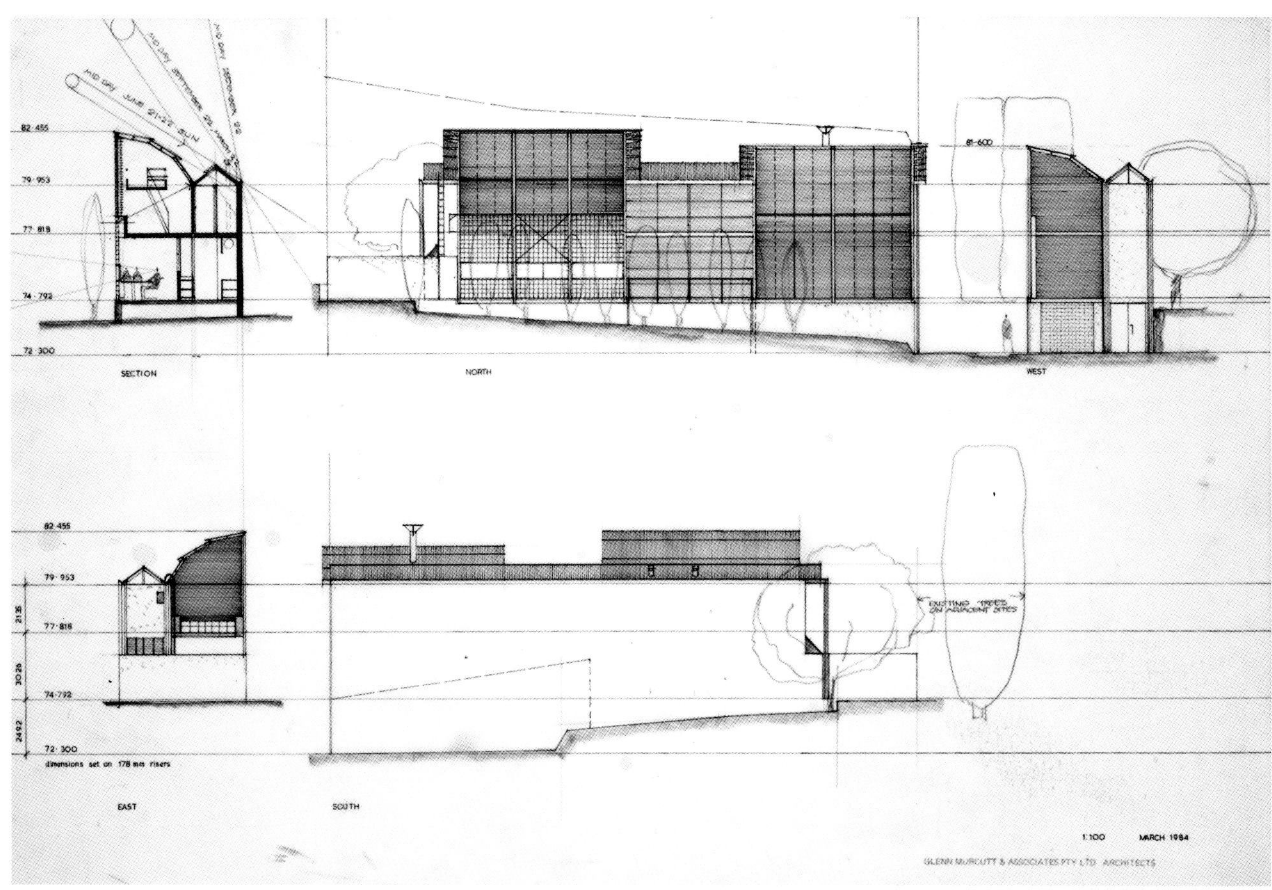

82·455
79·953
77·818
74·792
72·300
SECTION
NORTH
WEST
EAST
SOUTH
dimensions set on 178 mm risers
1:100
MARCH 1984
GLENN MURCUTT & ASSOCIATES PTY LTD ARCHITECTS

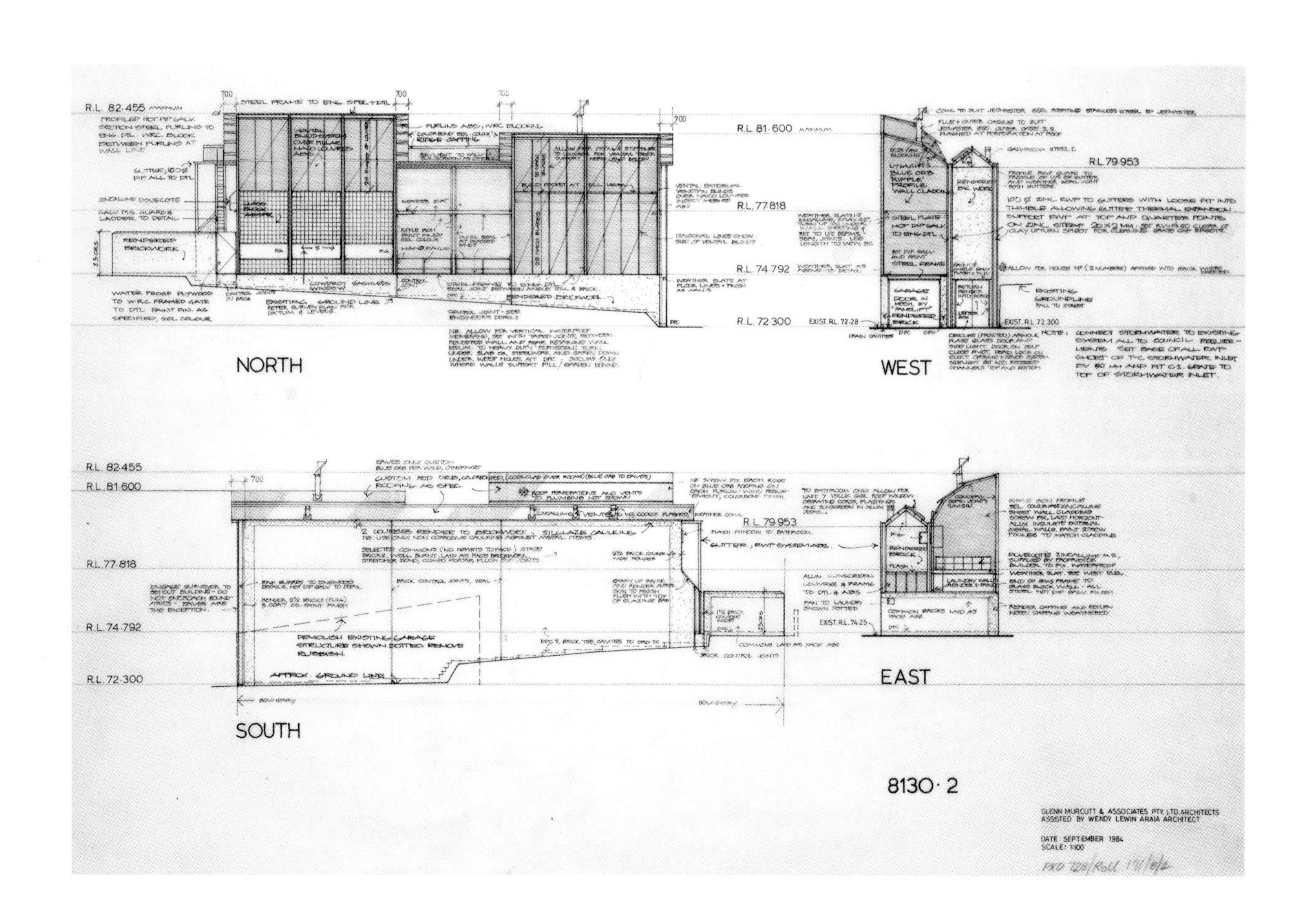

R.L. 82·455
R.L. 81·600
R.L. 79·953
R.L. 77·818
R.L. 74·792
R.L. 72·300
NORTH
WEST
SOUTH
EAST
8130 · 2
GLENN MURCUTT & ASSOCIATES PTY. LTD. ARCHITECTS
ASSISTED BY WENDY LEWIN ARAIA ARCHITECT
DATE: SEPTEMBER 1984
SCALE: 1:100

Littlemore house

Woollahra Sydney New South Wales

1983 to 1986

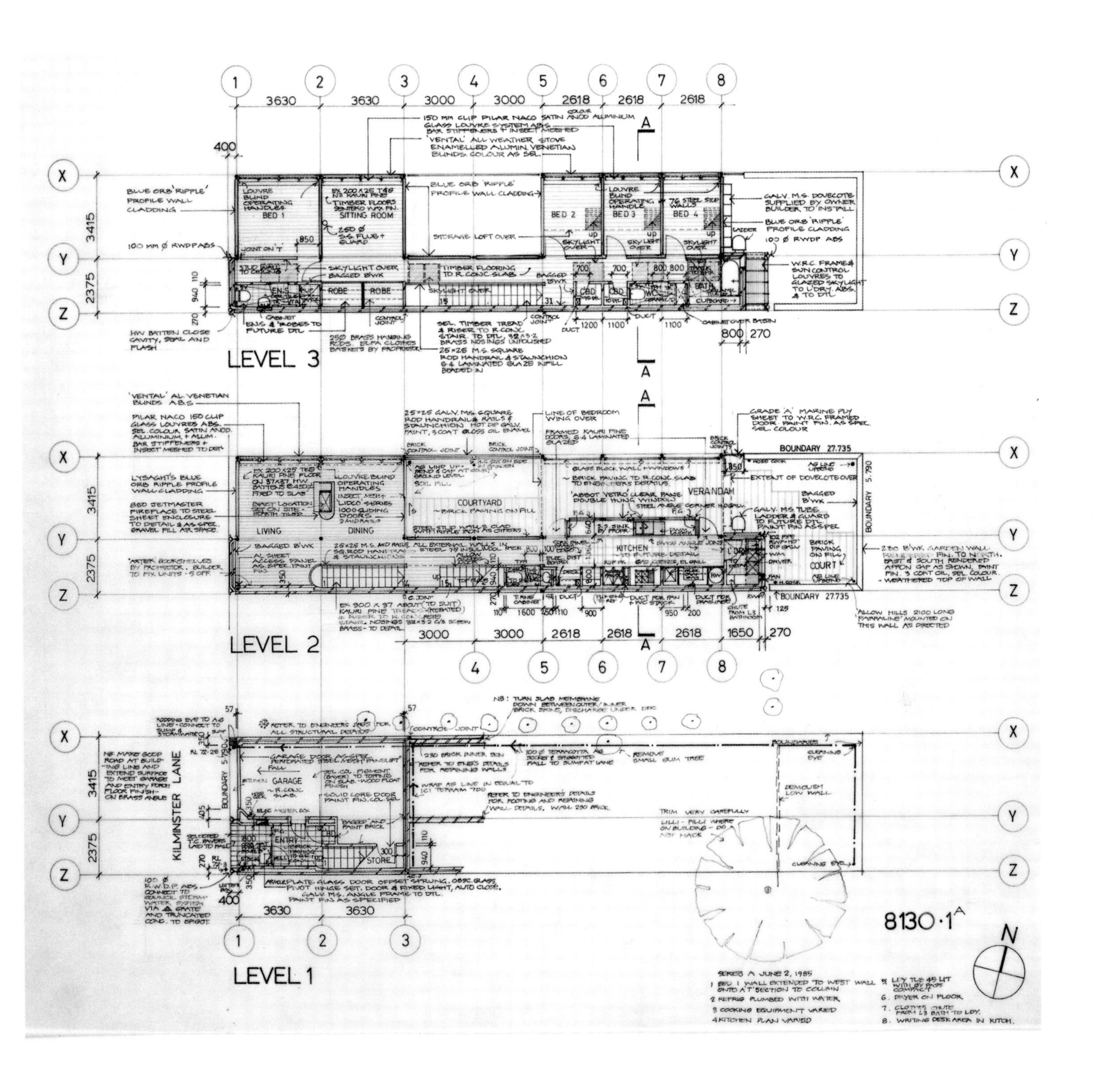

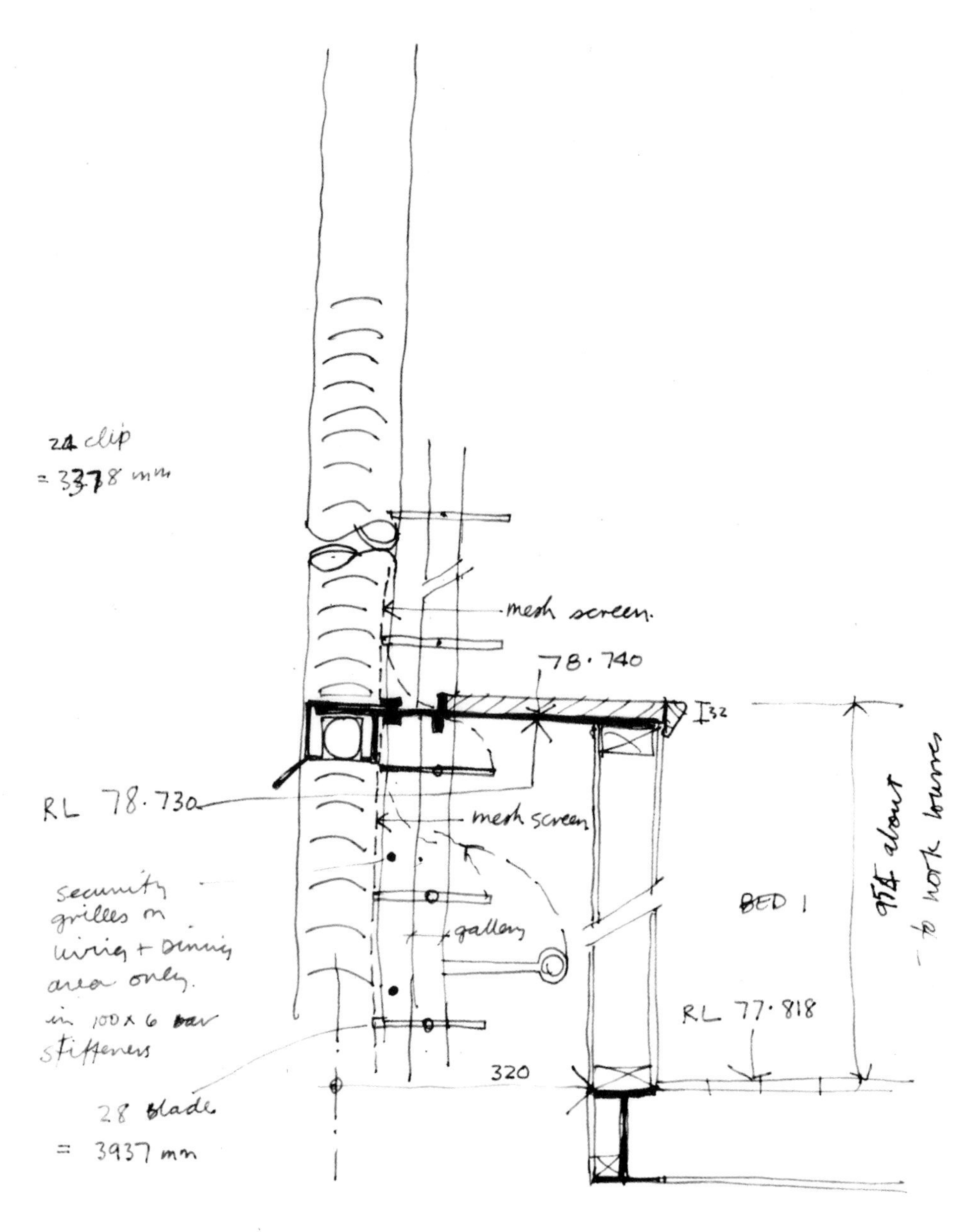
24 clip
= 3378 mm
mesh screen.
78·740
32
RL 78·730
mesh screen
security grilles on living + dining area only.
in 100 x 6 bar stiffeners
gallery
BED 1
about - to work louvres
RL 77·818
320
28 blade
= 3937 mm
LIVING
DINING
1:5 SECTION
PXD 728/Roll 191/A/65

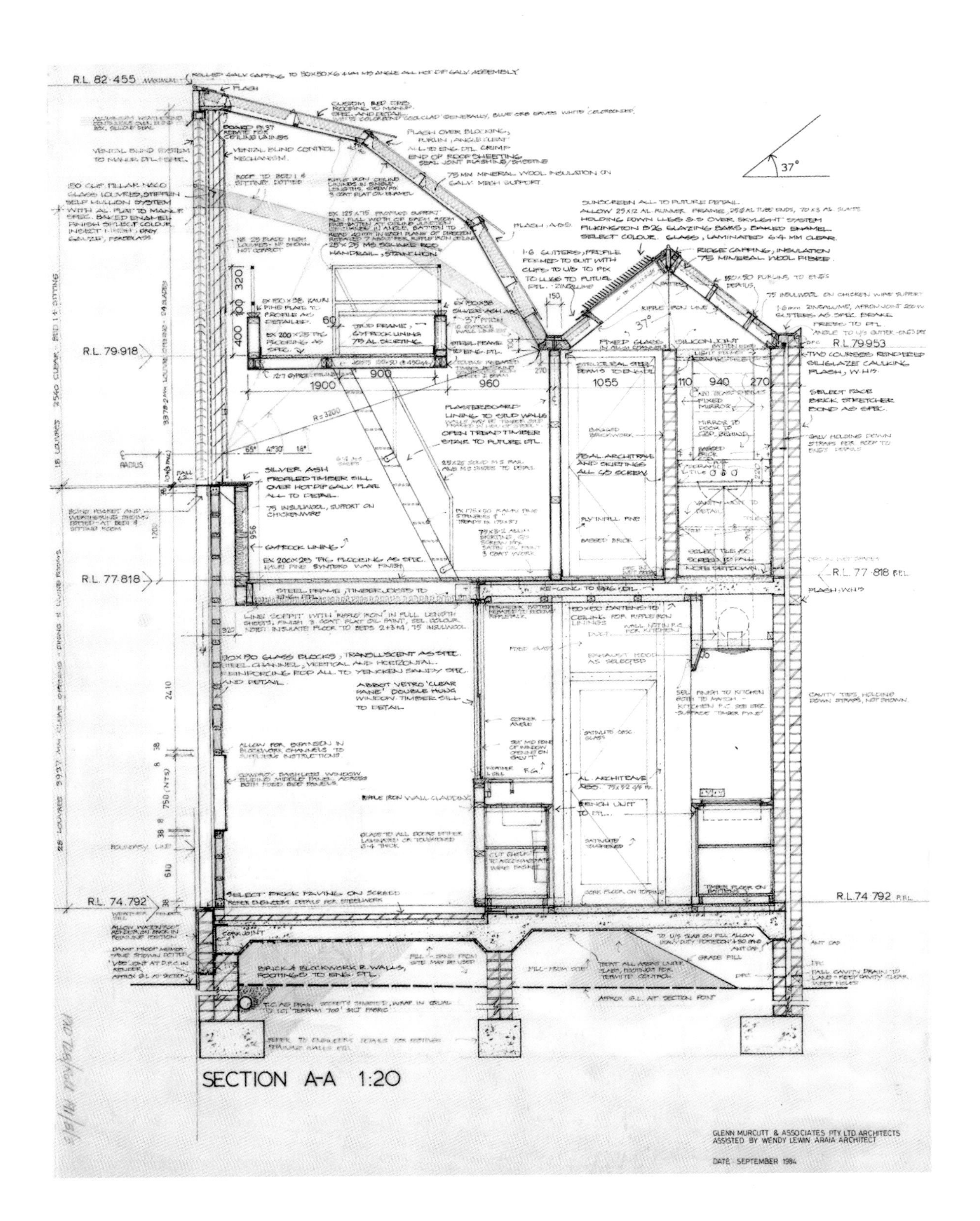
R.L. 82·455
R.L. 79·918
R.L. 77·818
R.L. 74·792
R.L. 79·953
R.L. 77·818 F.F.L.
R.L. 74·792 F.F.L.
37°
1900
900
960
1055
110
940
270
SECTION A-A 1:20
GLENN MURCUTT & ASSOCIATES PTY. LTD. ARCHITECTS
ASSISTED BY WENDY LEWIN ARAIA ARCHITECT
DATE: SEPTEMBER 1984

Magney house
Paddington Sydney New South Wales
1986 to 1990

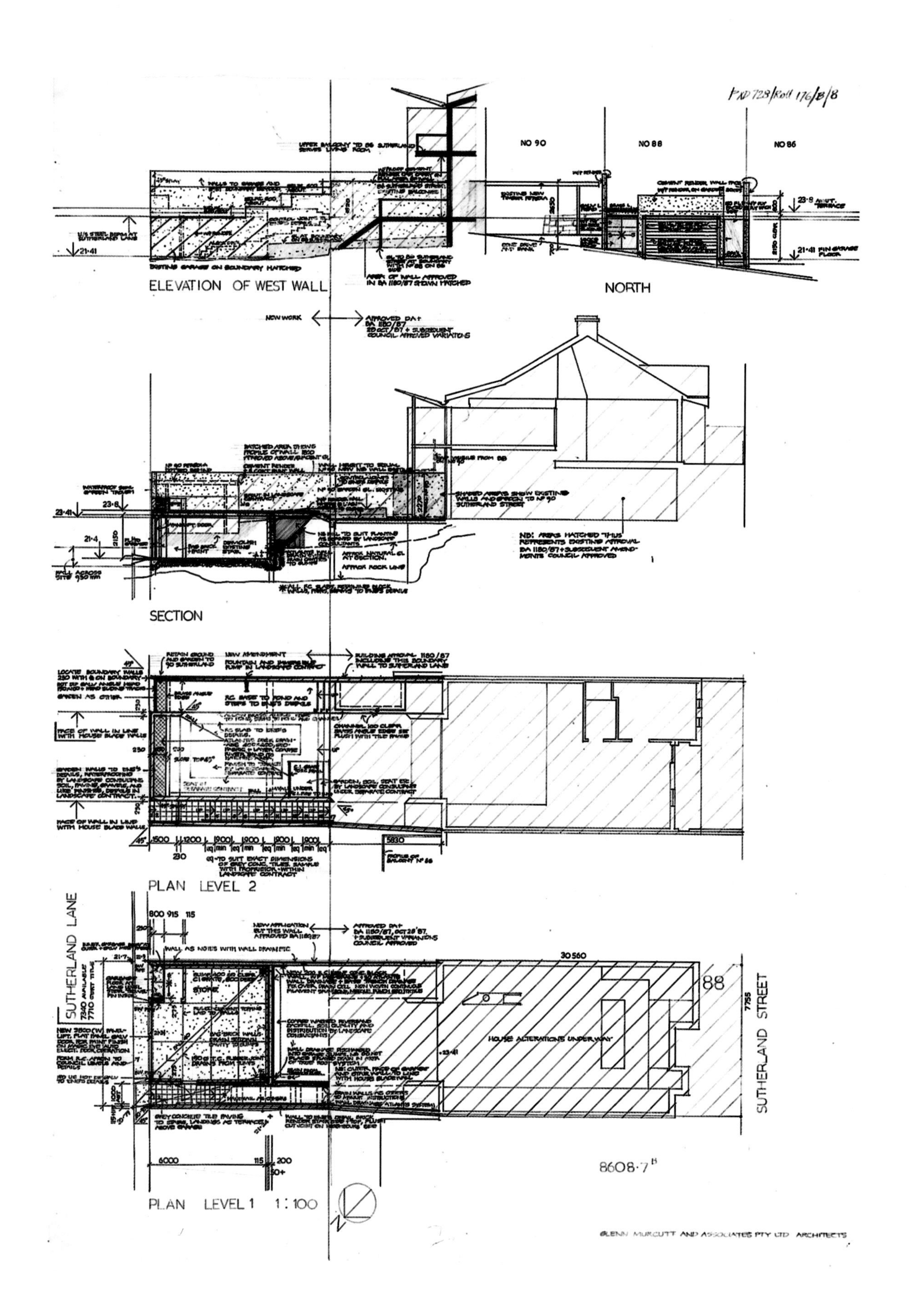

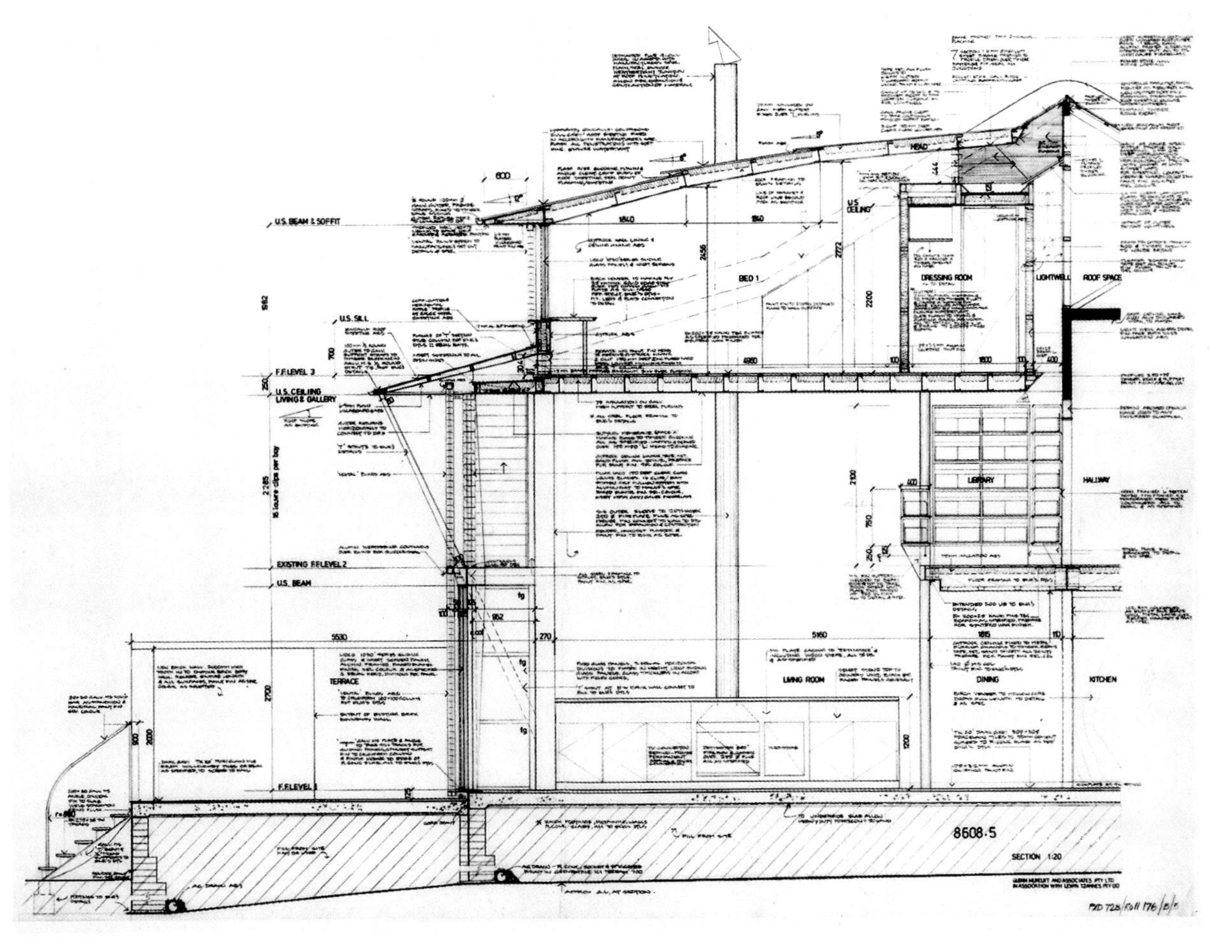

original proposal

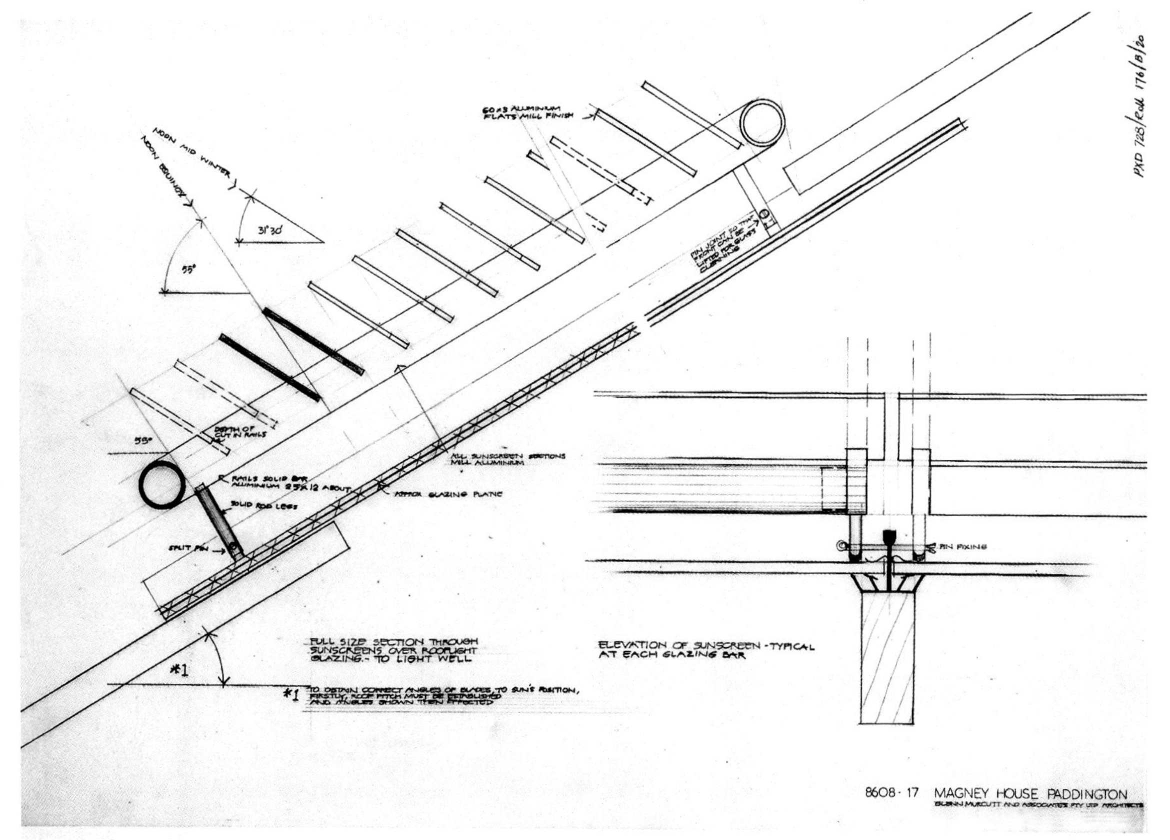

section of sun screen, typical at each glazing bar

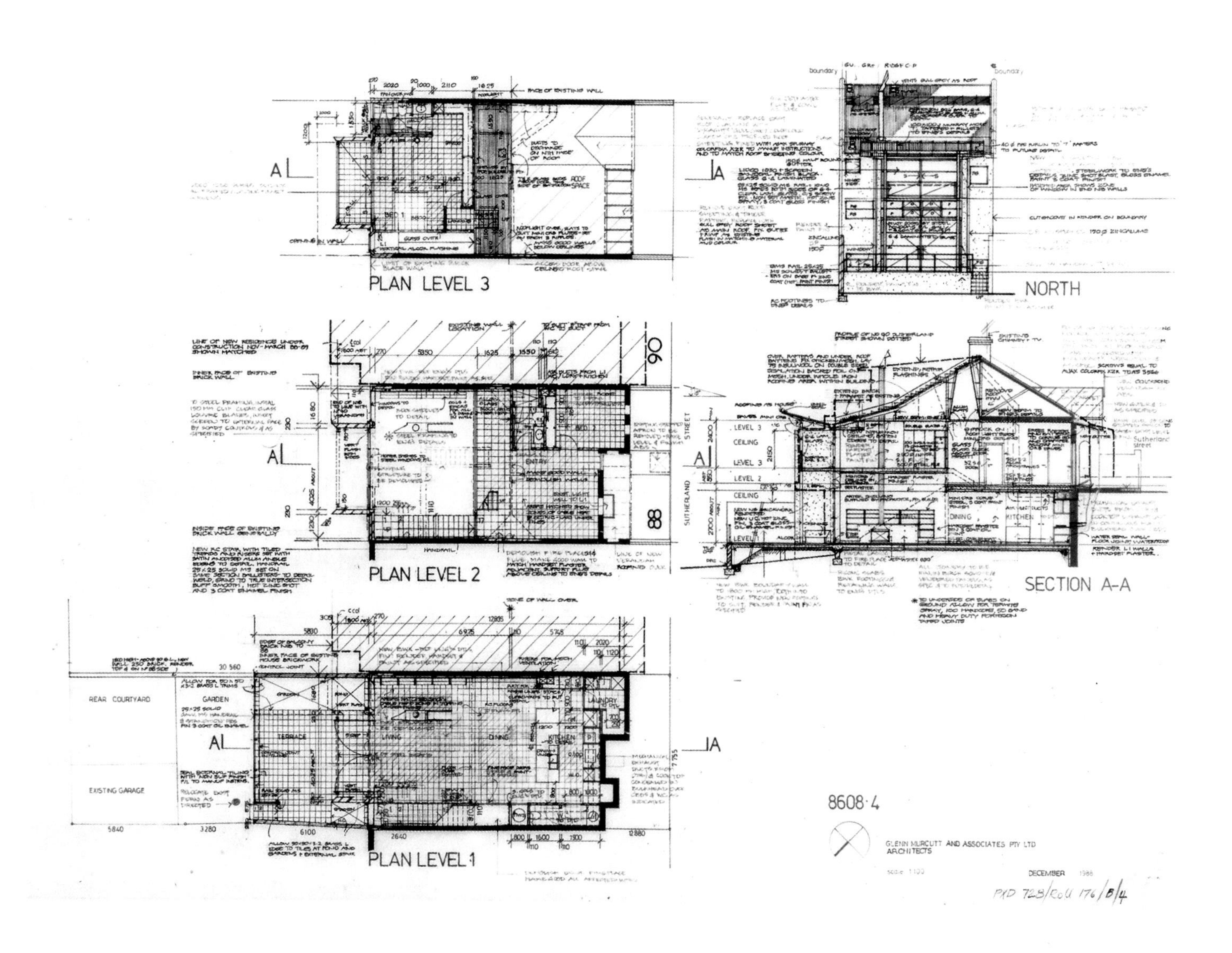
PLAN LEVEL 3
NORTH
PLAN LEVEL 2
SECTION A-A
LEVEL 3
CEILING
LEVEL 2
LEVEL 1
DINING
KITCHEN
SUTHERLAND STREET
REAR COURTYARD
GARDEN
TERRACE
LIVING
DINING
KITCHEN
LAUNDRY
EXISTING GARAGE
PLAN LEVEL 1
8608·4
GLENN MURCUTT AND ASSOCIATES PTY LTD
ARCHITECTS
DECEMBER 1986

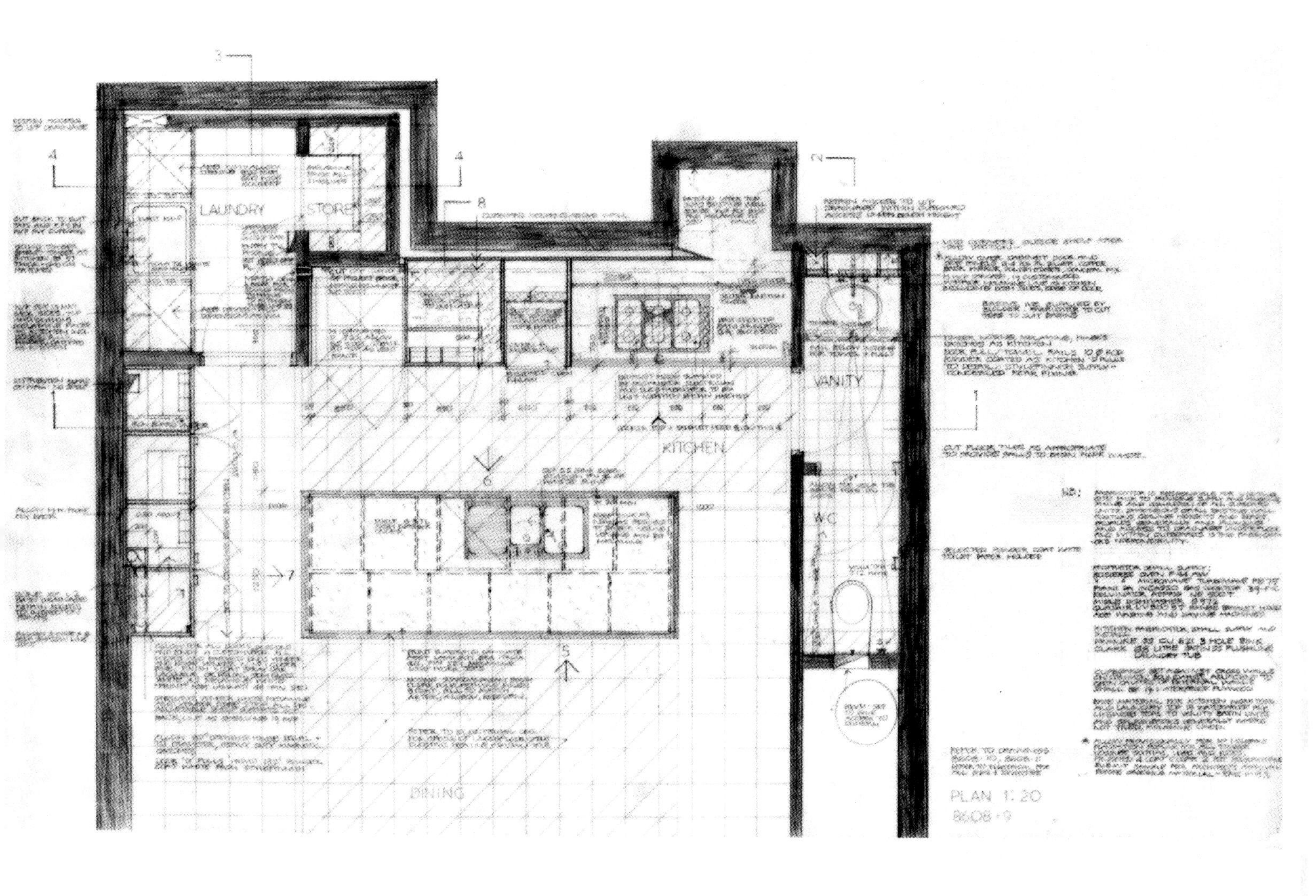
LAUNDRY
STORE
KITCHEN
VANITY
WC
DINING
PLAN 1:20
8608·9

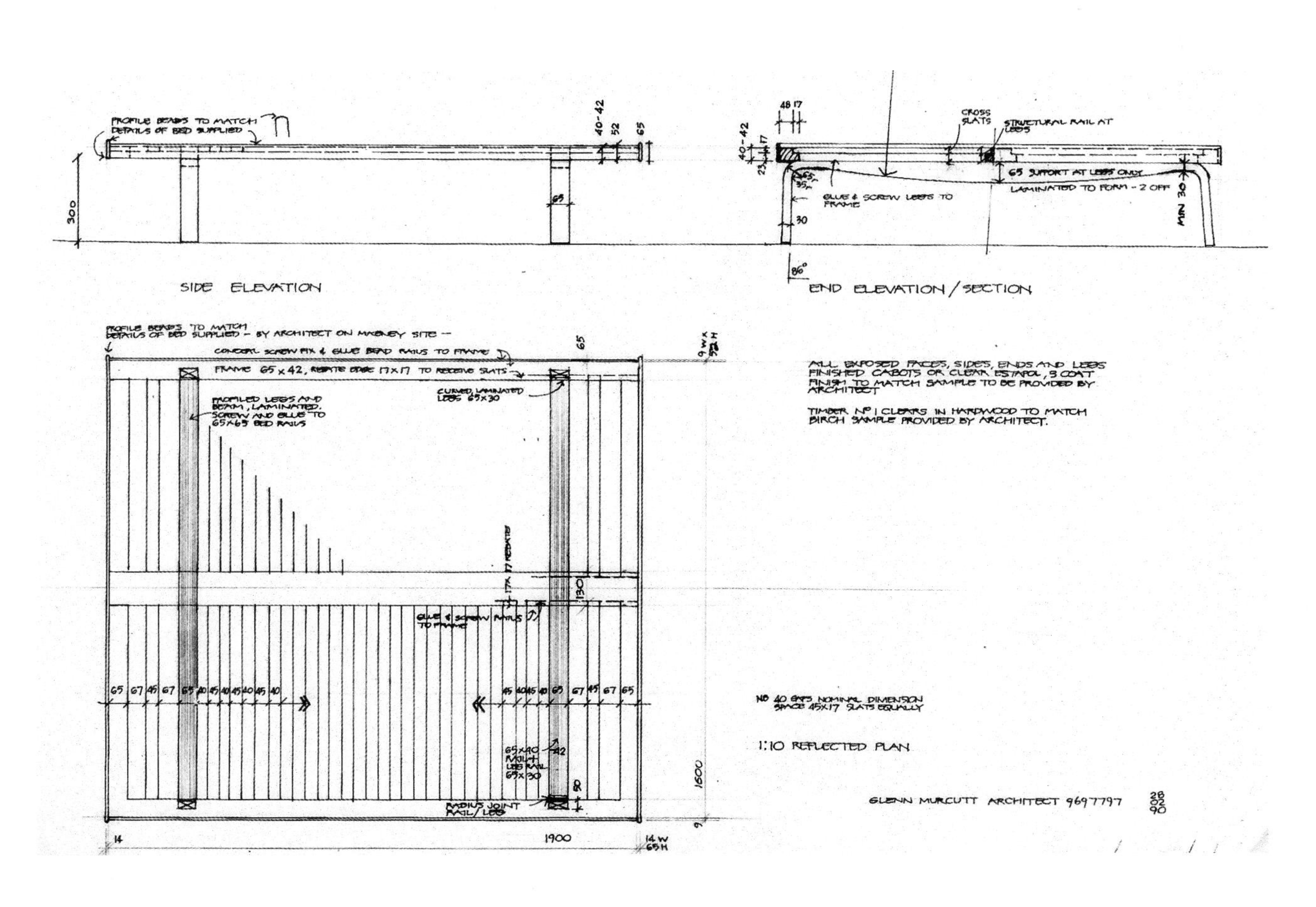
PROFILE BEADS TO MATCH DETAILS OF BED SUPPLIED
SIDE ELEVATION
CROSS SLATS
STRUCTURAL RAIL AT LEGS
65 SUPPORT AT LEGS ONLY
LAMINATED TO FORM - 2 OFF
GLUE & SCREW LEGS TO FRAME
END ELEVATION / SECTION
FRAME 65 x 42, REBATE EDGE 17 x 17 TO RECEIVE SLATS
CURVED LAMINATED LEGS 65x30
PROFILED LEGS AND BEAM, LAMINATED. SCREW AND GLUE TO 65x65 BED RAILS
ALL EXPOSED FACES, SIDES, ENDS AND LEGS FINISHED CABOTS OR CLEAR ESTAPOL, 3 COAT FINISH TO MATCH SAMPLE TO BE PROVIDED BY ARCHITECT
TIMBER Nº 1 CLEARS IN HARDWOOD TO MATCH BIRCH SAMPLE PROVIDED BY ARCHITECT.
RADIUS JOINT RAIL / LEG
1:10 REFLECTED PLAN
GLENN MURCUTT ARCHITECT 9697797
1900
1600

Minerals and Mining Museum
Broken Hill New South Wales
1987 to 1989 (unbuilt)

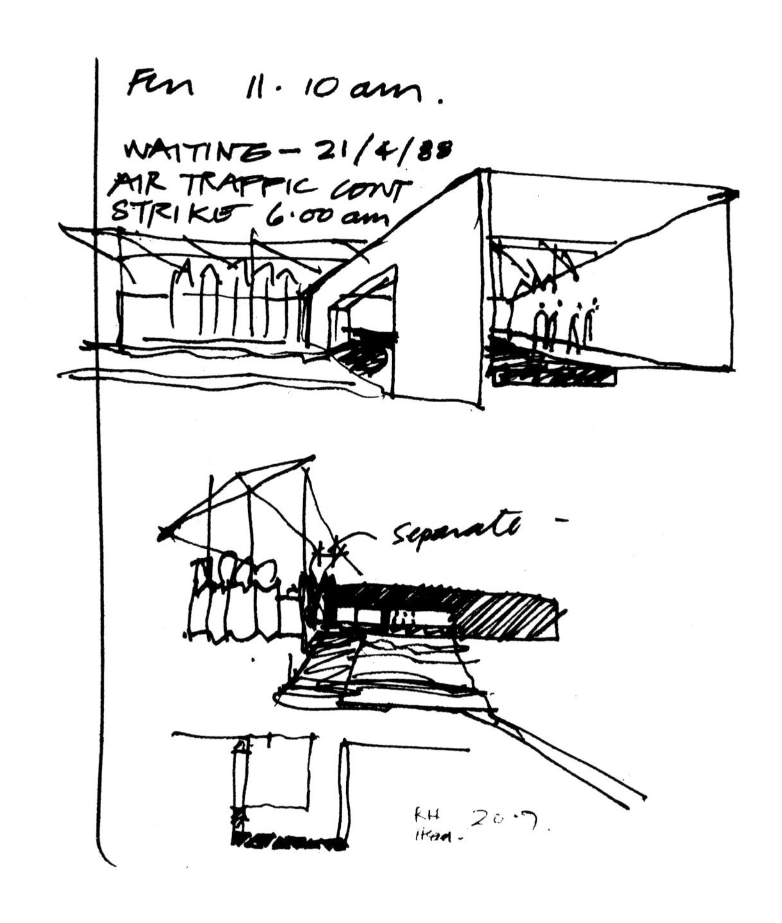

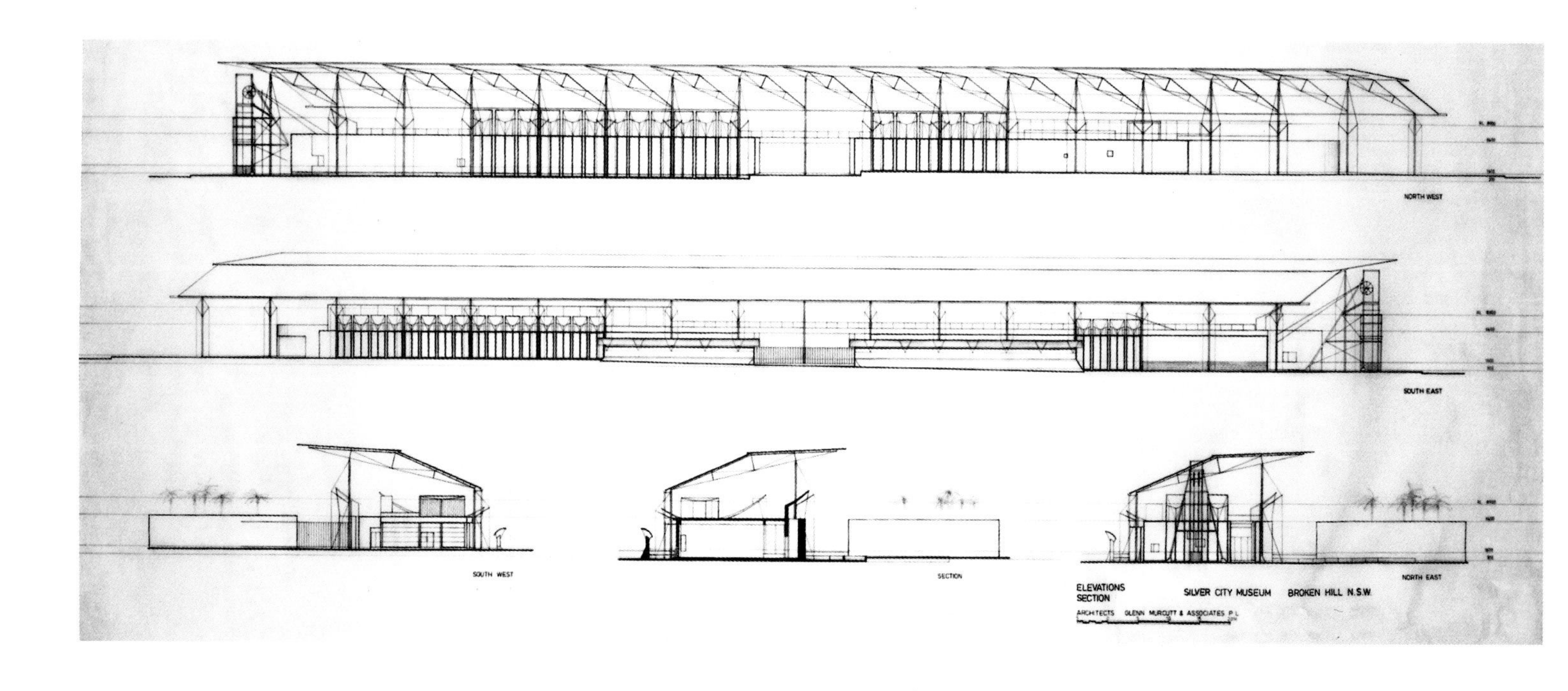

For the preliminary design sketches of this project, illustrating Murcutt's design process, see pages 25 to 31.

Reg Lark assisted with the working drawings.
Structural engineer James Taylor of James Taylor and Associates was involved in all critical stages of the design process. 'I've always worked with Dick Taylor of Taylor Thompson Whitting, and his son, James Taylor, of James Taylor and Associates. They are very supportive, creative engineers.'
Wind tunnel testing: Victorian Technology Centre

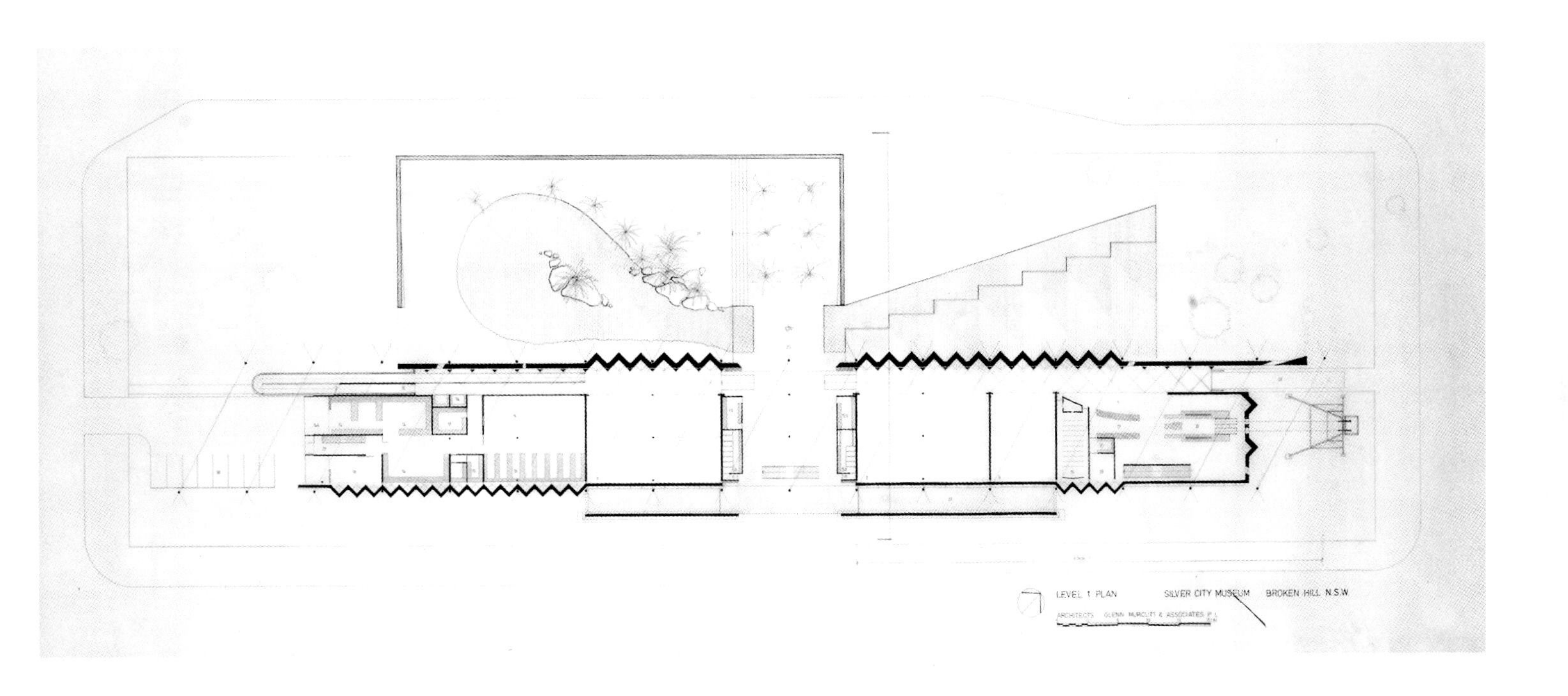

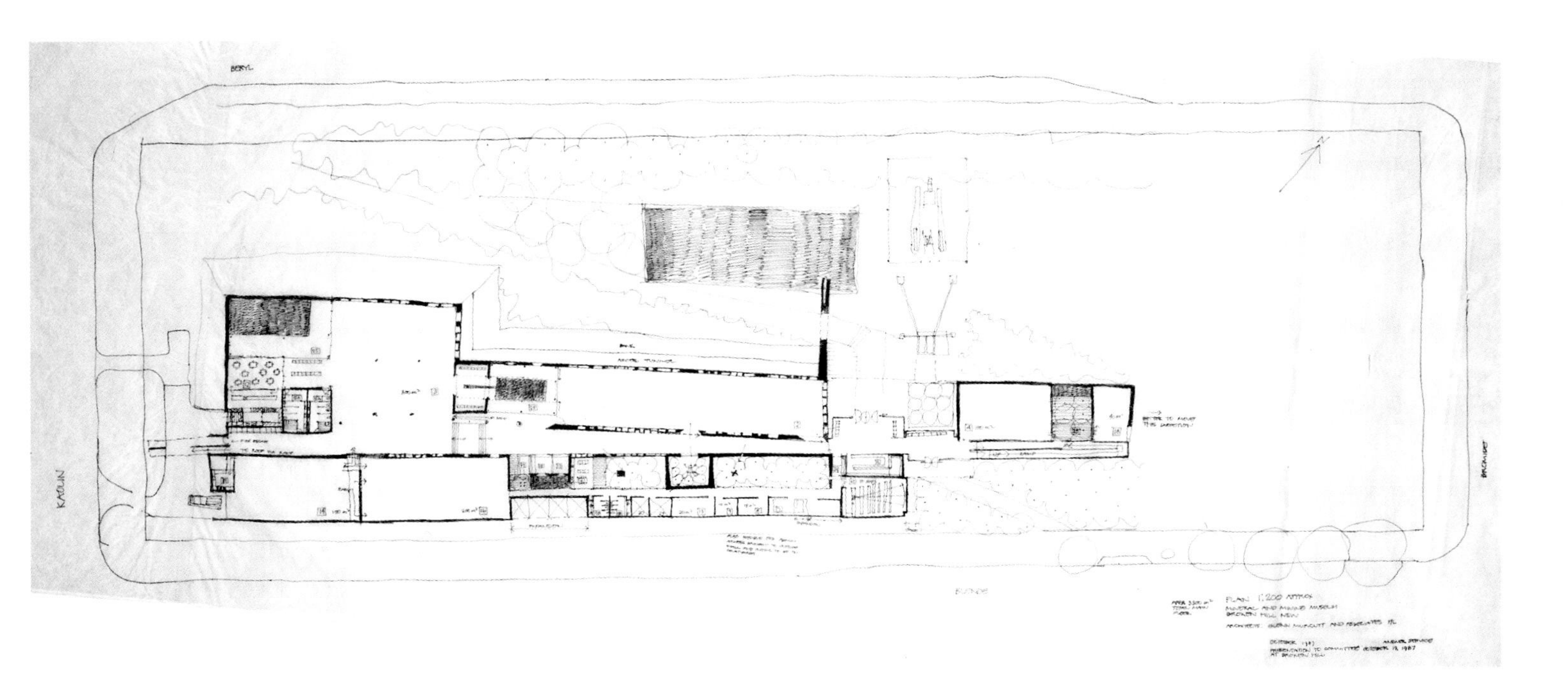

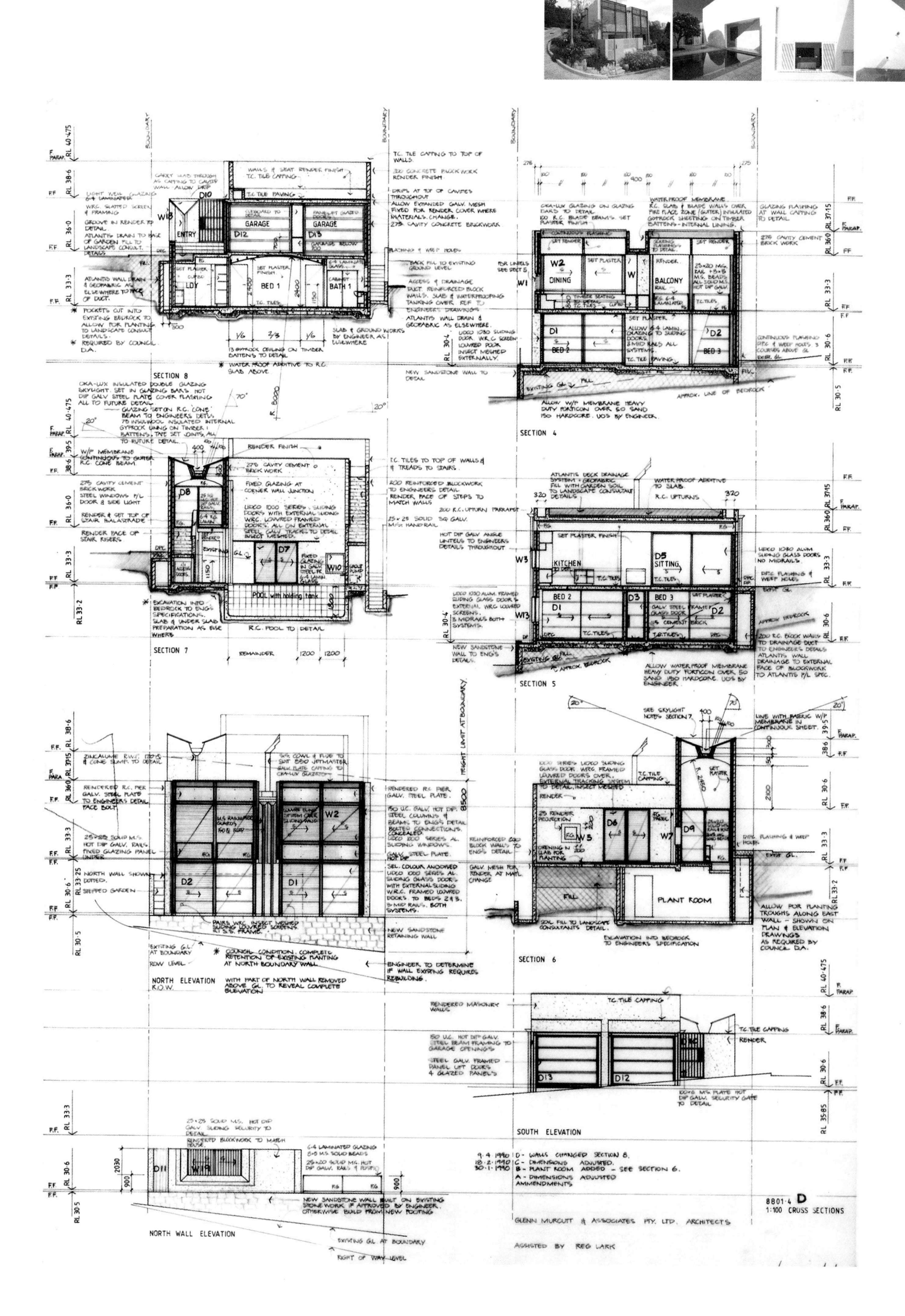
SECTION 8
SECTION 4
SECTION 7
SECTION 5
SECTION 6
NORTH ELEVATION R.O.W.
SOUTH ELEVATION
NORTH WALL ELEVATION
GARAGE
BED 1
BATH 1
LDY
ENTRY
DINING
BALCONY
BED 2
BED 3
KITCHEN
SITTING
PLANT ROOM
POOL with holding tank
R.C. POOL TO DETAIL
9.4.1990 D - WALLS CHANGED SECTION 8.
18.2.1990 C - DIMENSIONS ADJUSTED.
30.1.1990 B - PLANT ROOM ADDED - SEE SECTION 6.
A - DIMENSIONS ADJUSTED AMMENDMENTS
8801.4 D
1:100 CROSS SECTIONS
GLENN MURCUTT & ASSOCIATES PTY. LTD. ARCHITECTS
ASSISTED BY REG LARK

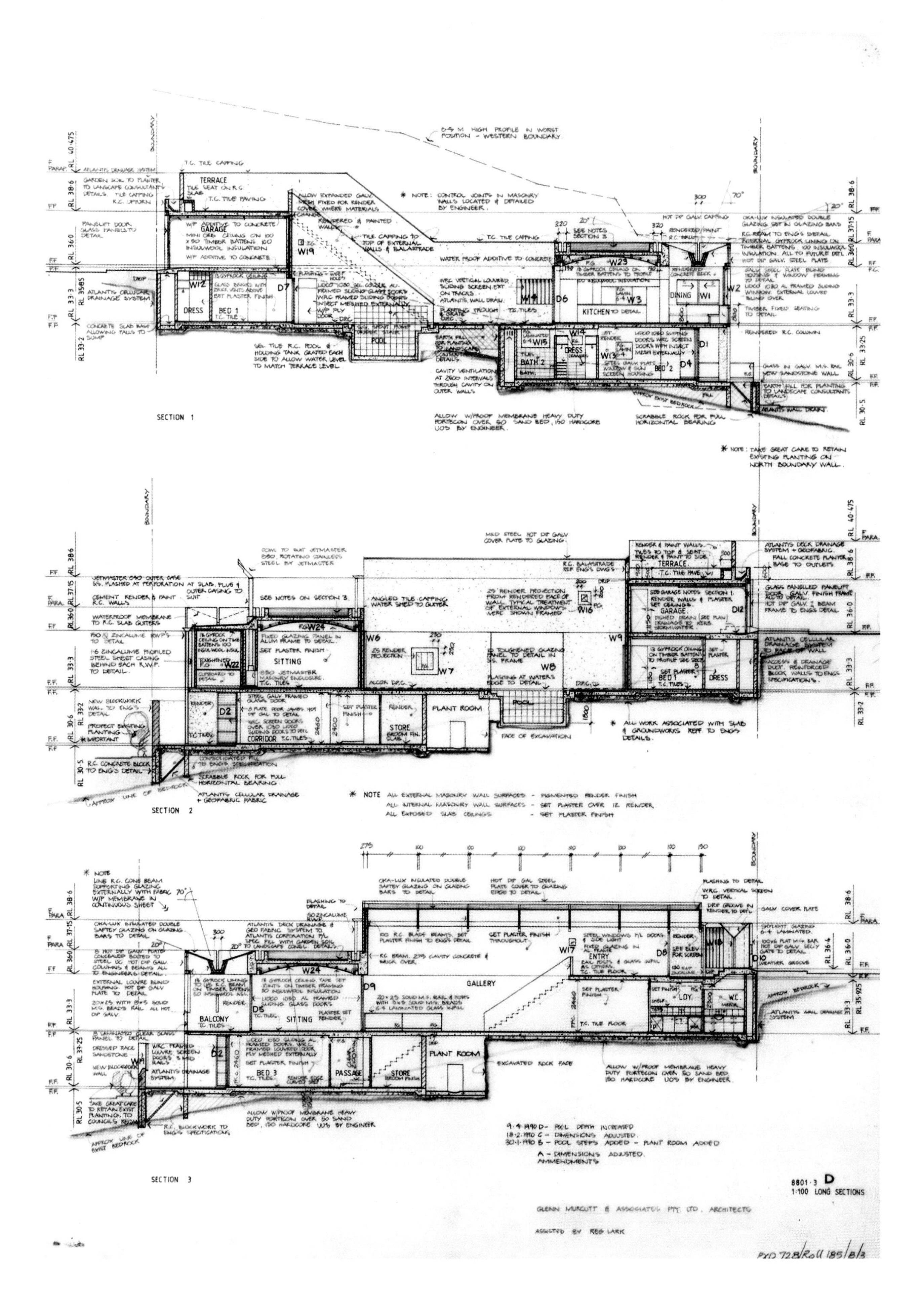
SECTION 1
SECTION 2
SECTION 3
TERRACE
GARAGE
POOL
DRESS
BED 1
BATH 2
BED 2
KITCHEN
DINING
SITTING
PLANT ROOM
STORE
CORRIDOR
BALCONY
BED 3
PASSAGE
GALLERY
ENTRY
LDY.
W.C.
* NOTE ALL EXTERNAL MASONRY WALL SURFACES - PIGMENTED RENDER FINISH
ALL INTERNAL MASONRY WALL SURFACES - SET PLASTER OVER 12 RENDER
ALL EXPOSED SLAB CEILINGS - SET PLASTER FINISH
* NOTE: TAKE GREAT CARE TO RETAIN EXISTING PLANTING ON NORTH BOUNDARY WALL.
9.4.1990 D - POOL DEPTH INCREASED
18.2.1990 C - DIMENSIONS ADJUSTED.
30.1.1990 B - POOL STEPS ADDED - PLANT ROOM ADDED
A - DIMENSIONS ADJUSTED. AMMENDMENTS
8801-3 D
1:100 LONG SECTIONS
GLENN MURCUTT & ASSOCIATES PTY. LTD. ARCHITECTS
ASSISTED BY REG LARK
PXD 728/Roll 185/8/3

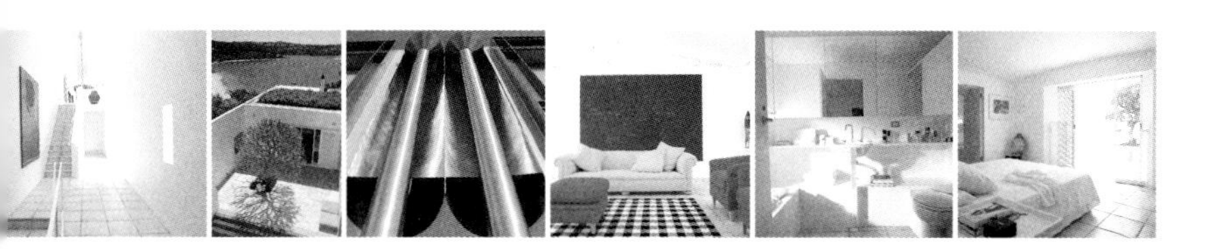

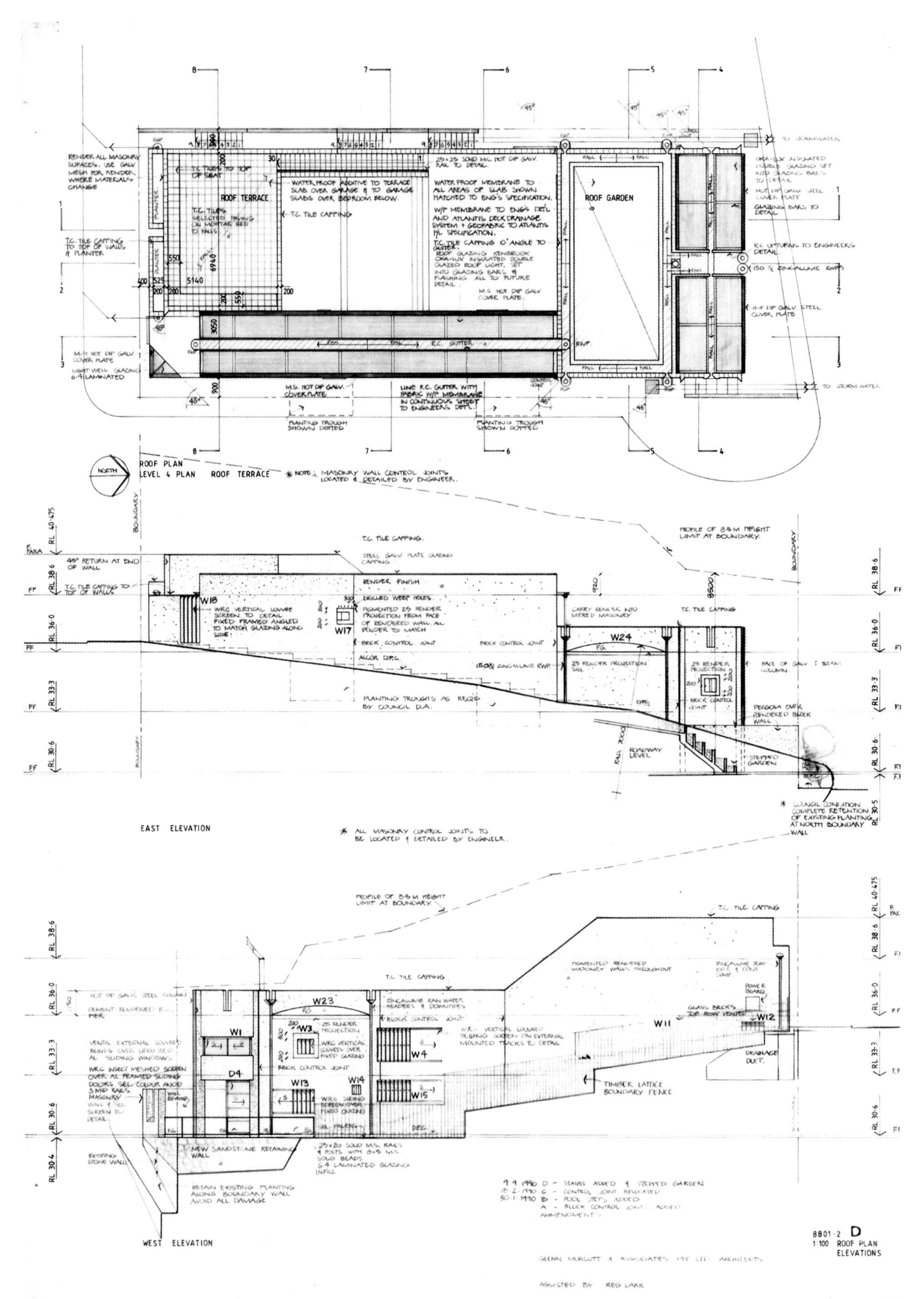

ROOF TERRACE
ROOF GARDEN
ROOF PLAN
LEVEL 4 PLAN ROOF TERRACE
NORTH
EAST ELEVATION
WEST ELEVATION
W18
W17
W24
W23
W1
W3
W4
D4
W13
W14
W15
W11
W12
T.C. TILE CAPPING
RENDER FINISH
PLANTING TROUGHS AS REQ'D BY COUNCIL D.A.
ALL MASONRY CONTROL JOINTS TO BE LOCATED & DETAILED BY ENGINEER.
TIMBER LATTICE BOUNDARY FENCE
NEW SANDSTONE RETAINING WALL
RETAIN EXISTING PLANTING ALONG BOUNDARY WALL AVOID ALL DAMAGE
9.4.1990 D - STAIRS ADDED & STEPPED GARDEN
18.2.1990 C - CONTROL JOINT RELOCATED
30.1.1990 B - POOL STEPS ADDED
A - BLOCK CONTROL JOINT ADDED
AMMENDMENTS
8801-2 D
1:100 ROOF PLAN ELEVATIONS
GLENN MURCUTT & ASSOCIATES PTY LTD ARCHITECTS
ASSISTED BY REG LARK

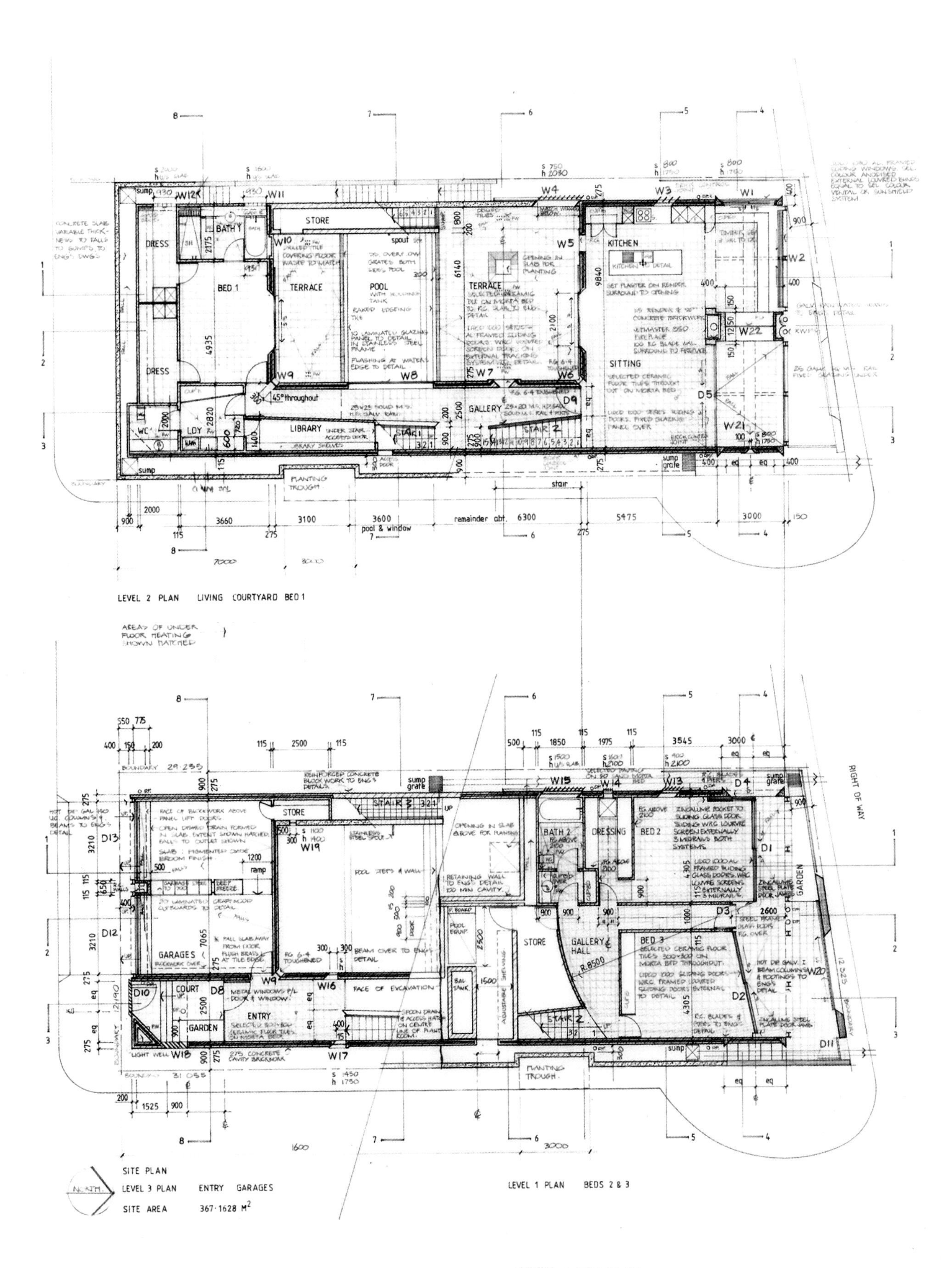

9·4·1990 D - WALLS CHANGED
28·2·1990 C - DIMENSIONS ADJUSTED
30·1·1990 B - PLANT ROOM & POOL STEPS ADDED
A - DIMENSIONS ADJUSTED AMMENDMENTS

8801·1 D
1:100 PLANS

GLENN MURCUTT & ASSOCIATES PTY LTD ARCHITECTS

ASSISTED BY REG LARK

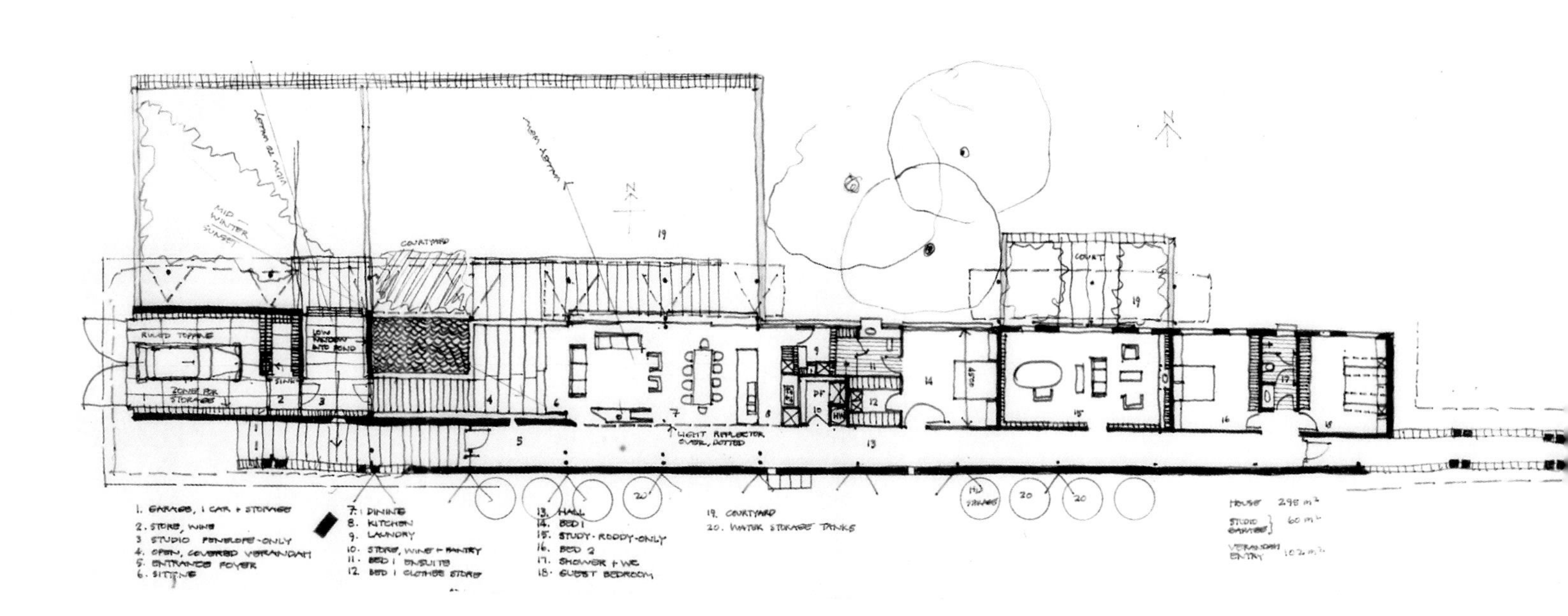

1. GARAGE, 1 CAR + STORAGE
2. STORE, WINE
3. STUDIO PENELOPE-ONLY
4. OPEN, COVERED VERANDAH
5. ENTRANCE FOYER
6. SITTING
7. DINING
8. KITCHEN
9. LAUNDRY
10. STORE, WINE + PANTRY
11. BED 1 ENSUITE
12. BED 1 CLOTHES STORE
13. HALL
14. BED 1
15. STUDY - RODDY - ONLY
16. BED 2
17. SHOWER + WC
18. GUEST BEDROOM
19. COURTYARD
20. WATER STORAGE TANKS
COURTYARD
COURT

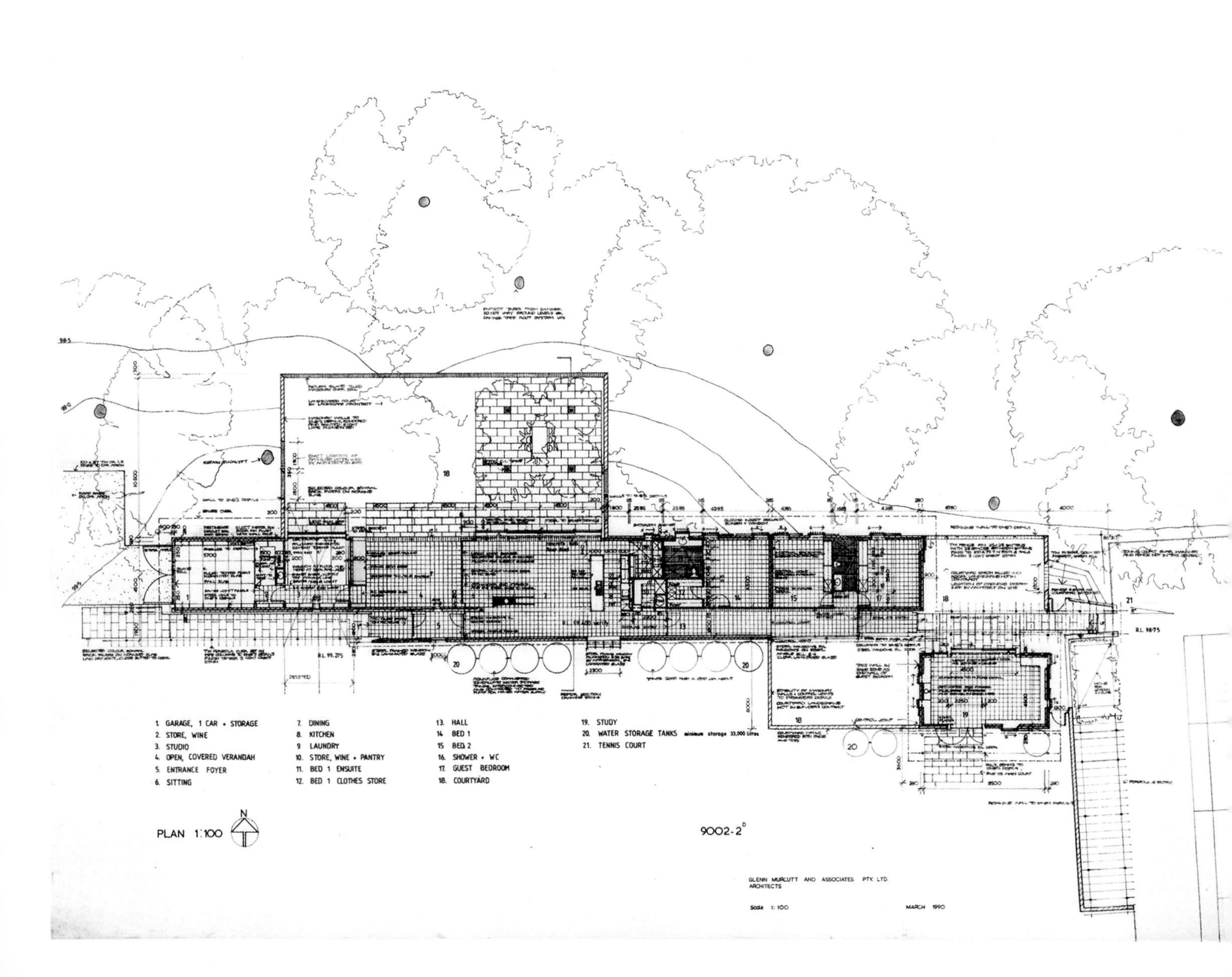

1. GARAGE, 1 CAR + STORAGE
2. STORE, WINE
3. STUDIO
4. OPEN, COVERED VERANDAH
5. ENTRANCE FOYER
6. SITTING
7. DINING
8. KITCHEN
9. LAUNDRY
10. STORE, WINE + PANTRY
11. BED 1 ENSUITE
12. BED 1 CLOTHES STORE
13. HALL
14. BED 1
15. BED 2
16. SHOWER + WC
17. GUEST BEDROOM
18. COURTYARD
19. STUDY
20. WATER STORAGE TANKS minimum storage 33,000 litres
21. TENNIS COURT
PLAN 1:100
N
9002-2D
GLENN MURCUTT AND ASSOCIATES PTY. LTD.
ARCHITECTS
Scale 1:100
MARCH 1990

House
Southern Highlands New South Wales
1988 to 1992

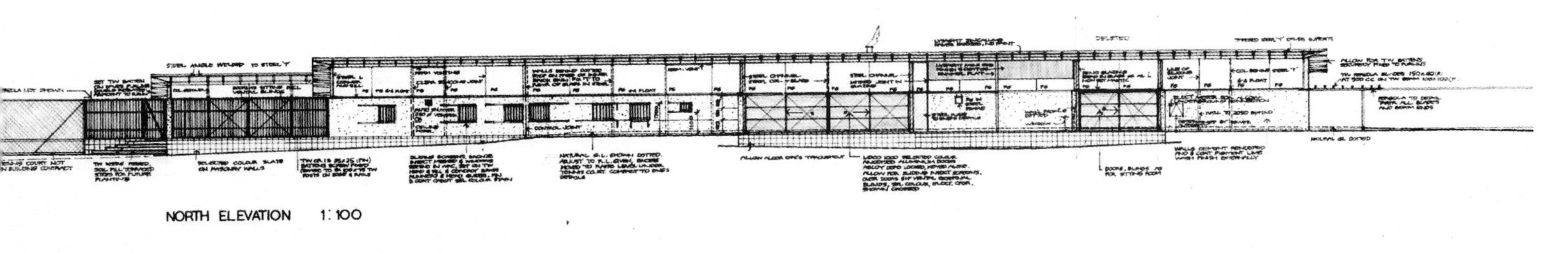

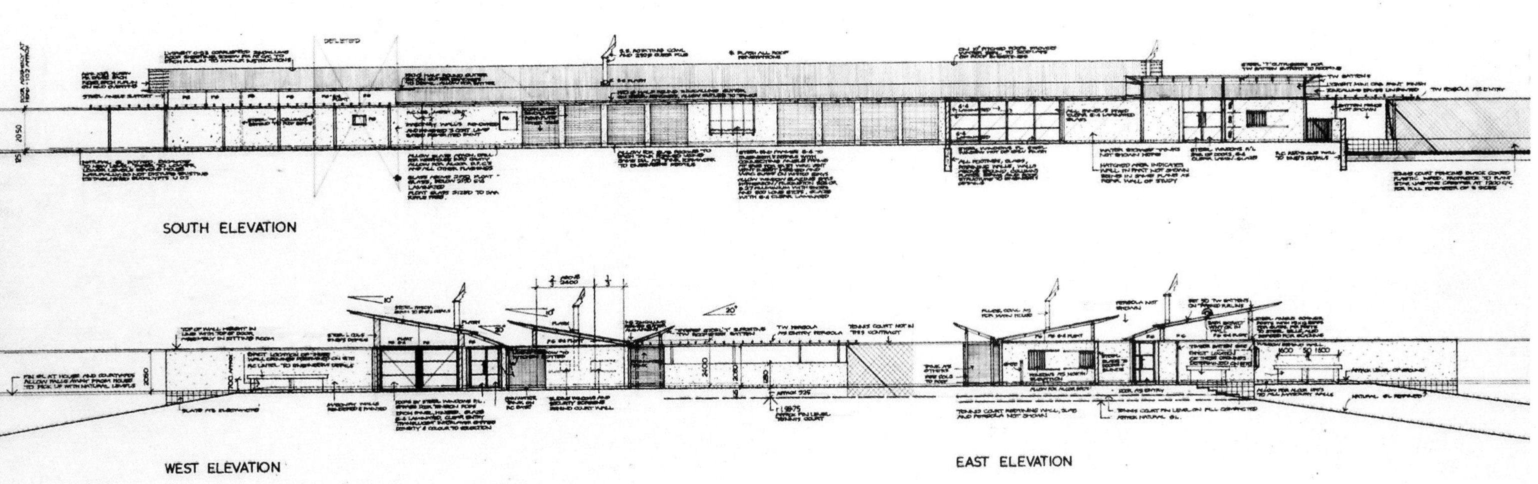

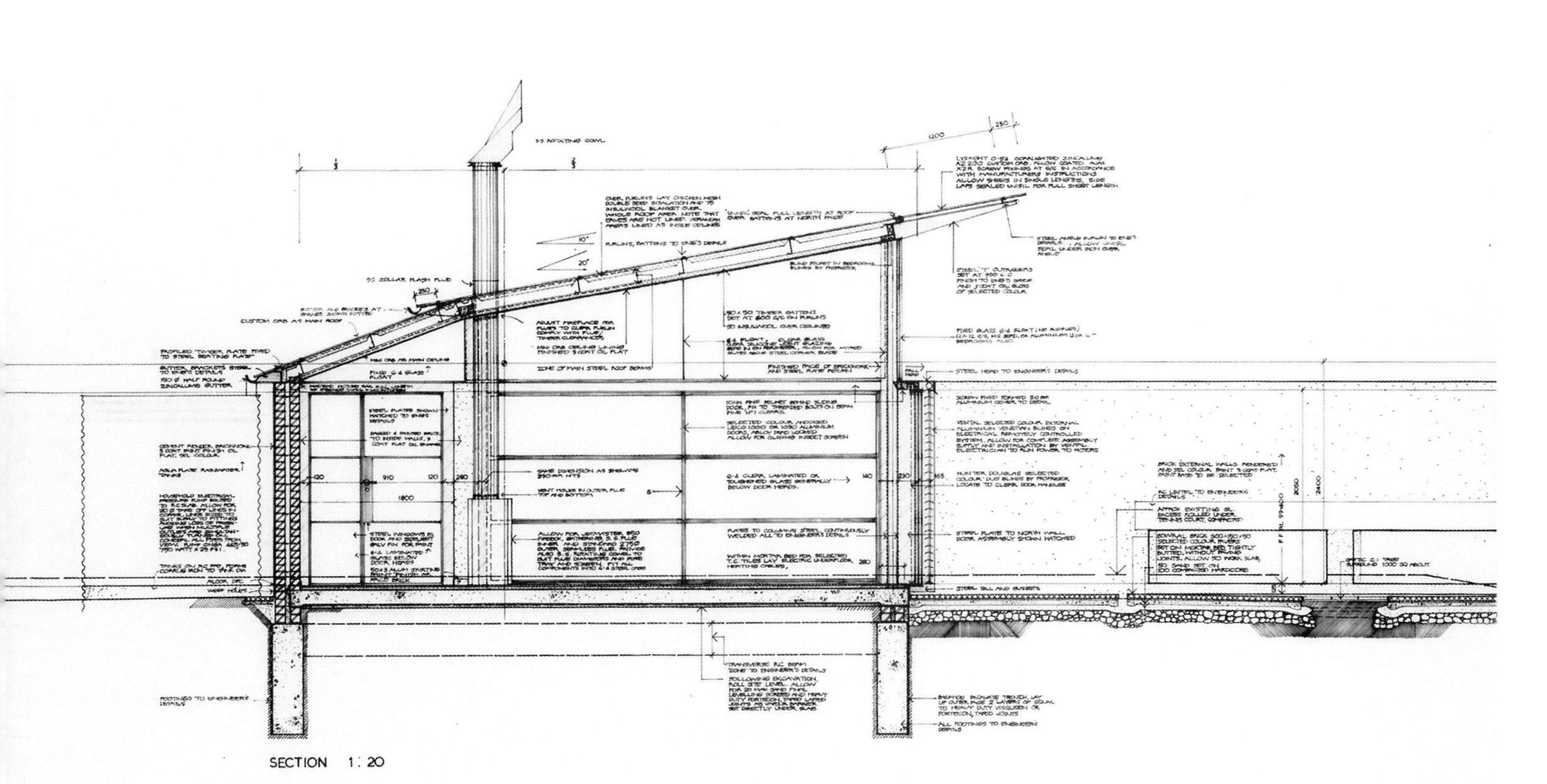

Simpson-Lee house
Mount Wilson New South Wales
1989 to 1994

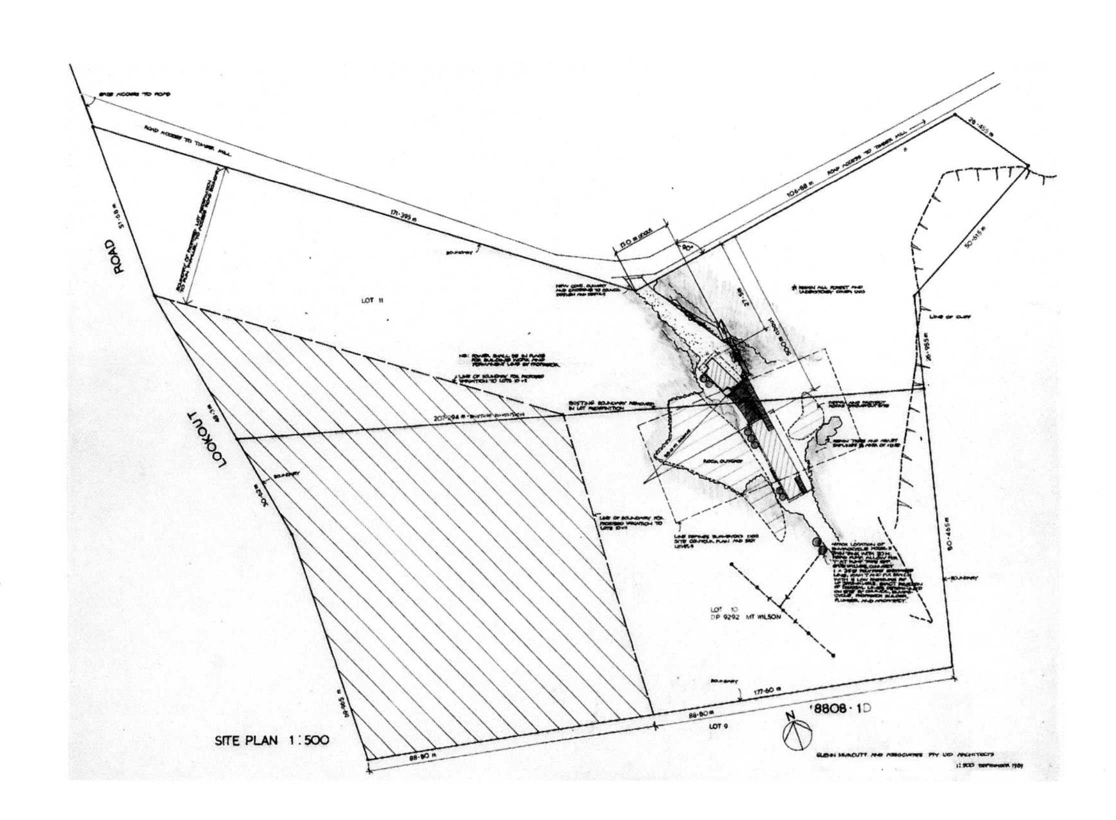

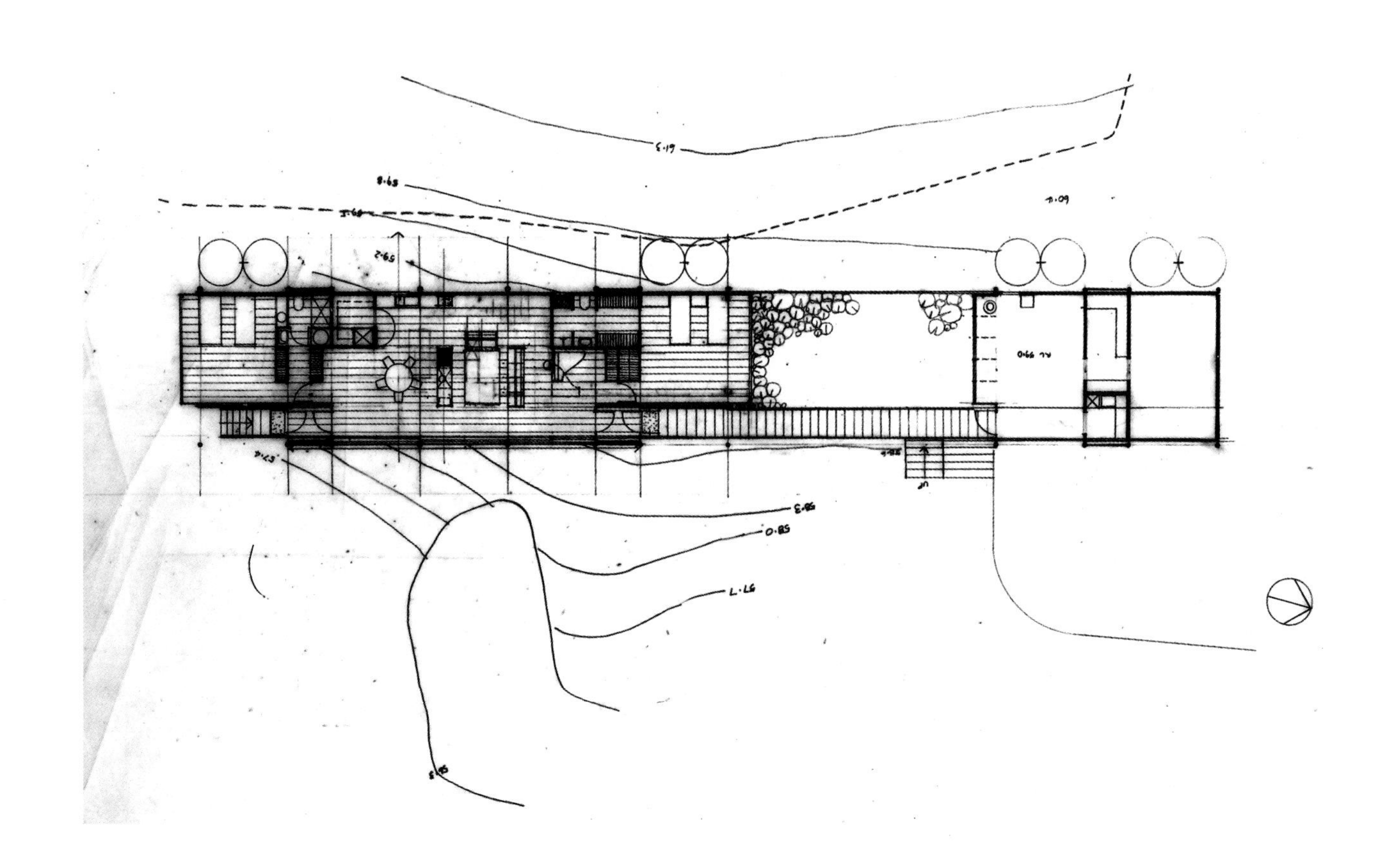

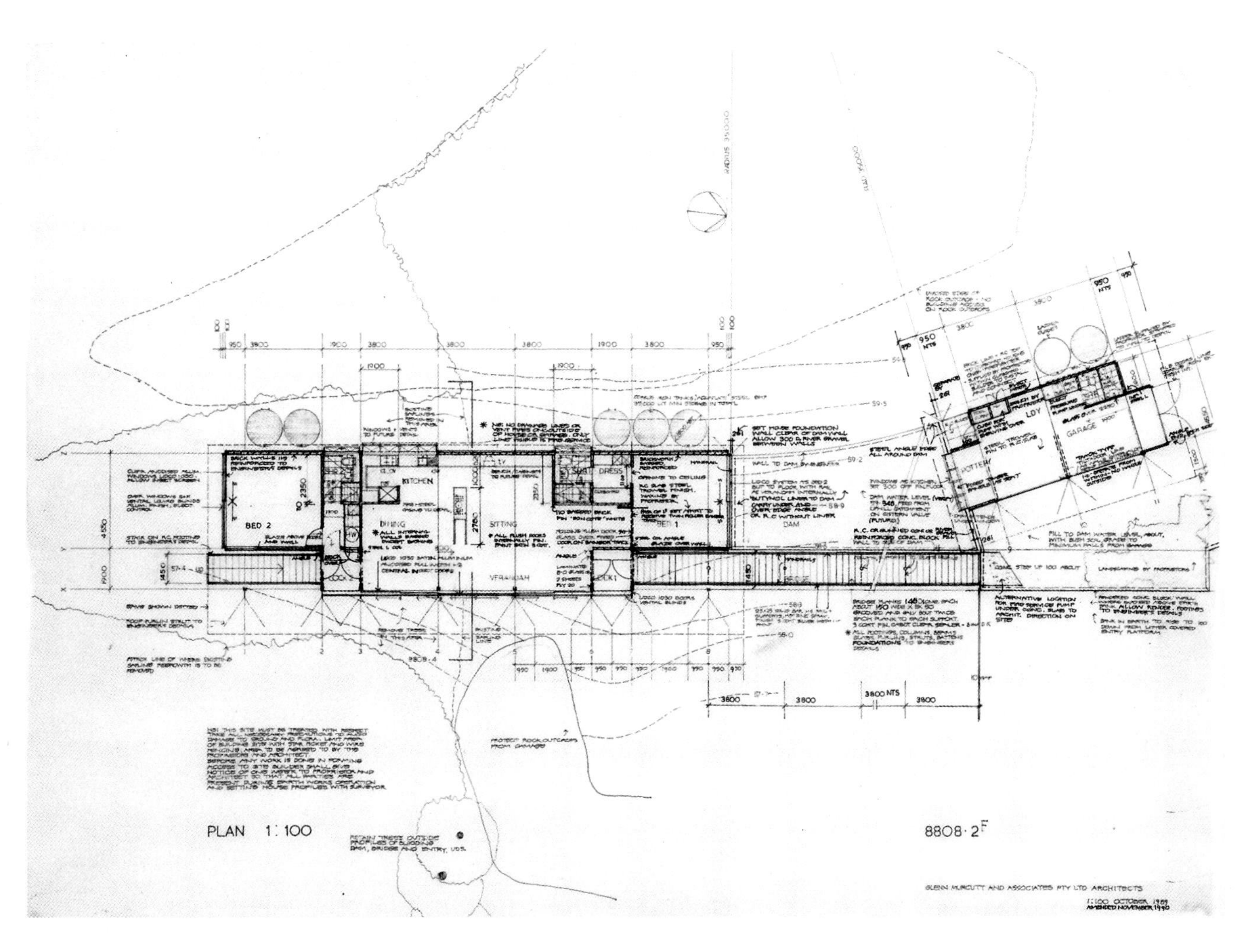

BED 2
KITCHEN
DINING
SITTING
DRESS
BED 1
VERANDAH
DAM
LDY
GARAGE
PLAN 1:100
8808·2F
GLENN MURCUTT AND ASSOCIATES PTY LTD ARCHITECTS

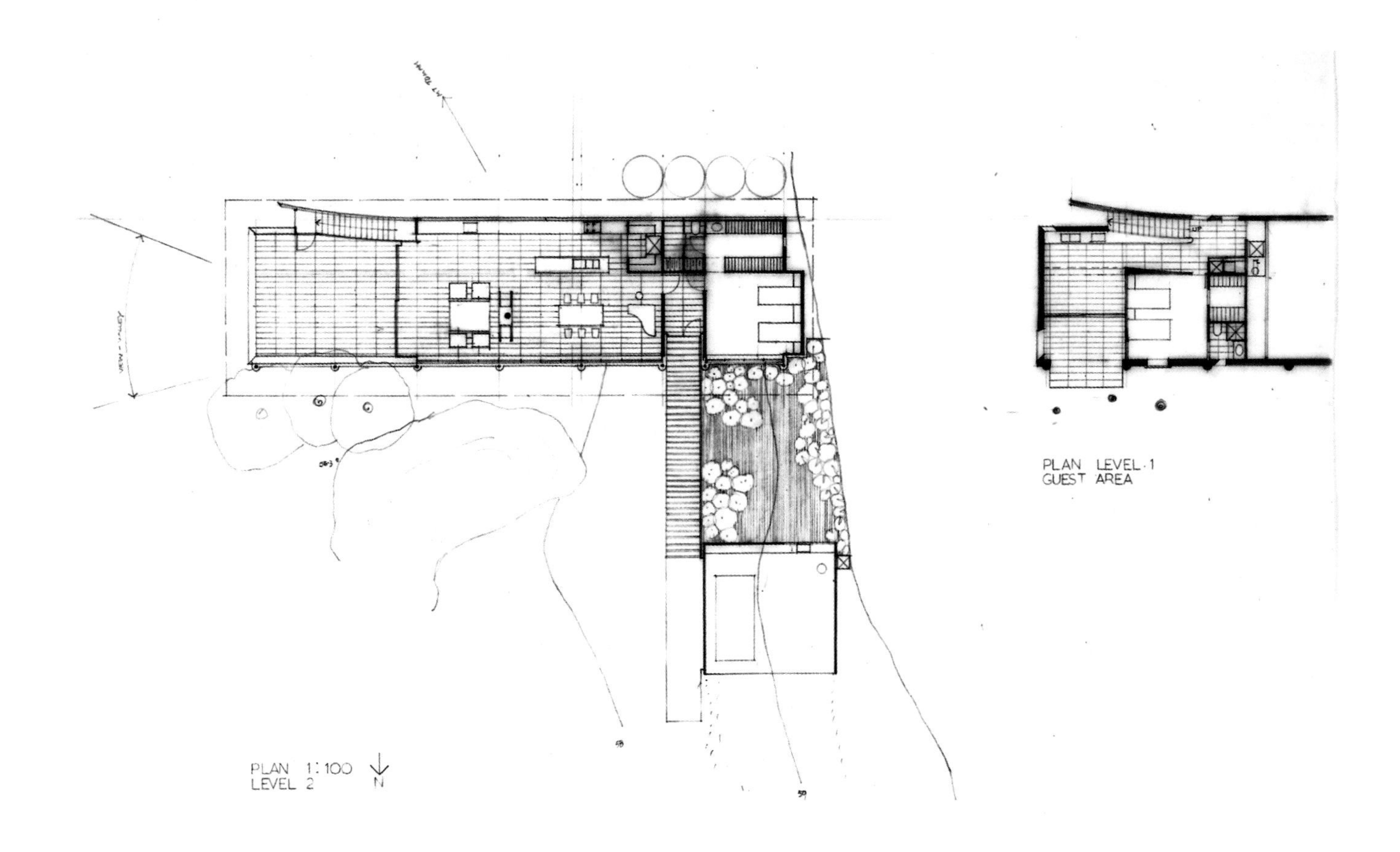

PLAN LEVEL·1
GUEST AREA
PLAN 1:100
LEVEL 2
N

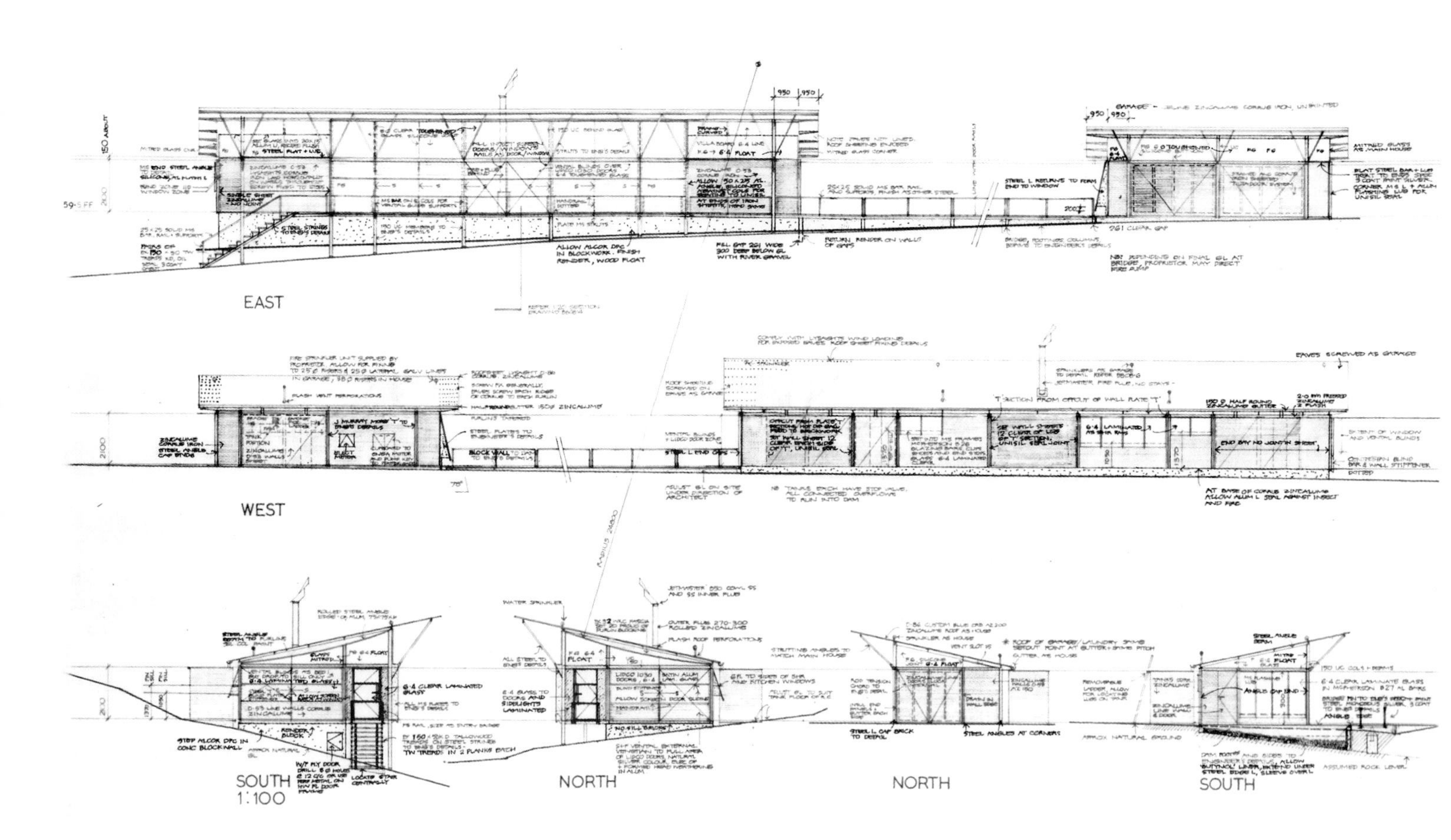
EAST
WEST
SOUTH
1:100
NORTH
NORTH
SOUTH

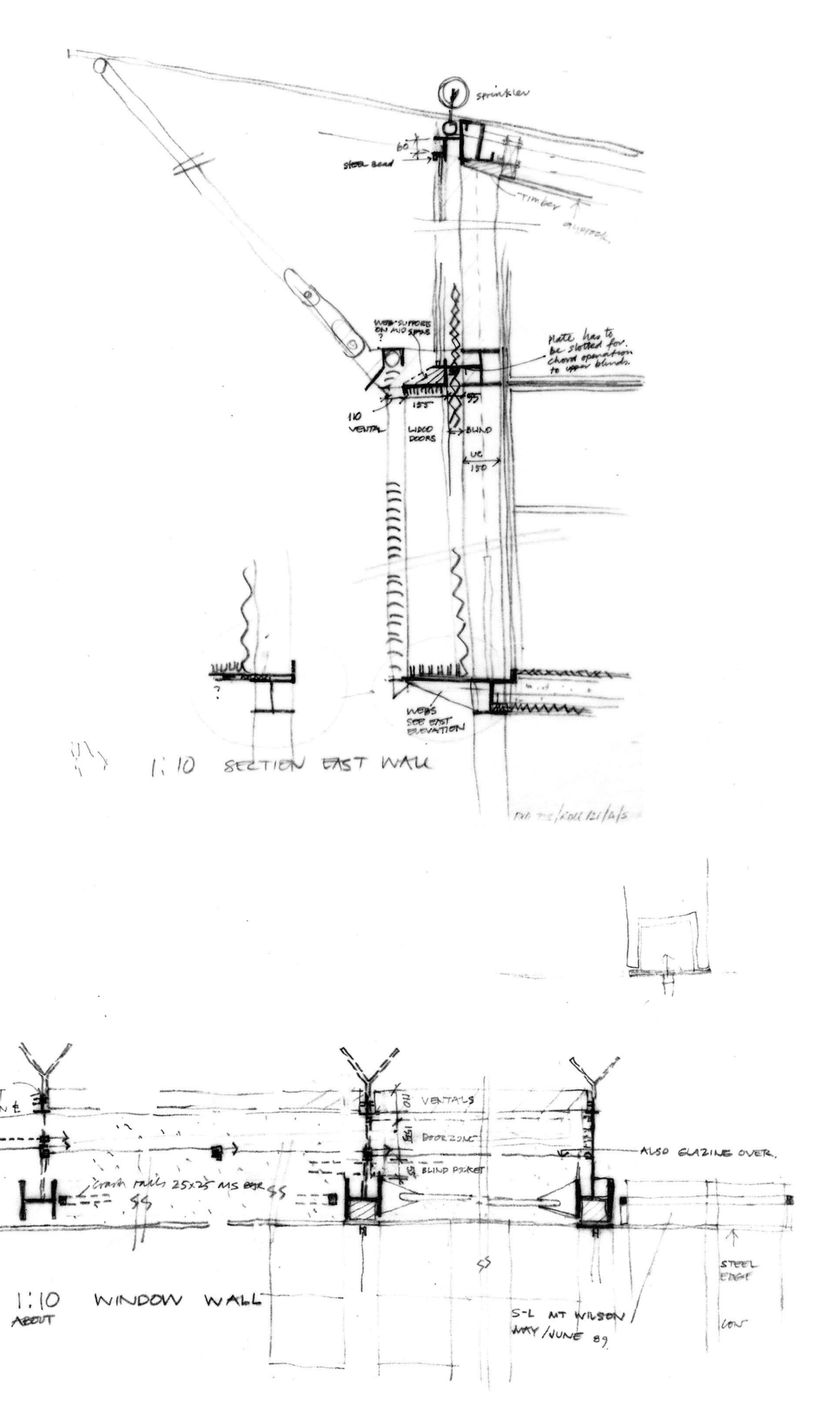
sprinkler
60
steel bead
Timber
Plate has to be slotted for chord operation to upper blinds.
WEB SUPPORTS ON AXIO SPINS ?
110 VENTAL
155
55
LIDCO DOORS
BLIND
UC 150
WEBS SEE EAST ELEVATION
1:10 SECTION EAST WALL
T AT COLUMN ℄
VENTALS
DOORZONE
BLIND POCKET
ALSO GLAZING OVER.
crash rails 25x25 MS BAR SS
SS
STEEL EDGE
1:10 WINDOW WALL
ABOUT
S-L MT WILSON /
MAY / JUNE 89

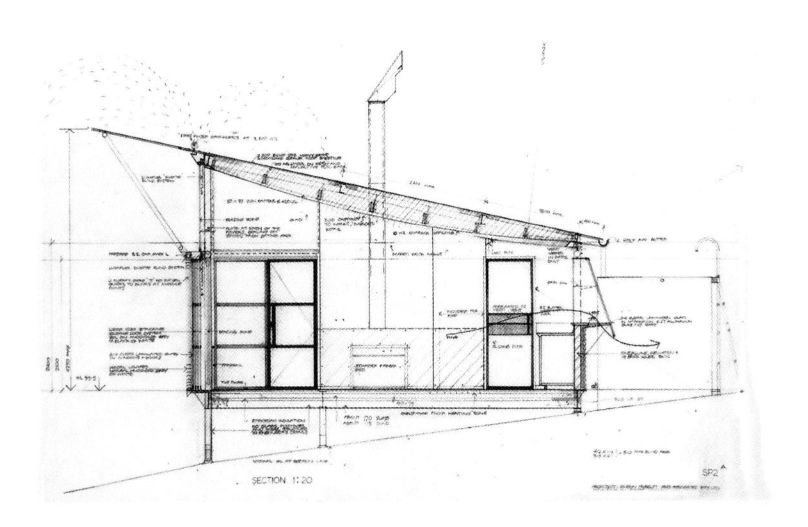
SECTION 1:20
SP2

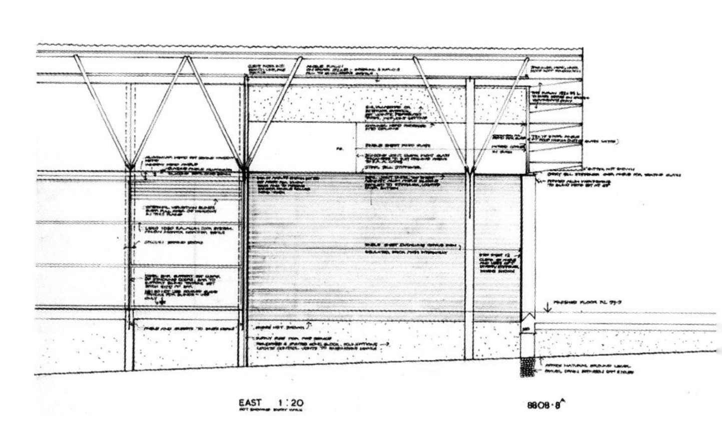
EAST 1:20
8808·8

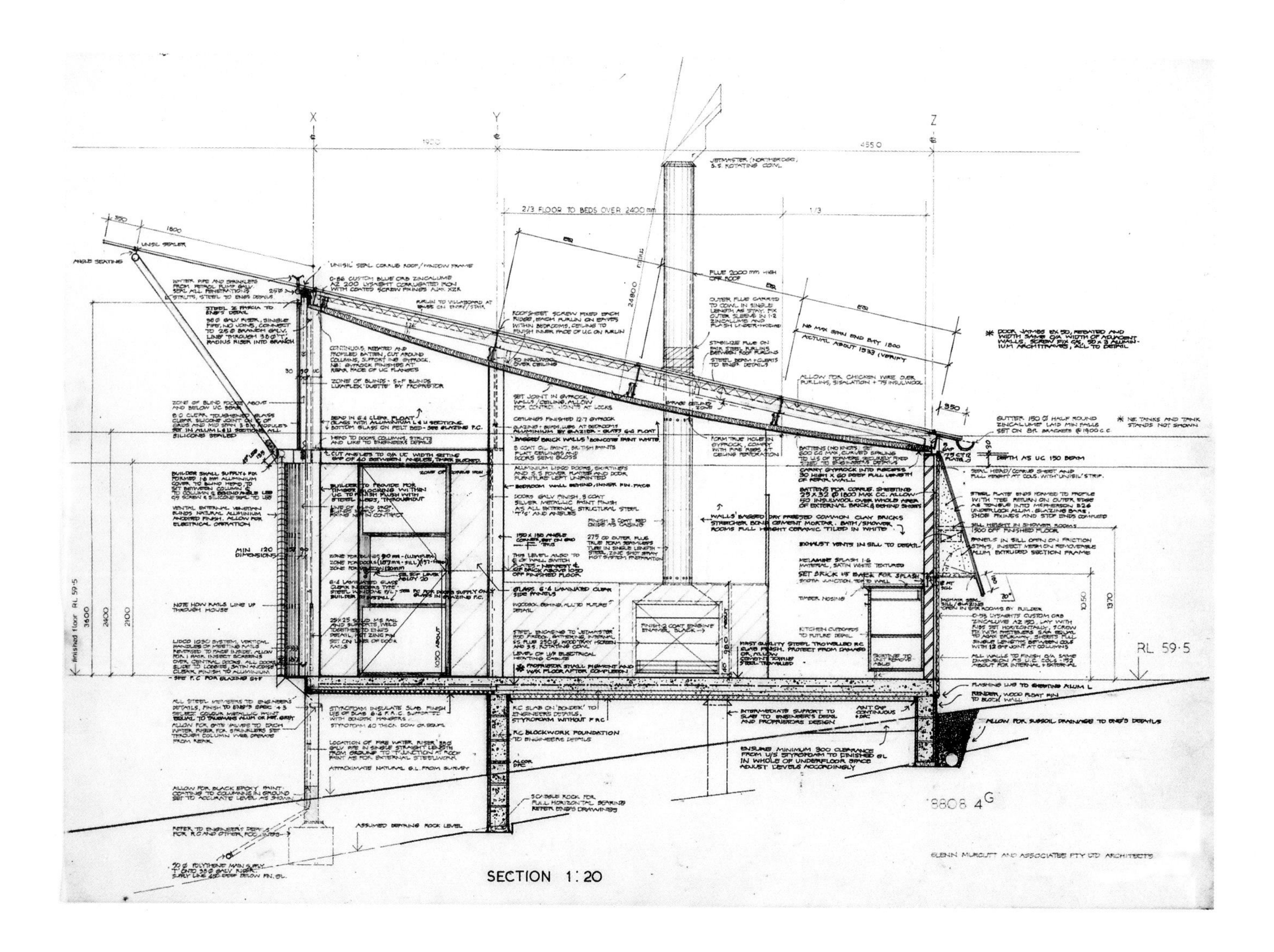
X
Y
Z
1900
4950
2/3 FLOOR TO BEDS OVER 2400 mm
1/3
RL 59·5
8808 4G
SECTION 1:20
GLENN MURCUTT AND ASSOCIATES PTY LTD ARCHITECTS

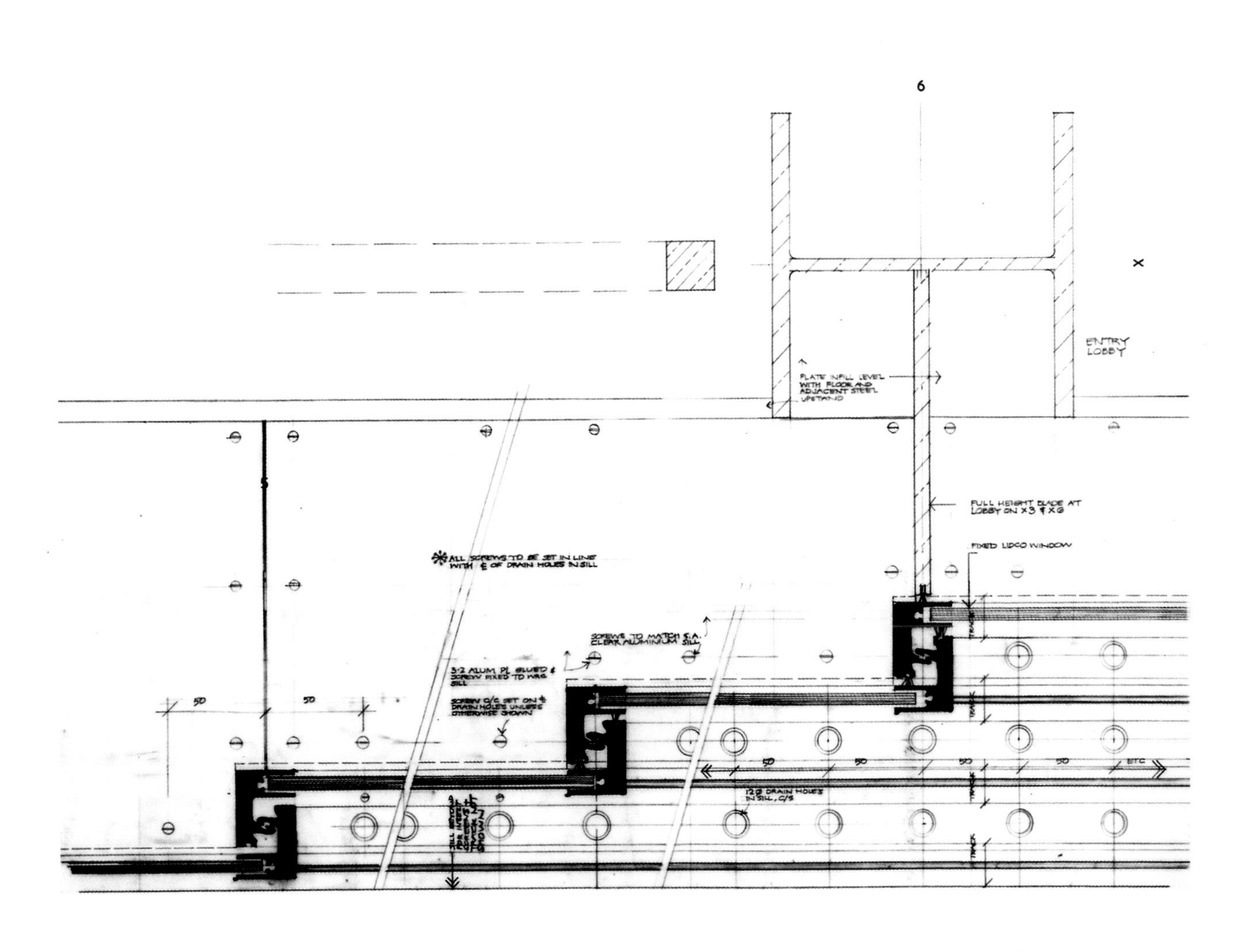

6
X
ENTRY LOBBY
PLATE INFILL LEVEL WITH FLOOR AND ADJACENT STEEL UPSTAND
FULL HEIGHT BLADE AT LOBBY ON X3 & X6
FIXED LIDCO WINDOW
ALL SCREWS TO BE SET IN LINE WITH ℄ OF DRAIN HOLES IN SILL
SCREWS TO MATCH S.A. CLEAR ALUMINIUM SILL
3.2 ALUM PL GLUED & SCREW FIXED TO W&G SILL
SCREW C/C SET ON ℄ DRAIN HOLES UNLESS OTHERWISE SHOWN
12Ø DRAIN HOLES IN SILL, C/S
50
ETC

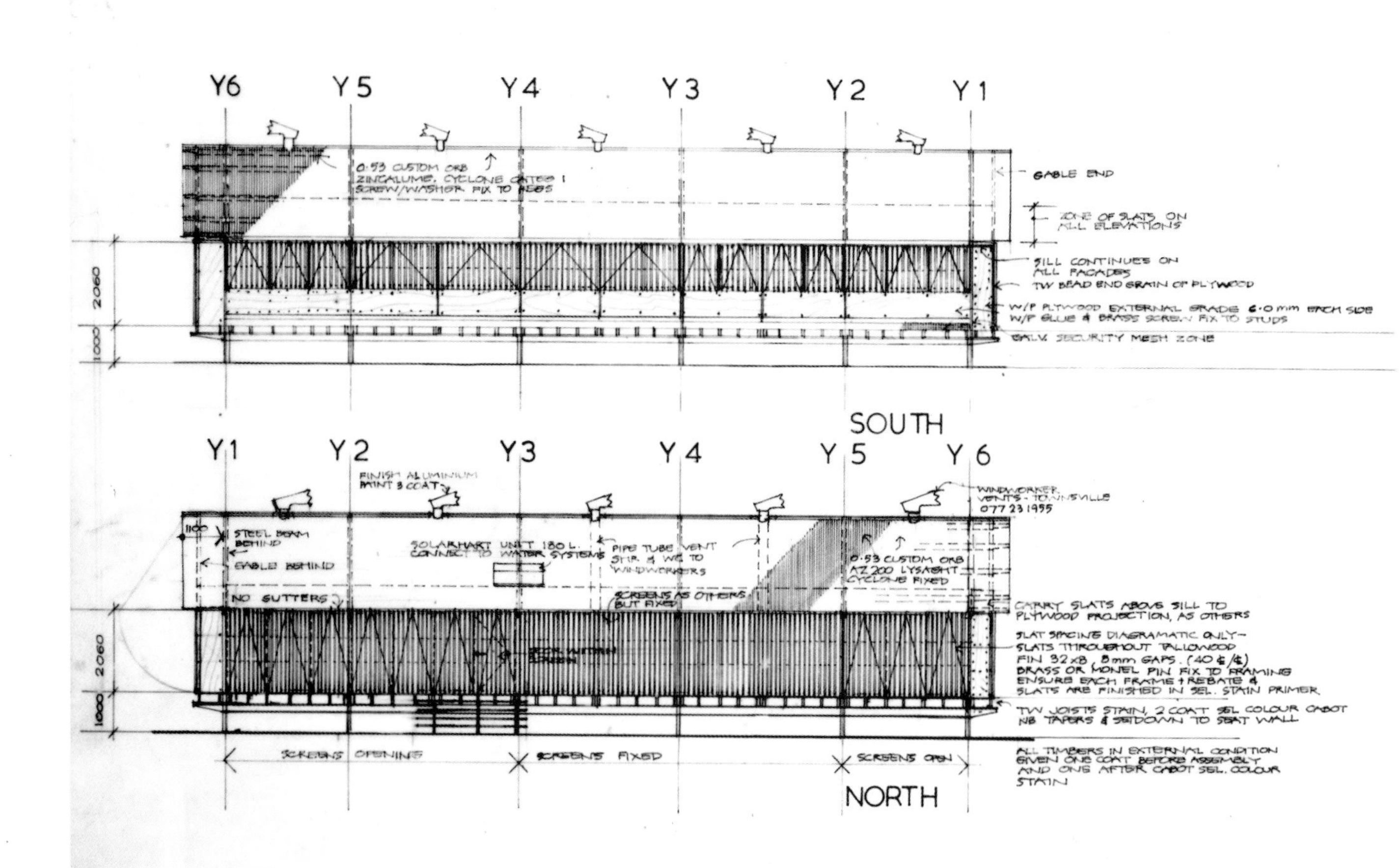

Y6
Y5
Y4
Y3
Y2
Y1
GABLE END
ZONE OF SLATS ON ALL ELEVATIONS
SILL CONTINUES ON ALL FACADES
SOUTH
Y1
Y2
Y3
Y4
Y5
Y6
NORTH

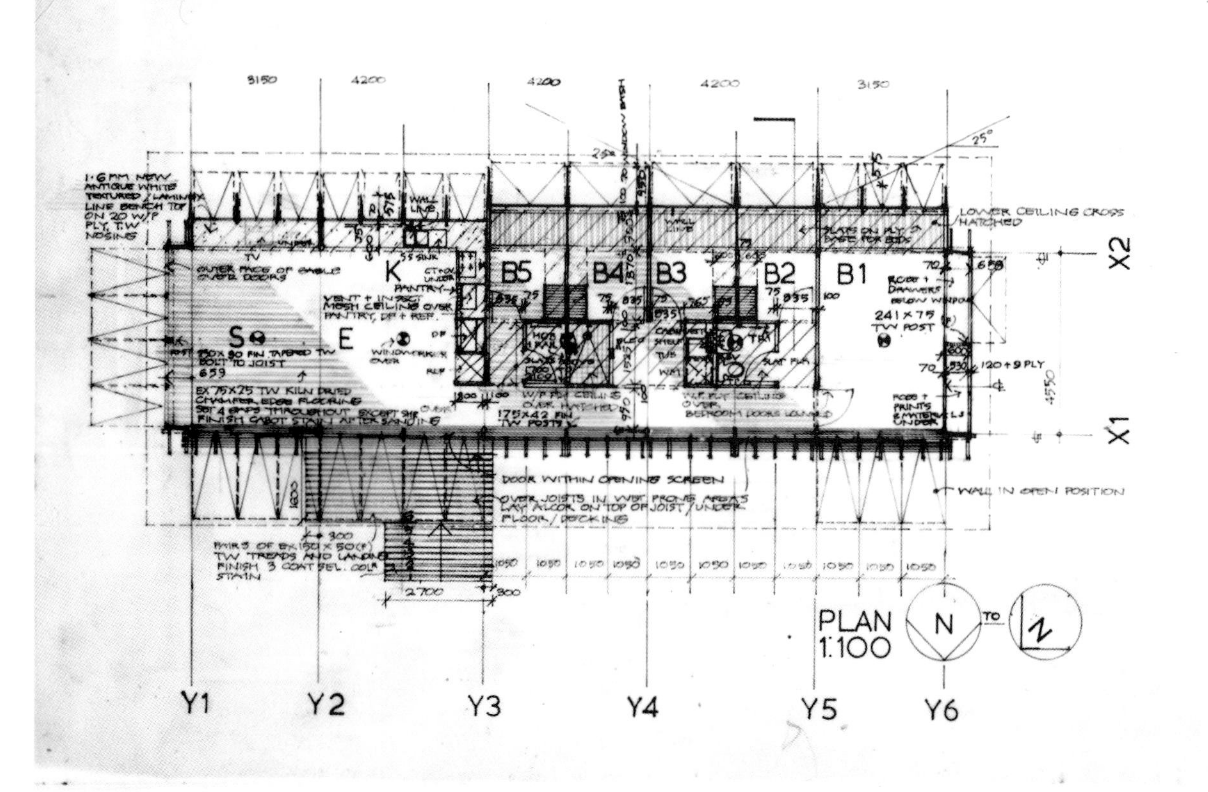

PLAN 1:100
Y1
Y2
Y3
Y4
Y5
Y6
X1
X2

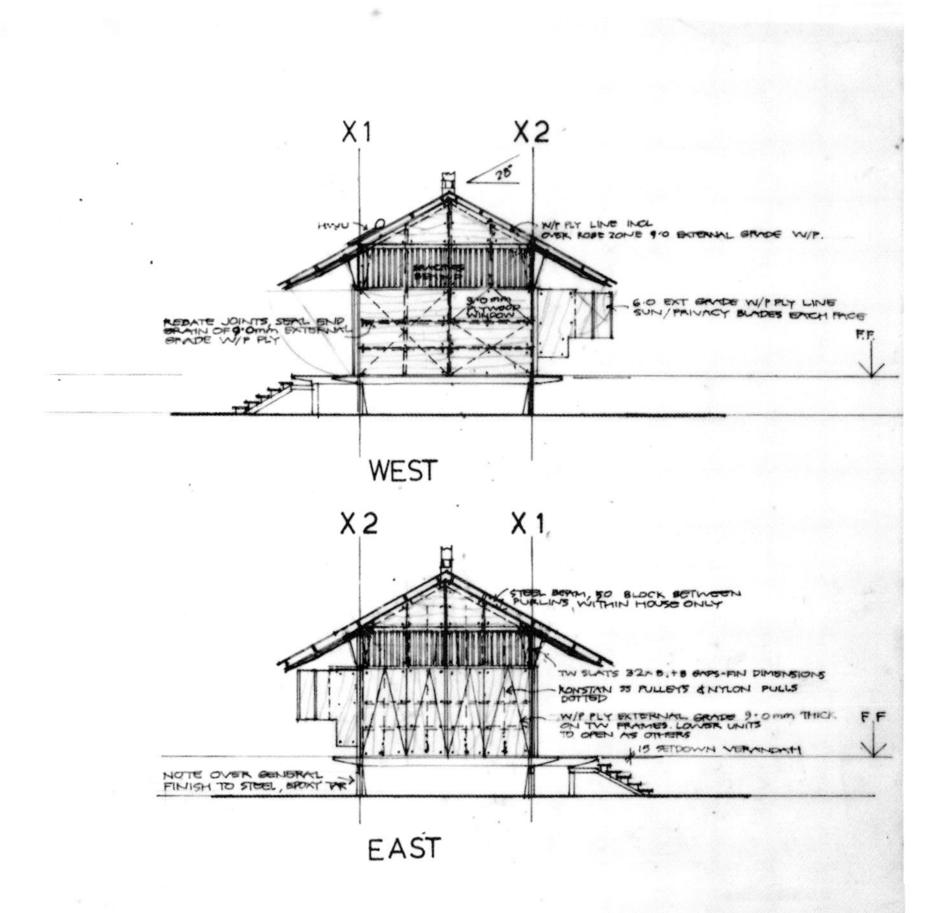

DOORS : TO BED 1, 820 X 2035 TIMBER LOUVRE, VENT.
TO BEDS 2-5, 765 X 2035 " "
SHOWER & WC DOORS H.C. VENEER AS WALLS W/P EXTERNAL GRADE

DOOR LOCKS + FURNITURE : STYLEFINNISH ABLOY. ALLOW LOCKSETS KEYED ALIKE AND DEAD LOCK + INTERNAL SNIB ENTRY. TO WC & SHOWER ALLOW FOR PRIVACY LOCKS, ALL S.C.P. FINISH.
TO ALL DOORS TO ROOMS, SHR & WC ALLOW FOR STYLEFINNISH S.C.P. LEVER 20
CUPBOARD 'D' PULLS STYLEFINNISH SCP PRIMO 142, HEAVY DUTY MAGNETIC LOCKS. HINGES 1 1/2 PAIR/DOOR INTERNALLY S.S.
CUPBOARD HINGES S.S./BRASS 180° OPENING OFFSET PIVOT OR BUTT HINGE ON JAMB.
DRAWER SLIDES BLUM. (STYLEFINNISH 02 9576344)

WALL LINING : GENERALLY 75 & 100 X 50 STUD FRAMED WALLS TO COMPLY WITH ASA TIMBER FRAMING INCL PLATES, NOGGING, BRACING AND HOLDING DOWN FOR CATEGORY 1 TERRAIN CYCLONE. INTERNAL WALLS LINED WITH 6.0MM EXTERNAL GRADE W/P, SEALED END GRAIN EXTERNAL PLY AS INTERNAL BUT THICKNESS TO ENGINEER'S DETAILS, SCREWS BRASS + GLUE.

TIMBER FINISHES : FINISH SANDING + 3 COAT CLEAR SATIN POLYURETHANE INTERNALLY & 2 COAT OF SELECTED COLOUR CABOT STAIN OVER 1 COAT CABOT SEALER. EXTERNALLY

⊗ : WINDWORKER VENTILATOR RIDGE MOUNT FOR 28° ROOF PITCH. ISOLATE GALV WINDWORKER WITH 3 COATS OF EPOXY PAINT, FROM ZINCALUME

ROOF SHEET : ALLOW FOR LYSAGHTS 0·53 CUSTOM ORB ZINCALUME AZ 200 CORRUGATED IRON IN SINGLE LENGTHS. FIXING SHALL COMPLY WITH TERRAIN CATEGORY 1, ZINCALUME CYCLONE WASHERS & SCREWS. ALLOW FOR ZINCALUME AZ 200 ROLL RIDGE CAP FIXED AS FOR ROOF SHEETING, + THS 1450 / 17 SCREWS + CYCLONE WASHERS.

BOLTS : ALL BOLTS HOT DIP HEX HEAD GALV INCL WASHERS SIZED TO ENG'S DETAILS

TIMBERS : UOS SHALL BE Nº1 CLEAR TALLOWOOD (EUCALYPTUS MICROCORYS) K.D. FOR DOORS, SLATS AND JOINERY AND DECKING/FLOORING TO M.C. OF 15% APPROX. FOR LOCAL CONDITIONS. TIMBER SIZING TO ENGINEERS DETAILS

GLAZING : ALLOW OVER SHR ALCOVE 2 SHEETS OF 8·0 CLEAR LAMINATED GLASS AND WC 1 SHEET 8·0 CLEAR LAMINATED. SHEETS 520 X 1550 EACH SILICONED & CLIPPED ONTO JOISTS

PLUMBING

WC : FOWLER PACIFIC COMPACT VIT. CHINA WHITE
WC SEAT : FOWLER PREMIER TOP FIX WHITE
BASIN : FOWLER HAMILTON 600 VIT CHINA WHITE - 3 TAP HOLES
WM : BY PROPRIETOR
LAUNDRY TUB : CLARK 70 LIT. SUDSAVER MK II COMPACT SS + WHITE CABINET
REFRIG + DF : BY PROPRIETOR
COOKER + OVEN : ST GEORGE. NOTE COOKTOP COUNTER + SEP OVEN UNDER - WHITE
SINK : CLARK MONACO 5000 F RH 1 TAP HOLE SS FLUSHLINE, CUTTING BOARD, BASKET COLANDER
HWU : SOLARHART 180 LIT. UNIT FOR ROOF MOUNTING
PIPING : COPPER, SIZE AND HARDNESS TO SUIT PRESSURE AND FITTING DEMAND
TAPS + FITTINGS : RAYMOR T4 SERIES, WHITE HANDLES, SCP BRASS SKIRTS
ALLOW FOR STOP VALVES, MIXERS, TWINNER FOR SINGLE HOLE KITCHEN SINK AND 190 MM AERATED CURVED SPOUT; RECESSED SINK SET FOR LAUNDRY WITH WALL MOUNTED 190 MM CURVED SPOUT; FOR BASIN, 110 MM CONICAL SPOUT AERATED; FOR SHOWER MIXER AND 270 MM SCP DOUBLE ELBOW ADJUST. SET ROSE 1800 TO MOUNTING OFF FLOOR. LDRY HOSE COCKS, + SINK SET, 190 WALL SPOUT.

GARDEN TAPS : ALLOW 4 HOSE COCKS SET ON EACH CORNER OF HOUSE AT REAR OF COLUMNS - OUT OF VIEW, TURN SIDEWAYS. RISER SET AGAINST A WASTE LINE BACK FROM EDGE OF HOUSE

SUPPLY & WASTE LINES : CONNECT TO TOWN WATER AND SEWER LOCATED TO NORTH SIDE OF SITE ALL LINES CONCEALED FROM VIEW, SET MIN 1500 FROM EDGE OF BUILDING COLUMNS. VENTS CARRIED IN WALLS AND SET VERTICAL AND CLEAR OF VENT PIPE TO WINDWORKER BY 30 MM. COMPLY WITH THE REQUIREMENTS OF LOCAL W.S. & DRAINAGE AUTHORITY. CONNECTION TO TOWN WATER IN COPPER - NO METER -
ALL WASTE, SUPPLY AND VENT LINES SET VERTICAL, TRAPS SET HARD AGAINST U/S OF FLOOR. WASTE FITTINGS C.P. BRASS BODIES.

TILING : ALLOW FOR TILING WALLS AND HOB TO SHOWER TO 2035, TO LAUNDRY AND TOILET TO 1200, JOHNSON 200 X 100, SATIN ALIBASTER. BOND 1/2 ON END. FLOOR TILED IN SHOWER MIRAGE TK9 GREY 100 X 100 X 10 OR SQ SET ON 20 GRC SHEET (NO JOINT), GRC L AT WALL JUNCTION, W/P GLUE ALL TO LOCAL AUTHORITY REQUIREMENTS.
NB: IN AREAS OF WATER ADJACENT TO SHOWER, KITCHEN SINK, WC + BASIN, N. WALL AND LAUNDRY ALLOW FOR ALCOR LAID OVER JOISTS PRIOR TO NAILING FLOOR. TOILET PAPER HOLDER + 3 TOWEL RAILS SHR + 1 IN WC, SCP LANE 770, 970, 820 L.

NB: READ IN CONJUNCTION WITH 1:20 SECTION DRAWING 9006 4 ^A
REFER TO ENGINEERS DRAWING FOR ALL STRUCTURAL ELEMENTS INCLUDING FOOTINGS, COLUMNS, BEAMS, PURLINS, JOISTS, EAVES PURLIN PROFILES AND EXTERNAL GRADE WATERPROOF PLY USED THROUGHOUT.

ALLOW FOR RONSTAN PULLEY BLOCKS IN SS AND SYNTHETIC HORN CLEATS MONEL BOLT OR SCREW LOCATED, SS EYEBOLTS AND HOOKS & NYLON CHORD + SS HINGES SCP BOLTS FOR OPENING SCREENS AND WINDOWS 2/UNIT.

9006·3 B

GLENN MURCUTT AND ASSOCIATES PTY LTD ARCHITECTS
JAN 1992

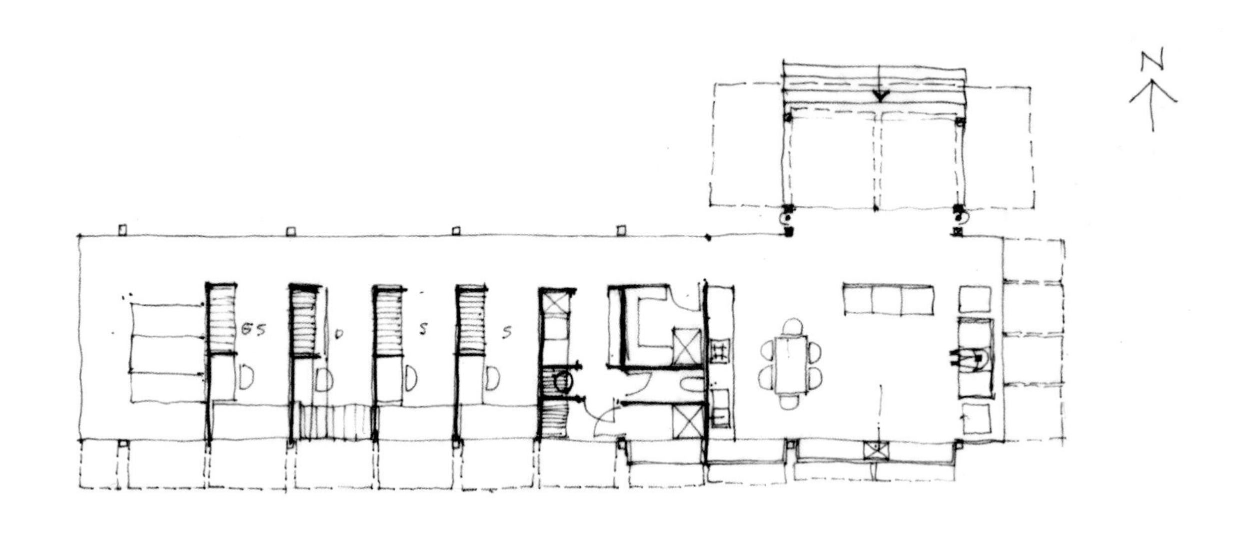
N
ES
D
S
S

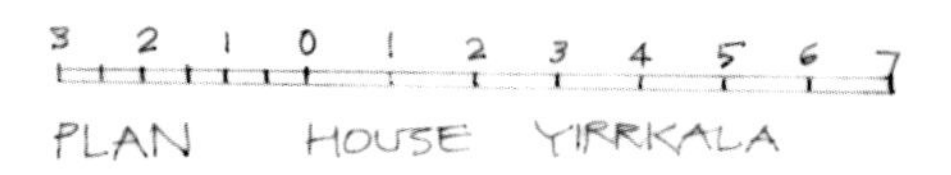
3 2 1 0 1 2 3 4 5 6 7
PLAN HOUSE YIRRKALA

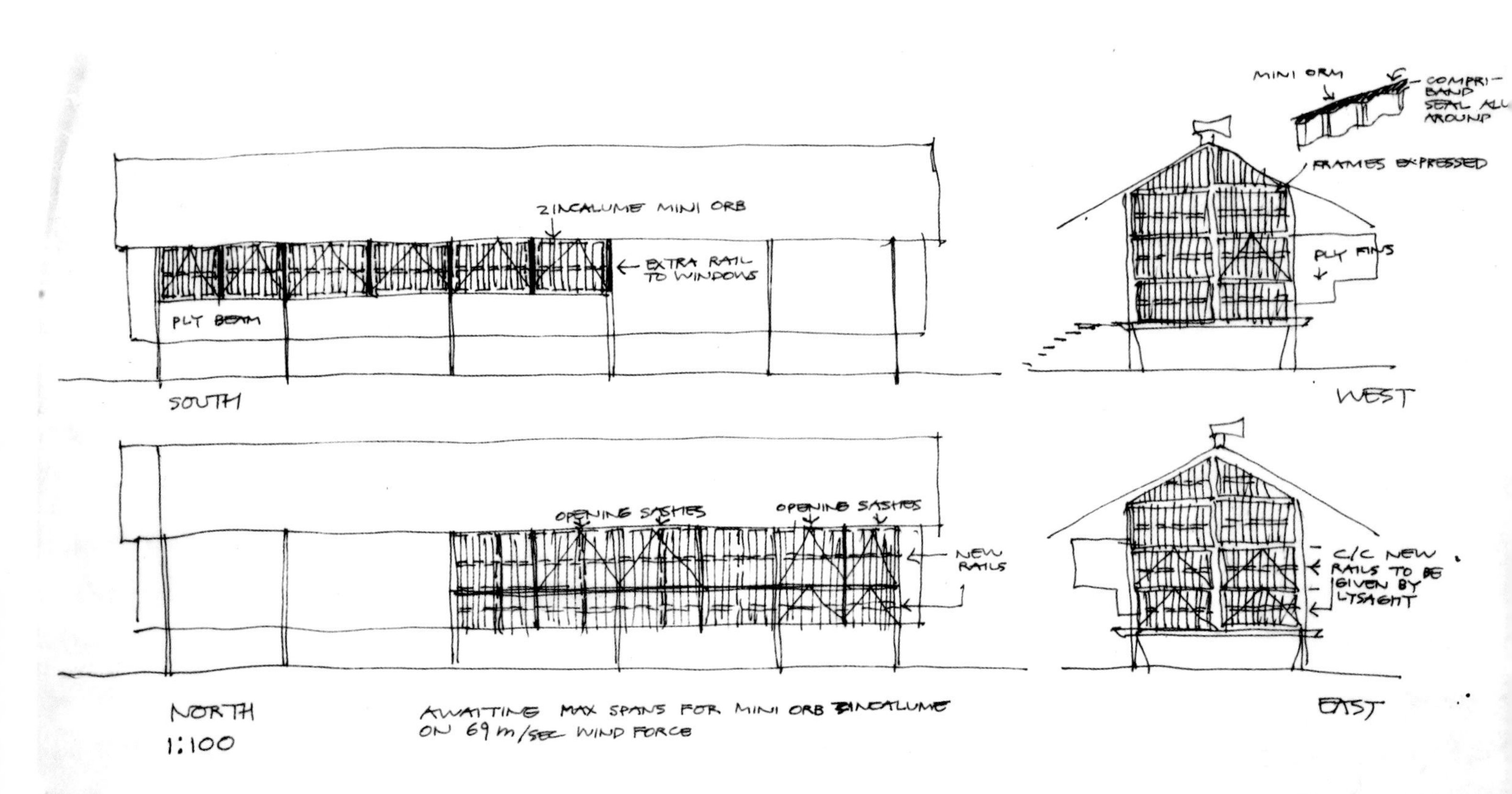
ZINCALUME MINI ORB
EXTRA RAIL TO WINDOWS
PLY BEAM
SOUTH
MINI ORM
COMPRI-BAND SEAL ALL AROUND
FRAMES EXPRESSED
PLY FINS
WEST
OPENING SASHES
OPENING SASHES
NEW RAILS
C/C NEW RAILS TO BE GIVEN BY LYSAGHT
NORTH
1:100
AWAITING MAX SPANS FOR MINI ORB ZINCALUME
ON 69 m/sec WIND FORCE
EAST

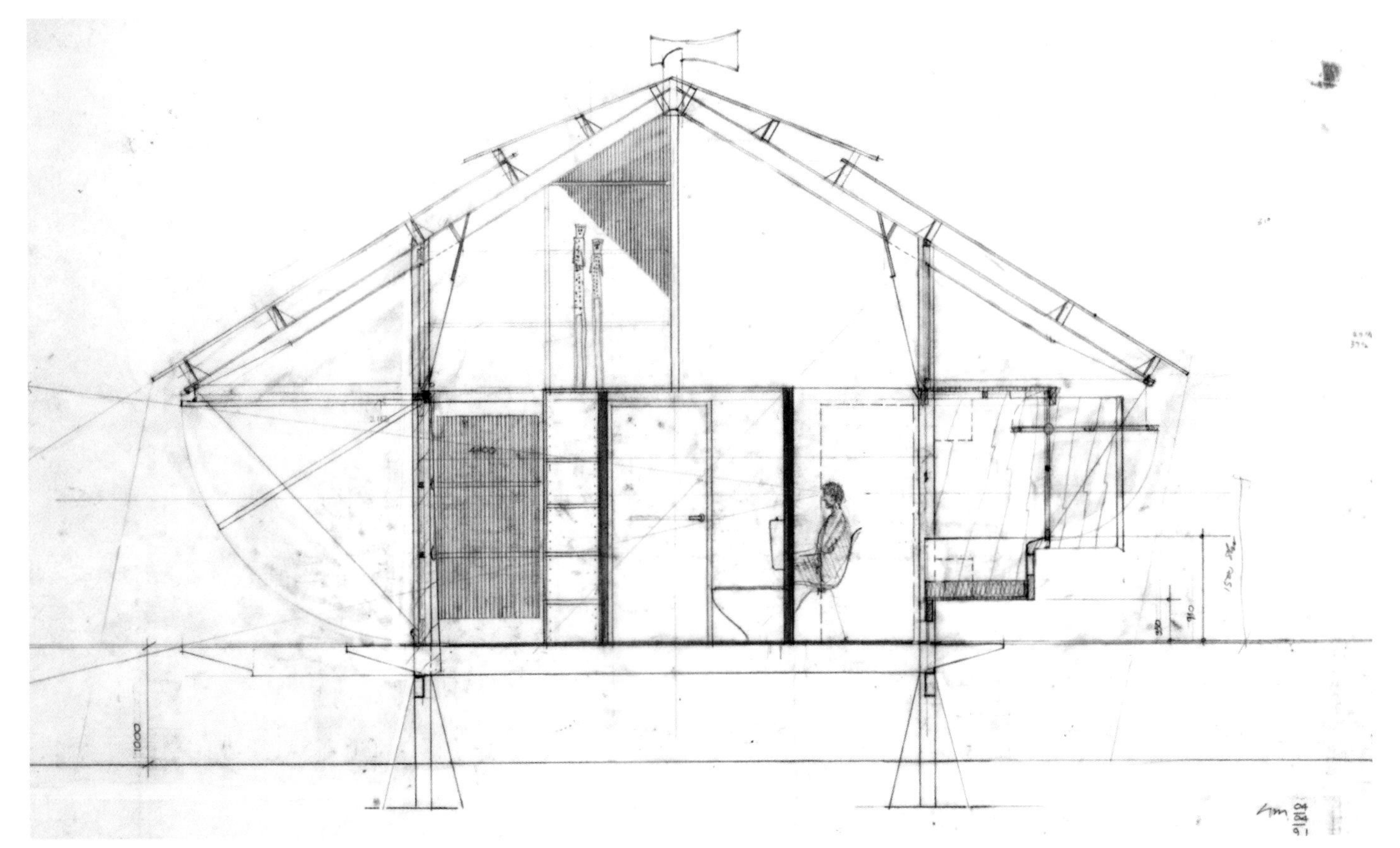

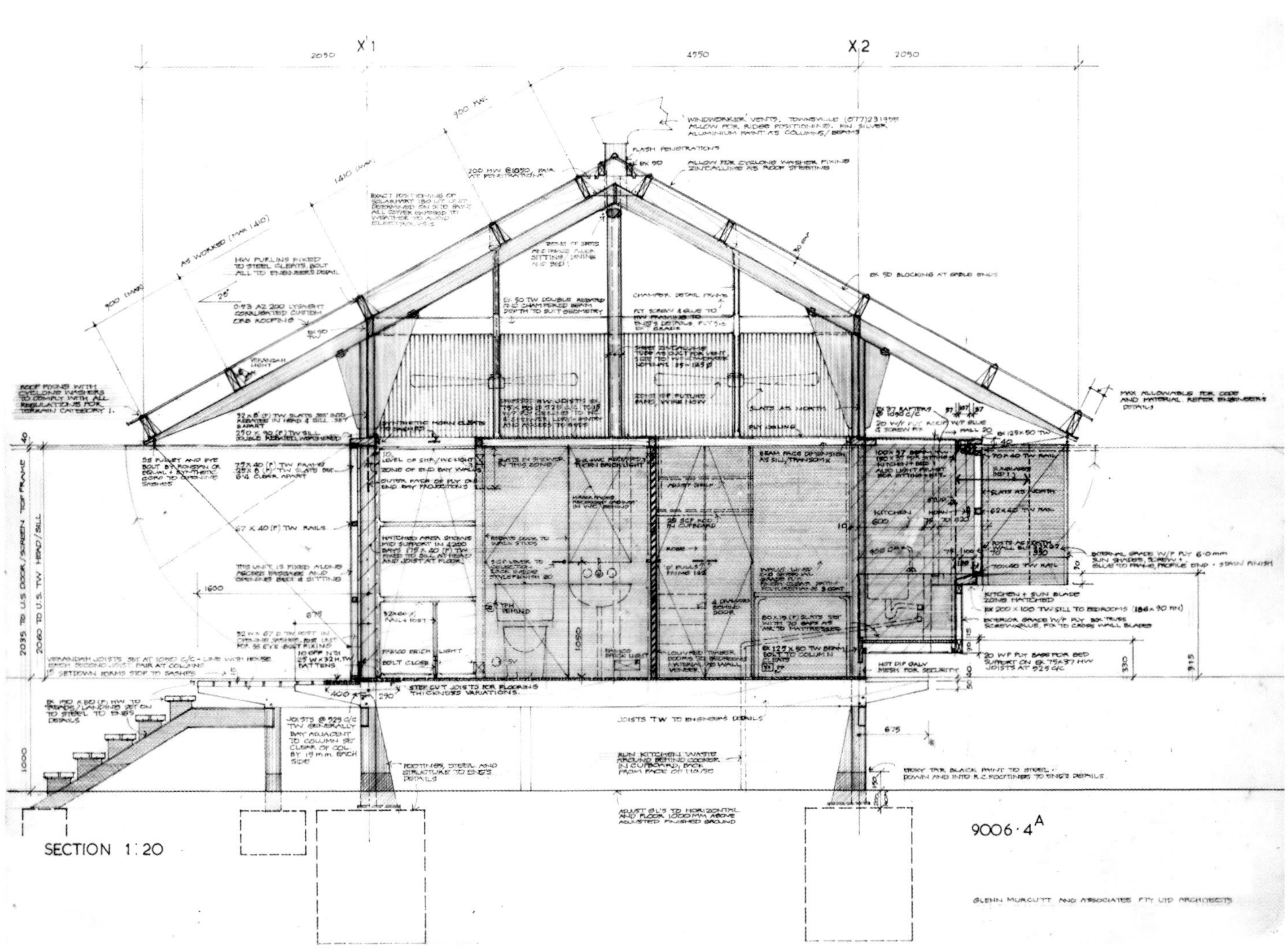
X1
X2
2050
4550
2050
SECTION 1:20
9006·4A
GLENN MURCUTT AND ASSOCIATES PTY LTD ARCHITECTS

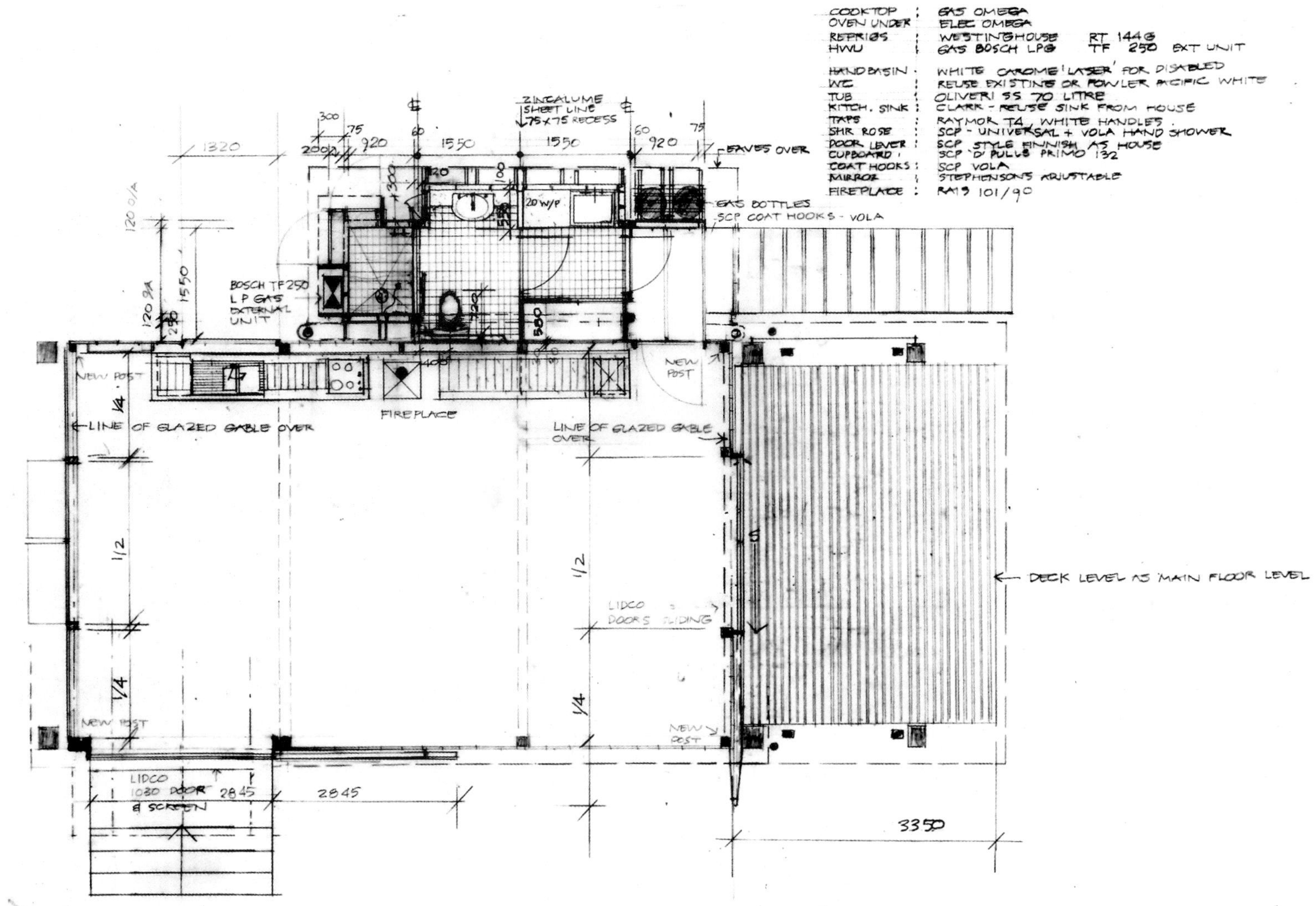

COOKTOP : GAS OMEGA
OVEN UNDER : ELEC OMEGA
REFRIGS : WESTINGHOUSE RT 144G
HWU : GAS BOSCH LPG TF 250 EXT UNIT
HAND BASIN : WHITE CHROME 'LASER' FOR DISABLED
WC : REUSE EXISTING OR FOWLER PACIFIC WHITE
TUB : OLIVERI SS 70 LITRE
KITCH. SINK : CLARK - REUSE SINK FROM HOUSE
TAPS : RAYMOR T4, WHITE HANDLES
SHR ROSE : SCP - UNIVERSAL + VOLA HAND SHOWER
DOOR LEVER : SCP - STYLE FINNISH AS HOUSE
CUPBOARD : SCP D' PULLS PRIMO 132
COAT HOOKS : SCP VOLA
MIRROR : STEPHENSONS ADJUSTABLE
FIREPLACE : RAIS 101/90
ZINCALUME SHEET LINE 75 X 75 RECESS
EAVES OVER
GAS BOTTLES
SCP COAT HOOKS - VOLA
BOSCH TF250 L P GAS EXTERNAL UNIT
NEW POST
FIREPLACE
LINE OF GLAZED GABLE OVER
LIDCO DOORS SLIDING
DECK LEVEL AS MAIN FLOOR LEVEL
LIDCO 1030 DOOR & SCREEN
1320
1550
920
2845
3350

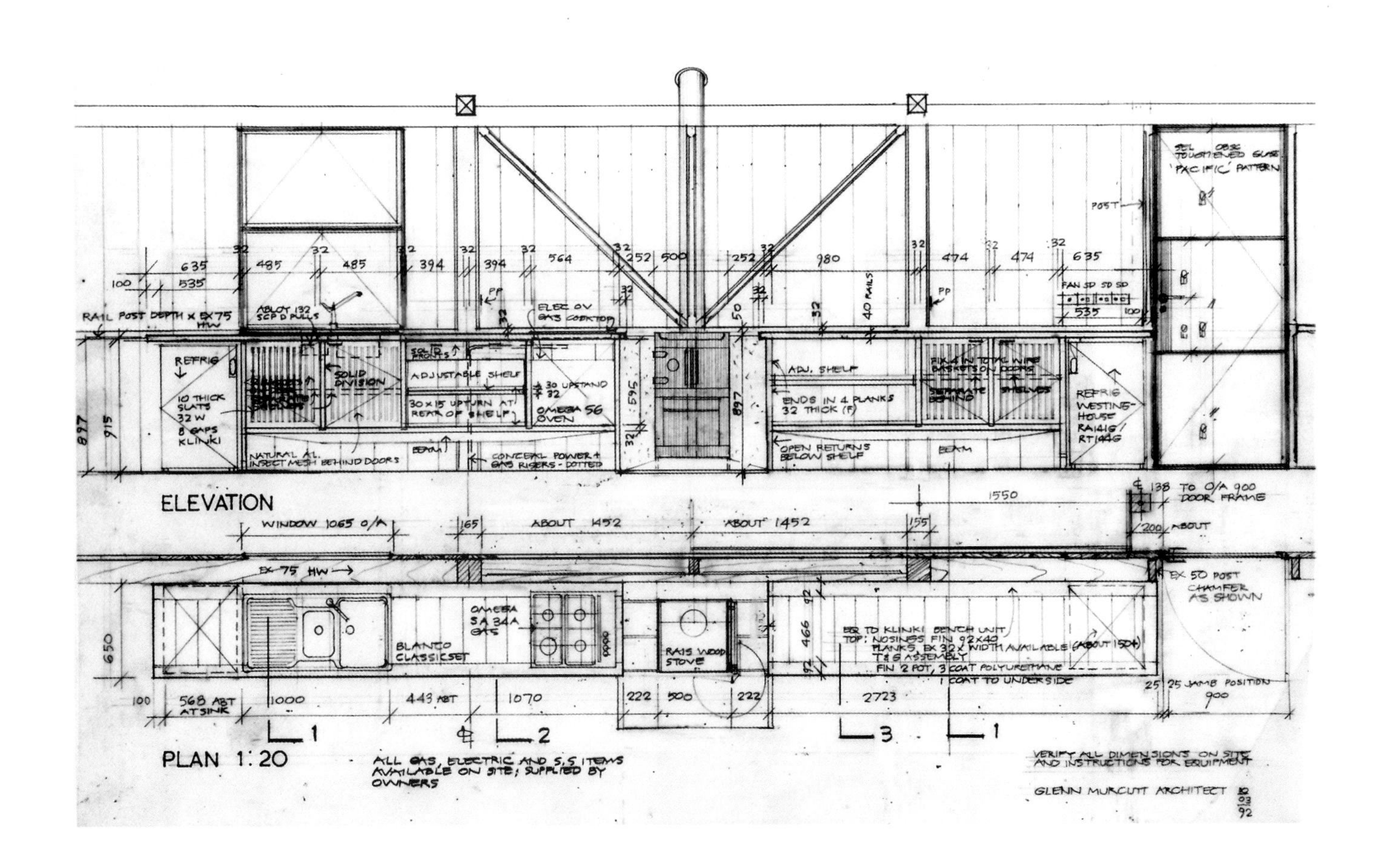

ELEVATION
REFRIG
10 THICK SLATS 32 W 8 GAPS KLINKI
SOLID DIVISION
ADJUSTABLE SHELF
30 X 15 UPTURN AT REAR OF SHELF
OMEGA 56 OVEN
ELEC OV GAS COOKTOP
NATURAL AL. INSECT MESH BEHIND DOORS
CONCEAL POWER + GAS RISERS - DOTTED
BEAM
ADJ. SHELF
ENDS IN 4 PLANKS 32 THICK (F)
OPEN RETURNS BELOW SHELF
REFRIG WESTINGHOUSE RA1416/RT144G
'PACIFIC' PATTERN
POST
WINDOW 1065 O/A
ABOUT 1452
1550
DOOR FRAME
OMEGA SA 34A GAS
BLANCO CLASSICSET
RAIS WOOD STOVE
FIN 2 POT, 3 COAT POLYURETHANE 1 COAT TO UNDERSIDE
CHAMFER AS SHOWN
JAMB POSITION
PLAN 1:20
ALL GAS, ELECTRIC AND S.S ITEMS AVAILABLE ON SITE; SUPPLIED BY OWNERS
VERIFY ALL DIMENSIONS ON SITE AND INSTRUCTIONS FOR EQUIPMENT
GLENN MURCUTT ARCHITECT

Murcutt guest studio

Kempsey New South Wales

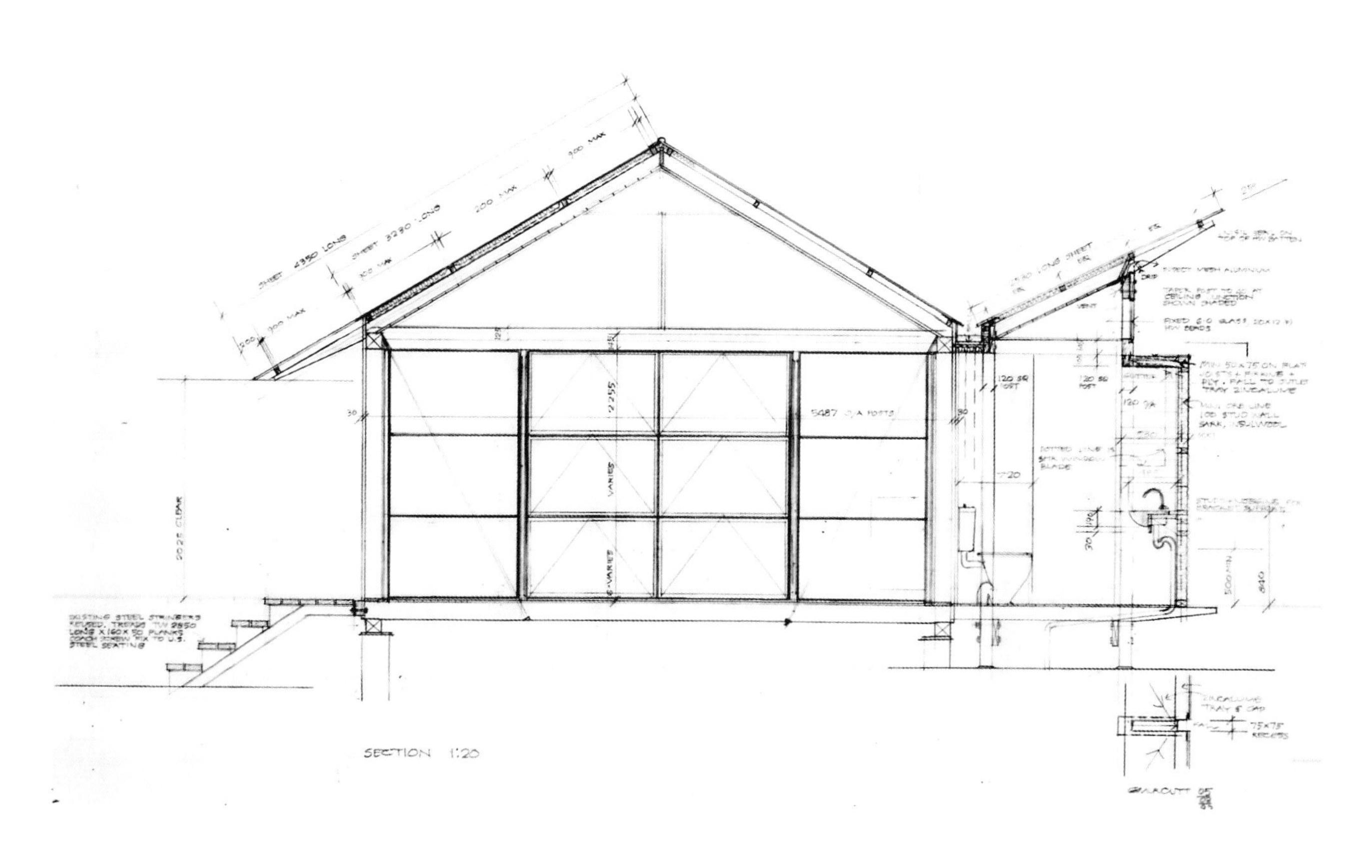

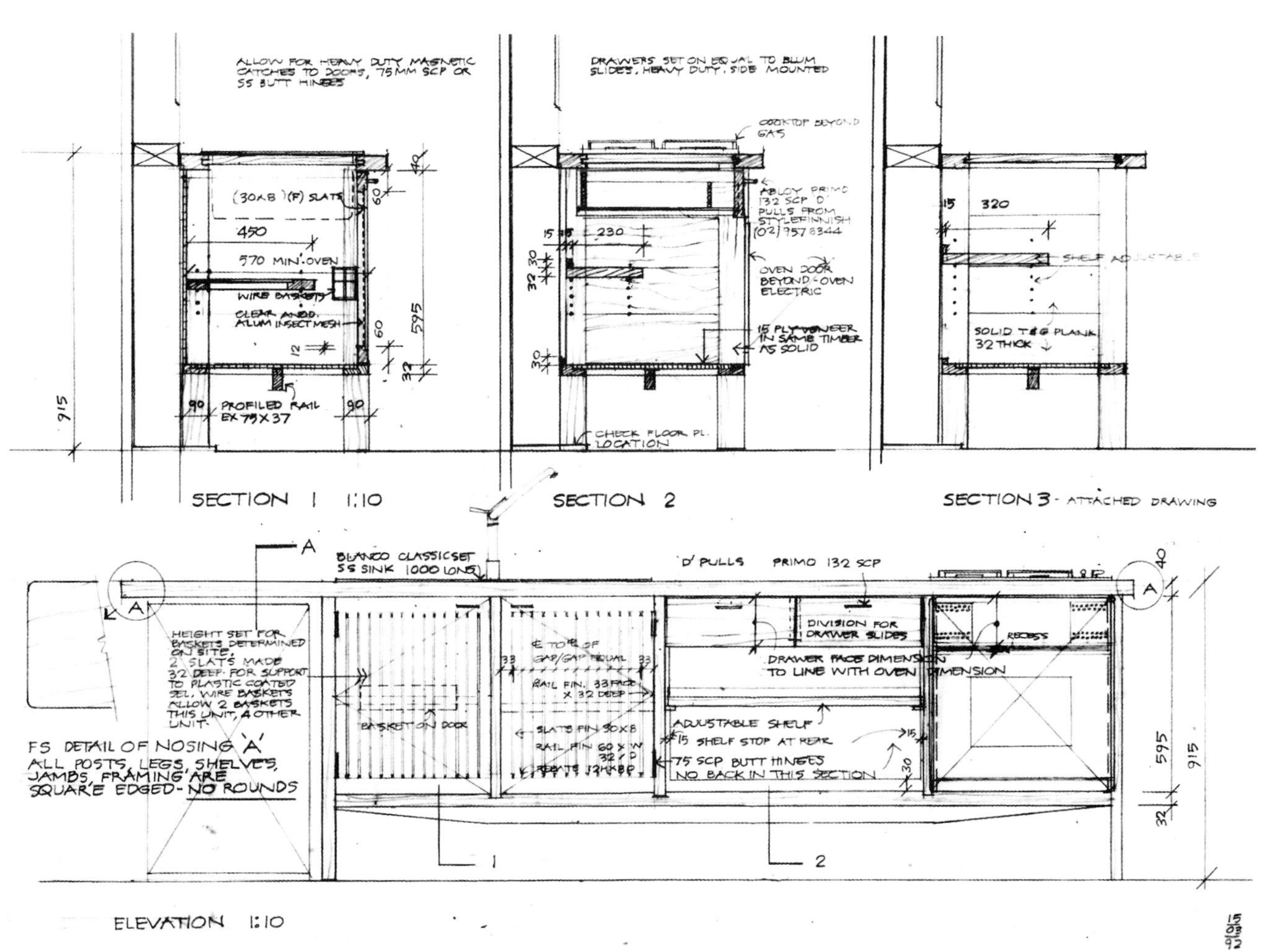

Schnaxl house
Bilgola Sydney New South Wales
1994 to 1996

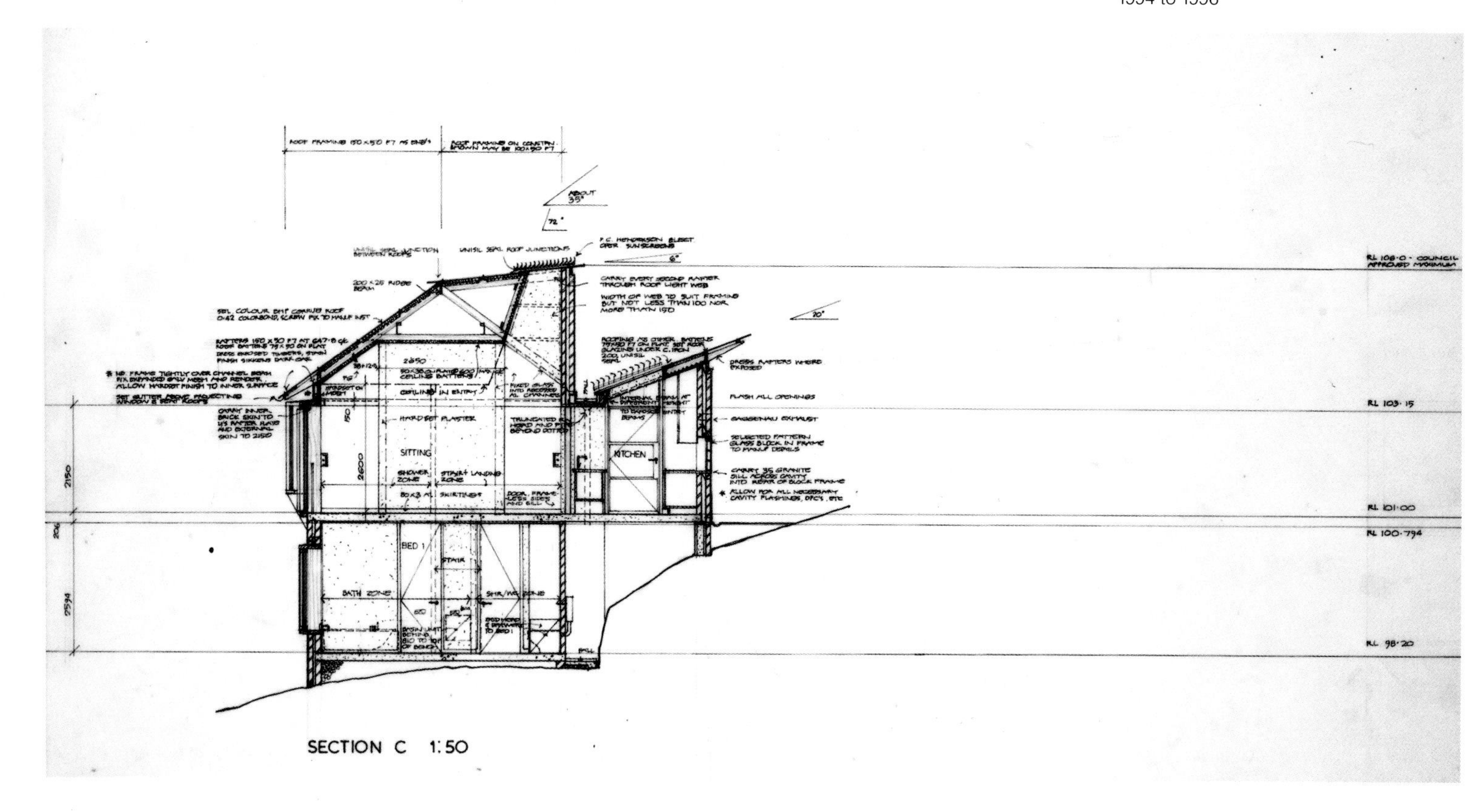

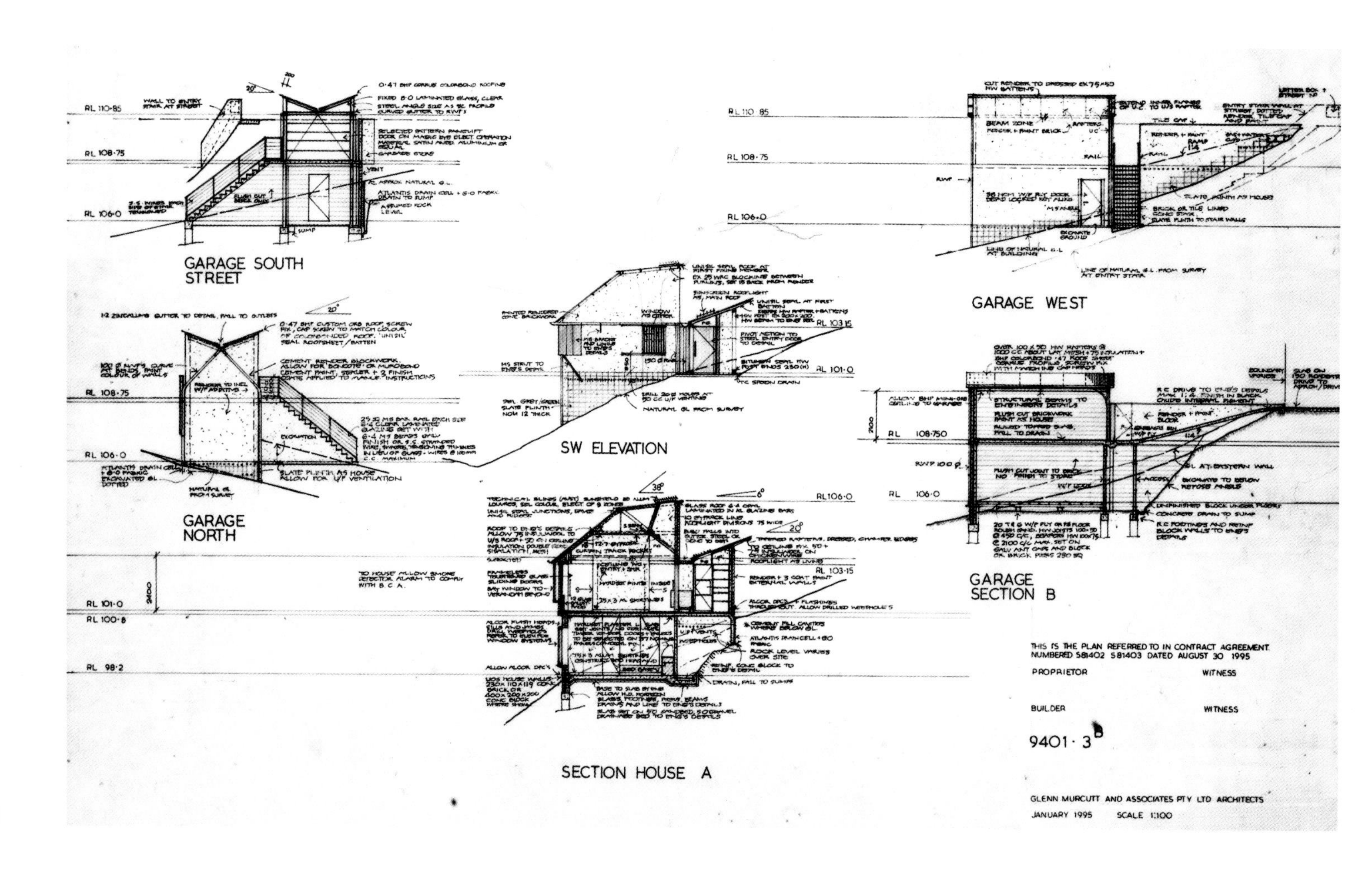

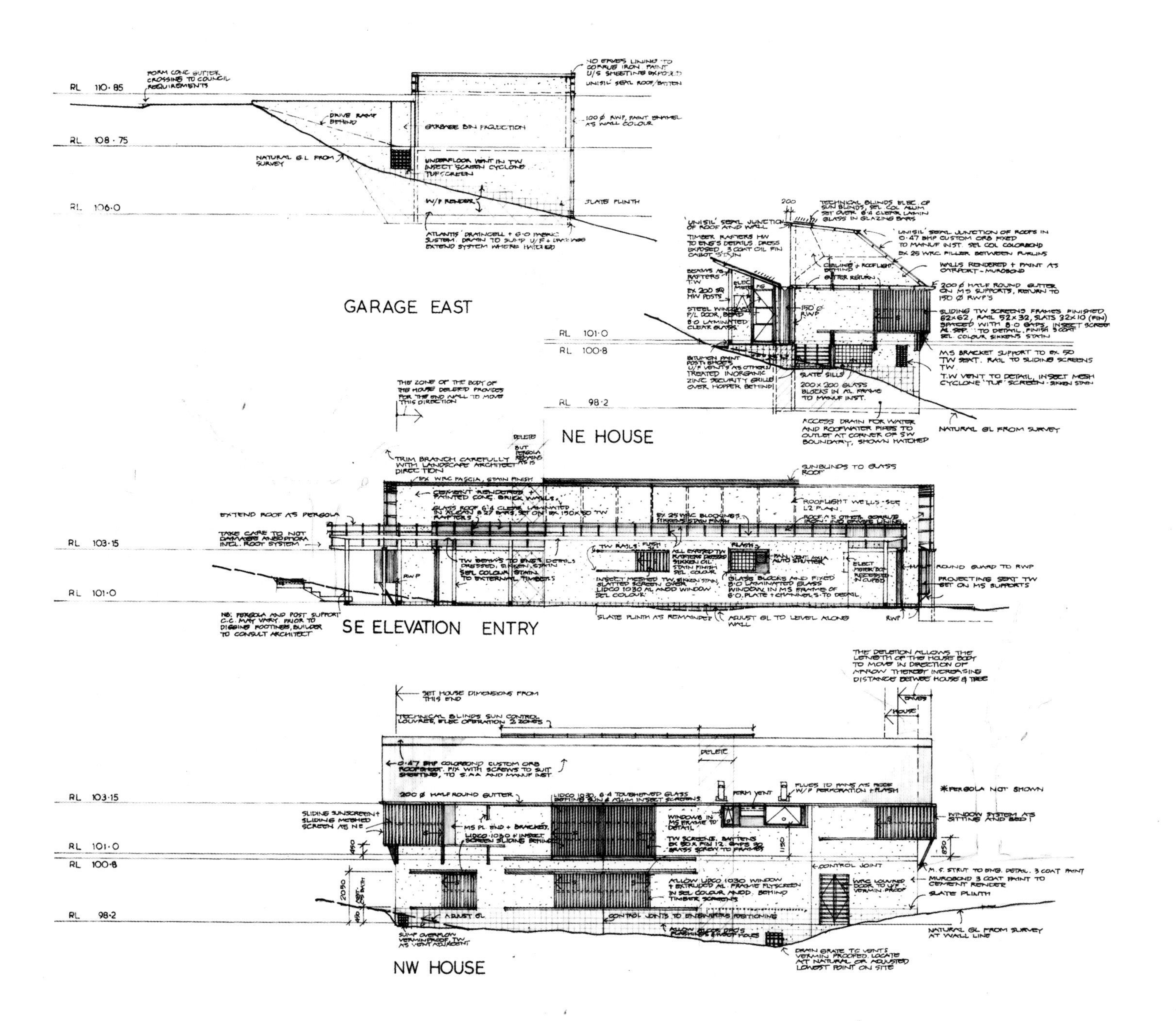

GARAGE EAST
RL 110·85
RL 108·75
RL 106·0
GARBAGE BIN PRODUCTION
SLATE PLINTH
NE HOUSE
RL 101·0
RL 100·8
RL 98·2
NATURAL GL FROM SURVEY
SE ELEVATION ENTRY
RL 103·15
RL 101·0
EXTEND ROOF AS PERGOLA
ROUND GUARD TO RWP
NW HOUSE
RL 103·15
RL 101·0
RL 100·8
RL 98·2
SLATE PLINTH
*PERGOLA NOT SHOWN
CONTROL JOINT

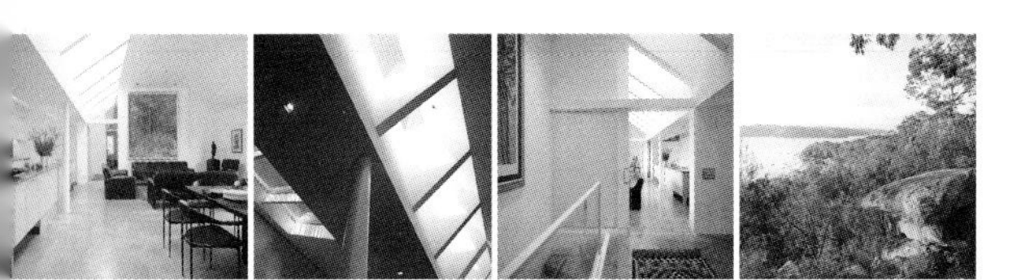

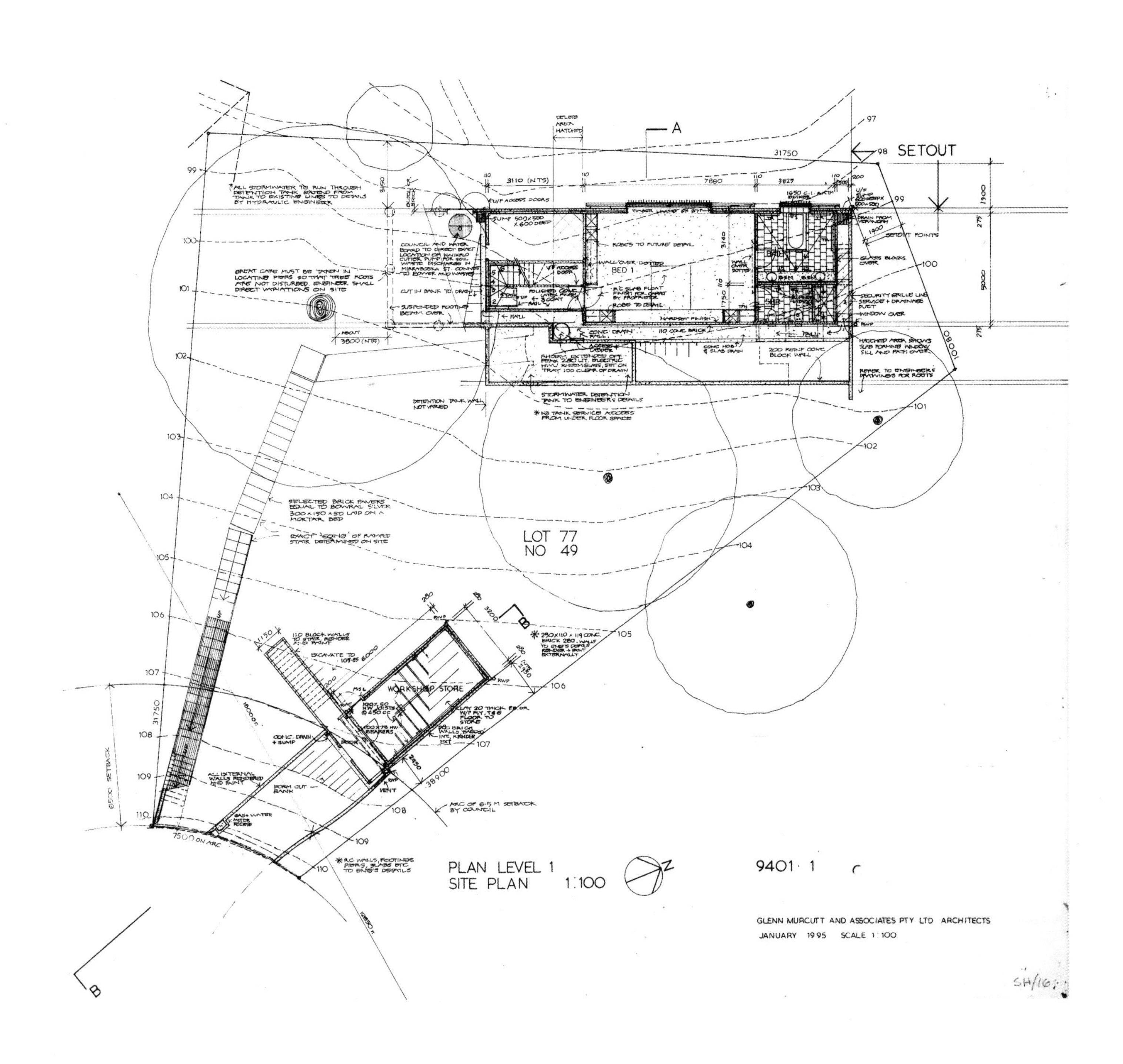

A
SETOUT
31750
BED 1
LOT 77
NO 49
WORKSHOP STORE
PLAN LEVEL 1
SITE PLAN 1:100
9401·1
GLENN MURCUTT AND ASSOCIATES PTY LTD ARCHITECTS
JANUARY 1995 SCALE 1:100
B

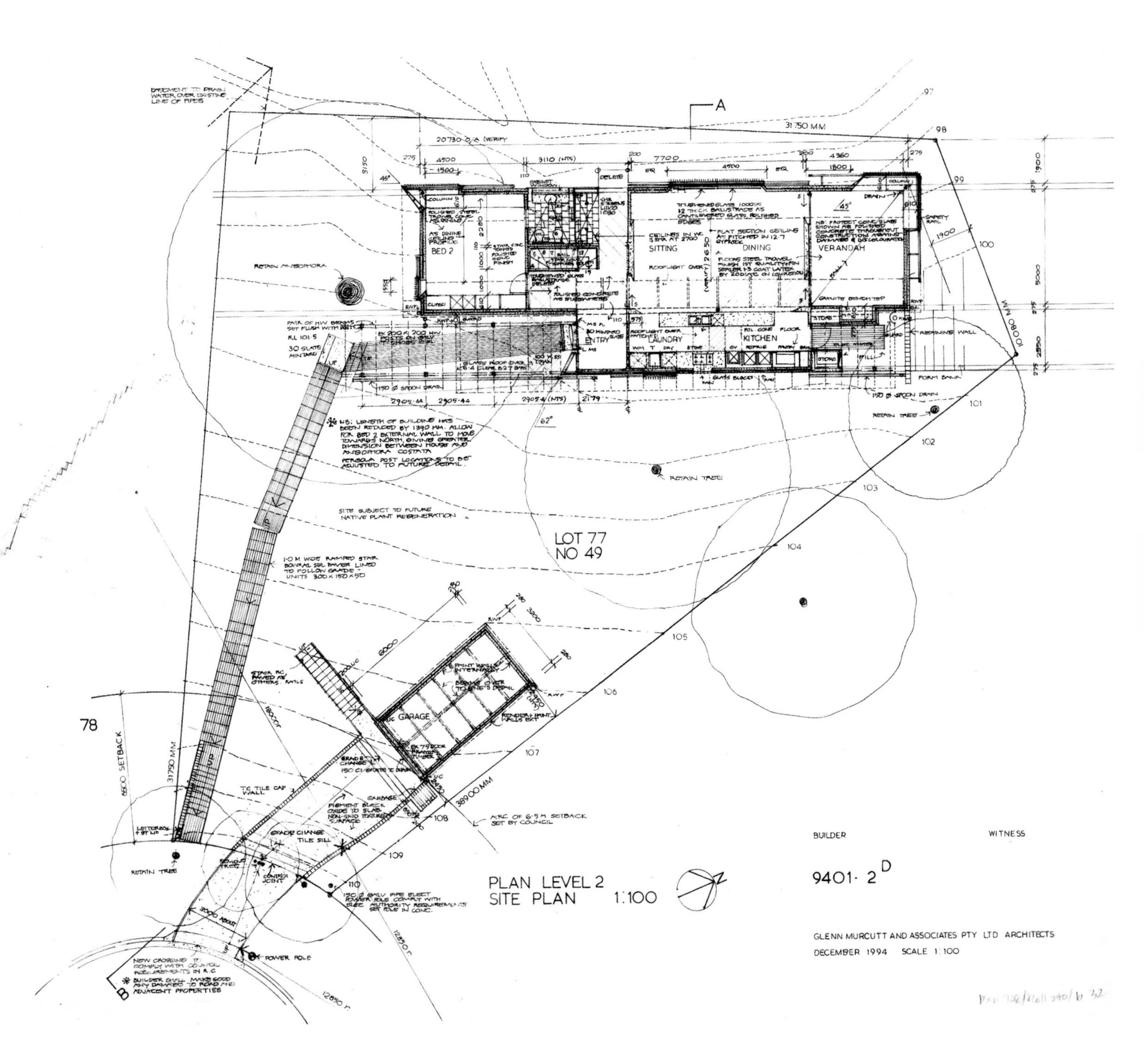
PLAN LEVEL 2
SITE PLAN 1:100
9401- 2 D
BUILDER
WITNESS
GLENN MURCUTT AND ASSOCIATES PTY LTD ARCHITECTS
DECEMBER 1994 SCALE 1:100
LOT 77
NO 49
BED 2
SITTING
DINING
VERANDAH
ENTRY
LAUNDRY
KITCHEN
GARAGE
31750 MM
38900 MM
10080 MM
5500 SETBACK
78

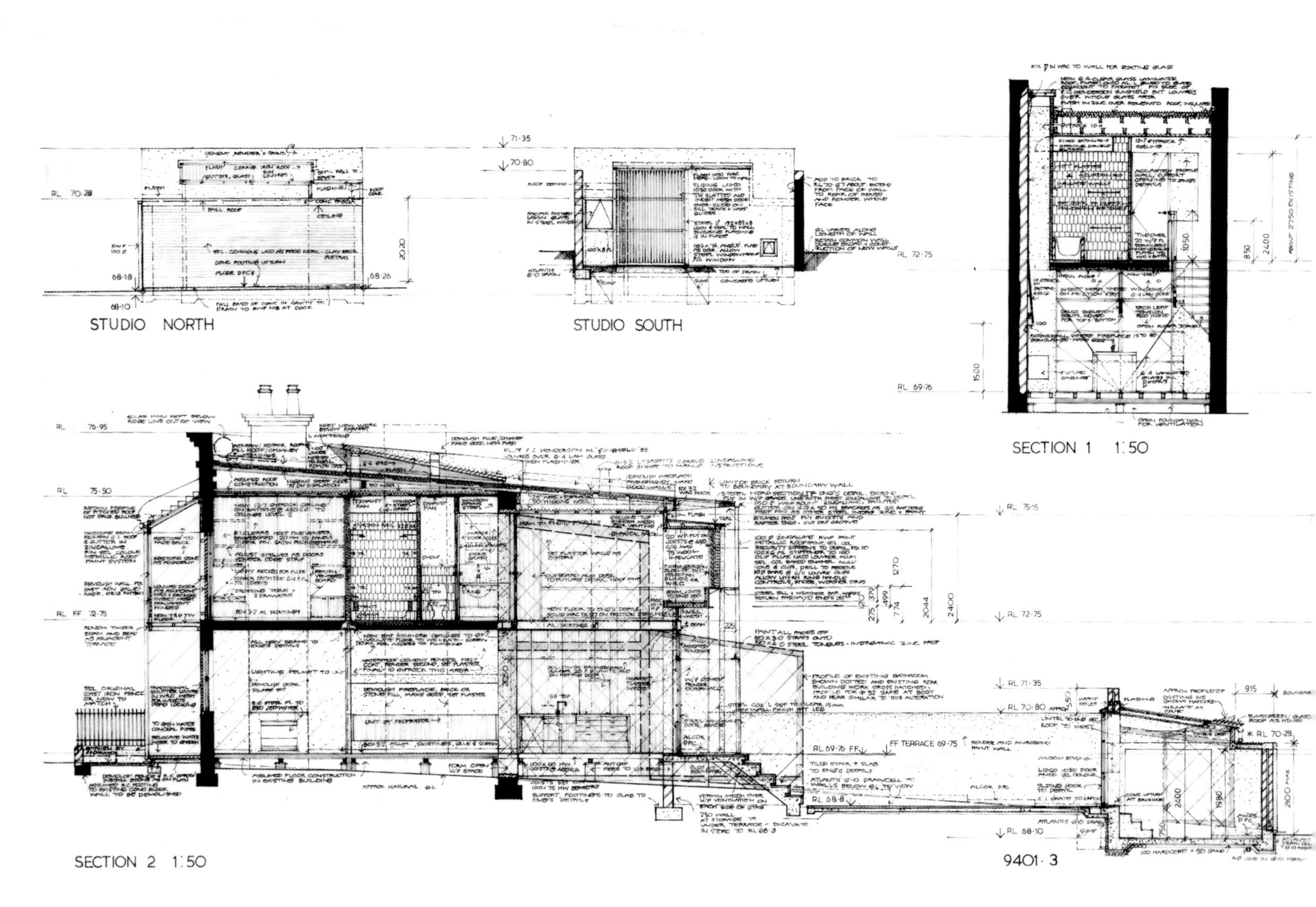
STUDIO NORTH
STUDIO SOUTH
SECTION 1 1:50
SECTION 2 1:50
9401·3

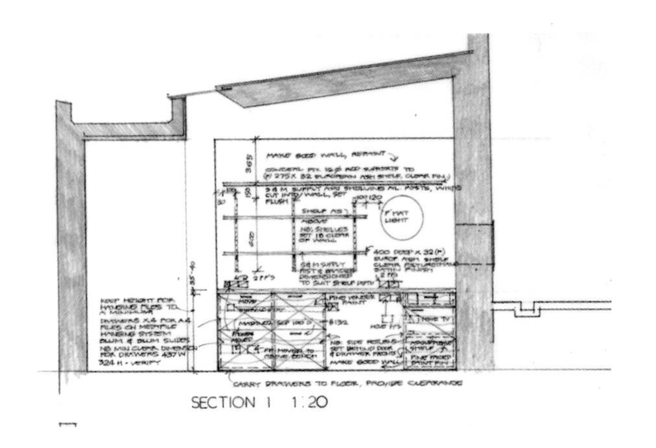
SECTION 1 1:20

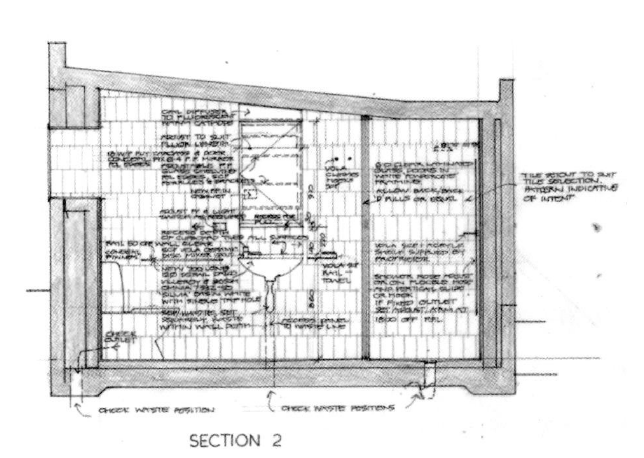
SECTION 2

Deakins-Beckwith house
in collaboration with Nicholas Murcutt
Woollahra Sydney New South Wales
1994 to 1997

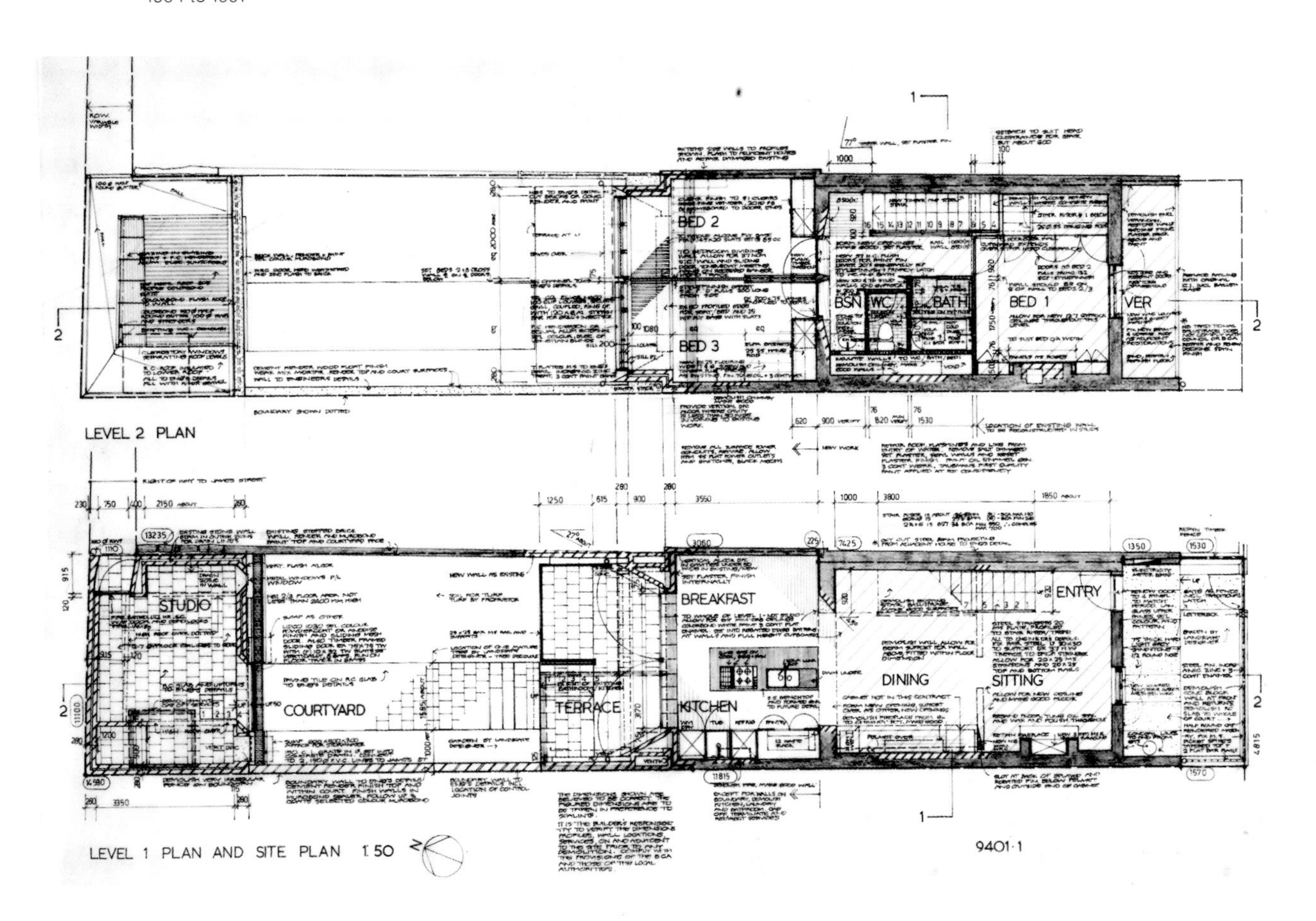

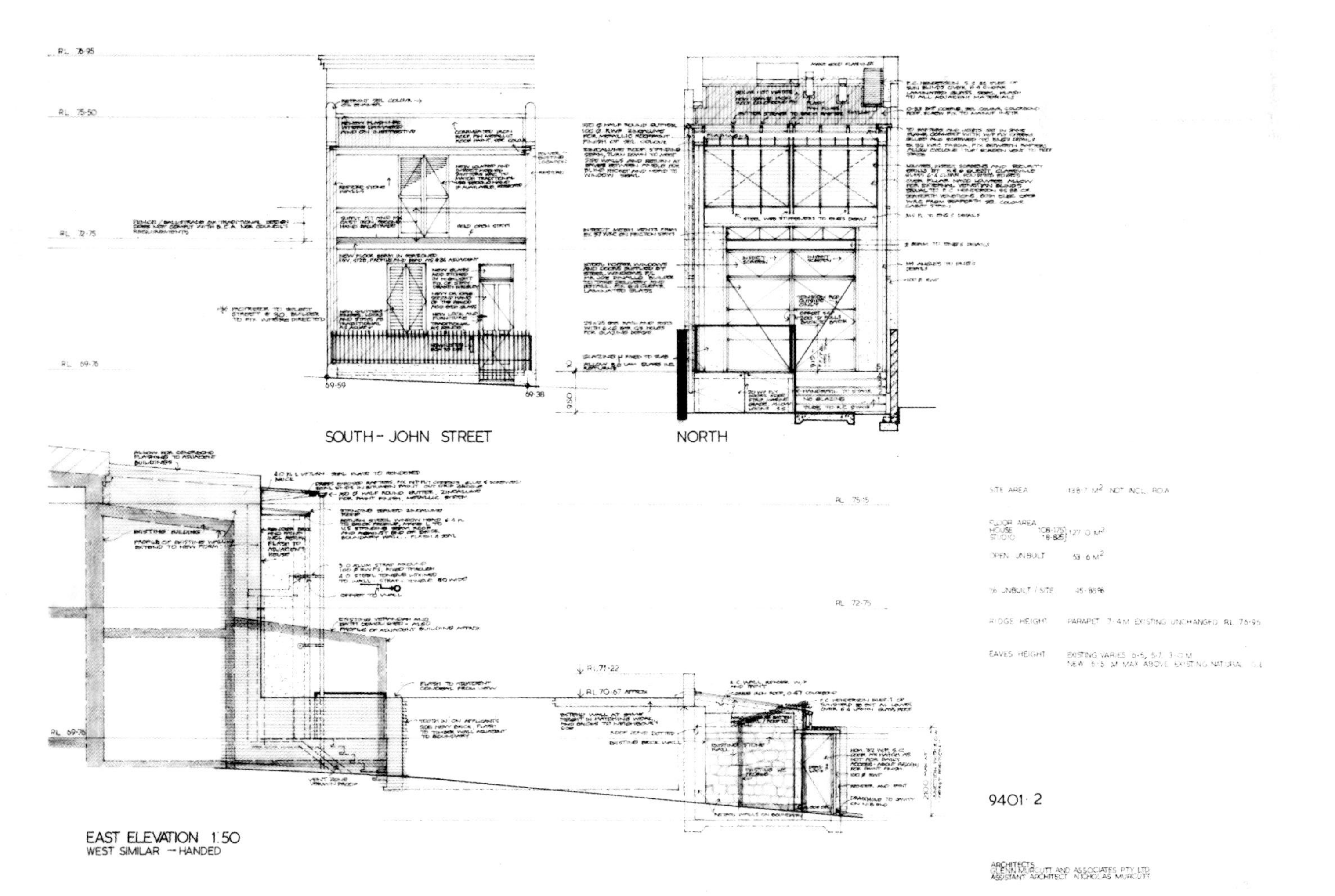

Fletcher-Page house

Kangaroo Valley New South Wales
1996–1998

Site Plan
Scale 1:500

sections, north/south/east/west

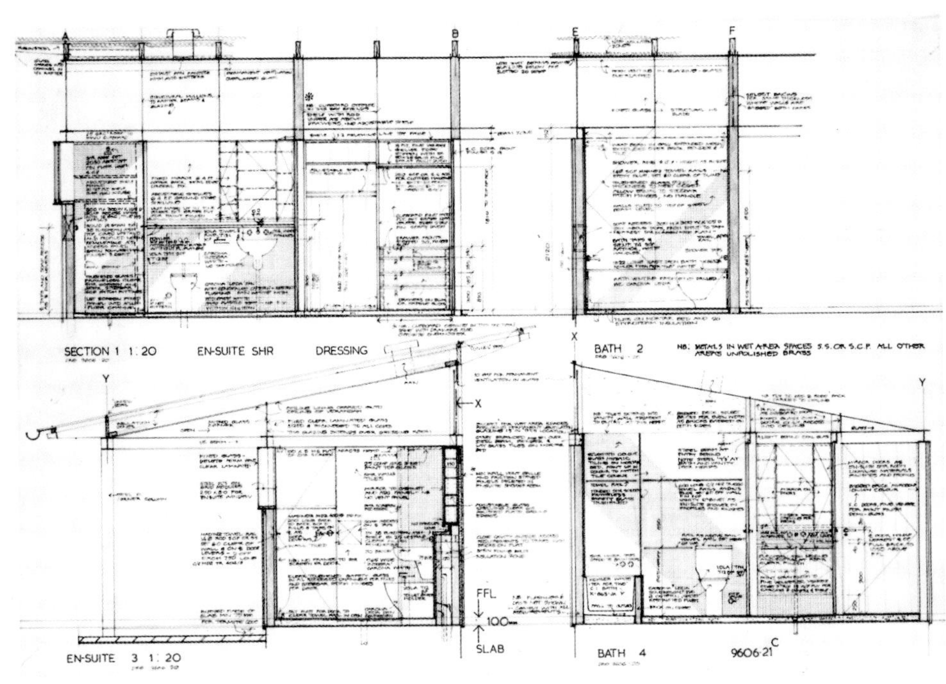
SECTION 1 1:20
EN-SUITE SHR
DRESSING
BATH 2
NB: METALS IN WET AREA SPACES S.S. OR S.C.P. ALL OTHER AREAS UNPOLISHED BRASS
FFL
100
SLAB
EN-SUITE 3 1:20
BATH 4
9606·21

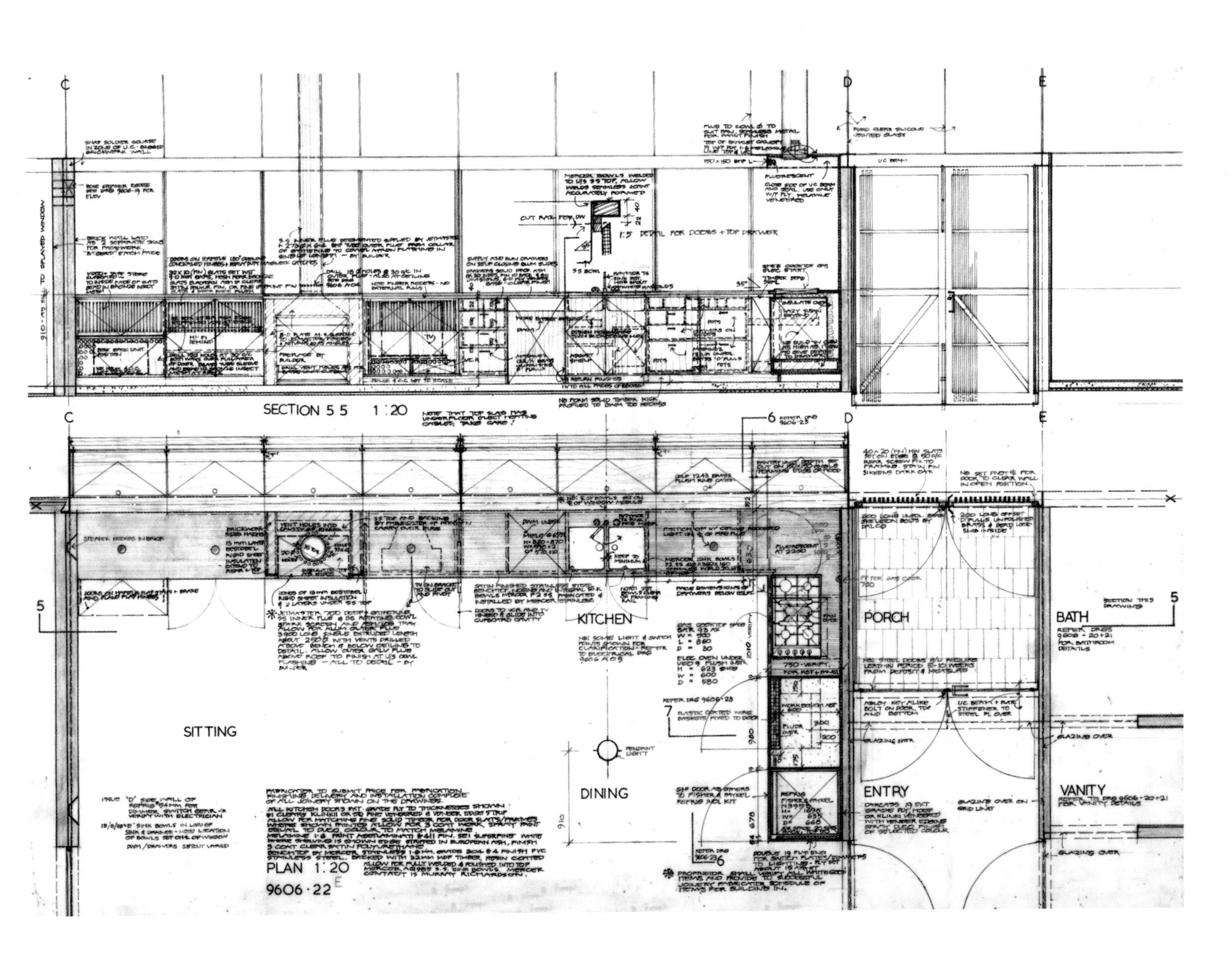
SECTION 5 5 1:20
KITCHEN
PORCH
BATH
SITTING
DINING
ENTRY
VANITY
PLAN 1:20
9606·22

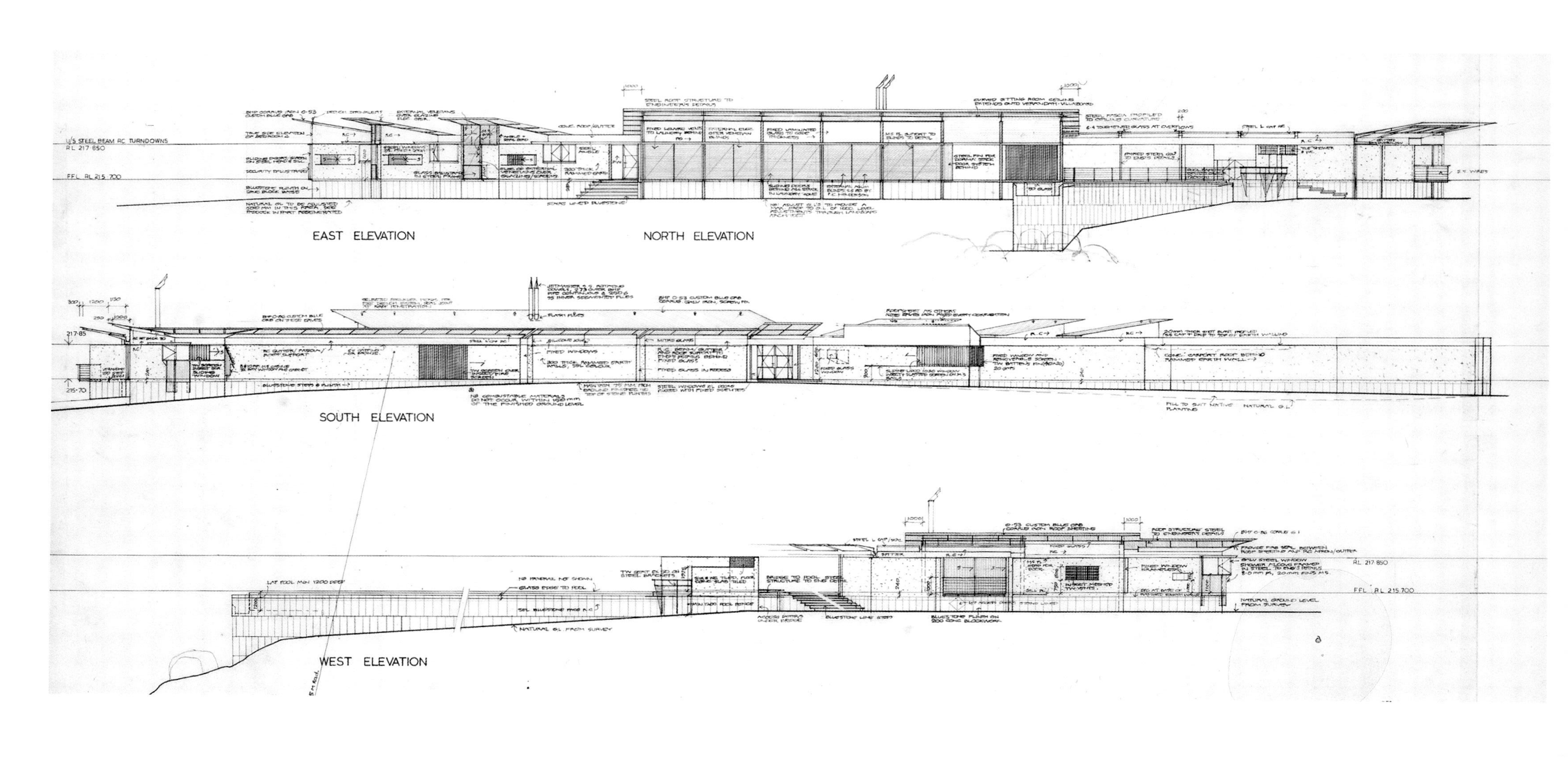
U/S STEEL BEAM RC TURNDOWNS
RL 217 850
FFL RL 215 700
EAST ELEVATION
NORTH ELEVATION
217·85
215·70
SOUTH ELEVATION
RL 217 850
FFL RL 215 700
WEST ELEVATION

House
Mount White New South Wales
1996 (unbuilt)

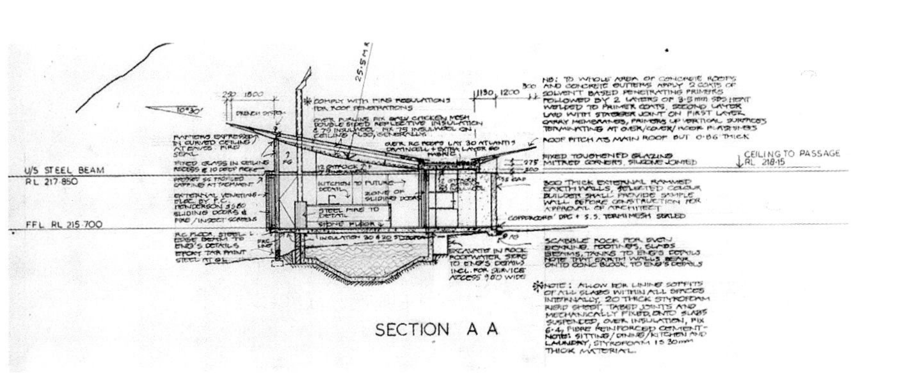

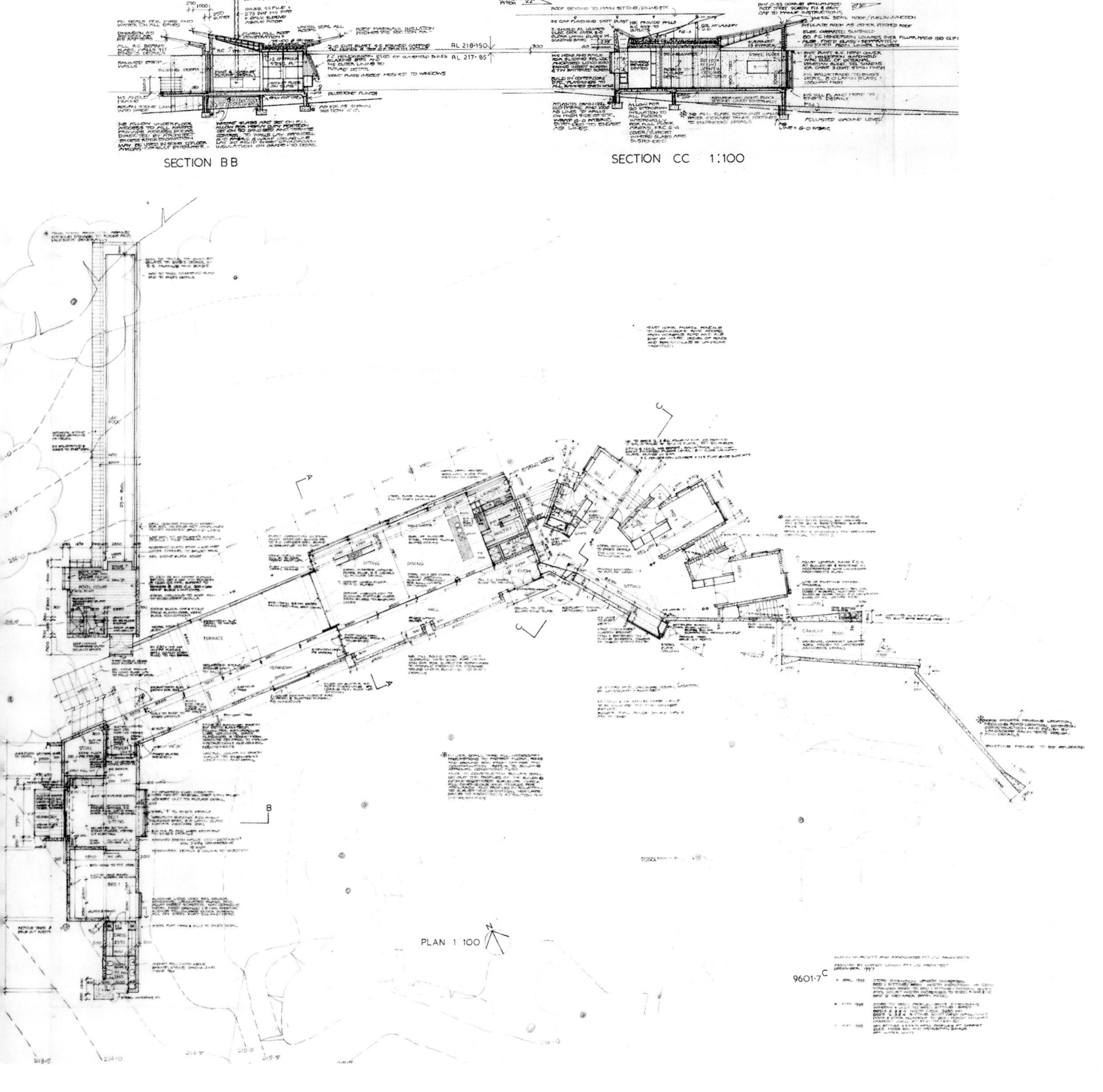

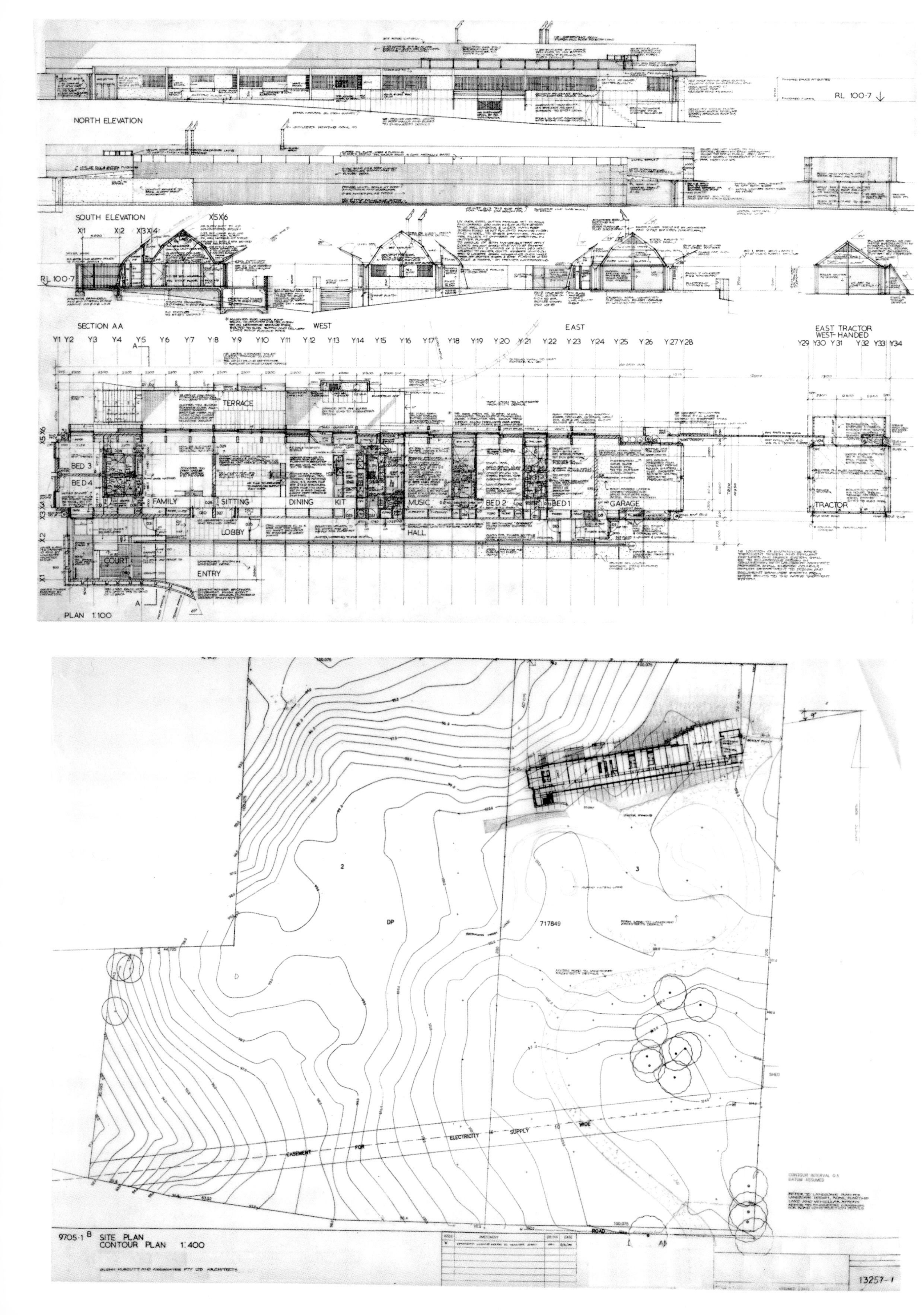
NORTH ELEVATION
RL 100·7
SOUTH ELEVATION
SECTION AA
WEST
EAST
EAST TRACTOR
WEST-HANDED
TERRACE
BED 3
BED 4
FAMILY
SITTING
DINING
KIT
MUSIC
BED 2
BED 1
GARAGE
TRACTOR
LOBBY
HALL
COURT
ENTRY
PLAN 1:100
2
DP
3
717849
EASEMENT FOR ELECTRICITY SUPPLY 10 WIDE
ROAD
SHED
CONTOUR INTERVAL 0.5
DATUM ASSUMED
9705·1 B SITE PLAN
CONTOUR PLAN 1:400
13257-1

House
Southern Highlands New South Wales
1997 to 2000

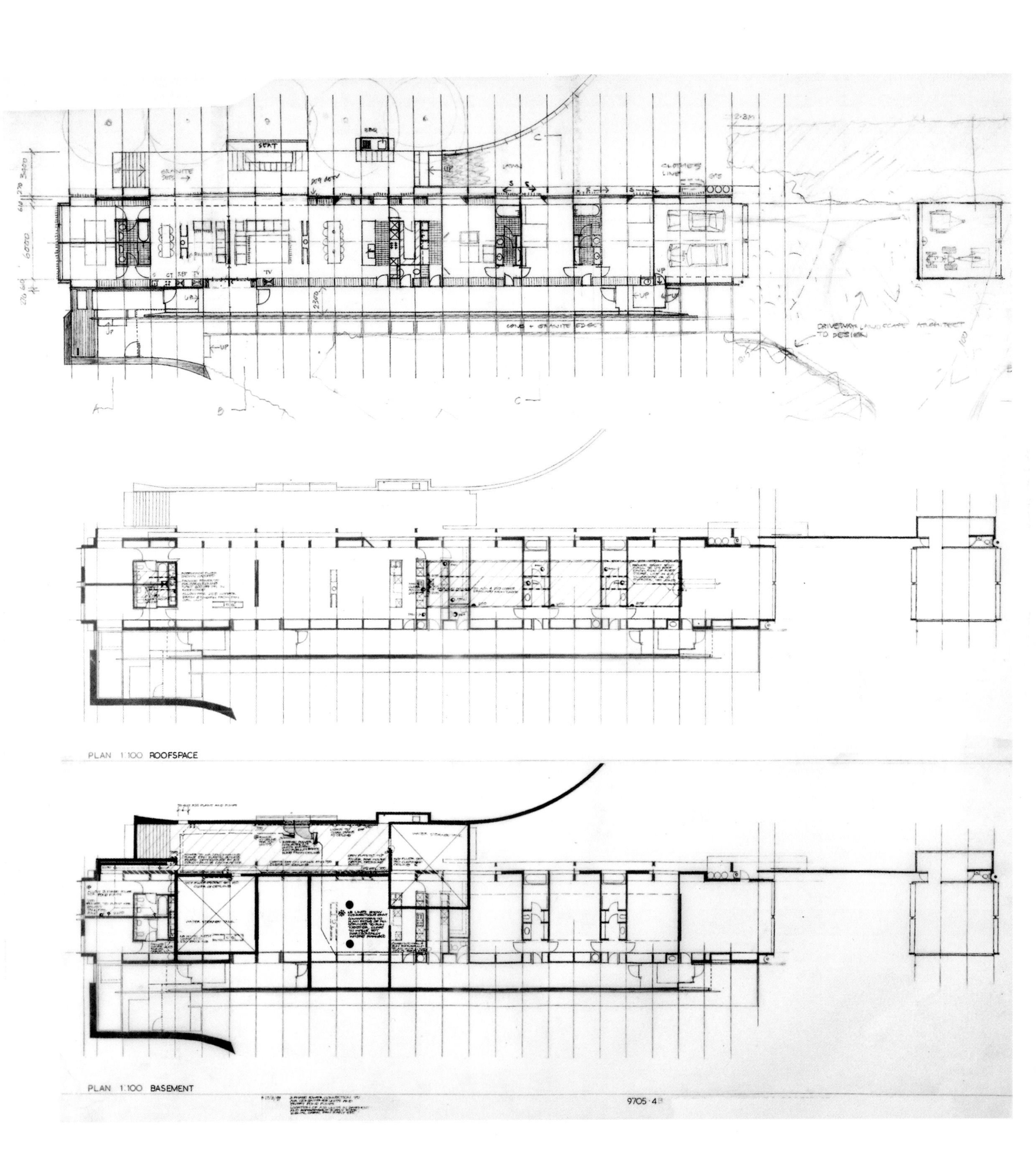

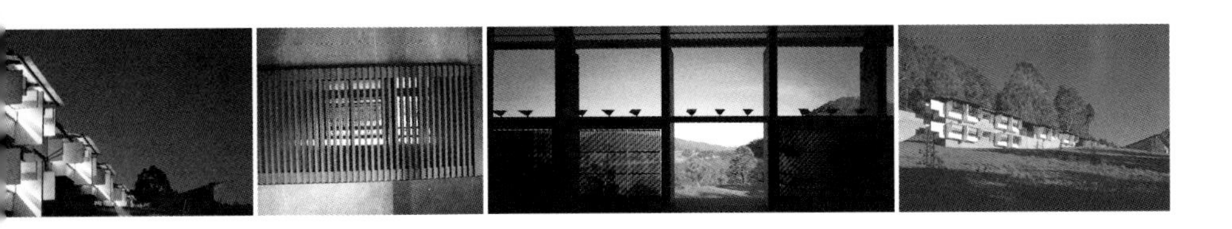

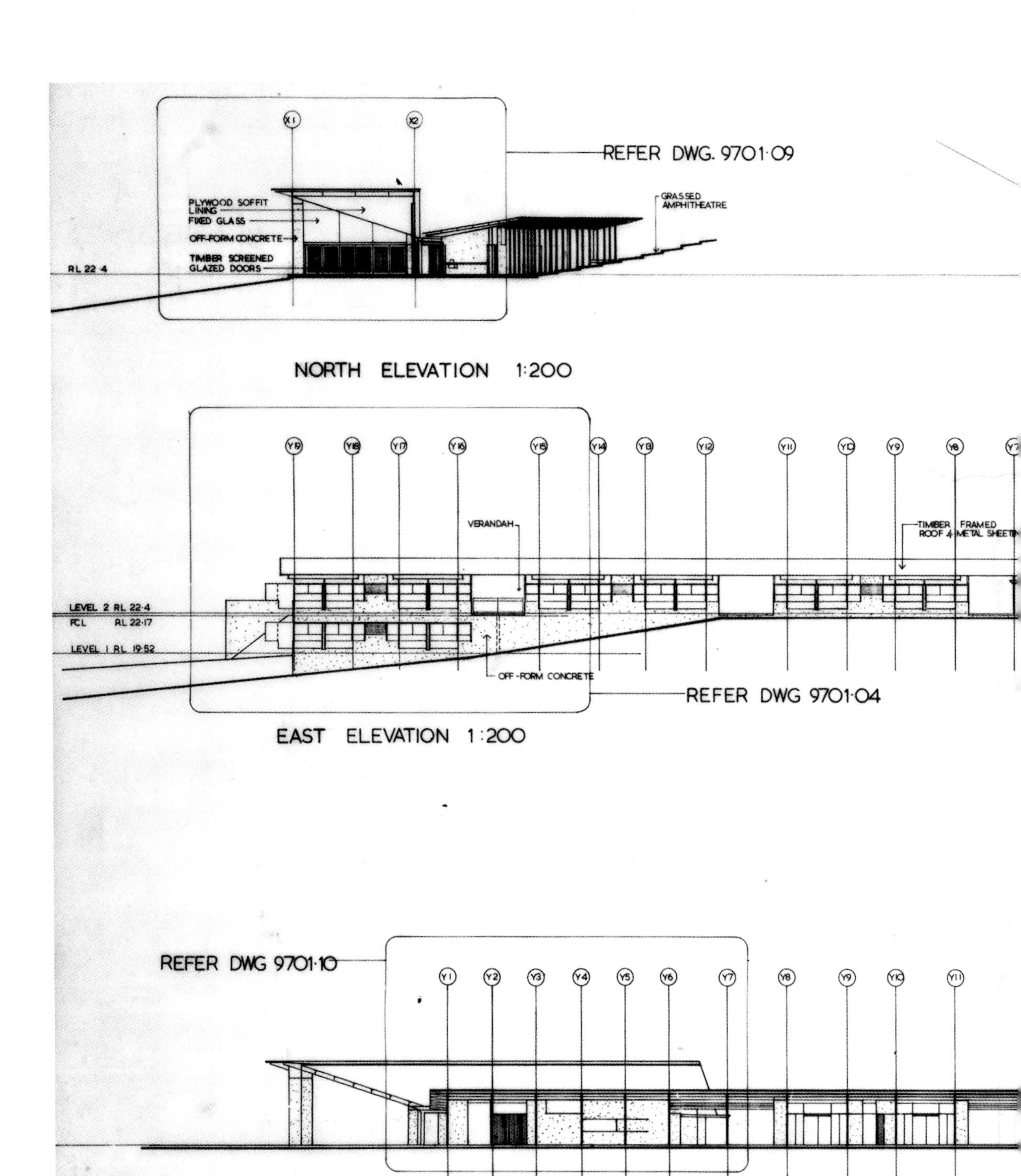

REFER DWG. 9701·09
PLYWOOD SOFFIT LINING
FIXED GLASS
OFF-FORM CONCRETE
TIMBER SCREENED GLAZED DOORS
RL 22·4
GRASSED AMPHITHEATRE
NORTH ELEVATION 1:200
VERANDAH
TIMBER FRAMED ROOF & METAL SHEETIN
LEVEL 2 RL 22·4
FCL RL 22·17
LEVEL 1 RL 19·52
OFF-FORM CONCRETE
REFER DWG 9701·04
EAST ELEVATION 1:200
REFER DWG 9701·10
WEST ELEVATION 1:200
NOTES GENERALLY AS ABOVE

Arthur and Yvonne Boyd Education Centre
in collaboration with Wendy Lewin and Reg Lark
Riversdale West Cambewarra New South Wales
1996 to 1999

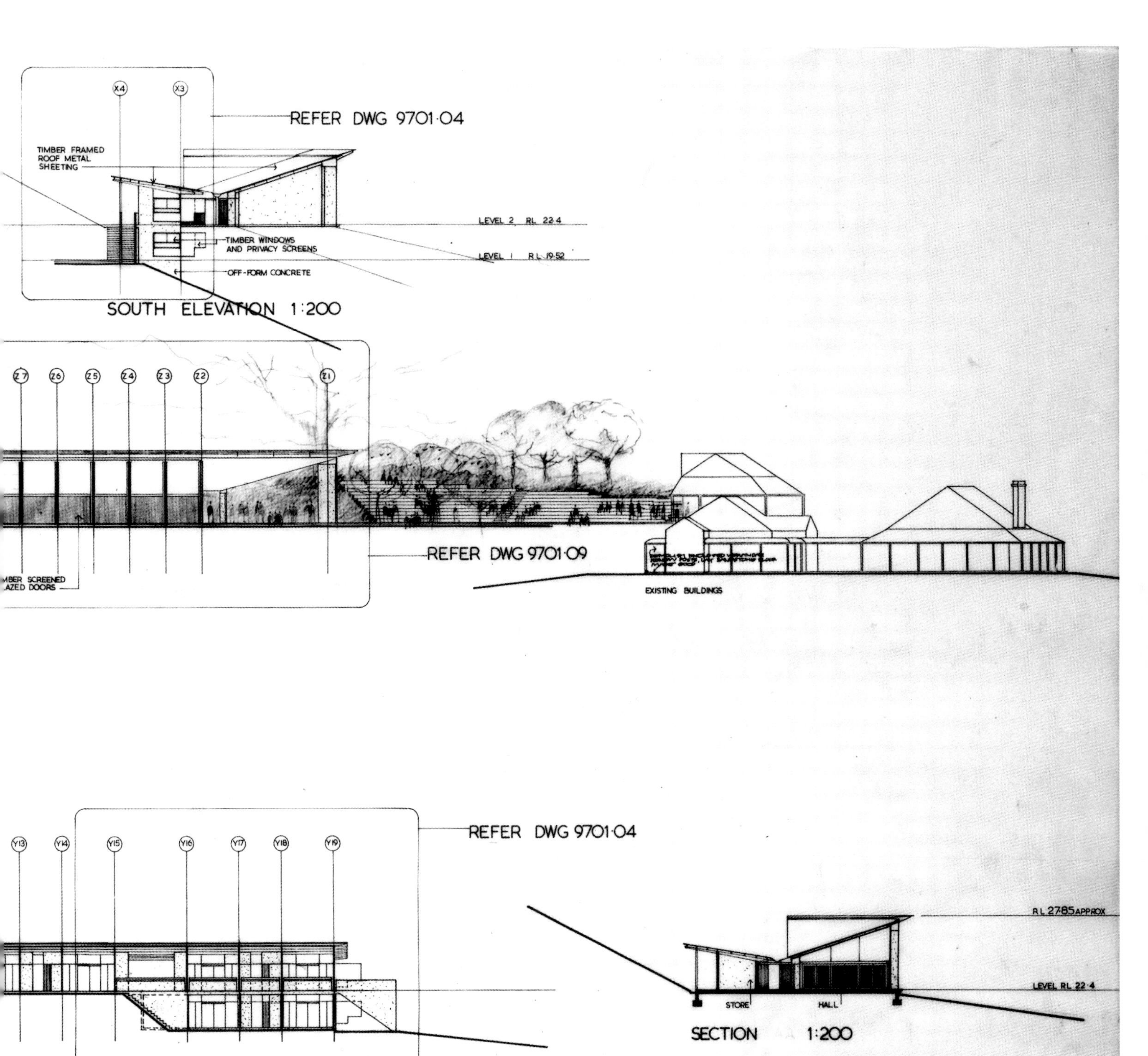

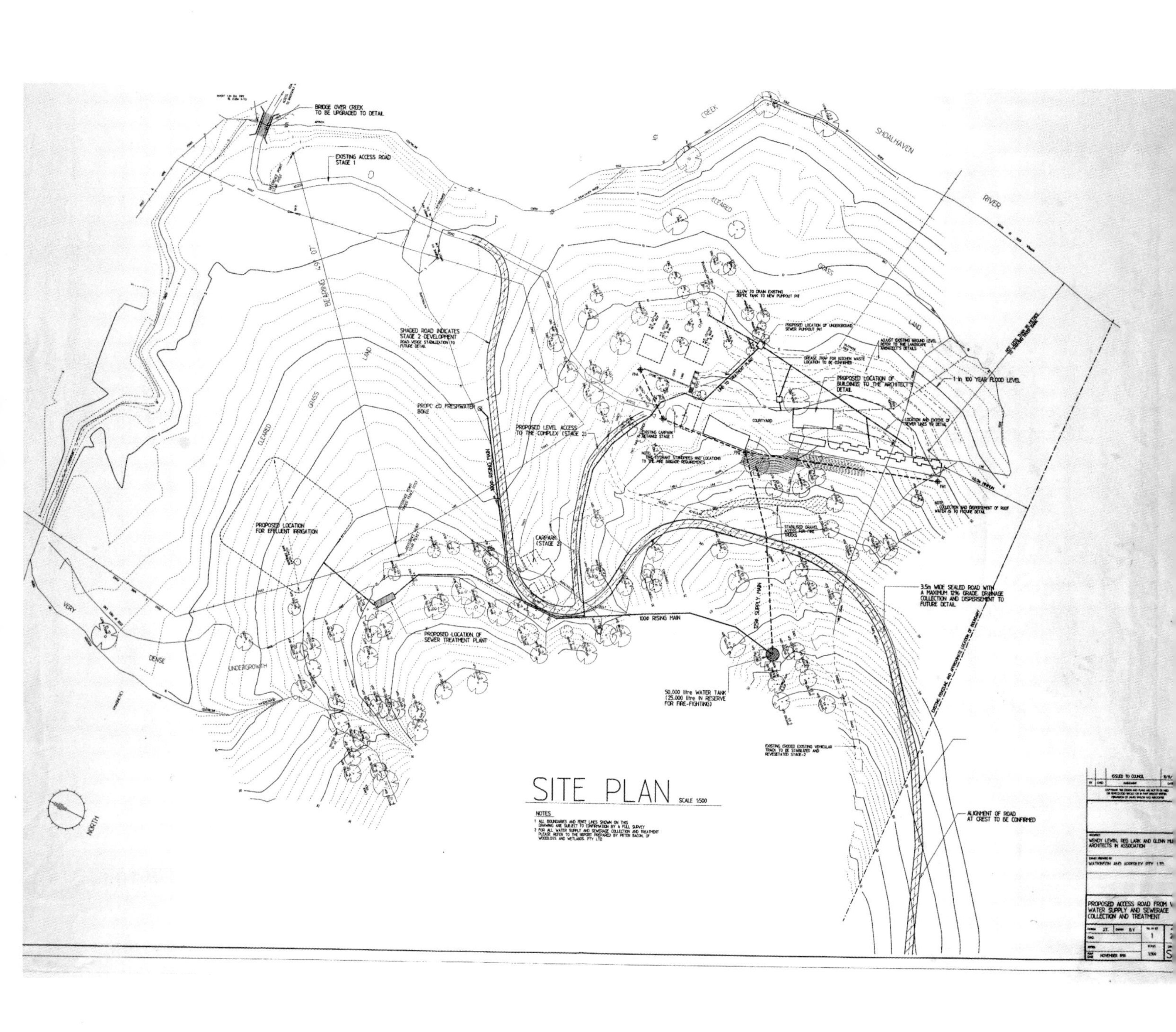

BRIDGE OVER CREEK
TO BE UPGRADED TO DETAIL
EXISTING ACCESS ROAD
STAGE 1
CREEK
SHOALHAVEN
RIVER
CLEARED
GRASS
LAND
SHADED ROAD INDICATES
STAGE 2 DEVELOPMENT
PROPOSED LOCATION OF
BUILDINGS TO THE ARCHITECT'S
DETAIL
1 in 100 YEAR FLOOD LEVEL
PROPOSED LEVEL ACCESS
TO THE COMPLEX (STAGE 2)
COURTYARD
PROPOSED LOCATION
FOR EFFLUENT IRRIGATION
CARPARK
(STAGE 2)
100Ø RISING MAIN
PROPOSED LOCATION OF
SEWER TREATMENT PLANT
50,000 litre WATER TANK
(25,000 litre IN RESERVE
FOR FIRE-FIGHTING)
3.5m WIDE SEALED ROAD WITH
A MAXIMUM 12% GRADE. DRAINAGE
COLLECTION AND DISPERSEMENT TO
FUTURE DETAIL
ALIGNMENT OF ROAD
AT CREST TO BE CONFIRMED
VERY
DENSE
UNDERGROWTH
NORTH
SITE PLAN
SCALE 1:500
NOTES
ISSUED TO COUNCIL

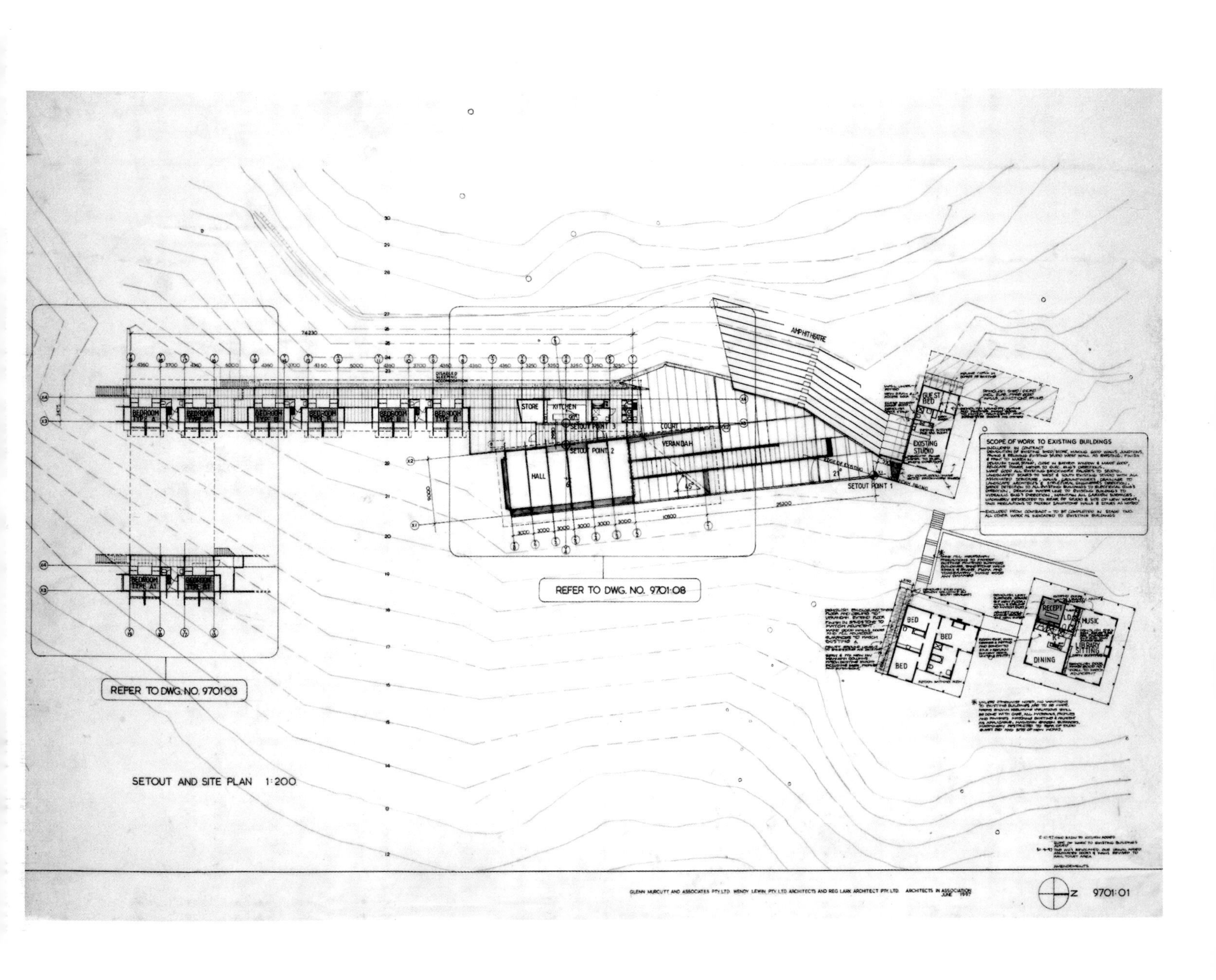
AMPHITHEATRE
BEDROOM TYPE A
STORE
KITCHEN
SETOUT POINT 3
SETOUT POINT 2
COURT
VERANDAH
HALL
GUEST BED
EXISTING STUDIO
SETOUT POINT 1
SCOPE OF WORK TO EXISTING BUILDINGS
REFER TO DWG. NO. 9701·08
BED
RECEPT
MUSIC
LIBRARY
DINING
REFER TO DWG. NO. 9701·03
SETOUT AND SITE PLAN 1:200
9701·01

Acknowledgments

The photographs used in this publication have kindly been provided by:
Reiner Blunck
Anthony Browell
Max Dupain (courtesy of Eric Sierens)
Peter Hyatt
Geoff Leung
Glenn Murcutt

The publisher would be pleased to supply details of any specific photograph upon request.

The photographs of models included in the book have been reproduced courtesy of the Powerhouse Museum, Sydney, Australia. Photography of the models is by Sue Stafford.

The drawings included are held by the Image Library of the State Library of New South Wales, Sydney, Australia and have been reproduced with permission.

plinth
water